Fundamentals of

ecology

Two types of ponds which are contrasting ecological systems, one "generalized," the other "specialized." Food-producing green plants in the upper pond (Delaware) consist of both microscopic floating algae (phytoplankton) and rooted vegetation submerged in the shallow water or emerging along the shore. The pond in the lower picture (Georgia) is so managed that rooted plants are eliminated, and all the food producers are of the microscopic type. The upper pond supports not only a greater variety of plants but also more kinds of animals, including the waterfowl which feed on and nest in the rooted vegetation. The lower pond has fewer species of organisms but large numbers of individuals of those present; it is a better game fish pond because more of the available energy is channeled into a few species harvestable by man. (U. S. Soil Conservation Service Photos.)

Fundamentals of

ecology

Eugene P. Odum

Alumni Foundation Professor of Zoology
University of Georgia
Athens, Georgia

In collaboration with

Howard T. Odum

Director, Institute of Marine Science
University of Texas
Port Aransas, Texas

SECOND EDITION

W. B. Saunders Company

Philadelphia and London

The Library of Congress has cataloged this book as follows:

Odum, Eugene Pleasants, 1913–   Fundamentals of ecology (by) Eugene P.
   Odum in collaboration with Howard T. Odum.   2d ed.   Philadelphia,
   Saunders, 1959.   546 p.   illus.   24 cm.   Includes bibliography.
   1. Ecology.   QH541.O3   1959   (574.5   575.3)   58–12125

Reprinted, June, 1959, March, 1960, March, 1961, November, 1961, April,
1962, May, 1963 and September, 1963

Made in the United States of America.   Press of W. B. Saunders Company

Preface to the second edition

In the short span of five years since the publication of the first edition, interest in ecology has increased considerably. Applications and potential applications have particularly focused attention on basic principles and have necessitated new orders of thinking. I was impressed with the new orders of magnitude at the 1955 Geneva Conference on the Peaceful Uses of Atomic Energy, which was essentially a preview of an era rapidly approaching. In his opening remarks the chairman of the conference, Homi J. Bhabha of India, pointed out that from the standpoint of the most basic need of all, namely energy, there were three ages of mankind: the age of muscle power, the age of fossil fuels and the atomic age. Since the supply of fossil fuels is rapidly being depleted, civilization must look to atomic energy and sun energy to an increasing extent. It is generally conceded that environmental contamination, with its concurrent dangers of genetic damage, stands as the most important limiting factor in the large scale use of atomic energy in the immediate future. Even more important is the upsurge of the world's human population and its skyrocketing demands for water, food and living space. Both increasing human populations and increasing radioactivity (not to mention other forms of environmental pollution) pose difficult problems in which ecological considerations are paramount.

Fortunately, biologists and the public alike are beginning to realize that ecological research of the most basic nature is vital to the solution of mankind's environmental problems. Some of the things which we fear most in the future, radioactivity, for example, if intelligently studied, help solve the very problems they create. Thus, isotopes used as tracers in the environment elucidate turnover processes which we must understand before radioactive waste materials can be safely released into the environment. Above all, thorough studies of nature's population problems and nature's use of sun energy can help provide a realistic approach to what may be the greatest problem of all, the avoidance of "over-population."* Therefore, the need for a functional approach and a critical examination of principles, the twin motivations for the preparation of the first edition, have provided the impetus for the present attempt to keep the subject of ecology up to date.

The organization of the second edition is essentially the same as that of the first although many sections have been extensively revised in the light of recent advances. I have been gratified to find that the general organization of the book and especially the arrangement of principles in Part I, which was without precedent in previous texts, have been well received by students, teachers and investigators. The widespread use of the first edition both abroad and in this country has indicated that the original presentation was both useful and cosmopolitan; hence the same general plan has been followed in the revision.

Part I is concerned with basic principles, that is, the general truths and concepts which apply widely and are not restricted to any particular environment or group of organisms. To make the meaning clear to the beginner, as well as to the specialist, an attempt has been made to state principles briefly and concisely without complicating detail. One or two clear-cut and well documented examples, illustrated wherever possible with tables, diagrams or graphs, are given for each principle. Principles are arranged in a logical sequence based on the theory that the whole environmental complex and its functional aspects are best presented first, and then followed by ideas and concepts which deal with smaller units. I am more convinced than ever that the "ecosystem" or "whole-before-the-parts" approach with its functional emphasis is sound because it avoids several stumbling blocks which can make the presentation of ecology either to students or to scientists in other fields very difficult. That is to say, the reverse approach, which starts with individual environmental factors or organisms, often bogs down in details of description, sampling methodology and taxonomy; such details, of course, are vitally

---

* The results for mankind are just as tragic regardless of whether one considers overpopulation to be the result of too many people for the resources or too few resources for the people!

important in the carrying out of specific investigations, but they need not obscure the presentation of principles which must be understood by the beginner before he can possibly design research of his own or judge critically the work of others. I need not belabor this pedagogic point since I can refer the reader to two published essays on this subject which are cited in the bibliography of this edition (E. P. Odum, 1957; 1957a).

In many cases new material added to Part I of this edition has been placed in "discussion" sections following the brief statement and explanation of the principle. One may skip over this material or return to it later (as might be desirable in teaching students who have only a minimum background in biology) without breaking the continuity of the presentation of basic principles.

Part II is organized along the lines followed in field work, and emphasizes the descriptive phase of ecology. By means of frequent cross references between Part I and Part II, I have attempted to make it possible to begin—either in reading or in formal course work—with either Part I or Part II. Thus, if the instructor or the reader wishes to cover theory first, he may begin with Part I. If, on the other hand, he wishes to start immediately with the study of outdoor habitats, as when the course is given in summer or fall, he may start with Part II and follow with consideration of the unifying principles that have been illustrated by the field and laboratory work. Another possibility, of course, is to work the two sections simultaneously. Thus, I have tried to make the arrangement flexible and adaptable to various uses and situations.

Part III deals essentially with applications and borderline fields. The attempt is made to show how the principles outlined in Part I and the results of the study of environments covered in Part II are applied. This section is of necessity brief. The applied worker generally learns most of the needed details in the actual practice of his profession and from consulting books and research papers dealing entirely with his specialty. He will learn faster, however, and his work will be sounder, if he can see the connection between the basic principles of ecology and his particular application. As is the case in Parts I and II, a few clear-cut examples are presented to illustrate key points. Selected references are cited for further reading, but no attempt is made to survey or analyze the vast and often confusing literature which has mushroomed around the various applied fields. Essentially this portion of the book has been designed to give the beginner some idea of the professions open to the trained ecologist.

In this revision a new section entitled "Radiation Ecology" has been added to Part III. It should be emphasized that this new hybrid field is not only becoming an area of applied science of the greatest importance but also is bringing with it exciting new techniques, which may be expected to contribute to better understanding of fundamental problems, as outlined in Part I.

Traditionally, a book on ecology, like books on other sciences, is supposed to have a lengthy glossary because of the alleged difficulty of the terminology. I feel strongly that stereotyped definitions are of little value; the reader should *understand* the terms and the principles to which they refer, rather than *memorize* mere definitions. Consequently, I have not prepared a glossary as a separate section. Instead, the index serves as a "reference glossary." The page on which a specific term or concept is defined, explained, and illustrated being indicated by bold-face type.

Broadly speaking, the energy and ecosystem chapters in Part I and the terrestrial chapter in Part II have been the most extensively revised, reflecting, perhaps, the considerable advances in these areas. A serious bottleneck in our attempts to understand natural systems is the lack of knowledge in what is undoubtedly the weakest area in modern ecology, the "decomposer" phase of nature. During the past several years there has been a marked increase in interest in microbial ecology, as shown by the publication of the first comprehensive symposium on the subject by the Society of General Microbiology in 1957. I have tried to incorporate as much new material as possible in this aspect, but I fear it will be some years yet before one can do justice to this subject in an elementary textbook. The rewards for microbiologists who are willing to leave the comparative security of pure cultures and test tubes and grapple with the problems of natural populations are very great. The role of growth substances in the regulation of population growth, and the means of assaying the total activity of microorganisms in nature are but two of the exciting fields which need attention. I hope that the frequent questions and the obvious gaps in knowledge pointed up in this book will stimulate students to obtain the training needed to develop the field of microbial ecology.

In deciding what to include in and what to leave out of the

revision, I have resisted all temptation to include anything on methods, except what is needed to bring out principles—not because I think methods are unimportant, but because I believe they should be treated in a different kind of book or manual. Methods, unlike principles, are often highly specific for different populations and environments. Thus, any effective treatment of methods, which was intended for wide use, would have to be a compilation rather than a synthesis, as this book is intended to be. Also, teaching methods have to be developed by the individual to suit the local situation. Finally, I feel strongly that the student should know why things are measured before he becomes too involved in the how. I have found in actual practice that counting trees in a forest or plankton in a water sample is much less boring to the beginning student if he understands what principle is being tested or what problem might be solved by so doing. (If no principle or problem is involved, then we discard the counting and do something more meaningful!)

In working with the literature of the past few years, I have been more impressed than ever with the fact that ecology has emerged from a primarily descriptive subject to one which is also functional in approach. Until comparatively recently, ecologists were content to describe how nature "looks" (sometimes by means of fantastic terms!) and to speculate on what she may have looked like in the past or might look like in the future. Now, an equal emphasis is being placed on what nature "does," and rightly so, because the changing face of nature can never be understood unless her metabolism is also studied! This change in approach brings the small organisms into true perspective with the large and encourages the use of experimental methods to supplement the analytical. It is evident that so long as a purely descriptive viewpoint is maintained there is very little in common between such structurally diverse organisms as spermatophytes, vertebrates and bacteria. In real life, however, all these are intimately linked functionally in ecological systems, according to well defined laws. Thus, the only kind of general ecology is that which I call a "functional ecology," and this kind is of the greatest interest to all students of the subject, regardless of present or future specializations. Truly general or basic courses in ecology have often not been available in our largest universities because the subject is fragmented by departmental lines, which traditionally are drawn along morphological or taxonomic rather than physiological lines. Such lines need not be a barrier because, as I have tried to show in this book, any ecologist can present the general principles to students, regardless of departmental affiliations or of whether his training and special- ization may be in botanical, zoological or microbiological sciences.

To summarize, this book has two purposes: (1) to serve as a textbook in a college course, especially one designed to precede (but not replace) courses in plant (i.e., spermatophyte) ecology, vertebrate ecology, microbial ecology, marine ecology, etc., as well as various applied phases (conservation, forestry, etc.); such a basic course fits in logically with genetics, physiology, evolution and others in a core curriculum for undergraduate majors in biology; and (2) to serve as a reference for the specialist, the naturalist and the interested workers in related fields, including the great and growing army of conservation workers, sanitary engi- neers and other applied ecologists who need to be familar with background work and theories.

In the preparation of both editions I have been especially for- tunate to have the close collaboration of my brother, Howard Thomas Odum, Director of the Institute of Marine Science, Uni- versity of Texas. Especially important has been his co-authorship of the chapter on energy relations, a field in which he is making important and highly original contributions. His contributions to all of the manuscript have helped insure a broad coverage of ideas and literature.

In the Preface of the First Edition the following persons were mentioned as having contributed to the task of bringing together diverse viewpoints: R. E. Coker, V. E. Shelford, S. Charles Ken- deigh, G. Evelyn Hutchinson, Edward Deevey and the late W. C. Allee. In the preparation of the Second Edition I am most grateful to the following for specific contributions: Frank A. Pitelka (nu- merous specific suggestions throughout the manuscript), Robert B. Platt (microenvironment), John T. Curtis (terrestrial plant ecology), Carl H. Oppenheimer (microbial ecology), John H. Ryther (biological oceanography), Stanley I. Auerbach, Kermit Larson, Robert G. Lindberg, Jerry J. Davis and Richard F. Foster (radiation ecology). Through correspondence, reviews and per- sonal discussions, I am especially indebted to the following for suggestions and for calling attention to errors or weak points in the first edition: L. C. Birch, W. D. Billings, F. H. Bormann, M. F. Buell, W. D. Burbanck, Paul Burkholder, Stanley A. Cain, Mel- bourne R. Carriker, George L. Clarke, Pierre Dansereau, Charles

Elton, Francis C. Evans, Reed W. Fautin, F. Raymond Fosberg, Peter W. Frank, David G. Frey, Gordon Gunter, A. D. Hasler, Joel Hedgpeth, R. W. Hiatt, Charles E. Jenner, Bostwick H. Ketchum, E. T. Moul, H. J. Oosting, W. T. Penfound, R. E. Shanks, James T. Tanner, R. H. Whittaker and John N. Wolfe.

Finally, my colleagues at the University of Georgia, especially George H. Boyd, D. C. Scott, Robert A. Ragotzkie, Lawrence R. Pomeroy, and John M. Teal, and my students and former students, especially Robert A. Norris, James H. Jenkins, William H. Cross, Clyde E. Connell, Edward J. Kuenzler and Alfred E. Smalley, have helped in many ways. When not otherwise credited, the illustrations are original. Many of the graphs and pictorial diagrams were done by my wife, Martha Ann, to whom I am deeply grateful.

EUGENE P. ODUM

Contents

I · Basic ecological principles and concepts

II · The habitat approach

III · Applied ecology

1 · Basic ecological principles and concepts

1 · Introduction: the scope of ecology

1. Ecology and its relation to other sciences

Man has been interested in ecology in a practical sort of way since early in his history. In primitive society every individual, to survive, needed to have definite knowledge of his environment, i.e., of the forces of nature and of the plants and animals around him. Civilization, in fact, began when man learned to use fire and other tools to modify his environment. It is still necessary, or perhaps even more necessary than ever, for mankind as a whole to have an intelligent knowledge of the environment if our complex civilization is to survive, since the basic "laws of nature" have not been repealed; only their complexion and quantitative relations have changed, as the world's human population has increased.

Like all phases of learning, the science of ecology has had a gradual, if spasmodic, development during recorded history. The writings of Hippocrates, Aristotle, and other philosophers of the Greek period contain material which is clearly ecological in nature. However, the Greeks literally did not have a word for it. The word "ecology" is of recent coinage, having been first proposed by the German biologist, Ernst Haeckel, in 1869. As a recognized distinct field of biology, the science of ecology is still younger, dating from about 1900, and only in the past few years has the word become part of the general vocabulary to the extent that one may find it in popular magazine articles.

The word ecology is derived from the Greek *oikos,* meaning

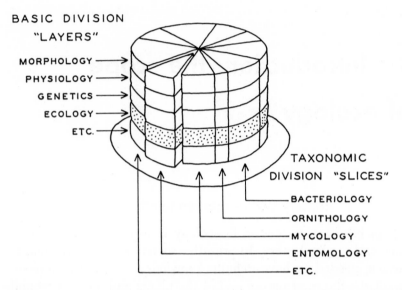

BASIC DIVISION

"LAYERS"

MORPHOLOGY ——→

PHYSIOLOGY ——→

GENETICS ——→

ECOLOGY ——→

ETC. ——→

TAXONOMIC

DIVISION "SLICES"

——BACTERIOLOGY

——ORNITHOLOGY

——MYCOLOGY

——ENTOMOLOGY

——ETC.

Figure 1.   The biology "layer cake," illustrating "basic" (horizontal) and "taxonomic" (vertical) divisions.

"house" or "place to live." Literally, ecology is the study of organisms "at home." Usually ecology is defined as the study of the relation of organisms or groups of organisms to their environment, or the science of the interrelations between living organisms and their environment. Because ecology is concerned especially with the biology of *groups* of organisms and with *functional* processes on the lands, in the oceans and in fresh waters, it is more in keeping with the modern emphasis, to define ecology as the study of the structure and function of nature (it being understood that mankind is a part of nature). In the long run the best definition for a broad subject field is probably the shortest and least technical one, as, for example, "the science of the living environment," or simply "environmental biology."

So much for definitions. To understand the scope of ecology, the subject must be considered in relation to other branches of biology and to *"ologies"* in general. In the present age of specialization in human endeavors, the inevitable connections between different fields are often obscured by the large masses of knowledge within the fields (and sometimes also, it must be admitted, by stereotyped college courses). At the other extreme, almost any field of learning may be so broadly defined as to take in an enormous range of subject material. Therefore, recognized "fields" must have bounds, even if these bounds are somewhat arbitrary and subject to shifting from time to time.

For the moment, let us look at the divisions of biology, "the science of life." When knowledge was limited, few subdivisions were needed, but now, to facilitate mental digestion, we cut the biology "layer cake," as it were, into small pieces in two distinct ways, as shown in Figure 1. We may divide it "horizontally" into what are usually called "basic" divisions, because they are concerned with fundamentals common to all life or at least are not restricted to particular organisms. Morphology, physiology, genetics, ecology, and embryology are examples of such divisions. We may also divide the cake "vertically" into what may be called "taxonomic" divisions, which deal with the morphology, physiology, ecology, etc., of specific kinds of organisms. Zoology, botany, and bacteriology are large divisions of this type, and phycology, protozoology, mycology, entomology, ornithology, etc., are divisions dealing with more limited groups of organisms. Thus ecology is a basic division of biology and, as such, is also an integral part of any and all of the taxonomic divisions. Both approaches are profitable. It is often very productive to restrict work to certain taxonomic groups, because different kinds of organisms require different methods of study (one cannot study eagles by the same methods used to study earthworms or oak trees) and because some groups of organisms are economically or otherwise much more important or interesting to man than others. Ultimately, however, unifying principles must be delimited and tested if the subject field is to qualify as "basic." It is the purpose of Part I of this book to outline briefly this aspect of ecology.

Perhaps the best way to delimit modern ecology is to consider it in terms of the concept of levels of organization. Although the number is arbitrary it is convenient to recognize ten levels of organization which are best visualized as a sort of "biological spectrum" as follows:

PROTOPLASM — CELLS — TISSUES — ORGANS — ORGAN SYSTEMS — ORGANISMS — POPULATIONS — COMMUNITIES — ECOSYSTEMS — BIOSPHERE

Ecology is concerned largely with the right-hand end of this spectrum, that is, the levels beyond that of the organism. In ecology the term *population,* originally coined to denote a group of people, is broadened to include groups of individuals of any one kind of organism. Likewise, *community* in the ecological sense (sometimes designated as "biotic community") includes all of the populations occupying a given area. The community and the nonliving environment function together as an ecological system or *ecosystem.* The portion of the earth in which ecosystems operate is conveniently designated as the *biosphere,* which is as far as we need go at the moment.* It is important to note that no sharp lines or breaks were indicated in the above "spectrum," not even between the organism and the population. Since introductory biology courses usually stop abruptly with the organism, and since in dealing with man and higher animals we are accustomed to think of the individual as the ultimate unit, the idea of a continuous spectrum may seem strange at first. However, from the standpoint of interdependence, interrelations and survival, there can be no sharp break anywhere along the line. The individual organism, for example, can not survive for long without its population any more than the organ would be able to survive

* Actually the "levels" spectrum, like a radiation spectrum or a logarithmic scale, theoretically can be extended infinitely in both directions.

for long without its organism. Similarly, the community can not exist without the cycling of materials and the flow of energy in the ecosystem.

One reason for listing the levels of organization horizontally instead of vertically is to emphasize that, in the long run, no one level is any more or less important, or any more or less deserving of scientific study than any other level. Some attributes, obviously, become more complex and variable as we proceed from the left to the right, but *it is an often overlooked fact that other attributes become less complex and less variable as we go from the small to the large unit.* Because homeostatic mechanisms, that is, checks and balances, forces and counter forces, operate all along the line, a certain amount of integration occurs as smaller units function within larger units. For example, the rate of photosynthesis of a whole community may be less variable than that of individuals or species within the community, because when one individual or species slows down another may speed up in a compensatory manner. *When we consider the unique characteristics which develop at each level,* there is no reason to suppose that any level is any more difficult or any easier to study quantitatively. The enumeration and study of the units of an organism (i.e., the cells and tissues) is not inherently easier nor more difficult than the enumeration and study of the units of a community (i.e., the organisms). Likewise, growth and metabolism may be effectively studied at the cellular level or at the ecosystem level by using units of measurement of a different order of magnitude. Furthermore, the findings at any one level *aid in the study of another level, but never completely explain the phenomena occurring at that level.* This is an important point because persons sometimes contend that it is useless to try to work on complex populations and communities when the smaller units are not yet fully understood. If this idea was pursued to its logical conclusion, all biologists would concentrate on one level, the cellular, for example, until they solved the problems of this level; then they would study tissues and organs. Actually, this philosophy was widely held until biologists discovered that each level had characteristics which knowledge of the next lower level explained only *in part.* It is now evident that science must advance along a broad front. This situation is analogous to the advance of an army; a breakthrough may occur anywhere, and when one does, the thrust will not penetrate far until the whole front moves up.

2. The subdivisions of ecology

In regard to subdivisions, ecology is commonly divided into *autecology* and *synecology*. Autecology deals with the study of the individual organism or an individual species. Life histories and behavior as a means of adaptation to the environment are usually emphasized. Synecology deals with the study of groups of organisms which are associated together as a unit. Thus, if a study is made of the relation of a white oak tree (or of white oak trees in general) or a wood thrush (or of wood thrushes in general) to the environment, the work would be autecological in nature. If the study concerned the forest in which the white oak or the wood thrush lives, the approach would be synecological. In the former instance attention is sharply focused on a particular organism with the purpose of seeing how it fits into the general ecological picture, much as one might focus attention on a particular object in a painting. In the latter instance the picture as a whole is considered, much as one might study the composition of a painting.

Synecology can be further subdivided according to the level of organization, as discussed in the previous section. Thus, we may speak of *population ecology, community ecology,* and *ecosystem ecology.* As a matter of fact, the present tendency is to divide ecology into four subdivisions, without reference to the terms autecology or synecology, namely: (1) species ecology, (2) population ecology, (3) community ecology, and (4) ecosystem ecology. As has already been stressed, the level-of-organization subdivisions are especially useful in the consideration of basic principles.

Useful subdivisions may also be based on the kind of environment or habitat. *Marine ecology, fresh-water ecology* and *terrestrial ecology* are the three broad subdivisions from this point of view; estuarine ecology, stream ecology, or grassland ecology represent more restricted interests. Although the basic principles are the same, the kinds of organisms and the methods of study are usually quite different for different environments. Therefore, subdivisions according to the natural environment are the most convenient for field research, as outlined in Part II of this book.

As is true of biology in general, ecology also may be subdivided along taxonomic lines, for example, plant ecology, insect ecology, microbial ecology and vertebrate ecology. Orientation within a restricted taxonomic group is profitable since attention is focused on the unique or special features in the ecology of that group, as well as on the development of detailed methods. In general, problems which pertain only to restricted groups are beyond the scope of this text since they are best considered after the general principles have been outlined.

Subdivisions in ecology, as in any other subject, are useful because they facilitate discussion and understanding as well as suggest profitable ways to specialize within the field of study. From the brief discussion in this section, we see that one might concentrate on processes, levels, environments or organisms and have equal opportunities to make valuable contributions to the overall understanding of environmental biology.

2 · Principles and concepts pertaining to the ecosystem and biogeochemical cycles

1. Concept of the ecosystem

Statement

Living organisms and their nonliving (abiotic) environment are inseparably interrelated and interact upon each other. Any area of nature that includes living organisms and nonliving substances interacting to produce an exchange of materials between the living and nonliving parts is an ecological system or ecosystem.* From a functional standpoint, an ecosystem has two components (which are usually partially separated in space and time), an *autotrophic component* (autotrophic = self-nourishing), in which fixation of light energy, use of simple inorganic substances, and buildup of complex substances predominate; and, secondly, a *heterotrophic component* (heterotrophic = other-nourishing) in which utilization, rearrangement and decomposition of complex materials predominate. It is convenient to recognize four constituents as comprising the ecosystem: (1) *abiotic substances*, basic inorganic and organic compounds of the environment; (2) *producers*, autotrophic organisms, largely green plants, which are able to manufacture

---

* The term ecosystem was first proposed by Tansley in 1935, but the concept is by no means so recent. Microcosm (Forbes, 1887), holocoen (Friederichs, 1930), biosystem (Thienemann, 1939), and bioinert body (Vernadsky, 1944) are terms which have been used to express similar ideas.

food from simple inorganic substances; (3) *consumers* (or macro-consumers), heterotrophic organisms, chiefly animals, which ingest other organisms or particulate organic matter; (4) *decomposers* (micro-consumers, saprobes or saprophytes), heterotrophic organisms, chiefly bacteria and fungi, which break down the complex compounds of dead protoplasms, absorb some of the decomposition products and release simple substances usable by the producers.

The ecosystem is the basic functional unit in ecology, since it includes both organisms (biotic communities) and abiotic environment, each influencing the properties of the other and both necessary for maintenance of life as we have it on the earth. A lake is an example of an ecosystem.

Explanation

Since no organism can exist by itself or without an environment, our first principle may well deal with the "interrelation" part of our basic definition of ecology given in Chapter 1, Section 1. The portion of the earth which contains living organisms and hence, in which ecosystems operate, is known as the *biosphere* (see page 6). Since life extends for only a relatively few feet below the earth's surface, the biosphere is the thin outer shell of the earth, including the oceans and the atmosphere. The biosphere is important not only as a place where living organisms can exist but also as a region where the incoming radiation energy of the sun brings about fundamental chemical and physical changes in the inert material of the earth. These changes result chiefly from the functioning of various ecosystems.

The concept of the ecosystem is and should be a broad one, its main function in ecological thought being to emphasize obligatory relationships, interdependence and causal relationships. Ecosystems may be conceived and studied in various sizes. A pond, a lake, a tract of forest or even a small aquarium could provide a convenient unit of study. As long as the major components are present and operate together to achieve some sort of functional stability, even if for only a short time, the entity may be considered an ecosystem. A temporary pond, for example, is a definite ecosystem with characteristic organisms and processes even though its active existence is limited to a short period of time.

One of the universal features of all ecosystems, whether terrestrial, freshwater or marine, or whether man-dominated (agricultural, etc.) or not, is the interaction of the autotrophic and heterotrophic components, as outlined in the Statement. Very frequently these functions and the organisms responsible for the processes are partially separated in space in that they are stratified one above the other. Also, the basic functions are partially separated in time in that there may be a considerable delay in the heterotrophic utilization of the products of autotrophic organisms. For example, photosynthesis predominates in the above-ground portion of a forest ecosystem. Only a part, often only a small part, of the photosynthate is immediately and directly used by the plant and by herbivores and parasites which feed on foliage and new wood; much of the synthesized material (in the form of leaves, wood and stored food in seeds and roots) eventually reaches the litter and soil which together constitute a well-defined heterotrophic system.

A further subdivision of the ecosystem into four components—abiotic substances, producers, consumers and decomposers—provides a convenient ecological classification. The three living components may be thought of as the three "functional kingdoms of nature" since they are based on the type of nutrition and the energy source used. These ecological categories should not be confused with taxonomic kingdoms, although there are certain parallels, as pointed out by Whittaker (1957). The ecological classification is one of function rather than of species as such. There are no hard and fast lines between the categories since some species of organisms occupy intermediate positions in the series and others are able to shift their mode of nutrition according to environmental circumstances. Separation of heterotrophs into large consumers and decomposers (i.e., small consumers) is especially arbitrary, but is justified in practice because of the very different study methods required. Organisms which we have designated as decomposers are those which obtain their energy by heterotrophic absorption of decomposition products. Such organisms are largely the heterotrophic microorganisms (bacteria, fungi, etc.); they are relatively immobile (usually imbeded in the medium being decomposed) and are very small with high rates of metabolism and turnover. Specialization is more evident biochemically than morphologically; consequently one cannot usually determine their role in the ecosystem by such direct methods as looking at them or counting their numbers. Organisms which we have designated as macro-consumers obtain their energy by heterotrophic ingestion of particulate organic matter. These are largely the "animals" in the broad sense. In contrast to the decomposers, the macro-consumers are larger, have slower rates of metabolism and are more readily studied by direct means. They tend to be morphologically adapted for active food seeking or food gathering, with the development of complex sensory-neuromotor as well as digestive, respiratory and circulatory systems in the higher forms.

It is possible to have a sizable ecosystem containing only producers and decomposers; pioneer aquatic communities, for example, may be composed of algae and heterotrophic microorganisms. Almost everywhere on our planet, however, the macro-consumers or animals invade sooner or later. Presumedly, a system without animals would be less efficient in the long run since the rate of energy transfer and the speed of recycling of materials would be slower. Large sections of the biosphere, such as the soil and the deep sea, lack producers but are kept going by the gravity flow of organic materials from above. We may conveniently consider soil, fallen logs or deep sea basins as ecosystems (since they do show consistent structural and functional characteristics), provided we recognize that these systems consist only of the heterotrophic component and are, therefore, incomplete.

For additional discussions of the ecosystem concept see Forbes' (1887) classic essay, Tansley (1935), and especially the important paper by Lindeman (1942).

Example

One of the best ways to begin the study of ecology is to go out and study a small pond. Ecologists have spent many years studying individual ponds and lakes without investigating all the details or understanding all the process, but the basic principles can be grasped by the student in a short time without resorting to a detailed study. Let us consider the pond as a whole as an ecosystem, leaving the study of smaller systems within the pond for the second section of this book. The inseparability of living organisms and the nonliving environment is at once apparent with the first sample collected. Not only is the pond a place where plants and animals live, but plants and animals make the pond what it is. Thus, a bottle full of the pond water or a scoop full of bottom

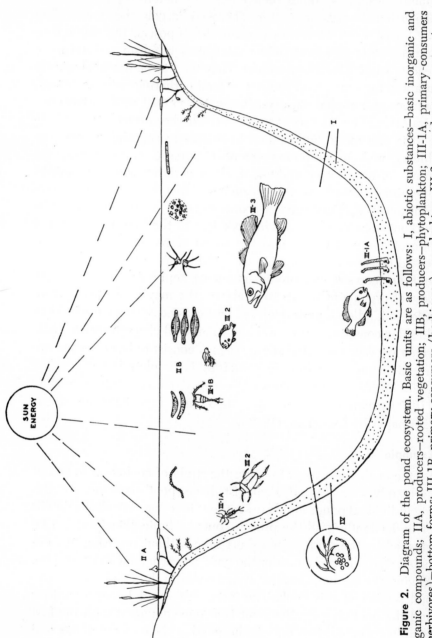

Figure 2. Diagram of the pond ecosystem. Basic units are as follows: I, abiotic substances—basic inorganic and organic compounds; IIA, producers—rooted vegetation; IIB, producers—phytoplankton; III-1A, primary-consumers (herbivores)—bottom forms; III-1B, primary consumers (herbivores)—zooplankton; III-2, secondary consumers (carnivores); III-3, tertiary consumers (secondary carnivores); IV, decomposers—bacteria and fungi of decay.

mud is a mixture of living organisms, both plant and animal, and inorganic and organic compounds. Some of the larger animals and plants can be separated from the sample for study or counting, but it would be difficult to completely separate the myriad of small living things from the nonliving matrix without changing the character of the fluid. True, one could autoclave the sample of water or bottom mud so that only nonliving material remained, but this residue would then no longer be pond water or pond soil but would have entirely different appearances and characteristics.

Despite the complexities, the pond ecosystem may be reduced to the four basic units, as shown in Figure 2.

1. *Abiotic substances* (Fig. 2, I), basic inorganic and organic compounds, such as water, carbon dioxide, oxygen, calcium, nitrogen and phosphorus salts, amino and humic acids, etc. A small portion of the vital nutrients is in solution and immediately available to organisms, but a much larger portion is held in reserve in particulate matter (especially in the bottom sediments), as well as in the organisms themselves. As Hayes (1951) has expressed it, a pond or lake "is not, as one might think, a body of water containing nutrients, but an equilibrated system of water and solids, and under ordinary conditions nearly all of the nutrients are in a solid stage." The rate of release of nutrients from the solids is one of the most important processes which regulate the rate of function of the entire ecosystem.

2. *Producer organisms.* In a pond the producers may be of two main types: (1) rooted or large floating plants generally growing in shallow water only (Fig. 2, IIA); and (2) minute floating plants, usually algae, called *phytoplankton* (Fig. 2, IIB), distributed throughout the pond as deep as light penetrates. In abundance, the phytoplankton gives the water a greenish color; otherwise, these producers are not visible to the casual observer, and their presence is not suspected by the layman. Yet, in large ponds and lakes, phytoplankton is generally more important than is rooted vegetation in the production of basic food for the ecosystem.

3. *Consumer organisms*, animals, such as insect larvae, crustacea, and fish. The primary consumers (herbivores) (Fig. 2, III-1A, III-1B) feed directly on living plants or plant remains, and are of two types, *zooplankton* and bottom forms, paralleling the two types of producers. The secondary consumers (carnivores) (Fig. 2, III-2, III-3) feed on the primary consumers, etc.

4. *Decomposer organisms* (Fig. 2, IV). The aquatic bacteria and fungi are distributed throughout the pond, but are especially abundant in the mud-water interface along the bottom where bodies of plants and animals accumulate, and in the photosynthetic zone where plankton and rooted vegetation are concentrated. There may be as many as a million bacteria associated with a gram of plankton, and as many with each gram of bottom surface mud. While a few of the bacteria and fungi are pathogenetic in that they will attack living organisms and cause disease, the great majority are saprobic and begin attack only after the organism dies. When temperature conditions are favorable, decomposition occurs rapidly in a body of water; dead organisms do not retain their identification for very long but are soon broken up into pieces and their nutrients released for reuse.

The partial stratification of the pond into an upper "production" zone and a lower "decomposition-nutrient regeneration" zone is evident from Figure 2. Some of the energy fixed in the sunlit or photic zone is dissipated within the zone by the respiration of all of the organisms, but a substantial amount ends up as *organic detritus* (a general term for fragments of bodies, feces, etc.), which is consumed and decomposed on the bottom of the pond.

The biological control of the chemical environment

Although everyone realizes that the abiotic environment ("physical factors") controls the activities of organisms, it is not always realized that organisms influence and control the abiotic environment in many ways. Changes in the physical and chemical nature of inert materials are constantly being effected by organisms which return new compounds and isotopes to the nonliving environment. The chemical content of the sea and of its bottom "oozes" is largely determined by the actions of marine organisms. Plants growing on a sand dune build up a soil radically different from the original substrate. A South Pacific coral island is a striking example of how organisms influence their abiotic environment. From simple raw materials of the sea, whole islands are built as the result of the activities of animals (corals, etc.) and plants. The very composition of our atmosphere is controlled by organisms. Indeed, without living organisms our world probably would be a relatively unchanging mass composed of fewer kinds of materials. Like our moon, it would be a dull world indeed.

For a discussion of the "biological control of the chemical environment," see Redfield (1958).

The Copper Basin at Copperhill, Tennessee, and a similar area east of Butte, Montana, provide impressive demonstrations of the result of the *absence* of living organisms (see Figure 3). In these regions fumes from copper smelters exterminated all the rooted plants over a wide area. All the soil eroded away, leaving a spectacular desert, as shown in Figure 3. Although modern smelting methods no longer release fumes, vegetation has failed to return, and artificial reforestation attempts have largely failed. The area is too "raw" for life to obtain an effective foothold and start the rebuilding process. Even the climate is different; temperatures are higher and less rain falls in the denuded area, compared with the nearby forest (Hursh, 1948a). Everyone should visit Copperhill as part of his general education!

Figure 3. The Copper Basin at Copperhill, Tennessee, is suggestive of what land without life would be like. A luxuriant forest once covered this area, until fumes from smelters killed all of the vegetation. Although fumes are no longer released by modern methods of ore preparation, the vegetation has not become re-established. (U. S. Forest Service Photo.)

Production and decomposition in nature

Just how chlorophyll-bearing plants manufacture carbohydrates, proteins, fats and other complex materials is not yet fully understood. However, the simplified photosynthesis formula is one of the first things learned in elementary biology. Written in word form, it goes something like this:

$$\begin{bmatrix} \text{Carbon} \\ \text{dioxide} \end{bmatrix} \text{plus [water] plus} \begin{bmatrix} \text{light energy in} \\ \text{presence of en-} \\ \text{zyme systems} \\ \text{associated with} \\ \text{chlorophyll} \end{bmatrix} \begin{array}{c} \text{results in [glucose]} \\ \text{plus} \\ \text{[oxygen].} \end{array}$$

Chemically the photosynthetic process involves the storage of a part of the sunlight energy as potential or "bound" energy of food. The process is much more complicated than indicated in the above word formula, but the basic idea is easily understood. The photosynthetic process of food manufacture is often called the "business of green plants." It is now believed that the synthesis of amino acids, proteins, and other vital materials occurs simultaneously with the synthesis of carbohydrates (glucose), some of the basic steps involved being the same. The reverse of photosynthesis, or respiration, results in the oxidation of foods with the release of energy (making possible growth, movement, heat production, etc.) and is, of course, the "business of all organisms." A part of the synthesized food is used, of course, by the producers themselves. The excess as well as the producer protoplasm is then utilized by the consumers and decomposers, or, as is frequently the case, part of it is stored or transported into other systems. The dynamics of "production" will be considered in detail in Chapter 3.

Two very interesting groups of producers, the photosynthetic bacteria and the chemosynthetic bacteria, use methods of carbon fixation different from the method shown in the word formula above. In fact, these organisms are intermediate between producers and consumers, and producers and decomposers, respectively. In most ecosystems these bacteria play a very minor role in the production of organic matter, but they are able to function in situations which would be unfavorable for the general run of green plants. The photosynthetic bacteria use sunlight for energy but they can grow anaerobically; they do not produce oxygen as a byproduct, and are able to function as heterotrophs in the dark. The purple bacterium, *Rhodospirillum*, belongs to this group; these bacteria often occur as a conspicuous purple layer beneath a green algal layer in stagnant pools. The chemosynthetic bacteria obtain their energy not by photosynthesis but by the chemical oxidation of simple inorganic compounds, as, for example, ammonia to nitrite, nitrite to nitrate, sulfide to sulfur, and ferrous to ferric iron. They can grow in the dark either in the presence or absence of oxygen. The sulfur bacteria, often abundant in sulfur springs, and the nitrogen bacteria, which are important in the nitrogen cycle (see Figure 7), are examples of this group.

Most species of the higher plants (Spermatophytes) and many species of the algae require only simple inorganic nutrients and are, therefore, completely autotrophic. Some species of algae, however, require a single complex organic "growth substance" which they themselves cannot synthesize; still other species require one, two, three or many such growth substances (Provasoli and Pintner, 1953) and are, therefore, partly heterotrophic. In the land of "the midnight sun" in northern Sweden, Rodhe (1955) has presented evidence to indicate that during the summer, algae in lakes are producers; during the long winter "night" (which may last for several months), when they apparently are able to utilize the accumulated organic matter in the water, they are consumers.

Despite the fact that nature presents a broad spectrum of function, the simple producer-consumer-decomposer classification is a good working arrangement. Since specialization in function tends to result in greater efficiency under the competitive conditions of nature, most kinds of organisms, especially the evolutionally more advanced species, appear to be restricted to a rather narrow range of function, leaving the job of filling in the gaps to less specialized organisms. Just how important are the nonspecialists (or the "jack-of-all-trades", as it were) in the total metabolism of various ecosystems is a question which cannot be answered as yet.

The activities of consumers are familiar enough since man is the number one consumer with which we are concerned. The importance of decomposer activity in nature is also generally recognized but actually little understood. It has been only in the past few years that the ecology of bacteria and fungi has received the attention it deserves. Consequently, it may be worth while to consider the role of the decomposers in the ecosystem in more detail.*

Decomposition, of course, is the result of the process by which bacteria and fungi obtain food for themselves. It is an absolutely vital function, nevertheless, because, if it did not occur, all the nutrients would soon be tied up in dead bodies, and no new life could be produced. Within the bacterial cells and the fungi, mycelia, are sets of enzymes necessary to carry out specific chemical reactions. These enzymes are secreted into dead matter; some of the decomposition products are absorbed into the organism as food, and other products remain in the environment or are excreted from the cells. No single species of decomposer can produce complete decomposition of a dead body. However, populations of decomposers prevalent in the biosphere consist of many species which, by their graduated action, can effect complete decomposition. Not all parts of the bodies of plants and animals are broken down at the same rate. Fats, sugars and proteins are decomposed readily, but cellulose, lignin of wood and the hair and bones of animals, are acted on very slowly. This is illustrated by studies of the decomposition of marsh grass, shown in Figure 4. Note that under the most favorable conditions (Fig. 4, right), decomposition was rapid during the first 10 days, but proceeded at a much slower rate during the next two weeks. About 25 per cent of the dry weight of the organism was quickly decomposed and the remaining 75 per cent (mostly cellulose) acted on more slowly. Decomposition of grass left submerged in the water was much influenced by temperature, the rate of breakdown being more rapid in summer than in winter (Fig. 4, left). After almost a year, 10 per cent of the annual crop of grass still remained. The "delay in the complete heterotrophic utilization of the products of autotrophic organisms" may be even greater in dry or cold environments (see page 375).

The more resistant organic compounds are collectively called "humus." It is convenient to regard the decomposition as comprising two stages: the rapid production of humus and the slower mineralization of humus. The decomposition of cellulose, particularly, seems to be a bottleneck in ecosystems (see the review by Siu and Reese, 1953).

---

* The following discussion of decomposers is based in part on a series of notes contributed by Dr. Carl H. Oppenheimer, Institute of Marine Science, University of Texas.

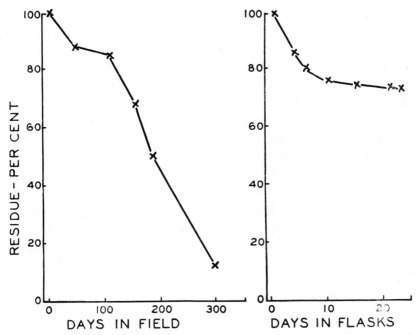

Figure 4.   Decomposition of marsh grass (*Spartina alterniflora*) in sea water, expressed as per cent of initial dry weight of grass after different periods of time. Left, dry residue remaining from freshly cut grass placed in crates submerged in a Georgia estuary from November to the following September; both small animals and microbes had ready access to the grass. Right, residues of ground-up grass in flasks inoculated with marine mud bacteria and shaken at 30° C. for 24 days. (After Burkholder and Bornside, 1957.)

The bacteria and the fungi may work together or alternate in the breakdown process. Bacteria appear to be more important in the breakdown of animal flesh while fungi perhaps are more important in the breakdown of wood. Tribe (Williams and Spicer, 1957) describes an interesting succession of organisms which completely decomposed cellulose film which he buried in the soil. Fungi were the first to invade the film; only later did bacteria appear in numbers. As soon as the film had been broken up, nematodes and other soil invertebrates arrived on the scene and gobbled up the small pieces (including, of course, the decomposers). Thus, decomposers also provide food, indirectly or directly, for various consumers which in turn hasten the breakdown process. While large organisms are being slowly decomposed, a special habitat is provided for a variety of organisms. For example, a fallen log in a forest supports a well developed subcommunity which changes with the state of decay.

One of the important characteristics of decomposers as a group is their ability to function under a variety of environmental conditions. Bacteria, for example, will grow either in the absence or presence of oxygen. However, the end products may be different. Figure 5 shows the results of an interesting study in which the same species of bacterium, *Aerobacter,* was grown under anaerobic and aerobic conditions with glucose as the sole carbon source. When oxygen was present almost all of the glucose was converted into bacterial protoplasm and CO_2, but in the absence of oxygen decomposition was incomplete, a much smaller portion of the glucose ended up as cell carbon, and a series of organic compounds was released into the environment. Bacteria, in fact, often create anaerobic conditions in sediments and soil by using oxygen faster than it can diffuse into the medium.

Although the "mineralization of organic matter" and the production of plant nutrients has been stressed as the primary function of decomposition, there is yet another function which is receiving increasing attention from ecologists. Apart from possible use as food by other organisms, the organic substances released into the environment during decomposition may have profound effects on the growth of other organisms in the ecosystem. Julian Huxley, in 1935, suggested the term "external diffusion hormones" for those chemical substances which exert a correlative action on the system via the external medium; Lucas (1947) has proposed

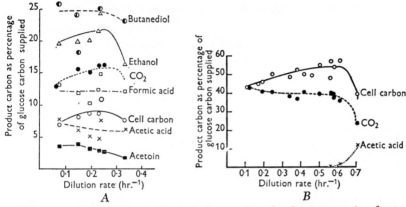

Figure 5. The decomposition of glucose by the bacterium *Aerobacter* under anaerobic (A) and aerobic (B) conditions. Note that under aerobic conditions decomposition is complete, and 40 to 50 per cent of the original carbon of glucose is converted into bacterial biomass. However, under anaerobic conditions only about 15 per cent glucose carbon is converted, and a number of incompletely decomposed organic substances remain in the environment. The decline in cell carbon and CO_2 and the beginning of acetic acid production in B indicate that oxygen is beginning to decrease, with the result that the situation shown in A is beginning to develop. (After Pirt, 1957.)

the term "ectocrine." The term "environmental hormone" also clearly indicates what is meant. These substances may be inhibitory, as in the case of the "antibiotic" penicillin (which is produced by a fungus), or stimulatory, as in the case of various vitamins and other growth substances, for example, thiamin, Vitamin B_{12}, biotin, histidine, uracil and others, many of which have not been identified chemically. Organic compounds frequently combine with trace metals in the environment to form hormone-like substances.

Interest in environmental hormones goes back to the famous Pütter-Krogh argument (which still continues) concerning the role of dissolved organic substances which are abundant in water and soil. The former contended that these substances were extensively used by higher plants and animals as food; the latter presented experimental evidence that they were insignificant as food, at least for such organisms as zooplankton. It is now becoming clear that many of the "waste products" of decomposition may be more important as chemical regulators than as food as such. This is exciting to the ecologist, because such regulators provide a mechanism for coordinating units of the ecosystem, and help to explain both the equilibria and the succession of species which he so commonly observes in nature. Before we become too enthusiastic about this, there is much work to be done. Vitamin B_{12}, for example, has been much studied in nature in recent years, and the investigators are not agreed on whether or not this substance is ecologically important. It is definitely required by many organisms, but it is also abundant and widely distributed; the question whether it ever becomes scarce enough to limit the growth of producers has not been satisfactorily determined (note, for example, the opposite views of Droop, 1957, and Daisley, 1957). The role of the inhibitory substances is perhaps more clearly defined. It should be mentioned at this point that although the decomposers seem to play the major role in the production of environmental hormones, the algae also excrete such substances (see, for example, Rice, 1954 and Proctor, 1957). The waste products of higher organisms, root excretions, for example, may also be important in this regard (see Bonner, 1950; Keever, 1950). In addition to papers cited above, additional discussion of this general subject may be found in the review by Saunders (1957) and the symposium edited by Williams and Spicer (1957).

In summary, then, it would appear that the decomposers have at least three functions in the ecosystem in addition to tending to their own needs for growth and survival: (1) the mineralization of dead organic matter, (2) production of food for other organisms and (3) production of "ectocrine" substances. Since microorganisms do bring about extensive changes in the chemical nature of the environment, they are also important in the formation of inert materials, for example, the extensive bacterial precipitation of carbonates in the sea (Lalou, 1957). Although decomposers are very numerous, as units they are so small that their total biomass is much less than that of producers and consumers. Decomposers compensate for their size by a high rate of metabolism and a rapid turnover of protoplasm. Some idea of this intense activity is obtained by observation of the increase in temperature which may accompany decomposition. Many people have observed the heat generated in an artificial compost pile. In the rapidly accumulating sediments of Lake Mead, which is formed by the huge Hoover Dam on the Colorado River, ZoBell, Sisler and Oppenheimer (1953) found that the temperature of the bottom mud was as much as 6° C. above that of the adjacent water; they demonstrated that a part of this heat, at least, was due to the immense populations of microorganisms which are doing their best to keep up with the man-accelerated erosion in the watershed.

Because decomposers are so small and relatively unspecialized morphologically, they are difficult to study. One cannot analyze a microbial population simply by looking at it and counting the individuals as one might do with a stand of trees or a population of mammals, since microbes which look alike might have an entirely different type of metabolism. Species have to be isolated and cultured or the total activity measured in situ: specific examples of the latter approach will be discussed in Chapter 3 and in Part II of this text. Because of the technical difficulties of study, microbial ecology is, unfortunately, often completely omitted from the general college course in ecology. This need not be the case. Certainly the cellulose film and marsh grass experiments described above could be adapted as a class exercise. Some idea of the activities of decomposers can be obtained by measuring the CO_2 evolution from soil, using fairly simple apparatus which can be designed for field use (see Wallis and Wilde, 1957).

In addition to the symposium on microbial ecology (Williams and Spicer, 1957) and the other works already cited, the review papers by ZoBell (1946) and Cooke (1958) contain additional ideas, data and references.

Homeostasis of the ecosystem

The existence of homeostatic mechanisms at different levels of biological organization was mentioned in the previous chapter. Homeostasis at the organism level is a well known concept in physiology as outlined, for example, by Walter B. Cannon in his readable little book entitled *The Wisdom of the Body* (Cannon, 1932). We find that equilibrium between organisms and environment may also be maintained by factors which resist change in the system as a whole. Much has been written about this "balance of nature" but only with the recent development of good methods for measuring rates of function of whole systems has a beginning been made in the understanding of the mechanisms involved.

These mechanisms include those which regulate the storage and release of nutrients, as well as those which regulate the growth of organisms and the production and decomposition of organic substances. The possible role of "ectocrine" substances in coordinating units of the ecosystem has already been mentioned. In subsequent sections and chapters, we shall have frequent occasion to discuss these mechanisms and to present specific data demonstrating that the whole is often not as variable as the part.

As a result of the evolution of the central nervous system and brain, man has gradually become the most powerful organism, as far as the ability to modify the operation of ecosystems is concerned.* Man's power to change and control seems to be increasing faster than man's realization and understanding of the results of the profound changes of which he is now capable. As many writers have pointed out, this is a dangerous situation, because tinkering with basic ecosystems of the world can result either in a glorious future for mankind, or in his complete destruction if too many large-scale mistakes are made. Although nature has remarkable resilience, the limits of homeostatic mechanisms can easily be exceeded by the actions of man. When treated sewage is introduced into a stream at a moderate rate, the system is able to "purify itself" and return to the previous condition within a comparatively few miles downstream. If the pollution is great or if toxic substances for which no natural homeostatic mechanisms have been evolved are included, the stream may be permanently altered or even destroyed as far as usefulness to man is concerned.

The idea of the ecosystem and the realization that mankind is a part of complex "biogeochemical" cycles with increasing power to modify the cycles are concepts basic to modern ecology and are also points of view of extreme importance in human affairs generally. Conservation of natural resources, the most important practical application of ecology, must be built around these view-

* So important is man's role becoming as "a mighty geological agent" that Vernadsky (1945) has suggested that we think of the "noosphere" (from Greek *noos*, mind), or the world dominated by the mind of man, as gradually replacing the biosphere, the naturally evolving world which has existed for billions of years. This is dangerous philosophy because it is based on the assumption that mankind is now wise enough to understand the results of all his actions. When the reader has finished with this book I am sure he will agree that we have yet much to learn before we can safely take over the management of everything!

points. Thus, if understanding of ecological systems and moral responsibility among mankind can keep pace with man's power to effect changes, the present-day concept of "unlimited exploitation of resources" will give way to "unlimited ingenuity in perpetuating a cyclic abundance of resources." Hutchinson (1948a) has aptly expressed this viewpoint somewhat as follows: the ecologist should be able to show that it is just as much fun and just as important to repair the biosphere and keep it in good running order as to mend the radio or the family car.

2. Concepts of habitat and ecological niche

Statement

The habitat of an organism is the place where it lives, or the place where one would go to find it. The ecological niche, on the other hand, is the position or status of an organism within its community and ecosystem resulting from the organism's structural adaptations, physiological responses and specific behavior (inherited and/or learned). The ecological niche of an organism depends not only on where it lives but also on what it does. By analogy, it may be said that the habitat is the organism's "address," and the niche is its "profession," biologically speaking.

Explanation and examples

The term habitat is widely used, not only in ecology but elsewhere. It is generally understood to mean simply the place where an organism lives. Thus, the habitat of the water "backswimmer," *Notonecta,* is the shallow, vegetation-choked areas (littoral zone) of ponds and lakes; that is where one would go to collect this particular organism. The habitat of a *Trillium* plant is a moist, shaded situation in a mature deciduous forest; that is where one would go to find *Trillium* plants. Different species in the genus *Notonecta* or *Trillium* may occur in the same general habitat but exhibit small differences in location, in which event we would say that the *microhabitat* is different. Other species in these genera exhibit large habitat, or *macrohabitat*, differences.

Habitat may also refer to the place occupied by an entire community. For example, the habitat of the "sand sage grassland community" is the series of ridges of sandy soil occurring along the north sides of rivers in the southern Great Plains region of the United States. Habitat in this case consists mostly of physical or abiotic complexes, whereas habitat as used with reference to *Notonecta* and *Trillium*, mentioned above, includes living as well as nonliving objects. Thus, the habitat of an organism or group of organisms (population) includes other organisms as well as the abiotic environment. A description of the habitat of the community would include only the latter. It is important to recognize these two possible uses of the term habitat in order to avoid confusion.

Ecological niche is a more recent concept and is not so generally understood outside the field of ecology. It is, however, a very important concept. Charles Elton in England was one of the first to begin using the term "niche" in the sense of the "functional status of an organism in its community"; it has gradually become generally accepted as it became clear that niche is by no means a synonym for habitat. Let us return, for the moment, to the simple analogy of the "address" and the "profession" mentioned above. If we wished to become acquainted with some person in our human community we would need to know, first of all, his address, that is, where he could be found. To really get to know him, however, we would have to learn more than the neighborhood where he lives or works. We would want to know something about his occupation, his interests, his associates, and the part he plays in general community life. So it is with the study of organisms; learning the habitat is just the beginning. To determine the organism's status in the natural community we would need to know something of its activities, especially its nutrition and energy source; also its rate of metabolism and growth, its effect on other organisms with which it comes into contact, and the extent to which it modifies or is capable of modifying important operations in the ecosystem.

Returning to the *Notonecta* and the *Trillium*, we can see that discovery of the habitat, or where to go to collect it, does not necessarily result in determination of the ecological niche. By studying the structure of organisms in the laboratory we can infer certain things about their activities, but we would most certainly also have to do some observing or experimenting in nature. We would soon find that *Notonecta* is an active predator, swimming about and grasping and eating other animals of its general size range. It is thus a secondary consumer in its marginal pond community, and is fed upon in turn by other, larger animals or tertiary consumers. In contrast, other water bugs of the genus *Corixa*, found in the same habitat and looking much like *Notonecta* (see Figure 6), feed on decaying vegetation. *Corixa* thus plays a very different role in community life and, therefore, occupies an entirely different niche. The *Trillium*, because it has chloroplasts and is capable of food manufacture, can be immediately classed as a producer. As far as the forest community as a whole is concerned, it is a very minor producer, in no way influencing and controlling community life, as do the great forest trees. However, be-cause of its ability to live in dense shade and to convert the sparse light energy into food energy, it does occupy a definite and important place within its particular stratum, the forest floor, of the forest community. It is important to other forest floor plants competing with it for nutrients and sunlight, and to the animals which eat its foliage, are attracted to its flowers or use its body as a resting or hiding place.

The description of ecological niches of organisms is necessary as a foundation for an understanding of the functioning of the community and ecosystems operating in major habitats, just as the knowledge of the basic morphology of the parts (cells, tissues, organs) of the individual organism is prerequisite to an understanding of its physiology. In attempting to discover and describe the niches of organisms, the number of individuals present (i.e., the population density), their collective metabolism, the effects of

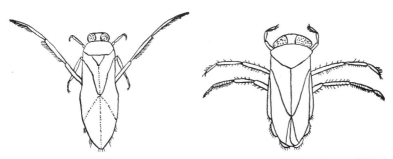

Figure 6. *Notonecta* (left) and *Corixa* (right), two aquatic bugs (Hemiptera) which occupy the same general habitat but very different ecological niches because of differences in food habits. (Redrawn from Mellanby, 1938.)

the abiotic environment on the organisms, the effect of the organisms on the abiotic environment, and the interaction of organisms on each other all enter the picture. Sometimes the niche is relatively easy to discover and describe, but usually it is not. There are various complications. The same species often occupies somewhat different niches in different regions, depending on the local community organization. Within the same taxonomic group, such as the genus or family, the species often show a similarity in niche relations (as might be expected from their similar morphological adaptations), but they almost never actually occupy the same niche in the same habitat. This is an important principle which will be discussed in Chapter 7 (Section 2). Many organisms, especially animals with distinct life history stages, occupy successively several widely different niches. Thus, the larval stage of a mosquito is a primary consumer in shallow water habitats of ponds, etc., whereas the adult occupies an entirely different habitat and niche— one that often brings it into violent interaction with mankind!

3. Biogeochemical cycles

Statement

The chemical elements, including all the essential elements of protoplasm, tend to circulate in the biosphere in characteristic paths from environment to organisms and back to the environment. These more or less circular paths are known as "inorganic-organic cycles," or *biogeochemical cycles*.

Explanation

The study of ecosystems may be approached not only from the consideration of the organism, but also from that of the abiotic environment. In other words, it is profitable in ecology to study not only organisms and their environmental relations but also the basic nonliving environment in relation to organisms. Of the 90-odd elements known to occur in nature, between 30 and 40 are known to be required by living organisms. Some elements such as carbon, hydrogen, oxygen, and nitrogen are needed in large quantities; others are needed in small, or even minute, quantities. Whatever the need may be, essential elements (as well as nonessential elements) appear to exhibit definite biogeochemical cycles. Some cycles, such as the one involving carbon, are more perfect than others; that is, the material is returned to the environment as fast as it is removed, and although critical "shortages" may occur in certain environments there is little or no permanent change in the distribution of the element in the various ecosystems of the biosphere. Other cycles may be less perfect; that is, some portion of the supply may get "lost" for long periods of time in places or in chemical forms inaccessible to organisms.

Hutchinson (1948a) points out that man is unique in that not only does he require the 40 essential elements but also in his complex culture he uses nearly all the other elements and the newer synthetic ones as well. He has so speeded up the movement of many materials that the cycles tend to become imperfect, or the process becomes "acyclic," with the result that man is continually running into shortages. The aim of conservation of natural re sources in the broadest sense is to make acyclic processes more cyclic. Fortunately, the more perfect cycles have so many compensating mechanisms that man has not yet done too much to modify them. Disturbance or manipulation of a cycle involving a vital element, however, could conceivably be much more dangerous than the disturbance of the less perfect cycles, because if such a cycle were disturbed beyond its compensatory powers, the whole thing might go completely to pieces.

Examples

Two examples will suffice to illustrate the principle of inorganic-organic cycles. The nitrogen cycle (Fig. 7) is an example of a very complex but more or less perfect cycle; the phosphorus cycle (Fig. 8) is an example of a simpler, possibly less perfect, one. As will be outlined in Chapter 4, both these elements are often very important factors, limiting or controlling the abundance of organisms, and hence they have received much attention and study.

As shown in Figure 7 (A) the nitrogen in protoplasm is broken down from organic to inorganic form by a series of decomposer bacteria, each specialized for a particular part of the job. Some of this nitrogen ends up as nitrate, the form most readily used by green plants (although some organisms can use nitrogen in other forms as illustrated), thus completing the cycle. The air, which contains 80 per cent nitrogen, is the greatest reservoir and safety

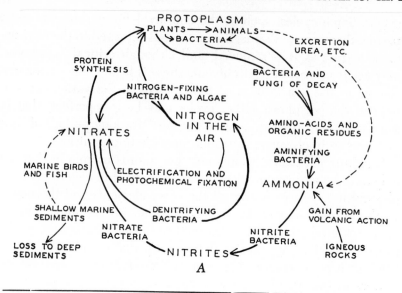

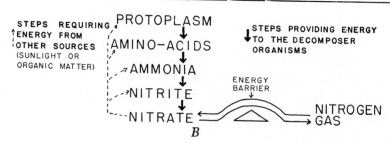

Figure 7. Two ways of picturing the nitrogen biogeochemical cycle, an example of a relatively perfect, self-regulating cycle in which there is little overall change in available nitrogen in *large* ecosystems or in the biosphere as a whole, despite rapid circulation of materials. In *A* the circulation of nitrogen between organisms and environment is depicted along with microorganisms which are responsible for key steps. In *B* the same basic steps are arranged in an ascending-descending series, with the high energy forms on top to distinguish steps which require energy from those which release energy.

Some quantitative estimates of interest are:

1. The loss of nitrogen from the atmosphere to sediments is apparently balanced by the gain from volcanic action; in fact, the nitrogen content of the air may possibly have increased throughout geological time.

2. According to Hutchinson (1944a), the amount of nitrogen fixed from the air (non-cyclic nitrogen) is estimated to lie between 140 and 700 mg. per square meter, or between 1 and 6 pounds per acre per year for the biosphere as a whole. Most of this is biological; only a small portion (not more than 35 mg. per square meter per year in temperate regions) is non-biological (electrification or photochemical fixation). Biological fixation in fertile areas may be much greater than the biosphere average, up to 200 pounds per acre, according to Fogg (1955).

(*Continued on facing page*)

valve of the system. Nitrogen is continually entering the air by the action of denitrifying bacteria and continually returning to the cycle through the action of nitrogen-fixing bacteria or blue-green algae and through the action of lightning (i.e., electrification). In Figure 7 (B) the components of the nitrogen cycle are shown in terms of the energy necessary for the operation of the cycle. The steps from proteins down to nitrates provide energy for organisms which accomplish the breakdown, whereas the return steps require energy from other sources, such as organic matter or sunlight. Likewise, nitrogen fixers must use up some of their carbohydrate or other energy stores in order to transform atmospheric nitrogen into nitrates.

The importance of the nitrogen-fixing bacteria associated with legumes (Fig. 9) is well known, of course, and in modern agriculture continuous fertility of a field is maintained as much by crop rotation involving legumes as by the application of nitrogen fertilizers. Secretion from the legume root stimulates growth of the nodule bacteria, and bacterial secretions cause root hair deformation, the first step in nodule formation (Nutman, 1956). Neither legume nor bacteria can fix nitrogen alone. Strains of bacteria have evolved which will grow only on certain species of legumes. The bacteria get carbohydrates from the host and the host gets nitrogen, some of which is excreted into the soil and may be used by other plants. Other nitrogen fixing bacteria live free in the soil and do not require the partnership of a vascular plant. In water and moist soil, blue-green algae often perform the vital operation of nitrogen fixation; these organisms may also be associated with higher plants but seem to be much less specialized symbionts. In the Orient it has been found that the blue-green algae which occur naturally in the rice paddies are very important

---

3. The capacity to fix atmospheric nitrogen was thought, until recently, to be limited to a few, but abundant, organisms, as follows:
   Free-living bacteria—*Azotobacter* and *Clostridium*
   Symbiotic nodule bacteria on legume plants—*Rhizobium* (see Figure 9);
   Blue-green algae (free-living or symbiotic)—*Anabaena*, *Nostoc*, and
       probably others.
In 1949 it was discovered that the purple bacterium *Rhodospirillum* and many other representatives of the photosynthetic bacteria are nitrogen fixers (see Kamen and Gest, 1949 and Kamen, 1953). Ability to fix nitrogen is proving to be widespread among photosynthetic, chemosynthetic and saprobic microorganisms. However, no higher plant is able to fix nitrogen alone; legumes and a few species of other families of vascular plants do so only with the aid of symbiotic bacteria.

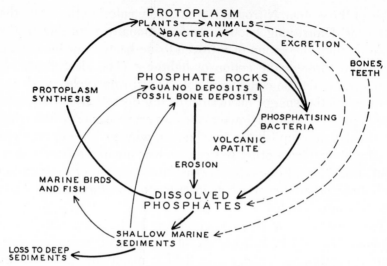

Figure 8. The phosphorus cycle. Phosphorus is a rare element compared with nitrogen. Its ratio to nitrogen in natural waters is about 1 to 23 (Hutchinson, 1944a). Chemical erosion in the United States has been estimated at 34 metric tons per square kilometer per year. Fifty-year cultivation of virgin soils of the Middle West reduced the P_2O_5 content by 36 per cent (Clarke, 1924). As shown in the diagram, the evidence indicates that return of phosphorus to the land has not been keeping up with the loss to the ocean.

in maintaining fertility under intensive cropping. Seeding the rice fields with extra algae often results in increased yields (Tamiya, 1957). Fogg (1955) has reviewed the entire subject of nitrogen fixation in a very readable manner, and Shields (1953) has reviewed the environmental factors which affect the nitrogen cycle as it pertains to the seed plants.

The self-regulating, feedback mechanisms, shown in a very simplified way by the arrows in the diagram (Fig. 7), make the nitrogen cycle a relatively perfect one, when large areas or the biosphere as a whole is considered. Thus, increased movement of materials along one path is quickly compensated for by adjustments along other paths. Some nitrogen from heavily populated regions of land, fresh water, and shallow seas is lost to the deep ocean sediments and thus gets out of circulation, at least for a while (a few million years perhaps). This loss is compensated for by nitrogen entering the air from volcanic gases. Thus, volcanic action is not to be entirely deplored but has some use after all! If nothing else, ecology teaches us not to make snap judgments as to whether a thing or an organism is "useful" or "harmful." One must consider all the aspects of a problem before arriving at a judgment. There will be many other examples of this in subsequent chapters.

The phosphorus cycle appears to be somewhat simpler. As shown in Figure 8, phosphorus, an important and necessary constituent of protoplasm, tends to "circulate," the organic compounds being broken down eventually to phosphates which are again available to plants. The great reservoir of phosphorus is not the air, however, but the rocks or other deposits which have been

Figure 9. Root nodules on a legume, the location of nitrogen-fixing bacteria of the symbiotic or mutualistic type (see also Figure 7). The legume shown is blue lupine, a cultivated variety used in southeastern U. S. (U. S. Soil Conservation Service Photo.)

formed in past geological ages. These are gradually eroding, releasing phosphates to ecosystems, but much phosphate escapes
into the sea, where part of it is deposited in the shallow sediments
and part of it is lost to the deep sediments. The means of returning
phosphorus to the cycle may presently be inadequate to compensate for the loss. In some parts of the world there is no extensive uplifting of sediments at present, and the action of marine
birds and fish (being brought to land by animals and man) is not
adequate. Sea birds have apparently played an important role in
returning phosphorus to the cycle (witness the fabulous guano
deposits on the coast of Peru). This transfer of phosphorus and
other materials by birds from the sea to land is continuing, but
apparently not at the rate which occurred in some of the past ages.
Man, unfortunately, appears to hasten the rate of loss of phosphorus and thus to make the phosphorus cycle less perfect.
Although man harvests a lot of marine fish, Hutchinson estimates
that only about 60,000 tons of elementary phosphorus per year is
returned in this manner, compared with one to two million tons
of phosphate rock which is mined and most of which is washed
away and lost. Agronomists tell us there is no immediate cause for
concern, since the known reserves of phosphate rock are large.
However, man may ultimately have to go about completing the
phosphorus cycle on a large scale if he is to avoid famine. Of
course a few geological upheavals raising the "lost sediments"
might accomplish it for us, who knows? At any rate, take a good
look at the diagram of the phosphorus cycle; its importance may
loom large in the future.

Quantitative study of biogeochemical cycles

Diagrams such as those in Figures 7 and 8 show only the broad
outlines of biogeochemical cycles. Quantitative relations, that is,
how much material passes along the routes shown by the arrows,
and how fast it moves, are but poorly known. However, an increasing number of studies on cycling rates in specific ecosystems
are being undertaken. Radioactive isotopes, which have become
generally available since 1946, are providing a tremendous stimulus for such studies since these isotopes can be used as "tracers"
or "tags" to follow the movement of materials. It should be emphasized that tracer studies in ecosystems, as in organisms, are
designed so that the amount of radioactive element introduced is
extremely small in comparison with the amount of non-radioactive

element already in the system. Therefore, neither the radioactivity nor the extra ions disturb the system; what happens to the tracer (which can be detected in extremely small amounts by the tell-tale radiations which it emits) simply reflects what is normally happening to the particular material in the system.

Ponds and lakes are especially good sites for study since they are relatively self-contained. Following the pioneer experiments of Coffin, Hayes, Jodrey, and Whiteway (1949), and Hutchinson and Bowen (1948, 1950), numerous papers have appeared reporting the results of the use of radiophosphorus (P^{32}) in studies of phosphorus circulation in lakes. Hutchinson (1957) has summarized these studies and reviewed the general knowledge on cycling of phosphorus and other vital elements in lakes.

Table 1. *Estimates of the turnover time of phosphorus in water and sediments of three lakes as determined with the use of P^{32} (after Hutchinson, 1957)*

Lake	Area Km.²	Depth m.	Turnover water	Time in days sediments	Ratio mobile P to total P in water
Bluff	0.4	7	5.4	39	6.4
Punchbowl	0.3	6	7.6	37	4.7
Crecy	2.04	3.8	17.0	176	8.7

It has been generally found that phosphorus does not move evenly and smoothly from organism to environment and back to organism as one might think from looking at the diagram in Figure 8, even though, as we have already indicated, a long-term equilibrium tends to be established. At any one time, most of the phosphorus is tied up either in organisms or in solid organic or inorganic particles which make up the sediments. In lakes, only about 10 per cent is the maximum likely to be in a soluble form at any one time. Although some back-and-forth movement or exchange occurs all of the time, extensive movement between solid and dissolved states is often irregular or "jerky," with periods of net release from the sediments followed by periods of net uptake by organisms or sediments, depending on seasonal temperature conditions and activities of organisms. Generally, uptake rate is more rapid than release rate. Plants readily take up phosphorus in the dark or under other conditions when they cannot use it. During periods of rapid growth of producers, which often occur in the spring, all of the available phosphorus may become tied up in producers and consumers. The system must then "slow down" since little new protoplasm can be synthesized until the bodies, feces, etc., are acted on by the decomposers. Thus, the concentration of phosphorus in the water may be higher after the "bloom" than during it. In other words, the concentration of dissolved phosphate in the water at any one time is not necessarily a good index to the total amount of phosphorus present. In general, the greater the surface area (as provided by both living organisms and inert particles) per unit of volume, the more rapidly will phosphorus be removed from the water.

Radiophosphorus has been especially useful in quantitative measurement of exchange rates in components of the ecosystem, that is, the rates at which phosphorus moves in and out of components after equilibrium has been established. To understand this it is necessary to introduce two concepts: *Turnover rate* is the fraction of the total amount of a substance in a component which is released (or which enters) in a given length of time. *Turnover time* is the reciprocal of this, that is, the time required to replace a quantity of substance equal to the amount in the component (see Robertson, 1957, for a discussion of these concepts). For example, if 1000 units are present in the component and 10 go out or enter each hour, the turnover rate is 10/1000 or 0.01 or 1 per cent per hour. Turnover time would then be 1000/10 or 100 hours. Data on turnover time for two large components, the water and the sediments, in three lakes are given in Table 1. The smaller lakes have a shorter turnover time presumedly because the ratio of bottom "mud" surface to the volume of water is greater. In general, the turnover time for the water of small or shallow lakes is about one week; for large lakes it may be two months or longer.

Studies with P^{32} tagged fertilizers in land ecosystems have revealed similar patterns; much of the phosphorus is "locked up" and unavailable to plants at any given time (see Comar, 1957, for a summary of some of these experiments). One very practical result of intensive studies of nutrient cycles has been the repeated demonstration that overfertilization can be just as "bad" from the standpoint of man's interest as underfertilization. When more materials are added than can be used by the organisms active at the time, the excess is often quickly tied up in soil or sediments or even lost completely (as by leaching), and is unavailable at the time when increased growth is most desired. In experiments with crops, little of tagged phosphate fertilizer added to soil ends up in the crop when the concentration of phosphate in the soil is already high. The "blind dumping" of fertilizers in ecosystems such as fish ponds is not only wasteful but may even backfire insofar as the desired results are concerned. Since different organisms are adapted to specific levels of materials, continued excess fertilization may result in a change in the kinds of organisms, perhaps discouraging the one man wants and encouraging the kinds he does not want. Among the algae, for example, *Botryococcus braunii* exhibits optimum growth at phosphorus concentration of 89 mg/M³ while *Nitzschia palea* grows best at 18 mg/M³. Increasing the amount of P from 18 to 89 would likely result in *Botryococcus* replacing *Nitzschia* (assuming other conditions favorable for both species), and this could have considerable effect on the kinds of animals that could be supported. The complete destruction of an oyster industry as a result of increased fertilization by phosphorus and nitrogen materials is described in Chapter 4 (see pages 96-97).

The sedimentary cycle

The nitrogen and phosphorus cycles in a very broad way illustrate the two general types of biogeochemical cycles. Cycles of oxygen, carbon dioxide and water resemble the cycle of nitrogen in that a gaseous phase is important in the continuous flow between inorganic and organic states. Most elements and compounds are more earthbound, and their cycles follow the pattern of phosphorus in that erosion, sedimentation, mountain building and volcanic activity, as well as biological transport, are the primary agents effecting circulation. A generalized picture of the sedimentary cycle of earthbound elements is shown in Figure 10. Some estimates of the amounts of material which pass through the cycle are marked on the arrows. Of course, very little is known about the flow of materials in the deep earth. The movement of solid matter through the air as dust is indicated as "fall out." To the natural fall out, atomic age man is adding additional materials, small in amount but significant biologically, as will be discussed later. The chemical elements which are available to the communities of the biosphere are those which by their geochemical nature tend to be enclosed within the types of rocks that come to the surface. Elements which are abundant in the mantle are scarce at the surface. As already indicated, phosphorus is one of the

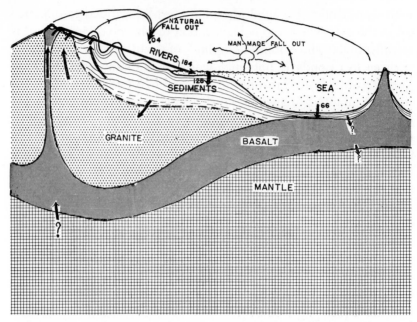

Figure 10. A diagram of the sedimentary cycle involving movement of the more "earthbound" elements. Where estimates are possible, the amounts of material are estimated in geograms per million year (one geogram = 10^{20} grams). The continents are sediment covered blocks of granite floating like corks on a layer of basalt which underlies the oceans. Below the black basalt is the Mantle layer which extends 2900 Km. down to the core of the earth. Granite is the light colored very resistant rock often used for tombstones; basalt is the black rock found in volcanoes. (Diagram prepared by H. T. Odum.)

elements whose scarcity on the earth's surface often limits plant growth.

The general "downhill" tendency of the sedimentary cycle is well shown in Figure 10; the lowlands and the oceans tend to gain soluble or usable mineral nutrients at the expense of the uplands during periods of minimum geological activity. Under such conditions, local biological recycling mechanisms are extremely important in keeping the downhill loss from exceeding the regeneration of new materials from underlying rocks. In other words, the longer vital elements can be kept within an area and used over and over again by successive generations of organisms, the less new material will be needed from the outside. Unfortunately, as already mentioned in the discussion of phosphorus, man tends to disrupt this homeostasis, often unwittingly, through a lack of understanding of the symbiosis between life and matter, which may have taken thousands of years to evolve. For example, it is now suspected, although not yet proved, that the stopping of salmon runs by dams is resulting in a decline not only of salmon but also of non-migratory fish, game and even timber production in certain high altitude regions of western United States. When salmon spawn and die in the uplands, they deposit a load of valuable nutrients recovered from the sea. The removal of large volumes of timber without the return of the contained minerals to soil (as would normally occur during the decay of logs) undoubtedly also contributes to the impoverishment of uplands in situations where the pool of nutrients was already limited. One can readily visualize how the destruction of such biological recycling mechanisms could result in the impoverishment of the whole ecosystem for many years to come, since it would require time for the re-establishment of a circulating pool of minerals. In such a case, devising means of returning limiting materials (and keeping them in situ) would be far more effective than the stocking of fish or planting of tree seedlings. It should also be emphasized that the sudden rush of materials into the lowlands, resulting from man-accelerated erosion, does not necessarily benefit the lowland ecosystems, because these systems may not get a chance to assimilate the nutrients before they pass into the sea beyond the range of light and, thus, completely out of biological circulation (at least for a time).

Cycling of non-essential elements

The biogeochemical cycles which we have been discussing involve elements essential to life. The non-essential elements also pass back and forth between organisms and environment and many of them are involved in the general sedimentary cycle, as pictured in Figure 10. Although they have no known value to the organism, many of these elements become concentrated in certain tissues, apparently because of chemical similarity to specific vital elements. Although a few of the non-essential elements become toxic when present in unusual quantities, most of them appear to have little effect in concentrations normally found in most natural ecosystems. Therefore, the ecologist would have little interest in most of the non-essential elements were it not for the fact that atomic bombs and nuclear power operations produce radioactive isotopes of some of these elements, which then find their way into the environment. Consequently, the new generation of ecologists must be concerned with the cycling of such things as strontium, cesium, cerium, ruthenium, yttrium and many others which the previous generation scarcely ever heard of! Even a very rare element, if in the form of a radioactive isotope, can become of biological concern, because a small amount of material (from the biogeochemical standpoint) can have marked biological effect. At present, strontium is receiving special attention, because radioactive strontium appears to be particularly dangerous to man and other vertebrates. Strontium behaves like calcium, with the result that radioactive strontium gets into close contact with blood-making tissue, which is very susceptible to radiation damage. Since various aspects of radioactivity in the environment are considered in some detail in Chapter 14, we need only consider strontium in relation to the calcium cycles in this chapter (see also H. T. Odum, 1951, 1957).

One of the most abundant elements that make up the sedimentary cycle is calcium; it washes down the rivers, deposits as limestone, is raised in mountain ranges and again washes down to the sea. About 7 per cent of the total sedimentary material flowing down the rivers is calcium. In comparison, the amount of phosphorus in the cycle is only about 1 per cent of the calcium. For every 1000 atoms of calcium, 2.4 atoms of strontium move to the sea like black sheep in a flock of white ones. As a result of nuclear weapons tests and production of waste materials from experimental and industrial uses of atomic energy, radioactive strontium is becoming widespread in the biosphere. This strontium is new material added to the biosphere since it is the result of the fission of uranium. Thus, a few new black sheep are being added, but these sheep are wolves in sheep's clothing, so-to-speak! Tiny amounts of radiostrontium have now followed calcium from soil and water into vegetation, animals, human food and human bones. In 1956 about 5 micromicrocuries (see page 456 for a definition of this unit of radioactivity) of radioactive strontium were present for every gram of calcium in milk, whereas about 0.7 micromicrocuries were present per gram of calcium in the bones of children. Studies on the effect of radiostrontium in producing cancer have led some scientists to suggest that, should these levels increase ten or one hundred fold, harmful effects on the human population might result over a period of time.

3 · Principles and concepts pertaining to energy in ecological systems

H. T. Odum and E. P. Odum

1. Review of fundamental concepts related to energy

Statement

Energy is defined as the ability to do work. The behavior of energy is described by the following laws. The *first law of thermodynamics* states that energy may be transformed from one type into another but is never created or destroyed. Light, for example, is a form of energy, for it can be transformed into work, heat, or potential energy of food, depending on the situation, but none of it is destroyed. The *second law of thermodynamics* may be stated in several ways, including the following: No process involving an energy transformation will spontaneously occur unless there is a degradation of the energy from a concentrated form into a dispersed form. For example, heat in a hot object will spontaneously tend to become dispersed into the cooler surroundings. The second law of thermodynamics may also be stated as follows: Because some energy is always dispersed into unavailable heat energy, no spontaneous transformation of energy (light, for example) into potential energy (protoplasm, for example) is 100 per cent efficient.

Explanation

It is readily apparent how the fundamental concepts of physics outlined in the above paragraph are related to ecology. The variety of manifestations of life are all accompanied by energy changes, even though no energy is created or destroyed (first law of thermodynamics). The energy that enters the earth's surface as light is balanced by the energy that leaves the earth's surface as invisible heat radiation. The essence of life is the progression of such changes as growth, self-duplication, and synthesis of complex relationships of matter. Without energy transfers, which accompany all such changes, there could be no life and no ecological systems. We, as human beings, should not forget that civilization is just one of the remarkable natural proliferations that are dependent on the continuous inflow of the concentrated energy of light radiation. In ecology, we are fundamentally concerned with the manner in which light is related to ecological systems, and with the manner in which energy is transformed within the system. Thus, the relationships between producer plants and consumer animals, between predator and prey, not to mention the numbers and kinds of organisms in a given environment, are all limited and controlled by the same basic laws which govern non-living systems, such as electric motors or automobiles.

Year in and year out light and other radiations associated with it leave the sun and pass into space. Some of this radiation falls on the earth, passes through the atmospheric film, and strikes forests, grasslands, lakes, oceans, cultivated fields, deserts, greenhouses, ice sheets and many hundreds of other types of ecological systems which blanket the earth and compose the biosphere. When light is absorbed by some object which becomes warmer as a result, the light energy has been transformed into another kind of energy, known as heat energy. Heat energy is composed of the vibrations and motions of the molecules that make up the object. The absorption of the sun's rays by land and water results in hot and cold areas, ultimately leading to the flow of air which may drive windmills and perform work such as the pumping of water against the force of gravity. Thus, in this case, light energy passes to heat energy of the land to *kinetic* energy of moving air which accomplishes work of raising water. The energy is not destroyed by lifting of the water, but becomes *potential energy*, because the latent energy inherent in having the water at an elevation can be turned back into some other type of energy by allowing the water to fall back down the well. As indicated in previous chapters, food resulting from photosynthetic activity of green plants contains potential energy which changes to other types when food is utilized by organisms. Since the amount of one type of energy is always equivalent to a particular quantity of another type into which it is transformed, we may calculate one from the other. For example, knowing the amount of light energy absorbed and knowing the conversion factor, we may determine the amount of heat energy which has been added.

The second law of thermodynamics deals with the transfer of energy toward an ever less available and more dispersed state. As far as the solar system is concerned, the dispersed state with respect to energy is one in which all energy is in the form of evenly distributed heat energy. That is, if left to itself, all energy where it undergoes a change of form will eventually tend to be transformed into the form of heat energy distributed at uniform temperature. This tendency has often been spoken of as "the running down of the solar system." Whether this tendency for energy to be leveled applies to the universe as a whole is not yet known.

At the present time the earth is far from being in a state of stability with respect to energy because there are vast potential energy and temperature differences which are maintained by the continual influx of light energy from the sun. However, it is the process of going *toward* the stable state that is responsible for the succession of energy changes that constitute natural phenomena on the earth as we know them. It is like a man on a treadmill; he never reaches the top of the hill, but his efforts to do so result in well defined processes. Thus, when the sun energy strikes the earth, it tends to be degraded into heat energy. Only a very small portion of the light energy absorbed by green plants is transformed into potential or food energy; most of it goes into heat, which then passes out of the plant, the ecosystem, and the biosphere. All the rest of the biological world obtains its potential chemical energy from organic substances produced by plant photosynthesis or microorganism chemosynthesis. An animal, for example, takes in chemical potential energy of food and converts a large part into heat to enable a small part of the energy to be re-established as the chemical potential energy of new protoplasm. At each step in the transfer of energy from one organism to another a large part of the energy is degraded into heat.

The second law of thermodynamics, which deals with the dispersal of energy, is related to the *stability principle*. According to this concept any natural enclosed system with energy flowing through it, whether the earth itself or a smaller unit, such as a lake, tends to change until a stable adjustment, with self-regulating mechanisms, is developed. Self-regulating mechanisms are mechanisms which bring about a return to constancy if a system is caused to change from the stable state by a momentary outside influence. A governor on a steam engine is an example of a self-regulating mechanical mechanism. If the engine goes faster than its set speed, the governor automatically reduces the speed. A mortality rate which increases automatically with increasing density of organisms is an example of a self-regulating mechanism that can make a living system stable. When a stable adjustment is reached, energy transfers tend to progress in a one-way fashion and at characteristic steady rates, according to the stability principle.

As we shall see in the next few sections, many important aspects of ecology, such as food chains, trophic structure, and productivity, result directly from the basic laws of energy transfer as we have outlined them in this section.

2. The food chain

Statement

The transfer of food energy from the source in plants through a series of organisms with repeated eating and being eaten is referred to as the *food chain*. At each transfer a large proportion of the potential energy is lost as heat. The number of steps or "links" in a sequence is limited, usually to four or five. The shorter the food chain (or the nearer the organism to the beginning of the chain) the greater the available energy which can be converted into *biomass* (= living weight, including stored food) and/or dissipated by respiration. Food chains are of three types: the *predator chain*, which, starting from a plant base, goes from smaller to larger animals; the *parasite chain*, which goes from larger to smaller organisms; and the *saprophytic chain*, which goes from dead matter into microorganisms. Food chains are not isolated sequences but are interconnected with one another. The interlocking pattern is often spoken of as the *food web*. In complex natural communities, organisms whose food is obtained from plants by the same number of steps are said to belong to the same *trophic level*. Thus, green plants occupy the first trophic level, plant-eaters the second level, carnivores which eat the herbivores the third level, secondary carnivores the fourth level. A given species population may occupy one, or more than one, trophic level according to the source of energy actually assimilated. The *energy flow* through a trophic level equals the total assimilation at that level which, in turn, equals the production of biomass plus respiration.

Explanation

The workings of the two laws of thermodynamics in natural communities are illustrated by the energy flow diagram in Figure 11. Energy inflows balance outflows as required by the first law; each energy transfer is accompanied by the dispersion of energy into an unavailable form (dispersed heat) as required by the second law.

Food chains are more or less familiar to everyone in a vague sort of way, at least, because man himself often occupies a position at or near the end of a chain of food items. What is not usually recognized by the layman, however, is that potential energy is lost at each food transfer. And only a very small percentage of the available sun energy was fixed by the plant in the first place. Figure 11 clearly shows how a large share of the potential en-

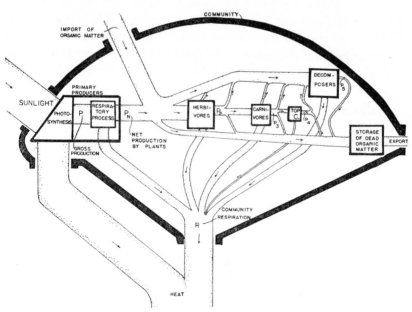

Figure 11. Energy flow diagram of a community showing successive fixation and transfer by components, and the large respiratory losses at each transfer. Compare the one-way flow of energy through the community as shown in this diagram with the circulation of materials as shown in Figures 7 and 8. P_G = gross primary production, P_N = net primary production and P_2, P_3, P_4 and P_5 = secondary production at the indicated levels. (Redrawn from H. T. Odum, 1956.)

ergy originally fixed by plants is lost preceding final predator action. Therefore, the "top carnivore" must be a relatively scarce, but not necessarily a "luxury" item in the ecosystem. In ecology, it is convenient to designate the total assimilation (that is, the production of biomass + respiration) of a trophic level as the *energy flow* through the level. We may also use this term with reference to individuals, populations or other components which we may wish to study. It is clear that the energy flow at each trophic level must always be less than that at the preceding level.

While respiration at all of the levels accounts for most of the energy losses in the ecosystem as a whole, there are other losses which affect the individual biotic components. As shown in the diagram (Fig. 11) some of the available food is not utilized, at least not immediately (this lag in the metabolism of the ecosystem was discussed in Chapter 2), and some of it may be exported from the community. Not all of the potential energy ingested or absorbed by heterotrophs is actually assimilated (such losses are indicated by the arrows leading from the tops of the herbivore and carnivore boxes in Figure 11). For example, the pig is generally considered the most efficient "converter" among farm animals; under good management a maximum of about 20 per cent of the gross energy fed to a pig can be returned in products that can be eaten by man (Maynard, 1954). Most of the 80 per cent loss is due to respiration, but some of it is food which the pig ate but did not assimilate; and some is converted into pig biomass but not utilized by man.

It is important to emphasize, as was done in the preceding chapter, that the classification of organisms according to trophic levels is one of function and not of species as such. A given species may occupy more than one trophic level. For example, if a population of animals obtains 80 per cent of its energy from eating plants and 20 per cent from eating animals, then 80 per cent of its energy flow can be assigned to the herbivore level and 20 per cent to the appropriate carnivore levels.

Examples

Many people think of the arctic as a barren region of no interest or value to man. Regardless of the outcome of present efforts by man to utilize the arctic, this vast region is of great interest if for no other reason than that its ecology is simplified. Because temperature exerts such a powerful limiting effect, only a relatively few kinds of organisms have become successfully adapted to the far northern conditions. Thus, the entire living part of the eco-system is built around a relatively few species. Studies in the arctic aid in the understanding of more complex conditions elsewhere, since such basic relationships as food chains, food webs and trophic levels are simplified and readily comprehended. Charles Elton early realized this and spent much time in the 1920's and 1930's studying the ecology of arctic lands, with the result that he was one of the first to clarify the above-mentioned principles and concepts. Consequently, we might well look to the arctic for our first examples of food chains.

The region between the limit of trees and the perpetual ice is generally known as the *tundra*. One of the important groups of plants on the tundra are the reindeer lichens (or "moss"), *Cladonia*, which represent a partnership between algae and fungi, the former being the producers, of course. These plants, together with the grasses, sedges, and dwarf willows, form the diet of the caribou of the North American tundra and of its ecological counterpart, the reindeer of the Old World tundra. These animals, in turn, are preyed upon by wolves and man. Tundra plants are also eaten by lemmings—shaggy haired voles with short tails and a bear-like appearance—and the ptarmigan or arctic grouse. Throughout the long winter, as well as during the brief summer, the arctic white fox and the snowy owl may depend largely on the lemming and related rodents. In each of these cases the food chain is relatively short and any radical change in numbers at any of the three trophic levels has violent repercussions on the other levels, because there is often little in the way of alternate choice of food. As will be discussed later, this may be one reason, at least, why some groups of arctic organisms undergo violent fluctuations in numbers, running the gamut from superabundance to near extinction. It is rather interesting to note, in passing, that the same sort of thing often happened to primitive human civilizations which depended on a single or on relatively few local food items.

During the brief arctic summer, insects emerge and migratory birds may be locally abundant. Food chains become longer and definite food webs develop, as in more southern regions. As far as is now known the principle behind food chains is the same north or south, but the details are extremely variable, being influenced not only by geography but by season and age of the organisms. Summerhayes and Elton (1923) describe the interesting situation on the island of Spitsbergen where there are no lemmings. Here foxes are able to feed on birds, insects, or plants in summer but

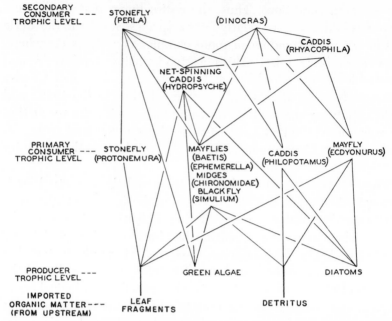

Figure 12. A portion of a food web in a small stream community in South Wales. The diagram illustrates: (1) the interlocking of food chains to form the food web, (2) three trophic levels, (3) the fact that organisms, such as Hydropsyche, may occupy an intermediate position between major trophic levels and (4) an "open" system in which part of the basic food is "imported" from outside the stream. (Redrawn from Jones, 1949.)

are forced to spend the winter out on the ice feeding on the remains of seals killed by polar bears and on the dung of the bears. The foxes thus become a part of the food web of the sea, which in arctic regions, at least, may be almost as productive as the land.

A food web which has been worked out for small organisms of a stream community is shown in Figure 12. This diagram not only illustrates the interlocking nature of food chains and three trophic levels, but also brings out the fact that some organisms occupy an intermediate position between the three major trophic levels. Thus, the net-spinning caddis feeds on both plant and animal material and is therefore intermediate between primary and secondary consumer levels.

A well managed farm or fish pond (see frontispiece), thousands of which are being built all over the country, provides excellent examples of food chains under fairly simplified conditions. Since the object of a fish pond is to provide the maximum number of fish of a particular species and a particular size, management procedures are designed to channel as much of the basic energy into the final product as possible. This is done by reducing the number of niches and "side food chains." Thus, an attempt is made to restrict the producers to one group, the floating algae or phytoplankton, other green plants (such as rooted aquatics and filamentous algae) being discouraged. As shown in Figure 2 (page 14), the phytoplankton is fed upon in turn by the zooplankton, and both these groups are taken by certain invertebrates, notably blood worms or chironomids, which are the preferred food of bluegills and other small fishes; these in turn are fed upon by bass. As will be outlined in Chapter 12, the balance between the last two food chain groups (i.e., bluegill-bass) is very important as far as harvest by man is concerned. Thus, a pond with bluegills as the only fish could actually produce a greater total weight or biomass of fish than one with bass and bluegills, but most of the bluegills would remain small because of high reproduction rate and competition for available food. Fishing by hook and line would soon be poor. Since man wants his fish in large sizes, and not as "sardines," the final predator is necessary for a good sport-fishing pond.* This brings up the very important point of food size. In addition to the operation of the second law of thermodynamics, size of food is one of the main reasons underlying the existence of food chains, as Elton (1927) pointed out. This is because there are usually rather definite upper and lower limits to the size of food that can efficiently support a given animal type. Man is somewhat an exception in that he can artificially concentrate or divide up food items and, theoretically at least, be independent of their original size. As indicated in the fish pond example, however, food item size can be an important factor with man, especially where esthetics as well as economics are considered important. Thus, we *could* eat insects, weeds, or bluegill fingerlings, but let us hope that we never allow our biosphere to get into such a state that we *have* to eat such items exclusively. It is more fun to live in a world where we can enjoy catching that large bass or eating that steak! In many overcrowded countries this is already impossible for the large mass of people (see Chapter 15).

Although man has become somewhat independent of food size, he has not yet figured out a way to get around the second law of thermodynamics. Thus, many people in crowded oriental countries eat rice rather than meat, partly, no doubt, through custom, but

---

* In the Philippines and the Orient, where food is of more vital concern than sport, larger yields are obtained by restricting the population to herbivorous species and harvesting pond fish in small sizes.

mostly through necessity. The shorter the food chain, the more people that can live on a given area of land.

The matter of size is involved, also, in the difference between a predator chain and a parasite chain; in the latter, organisms at successive levels are smaller and smaller instead of being generally larger and larger. Thus, roots of vegetable crops are parasitized by nematodes which may be attacked by bacteria or other smaller organisms. Mammals and birds are commonly parasitized by fleas, which in turn have protozoan parasites of the genus *Leptomonas*, to cite another example. However, from the energy standpoint there is no fundamental difference between predator and parasite chains, since both parasites and predators are "consumers." For this reason no distinction has been made in the energy flow diagram of Figure 11; a parasite of a green plant would have the same position in this diagram as a herbivore, whereas animal parasites would fall in the various carnivore categories. Theoretically, parasite chains should average shorter than predator chains since the metabolism per gram increases sharply with the diminishing size of the organism, resulting in a rapid decline in the biomass that can be supported, as will be discussed in the next section in this chapter.

The breakdown of dead matter and transfer of energy to decomposer microorganisms, which we have designated as the saprophytic (or saprobic) chain, involves a somewhat different pattern of energy flow, as shown in Figure 11. This pathway is an important and vital pattern in all ecosystems, and in some situations a large portion of the energy flow may follow this route. For example, in the extensive salt marshes found along the coasts in many parts of the world, a large part of the energy in the first trophic level is "detoured" via microorganisms before it gets into the herbivore-carnivore sequence. On the south Atlantic coast, for example, marsh grass (*Spartina*) remains to a considerable extent unconsumed until it dies and is washed into the estuaries where it is partly consumed, and, in the process, broken down by microorganisms into organic detritus (finely divided particulate matter). Then the detritus is fed upon by fiddler crabs (*Uca*) and other filter or deposit feeders, which in turn are preyed upon by other crabs, clapper rails, raccoons, etc. Thus, the fiddler crab occupies the "herbivore" position in the diagram of Figure 11. Although in this case microorganisms are "sharecroppers" with the crabs, the latter can make efficient use of their large share since they have to expend less energy than most herbivores to obtain their food; a fresh supply properly prepared is laid before them with each tide.

Saprophytic chains are presumedly short (i.e., involve few transfers) for the same reasons as indicated for parasite chains. A stream or pond heavily polluted with organic matter would represent an extreme case in which almost all of the potential energy ("imported," in this instance) follows a short chain through microorganisms, although the usual green plant-herbivore-carnivore sequence may also be present.

Ecological efficiencies

Ratios between energy flow at different points along the food chain are of considerable ecological interest. Such ratios, when expressed as percentages, are often called "ecological efficiencies." In Table 2 some of these ratios are listed and defined in terms of the energy flow diagram. For the most part, these ratios are meaningful in reference to component populations as well as to whole trophic levels. Since the several types of efficiencies are often confused, it is important to define exactly what relationship is meant; the energy flow diagram is a great help in this clarification. At this point we need only consider briefly the overall efficiency of energy transfer at successive trophic levels as indicated by the ratio of energy intakes (i.e., the first ratio listed in Table 2).

Rabinowitch (1951) estimates that the plant world in natural conditions fixes about 2 per cent of the usable light energy actually absorbed. Only about half of the incident radiation from the sun is in the visible range of wavelengths absorbed by chlorophyll. Thus, the efficiency of fixation of the total insolation reaching plants is about 1 per cent. In large bodies of water, much of the energy is absorbed by the water and its impurities so that efficiencies are lower relative to sunlight reaching the surface. For example, Riley (1944) estimates the efficiency for the ocean as a whole as 0.18 per cent of the total energy of radiation reaching the sea surface. It should be emphasized that these estimates are intended to represent averages for very large sections of the earth's surface; locally, trophic efficiencies at the primary level may be two or three times higher in the more productive agricultural, forest and shallow water communities.

The efficiency of transfer is higher at the higher trophic levels, but nature still levies a huge "tax" of heat energy each time food energy is transferred. Methods of determining trophic efficiency within whole communities are crude as yet; the best estimates are

Table 2. *Various types of ecological efficiencies*

Symbols are as follows (see diagram below): L—light (total); L_A—absorbed light; P_G—total photosynthesis (gross production); P—production of biomass; I—energy intake; R—respiration; A—assimilation; NA—ingested but not assimilated; NU—not used by trophic level shown; t—trophic level; t-1—preceding trophic level.

Ratio	Designation and Explanation

A. Ratios Between Trophic Levels

$\dfrac{I_t}{I_{t-1}}$ Trophic level energy intake (or Lindeman's) efficiency. For the primary level this is

$$\frac{P_G}{L} \quad \text{or} \quad \frac{P_G}{L_A}$$

$\dfrac{A_t}{A_{t-1}}$ Trophic level assimilation efficiency

$\dfrac{P_t}{P_{t-1}}$ Trophic level production efficiency

⎫ For the primary level P and A may be in terms of either L or L_A as above; $A_t/A_{t-1} = I_t/I_{t-1}$ for the primary level, but not for secondary levels.

$\dfrac{I_t}{P_{t-1}}$ or $\dfrac{A_t}{P_{t-1}}$ Utilization efficiencies

B. Ratios Within Trophic Levels

$\dfrac{P_t}{A_t}$ Tissue growth efficiency

$\dfrac{P_t}{I_t}$ Ecological growth efficiency

$\dfrac{A_t}{I_t}$ Assimilation efficiency

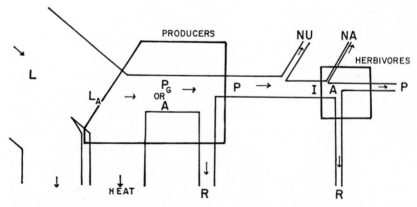

from aquatic communities as shown in Table 3. The primary or photosynthetic efficiencies in this table are given as a per cent of the total energy reaching the water surfaces which is converted into organic matter (the ratio P_G/L in Table 2). The efficiency in terms of absorbed light (P_G/L_A) would be somewhat higher,

Table 3. *Efficiency of energy transfer at various trophic levels in three aquatic ecosystems*

Trophic level	Trophic Level Energy Intake Efficiency (Per cent)		
	Cedar Bog Lake, Minnesota*	Lake Mendota, Wisconsin†	Silver Springs, Florida‡
Photosynthetic plants (producers)	0.10	0.40	1.2
Herbivores (primary consumers)	13.3	8.7	16
Small carnivores (secondary consumers)	22.3	5.5	11
Large carnivores (tertiary consumers)	not present	13.0	6

* After Lindeman (1941, 1942).
† Based on Juday (1940).
‡ H. T. Odum (1957).

5 per cent in Silver Springs, for example, instead of 1.2 per cent.

The very low primary efficiencies which seem to be characteristic of intact natural systems have puzzled many persons in view of the relatively high efficiencies obtained in electric motors and other mechanical systems. This has, quite naturally, led many to consider seriously ways of increasing nature's efficiency. Actually, long-time, large scale ecosystems are not directly comparable to short-time mechanical systems in this regard. For one thing, a considerable portion of fuel goes for repair and maintenance in living systems, and depreciation and repair are not included in calculating fuel efficiencies of engines. In other words, a lot of energy (human or otherwise) other than fuel is required to keep machines running, repaired and replaced; it is not fair to compare engines and biological systems unless this is considered because the latter are self-repairing and self-perpetuating. Secondly, it is likely that more rapid growth per unit time has greater survival value than maximum efficiency in the use of fuel. Thus, to use a simple analogy, it might be more important to reach a destination quickly at fifty miles per hour than to achieve maximum efficiency in fuel consumption by driving slowly!

Experiences with algal cultures are pertinent to the discussion of these points, because a serious effort is being made to increase man's food supply by developing techniques of mass culture of simple single-celled green plants (*Chlorella, Scenedesmus* and others). Numerous experiments have shown that quite high efficiencies (10, 20 or even 50 per cent) can be obtained in small cultures if the light intensity is low. However, the amount of food produced per unit of time is very small. When full daylight and large tanks are tried, the efficiency tends to drop rapidly with increasing yields until it is between 2 and 6 per cent, which is little, if any, higher than in productive natural communities or in the best grade of ordinary agriculture (Tamiya, 1957). Also, as the size of the operation increases, it becomes increasingly difficult to keep consumer organisms (zooplankton) from getting in on the harvest and thus reducing the yield to man. Therefore, it would appear at the present time that man should not count on increasing basic efficiency as a means of increasing world food supply. This does not mean that mass algal culture is not worthwhile. For other reasons it offers a promising supplement to other crops, especially in crowded countries like Japan, where suitable land for growing terrestrial crops is very scarce.

For further discussion of the idea that low efficiency is necessary for maximum power output see Odum and Pinkerton (1955) and H. T. Odum (1956a).

3. Metabolism and size of individuals

Statement

The standing crop biomass (expressed as the total dry weight of organisms present at any one time) which can be supported by a steady flow of energy in a food chain depends to a considerable extent on the size of the individual organisms. The smaller the organisms the greater its metabolism per gram of biomass. Consequently, the smaller the organism, the smaller the biomass which can be supported at a particular trophic level in the ecosystem. Conversely, the larger the organism, the larger the standing crop biomass. Thus, the amount of bacteria present at any one time would be very much smaller than the "crop" of fish or mammals even though the energy utilization was the same for both groups.

Explanation and examples

The metabolism per gram of biomass of the small plants and animals such as algae, bacteria, and protozoa is immensely greater than the metabolic rate of large organisms such as trees and vertebrates. This applies to both photosynthesis and respiration. In many cases the important parts of the community metabolically are not the few great conspicuous organisms but the numerous tiny organisms which are often invisible to the naked eye. Thus, the tiny algae (phytoplankton), comprising only a few pounds per acre at any one moment in a lake, can have as great a metabolism as a much larger volume of trees in a forest or hay in a meadow. Likewise, a few pounds of small crustacea (zooplankton) "grazing" on the algae can have a total respiration equal to many pounds of cows in a pasture.

The rate of metabolism of organisms or association of organisms is often estimated by measuring the rate at which oxygen is consumed (or produced in the case of photosynthesis). There is a broad general tendency for the metabolic rate per organism in animals to increase as the two-thirds power of the volume (or weight) increases, or the metabolic rate per gram biomass to decrease inversely as the length (Zeuthen, 1953). A similar relationship appears to exist in plants, although structural differences in plants and animals (see below) make direct comparisons in terms of volume and length difficult. These relations are shown in Figure 13 by the smoothed lines which indicate in an approximate manner the relation between size and metabolism. Various theories proposed to account for these trends have centered around diffusion processes; larger organisms have less surface area per gram through which diffusion processes might occur. However, the real explanation for the relationship between size and metabolism has not been agreed upon. Comparisons, of course, should be made at similar temperatures because metabolic rates are usually greater at higher temperatures than at lower temperatures (except with temperature adaptation; see page 90).

It should be pointed out that when organisms of the same general order of magnitude in size are compared the linear relationship shown in Figure 13 does not always hold. This is to be expected since there are many factors, secondary to size, which affect the rate of metabolism. For example, it is well known that warmblooded vertebrates have a greater respiration rate than coldblooded vertebrates of the same size. However, the difference is actually relatively small as compared with the difference between a vertebrate and a bacterium. Thus, given the same amount of available food energy, the standing crop of coldblooded herbivorous fish in a pond may be of the same order of magnitude as that of warmblooded herbivorous mammals on land. In the study of size-metabolism in plants, it is often difficult to decide what constitutes an "individual." Thus, we may commonly regard a large tree as one individual, but actually the leaves may act as "functional individuals" as far as size-surface area relationships are concerned. In a recent study of various species of seaweeds (large

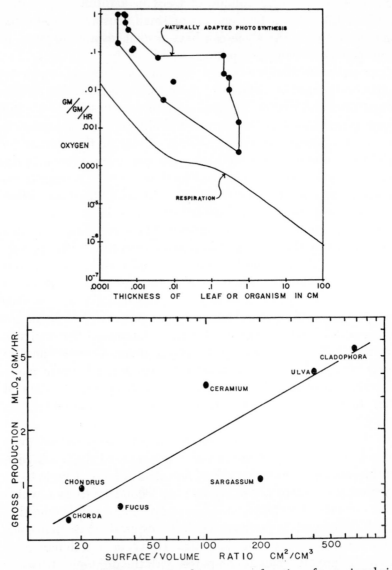

Figure 13. Metabolism per gram biomass as a function of organismal size. From top to bottom the curves represent: photosynthetic rate per gram biomass in a variety of algae and leafy plants in relation to length or thickness of leaf, respiration per gram biomass in heterotrophic organisms (animals and bacteria) in relation to the length of the organism, and gross production of several species of large marine seaweeds in relation to surface-to-volume ratio. In each case small organisms or thin organisms with a high surface-to-volume ratio have higher rates of metabolism per gram than large or thick organisms. Upper graph after H. T. Odum (1956a) from data of Verduin and Zeuthen. Lower graph after E. P. Odum et al. (1958).

multicellular algae), we found (see Figure 13) that species with thin or narrow "branches" (and consequently a high surface-to-volume ratio) had a higher rate per gram biomass of food manufacture, respiration, and uptake of radioactive phosphorus from the water than did species with thick branches (E. P. Odum, Kuenzler and Blunt, 1958). Thus, in this case the "branches" o1 even the individual cells were "functional individuals" and not the whole "plant," which might include numerous "branches" attached to the substrate by a single holdfast.

The inverse relationship between size and metabolism may also be observed in the ontogeny of a single species. Eggs, for example, usually show a higher rate per gram than the larger adults. In data reported by Hunter and Vernberg (1955), the metabolism per gram of trematode parasites was found to be ten times less than that of the small larval cercariae.

4. Trophic structure and ecological pyramids

Statement

The interaction of the food chain phenomena (energy loss at each transfer) and the size-metabolism relationship results in communities having a definite *trophic structure*, which is often characteristic of a particular type of ecosystem (lake, forest, coral reef, pasture, etc.). Trophic structure may be measured and described either in terms of the standing crop per unit area or in terms of the energy fixed per unit area per unit time at successive trophic levels. Trophic structure and also trophic function may be shown graphically by means of *ecological pyramids* in which the first or producer level forms the base and successive levels the tiers which make up the apex. Ecological pyramids may be of three general types: (1) the *pyramid of numbers* in which the number of individual organisms is depicted, (2) the *pyramid of biomass* based on the total dry weight, caloric value, or other measure of the total amount of living material and (3) the *pyramid of energy* in which the rate of energy flow and/or "productivity" at successive trophic levels is shown. The numbers and biomass pyramids may be inverted (or partly so), that is, the base may be smaller than one or more of the upper tiers if producer organisms average smaller than consumers in individual size. On the other hand, the energy pyramid must always take a true upright pyramid shape, provided all sources of food energy in the system are considered.

Explanation

The pyramid of numbers is actually the result of three phenomena which usually operate simultaneously. One of these phenomena is the familiar geometrical fact that a great many small units are required to equal the mass of one big unit, regardless of whether the units are organisms or building blocks. Thus, even if the weight of large organisms was equal to the weight of the smaller ones, the number of smaller organisms would be vastly greater than that of the larger ones. Because of the geometry, therefore, the existence of a valid pyramid of numbers in a natural group of organisms does not necessarily mean that there is less of the larger organisms on a weight basis.

The second phenomenon contributing to the pattern of many small organisms and few large ones is the food chain. As pointed out in Section 2, useful energy is always lost (into the form of heat) in the transfer through each step in the food chain. Consequently, except where there are imports or exports of organic matter, there is much less energy available to the higher trophic levels. The third factor involved in the pyramid of numbers is the inverse size-metabolic rate pattern discussed in the previous section.

Actually, the pyramid of numbers is not very fundamental or instructive as an illustrative device since the relative effects of the "geometric," "food chain" and "size" factors are not indicated. The form of the numbers pyramid will vary widely with different communities, depending on whether producing individuals are small (phytoplankton, grass) or large (oak trees). Likewise, numbers vary so widely that it is difficult to show the whole community on the same numerical scale. This does not mean that the number of individuals present is of no interest, but rather that such data are probably best presented in tabular form.

The pyramid of biomass is of more fundamental interest since the "geometric" factor is eliminated, and the quantitative relations of the "standing crop" are well shown. In general, the biomass pyramid gives a rough picture of the overall effect of the food chain relationships for the ecological group as a whole. When the total weight of individuals at successive trophic levels is plotted, a gradually sloping pyramid may be expected as long as the size of the organisms does not differ greatly. However, if organisms of lower levels average much smaller than those of higher levels, the biomass pyramid may be inverted. For example, where size of the producers is very small and that of the consumers large, the total weight of the latter may be greater at any one moment. In such cases, even though more energy is being passed through the producer trophic level than through consumer levels (which must always be the case), the rapid metabolism and turnover of the small producer organisms accomplish a larger output with a smaller standing crop biomass.

From the foregoing discussion it becomes clear that the number and weight of organisms which can be supported at any level in any situation depends, not on the amount of fixed energy present at any one time in the level just below, but rather on the *rate* at which food is being produced. The important time factor is introduced in the pyramid of energy which depicts the amount of organisms (usually expressed in terms of calories, a widely used unit of energy) produced within a given unit of time. Of the three types of ecological pyramids, the energy pyramid gives by far the best overall picture of the functional nature of communities; it actually shows "what goes on" in the living part of the ecosystem. In contrast with the numbers and biomass pyramids which are pictures of the standing states, i.e., organisms present at any one moment, the energy pyramid is a picture of the rates of passage of food mass through the food chain. Its shape is not affected by variations in the size and metabolic rate of individuals, and, if all sources of energy are considered, it must always be "right side up" because of the second law of thermodynamics. As will be discussed in more detail in the next section, the size of the various tiers is a direct measure of energy flow at successive levels. Theoretically, the form of the energy pyramid should be consistent and characteristic of a particular ecosystem if a reasonable time interval is considered. The one drawback to this form of graphic summary is that the data for its construction are often difficult to obtain.

Examples

The several types of ecological pyramids which we have discussed are illustrated in Figures 14 to 17. These are all constructed from published data, as indicated. In Figure 14, the numbers of all macroscopic organisms in one acre of a grassland community are arranged according to broad trophic levels to demonstrate an "upright" type of pyramid of numbers in which producers (plants) are individually more numerous than consumers (herbivorous insects, etc.) which in turn are associated with a very few tertiary consumers (birds and moles). As pointed out in the above state-

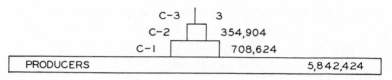

Figure 14.   An example of the "pyramid of numbers." The number of organisms (exclusive of decomposers) in a bluegrass field are arranged according to trophic levels as follows: Producers — green plants. C-1, herbivorous invertebrates. C-2, spiders, ants, predatory beetles, etc. C-3 birds and moles. (Plant data, Evans and Cain, 1952; animal data, Wolcott, 1937.)

ment, the relationship between the number of producers and primary consumers would be completely reversed in a forest where there would obviously be more insects than trees. The number of microorganism (decomposers) in grassland was not determined in the studies on which Figure 13 is based; their number, of course, would be extremely large and require a different scale to show on the same diagram with the other components.

Figure 15 illustrates biomass pyramids for a wide variety of communities in marine, freshwater and terrestrial environments. The diagram for the rich and beautiful Silver Springs, Florida, which is visited by thousands of tourists annually, is especially interesting since an estimate of all of the community, including the decomposers, is shown. Beds of freshwater eelgrass (*Sagittaria*) and attached algae make up the bulk of the standing crop of producers in this spring in which numerous aquatic insects, snails, herbivorous fish and turtles comprise the primary consumers. Other fish and invertebrates form the smaller "crop" of secondary consumers and bass and gar are the chief "top carnivores." Animal parasites were included in the latter level. Since the decomposers are primarily concerned with the breaking down of the large bulk of plants but also decompose all other levels as well, it is logical to show this component as a tall bar resting on the primary trophic level but extending to the top of the pyramid as well. Actually the biomass of decomposers is very small in relation to their importance in the functioning of the community. Thus, the pyramid of numbers greatly overrates the decomposers and the pyramid of biomass greatly underrates them. Neither numbers nor weights, in themselves, have much meaning in determining the role of decomposers in community dynamics; only measurements of actual energy utilization as could be shown on the energy pyramid will place the decomposers in true relationship with the macroscopic components. For this reason, and also because few estimates of total microbial populations have actually been made, the decomposer unit is not included on the other biomass pyramids illustrated in Figure 15.

Comparison of standing crop pyramids of springs, lakes, coral reefs, open oceans and fields as shown in Figure 15 brings out a number of interesting points. The examples have been chosen to illustrate the range of conditions found in nature. For reasons already discussed, biomass pyramids are usually upright but may be partly inverted. Only when the bulk of producer organisms are very small, for example, tiny algae or photosynthetic bacteria, is an inverted pyramid to be expected. Such inverted pyramids have been mainly reported from open water communities where plants growing on the bottom were not considered or where the water is

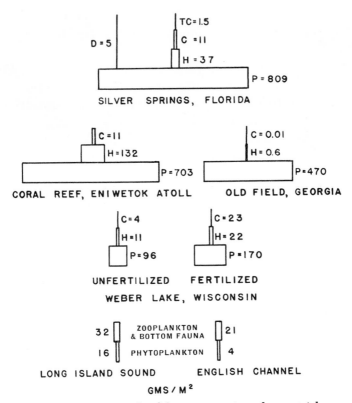

Figure 15. Biomass pyramids of diverse aquatic and terrestrial ecosystems. Pyramids are drawn approximately to same scale, and figures represent grams of dry biomass per square meter. P = producers, H = herbivores, C = carnivores, TC = top carnivores, and D = decomposers. Pyramids constructed from data as follows: Silver Springs—H. T. Odum, 1957; coral reef —Odum and Odum, 1955; old field—E. P. Odum, 1957a; Weber Lake—Juday, 1942; Long Island Sound—Riley, 1956; English Channel—Harvey, 1950.

too deep for bottom plants to exist (as in vast areas of the ocean). In such situations of rapid turnover, the standing crop structure (of the lower trophic levels, at least) is likely to be highly variable from time to time, with biomass pyramids sometimes being inverted, sometimes upright. What the average situation is in many of these open water communities has not been determined. In a recent study in which only the first two trophic levels of the open water were considered, Pennak (1955) found that the ratio by weight of the consumer crustaceans (zooplankton) to producer algae (phytoplankton) in 15 Colorado lakes varied from 0.4/1 to 9.9/1; in most lakes the standing crop of zooplankton was greater than the standing crop of phytoplankton on which they were feeding. In another study, Fleming and Laevastu (1956) report that ratio of zooplankton to phytoplankton in higher latitudes varies from 1/1 in winter to 1/25 in early summer, suggesting that the shape of the biomass pyramid may be expected to change with season.

If, for the moment, we may assume that the examples in Figure 15 are representative of the range of situations to be expected, we may make the following generalizations: (1) In terrestrial and shallow water ecosystems, where producers are large and relatively long-lived, a broad-based, relatively stable pyramid is to be expected. There is some evidence to show that pioneer or newly established communities will tend to have fewer consumers in proportion to producers (i.e., the apex of the biomass pyramid will be small) as illustrated by the "old-field" pyramid in comparison with that of the coral reef in Figure 15. Generally speaking, consumer animals in terrestrial and shallow water communities have more complicated life histories and habitat requirements (specialized shelter, etc.) than do green plants; hence animal populations may require a longer period of time for maximum development. (2) In open water or deep water situations where producers are small and short-lived the standing crop situation at any one moment may be widely variable and the biomass pyramid may be inverted. Also, the overall size of the total standing crop will likely be smaller (as indicated graphically by the area of the biomass pyramid) than that of land or shallow water communities, even if the total energy fixed annually is the same. Finally, (3) lakes and ponds where both large rooted plants and tiny algae are important may be expected to have an intermediate arrangement of standing crop units (as illustrated by Weber Lake, Fig. 15).

We may now turn to the consideration of energy pyramids as

illustrated in Figure 16. While a fairly complete picture could be presented in the case of biomass pyramids, our knowledge of energy fixation in *total* systems is extremely incomplete. Energy pyramids depict in a different way some of the same relationships shown in an energy flow diagram. Thus, each bar in Figure 16 represents total energy flow at each level while the shaded portion of the bar represents production of biomass and the unshaded portion represents the energy dissipated by respiration or exported downstream (compare with Figure 11 and Table 2). Energy pyramids put small organisms in their true perspective in relation to larger forms; for an example, compare biomass and energy flow estimates of the decomposer group in Silver Springs (Figs. 15 and 16).

The data in Table 4 provide a striking illustration of how the activities of decomposers and other small organisms may bear very little relation to the total numbers or biomass which are present at any one moment. Note that a fifteenfold increase in energy dissipated, which resulted from the addition of organic matter, was accompanied by less than a twofold increase in the number of bacteria and fungi. In other words, these small organisms merely "turnover" faster when they become more active, and do not increase their standing crop biomass proportionally as do large organisms. The protozoa, being somewhat larger than the bacteria, exhibited a somewhat greater increase in numbers (Table 4).

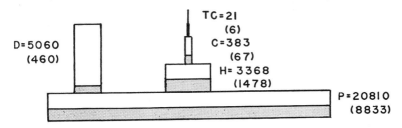

KILO-CALORIES / M² / YEAR

Figure 16. Energy pyramid for Silver Springs, Florida, on an annual basis. The portion of the total energy flow which is actually fixed as organic biomass, and which is potentially available as food for other populations in the next trophic level, is indicated by figures in parenthesis and by the shaded portion of each tier. Trophic levels are as follows: P = producers, H = herbivores, C = carnivores, TC = top carnivores, D = decomposers. Note that about half of the total assimilation ends up in the bodies of organisms (the rest being lost as heat or export), except for the decomposers level where per cent loss in respiration is much greater. (Diagram constructed from data of H. T. Odum, 1957.)

Table 4. *Comparison of total metabolism and population density of soil microorganisms under conditions of low and high organic matter**

	No manure added to the soil	Manure added to the soil
Energy Dissipated:		
Kilocalories x 10^6/acre/year	1	15
Average Population Density:		
Number/Gram of Soil		
Bacteria, x 10^8	1.6	2.9
Fungi mycelia, x 10^6	0.85	1.01
Protozoa, x 10^3	17	72

* Data from Russell and Russell, 1950.

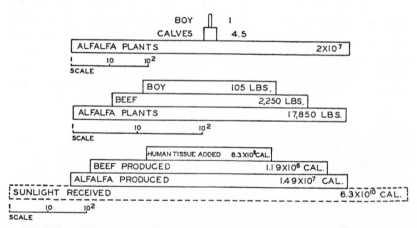

Figure 17. The three types of ecological pyramids illustrated for a hypothetical alfalfa-calf-boy food chain computed on the basis of 10 acres and one year and plotted on a log scale. Compiled from data obtained as follows: Sunlight: Haurwitz and Austin (1944), "Climatology." Alfalfa: "USDA Statistics, 1951"; "USDA Yearbook 1948"; Morrison (1947), "Feeds and Feeding." Beef calf: Brody (1945), "Bioenergetics and Growth." Growing boy: Fulton (1950), "Physiology"; Dearborn and Rothney (1941), "Predicting the Child's Development."

In Figure 17 data for a hypothetical alfalfa-calf-boy food chain situation are arranged in the form of all three types of pyramids. In the energy pyramid respiration is not included, only production of new biomass. While cows do not usually subsist entirely on alfalfa, nor boys entirely on meat, these diagrams are realistic *models* of the kind of ecosystem in which man is not merely an interested observer (as in Silver Springs) but is himself a vital part. Thus, most of man's domestic food animals are herbivores, and man could satisfy his nutritional requirements on a diet of meat (especially if he consumed various parts of the animal, not just muscle tissue). He could also be healthy as a vegetarian and assume the place of the calf, in which case more people could be supported with the same basic primary fixation of energy. Actually, of course, man usually occupies a variable position intermediate between a herbivore and a carnivore. The diagrams in Figure 17 also indicate the general situation to be expected in those terrestrial communities where producers and consumers are relatively large in individual size.

Although there is no evidence to indicate that "man controlled" systems are any different from "natural" systems in general energy relationships, there are many questions of far-reaching importance involving the relationships of number of species, number of individuals, biomass and trophic efficiency, which can not be answered at present. For example, what determines the efficiency at different levels? To what extent can man increase efficiency of energy fixation by plants and/or rate of transfer to higher levels? Can the slope of the pyramid be changed without changing the base? How does the trophic structure and energy relations of newly established communities compare with those which have had long periods of time for competition and adaptation to hold sway? How do "many"-species and "few"-species (as alfalfa-calf-boy situation) systems compare?

As graphic devices, ecological pyramids can also be used to illustrate quantitative relationships in specific parts of ecosystems in which one might have a special interest, for example, predator-prey or host-parasite groups. As already indicated a "parasite pyramid of numbers" would generally be reversed in contrast to biomass and energy pyramids. Unfortunately, almost no measurements have been made on entire populations of parasites and hyperparasites (parasites living on or in other parasites). One thing seems certain, however: One cannot take literally the well known jingle by Jonathan Swift, or the whimsical diagram* of Hegner:

> Big fleas have little fleas
> Upon their backs to bite 'em
> And little fleas have lesser fleas
> And so, ad infinitum.

* Reproduced from "Big Fleas Have Little Fleas, or Who's Who among the Protozoa," by Robert Hegner, Williams & Wilkins Co., 1938.

The number of levels or steps in the parasite chain or pyramid is not "ad infinitum" but is definitely limited, both by size relations and by our friend, the second law of thermodynamics!

5. Concept of productivity

Statement

Basic or *primary productivity* of an ecological system, community or any part thereof, is defined as the rate at which energy is stored by photosynthetic and chemosynthetic activity of producer organisms (chiefly green plants) in the form of organic substances which can be used as food materials. It is important to distinguish between two kinds of primary productivity as follows: *Gross primary productivity* is the total rate of photosynthesis including the organic matter used up in respiration during the measurement period. This is also known as "total photosynthesis" or "total assimilation." *Net primary productivity* is the rate of storage of organic matter in plant tissues in excess of the respiratory utilization by the plants during the period of measurement. This is also called "apparent photosynthesis" or "net assimilation." The amount of respiration is usually added to measurements of "apparent" photosynthesis as a correction in order to obtain estimates of gross production. The rates of energy storage at consumer and decomposer trophic levels are referred to as *secondary productivities* and are, of course, less and less at successive levels. There is only one kind of secondary production since consumers only utilize food materials already produced, with appropriate respiratory losses, and convert to different tissues by one, overall process. (In other words, the total energy flow at heterotrophic levels which is analogous to gross production of autotrophs should be designated as "assimilation" and not "production.") In all these definitions the term "productivity" and the phrase "rate of production" may be used interchangeably. The different stages in production within an ecosystem are shown in the energy flow diagram of Figure 11 as follows: P—Gross production. P_N—net production. P_2, P_3, P_4 and P_5—secondary productivities.

Explanation

The key word in the above definition is rate; the time element must be considered, that is, the amount of energy fixed in a given time. Biological productivity thus differs from "yield" in the chemical or industrial sense. In the latter case the reaction ends with the production of a given amount of material; in biological communities the process is continuous in time so that it is necessary to designate a time unit; for example, the amount of food manufactured per day or per year. In more general terms, productivity of an ecosystem refers to its "richness." While a rich or productive community may have a larger quantity of organisms than a less productive community, this is by no means always the case. *Standing biomass or standing crop present at any given time should not be confused with productivity.* This point has been brought out in the earlier discussions, but it will not hurt to emphasize it again since students of ecology often confuse these two quantities. Usually, one can not determine the productivity of a system simply by counting and weighing (i.e., "censusing") the organisms which happen to be present at any one moment, although good estimates of net productivity may be obtained from standing crop data in situations in which organisms are large and living materials accumulate over a period of time without being utilized (as in cultivated crops, for example). On the other hand, since small organisms "turnover" rapidly (see Table 4), and since organisms of all sizes are often "consumed" as they are being "produced," the size of the standing crop may bear little direct relation to productivity. For example, a fertile pasture which is being grazed by livestock would likely have a much smaller standing crop of grass than a less productive pasture which is not being grazed at the time of measurement. The "grazed pasture" situation is to be expected in a wide variety of natural communities where all trophic levels are present and active with the result that "consumption" occurs more or less simultaneously with "production."

The different kinds of production and the important distinction between gross and net primary production will become clear when the diagram in Figure 11 is carefully studied. Note that the respiration of plants reduces to an appreciable extent (at least 10 per cent, usually more) the food (net production) available for the higher trophic levels. The quantitative relationships between community production and total community respiration (including consumer and decomposer, as well as plant respiration) will be discussed in Chapter 8.

We now come to the point where we can relate the principles of biogeochemical cycles, as outlined in Chapter 2, to principles pertaining to energy in ecosystems. The important point is: materials circulate, but energy does not. Nitrogen, phosphorus, carbon, water and other materials of which living things are composed circulate through the system in a variable and complex manner. On the other hand, energy is used once by a given organism, is converted into heat and is lost to the ecosystem. Thus, there is a nitrogen cycle (as illustrated in Figure 7), which means that nitrogen may circulate many times between living and nonliving entities; but there is no energy cycle. Life is kept going by the continuous inflow of sun energy from outside. Productivity should ultimately lend itself to precise measurement if energy flow can be measured. As we shall see, this is not easy to do in practice.

Examples

Tables 5, 6, and 7 show some estimates of primary productivity of different ecological systems including experimental systems, field crops and a wide variety of natural aquatic and terrestrial communities. Values are expressed as grams of dry organic matter produced per square meter per day or per year. To visualize these figures in terms of approximate pounds per acre multiply by 10 (actually one gram/square meter = 8.9 lbs/acre). It should be pointed out that the estimates in the tables were obtained by different methods (discussed below) and by different workers. However, in each case the original data have been carefully studied, and necessary adjustments and corrections made to make the values comparable with one another. Also, it should be remembered that not all "dry matter" has the same energy value; a crop of sugar cane, for example, is chiefly carbohydrate and has a lower caloric value per gram than a crop of soybeans or wheat. Ultimately, all values should be converted to Calories per square meter (roughly four times dry weight), but methods of measuring productivity in many situations are still too crude to justify such conversions.

In Table 5, gross productivity is compared with net produc-

Table 5. *Comparison of gross and net primary productivity*

Ecosystem	Rate of production Gms/M²/day		Per cent of gross production lost to plant respiration (gross minus net)
	Gross	Net	
Silver Springs, Florida; year average[*]	17.5	7.4	57.5
Alfalfa, experimental plots[†]			
During period maximum growth	56.0	49.0	12.5
Average 6 months crop period	30.1	18.7	38.0
Sargasso Sea; year average[‡]	0.55	0.26	53.0

[*] H. T. Odum (1957).   [†] Thomas and Hill (1949).   [‡] Riley (1957).

tivity in situations where it has been possible to measure total photosynthesis and total plant respiration at the same time (as by gas exchange methods). We see from this table that producers may use as little as 10 per cent of their total food manufactured in case of small scale experimental crops, when all plants are growing rapidly under the most ideal conditions. However, where both rapidly growing, slow growing and senescent individuals (the latter using more food than they are making) are mixed together in some sort of balance, the case in any large scale community whether agricultural or natural, 50 per cent or more of the gross production may be used by the plants themselves. Thus, it is by no means safe to assume, as have many food technologists, that man can "get" 90 per cent of what plants make when any large area of the earth's surface is considered. To harvest 90 per cent one would have to continually replace individuals as they reach their peak of photosynthesis with other individuals, also at their peak. This, perhaps, can be done on a practical scale with algae, but as we have seen, the rapid respiratory rate which is inherent in small organisms counterbalances the greater efficiency in harvest (as compared with field crops), so we do well to harvest 50 per cent of gross, meaning that no more total food is obtained than with some other crops which may require less labor.

Measurements of gross productivity made in situ in intact natural aquatic communities are shown in Table 6. The more fertile systems, such as coral reefs, prove to be 40 times as productive as the infertile open oceans, when average production

Table 6.   *Gross primary productivity of various ecosystems as determined by gas exchange measurements of intact systems in nature*

Ecosystem	Rate of Production $Gms/M^2/day$
Averages for long periods—6 months to 1 year	
Infertile open ocean, Sargasso Sea[1]	0.5
Shallow, inshore waters, Long Island Sound; year average[3]	3.2
Texas estuaries, Laguna Madre[4]	4.4
Clear, deep (oligotrophic) Lake, Wisconsin[5]	0.7
Shallow (eutrophic) Lake, Japan[6]	2.1
Bog lake, Cedar Bog Lake, Minnesota (phytoplankton only)[7]	0.3
Lake Erie, Winter[8]	1.0
Lake Erie, Summer[8]	9.0
Silver Springs, Florida[9]	17.5
Coral reefs, average three Pacific reefs[10]	18.2
Values obtained for short favorable periods	
Fertilized pond, N. C. in May[11]	5.0
Pond with treated sewage wastes, Denmark, July[12]	9.0
Pond with untreated wastes, South Dakota, summer[13]	27
Silver Springs, Florida, May[9]	35
Turbid river, suspended clay, N. C., summer[11]	1.7
Polluted stream, Indiana, summer[14]	57
Estuaries, Texas[4]	23
Marine turtle-grass flats, Florida, August[14]	34
Mass algae culture, extra CO_2 added[15]	43

[1] Riley (1957); [3] Riley (1955); [4] H. T. Odum (unpublished); [5] Juday (1940); [6] Hogetsu and Ichimura (1954); [7] Lindeman (1942); [8] Verduin (1956); [9] H. T. Odum (1957); [10] Kohn and Helfrich (1957); [11] Hoskin, 1957 (unpublished); [12] Steeman-Nielsen (1955); [13] Bartsch and Allum (1957); [14] H. T. Odum (1957a); [15] Tamiya (1957).

throughout the year is considered. The data in Table 5 and Table 6 indicate that rates up to 60 gms./M^2/day may occur in the most fertile communities during favorable periods, but that it is unlikely that large scale ecosystems can maintain such a high rate throughout an annual cycle.

Table 7 summarizes estimates of net productivity, on both an annual and a daily basis, of crops, grasslands, forests, deserts and other ecosystems in which it is possible to use a "harvest" method (see below) to estimate the amount of organic matter available to higher trophic levels. Man and other consumers, of course, are most interested in this sort of net production. Estimates in Table 7 are "net yields" and are slightly lower than plant net production

Table 7. *Annual net primary productivity of various cultivated and natural ecosystems as determined by use of harvest methods*

Ecosystem	Net Primary Production Grams per square meter	
	Per year	Per day
CULTIVATED CROPS[1]		
Wheat, world average	344	0.94 (2.3)*
Wheat, average in area of highest yields (Netherlands)	1250	3.43 (8.3)
Oats, world average	359	0.98 (2.4)
Oats, average in area of highest yields (Denmark)	926	2.54 (6.2)
Corn, world average	412	1.13 (2.3)
Corn, average in area of highest yields (Canada)	790	2.16 (4.4)
Rice, world average	497	1.36 (2.7)
Rice, average in area of highest yields (Italy and Japan)	1440	3.95 (8.0)
Hay, U.S. average	420	1.15 (2.3)
Hay, average in area of highest yields (California)	940	2.58 (5.2)
Potatoes, world average	385	1.10 (2.6)
Potatoes, average in area of highest yields (Netherlands)	845	2.31 (5.6)
Sugar beets, world average	765	2.10 (4.3)
Sugar beets, average in area of highest yields (Netherlands)	1470	4.03 (8.2)
Sugar cane, world average	1725	4.73 (4.7)
Sugar cane, average Hawaii	3430	9.40 (9.4)
Sugar cane, maximum Hawaii under intensive culture[2]	6700	18.35 (18.4)
Mass algae culture, best yields under intensive culture outdoors, Tokyo[3]	4530	12.4 (12.4)
NON-CULTIVATED ECOSYSTEMS		
Giant ragweed, fertile bottomland, Oklahoma[4]	1440	3.95 (9.6)
Tall Spartina salt marsh, Georgia[5]	3300	9.0 (9.0)
Forest, pine plantation, average during years of most rapid growth (20-35 years old), England[6]	3180	6.0 (6.0)
Forest, deciduous plantation, England, comparable to the above pine plantation[7]	1560	3.0 (6.0)
Tall grass prairies, Oklahoma and Nebraska[8]	446	1.22 (3.0)
Short grass grassland, 13 in. rainfall; Wyoming[9]	69	0.19 (0.5)
Desert, 5 inches rainfall, Nevada[10]	40	0.11 (0.2)
Seaweed beds, Nova Scotia[11]	358	1.98 (1.0)

* Values in parenthesis are rates for growing season only, which is often less than a year.

[1] Values for crops obtained from Woytinsky (1953) and from 1957 U.S. Government "Statistical Abstracts" and corrected to include dry weight of unharvested parts of plant and to exclude water in case of crops such as potatoes, sugar cane, etc., which are harvested "wet." All averages are for several post-war years.

[2] Based on Burr, et al. (1957) who gives dry weight data on an exceptionally large crop. [3] Tamiya (1957); [4] Penfound (1956); [5] E. P. Odum & Smalley (1957); [6] Ovington (1957); [7] Ovington & Pearsall (1956); [8] Penfound (1956) and Weaver (1954); [9] Lang & Barnes (1942); [10] E. P. Odum (unpublished); [11] MacFarlane (1952).

as measured by gas exchange methods since some losses other than plant respiration occur while the crop awaits harvest. The range of productivity encountered in various terrestrial situa-

Table 8.   *Distribution of primary gross productivity. The range of values found in major environments of the world*

Types of ecosystems	Range of average gross productivity Gms/M^2/day
Deserts and Semi-arid Grasslands	less than 0.5
Open Oceans (probably also deep lakes)	less than 1.0
Continental Shelf Ocean Waters, Shallow Lakes and Ponds, Average Forests, Moist Grasslands, and Ordinary Agriculture	0.5 to 5.0
Coral Reefs, Estuaries, Some Mineral Springs, Semi-aquatic and Terrestrial Communities on Alluvial Planes, Evergreen Forests, and Intensive Agriculture	5.0 to 20.0
Maximum rates which may be maintained for short periods in the more productive natural and cultivated ecosystems	up to 60.0

Note: This table is based on data in Tables 1 to 4. Net production values of Table 4 converted to approximate gross production by the addition of 30 per cent (estimate of average plant respiration in intact systems).

tions is well shown in Table 7; also, the importance of considering both time and space are brought out. For example, deciduous and pine forests growing in the same climate and on the same soils in England had similar rates of production when the growing season only was considered, but the pine forest had a much higher annual yield because of the longer growing season. Thus, most cultivated crops have a high rate of production for several months and then zero production for long periods of the year. With a few crops (sugar cane, for example) and many aquatic and terrestrial natural communities, production continues throughout the year. With respect to space, note that average world production of crops is always much lower than averages obtained in small European countries where intense cultivation is practiced only under the most favorable soil and climatic conditions. Americans generally consider their agriculture the most efficient in the world, but in every case the average yield per acre of staple crops for the U.S. as a whole is lower than for small European countries or Japan. This simply means, of course, that in such a large heterogeneous area as the U.S., locally favorable areas (which would compare with any in Europe) are lumped with less favorable areas in obtaining the average. For the moment, we need only make the observation that large areas usually show considerable less productivity than small favorable areas (see also discussion of algal cultures, page 55-56). What man might do about closing the large gap between the "average" and the "maximum" will be discussed later.

Finally, we come to Table 8, which, in effect, summarizes all that we know about the world distribution of primary productivity. In this table what appear to be reasonable estimates of the range of *gross* productivity are given in round figures in order to present a picture of the order of magnitude found in basic types of ecosystems of the world. The data of Table 8 are shown graphically and dramatically in Figure 18, which depicts a "cross section" of the biosphere. As we see from Figure 18 there are about three orders of magnitude in productivity as follows: (1) Some parts of open oceans (also very deep lakes) and land deserts range around 0.1 gms/M²/day; thus, although limiting factors are quite different (nutrients in ocean, water on land) and the organisms entirely different (algae instead of spermatophytes), both deep oceans and arid lands are "deserts." (2) Grasslands, coastal seas, shallow lakes, and ordinary agriculture range from 1 gm/M²/day upwards. (3) Certain shallow-water systems such as estuaries, coral reefs or mineral springs, together with moist forests, intensive agriculture and natural communities on alluvial planes may range from 10 to 20 gms/M²/day. Production rates higher than 20 have frequently been reported for experimental crops, polluted waters, and limited natural communities (Table 6), but these values are usually based on short time measurements and small areas. It seems doubtful that any extensive ecosystem can maintain a rate higher than 25 gms/M²/day for periods of years.

Two tentative generalizations can be made from the data in Table 8 and Figure 18. First, a very large proportion of the earth's

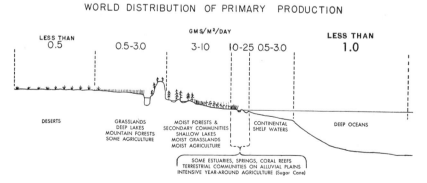

WORLD DISTRIBUTION OF PRIMARY PRODUCTION

Figure 18.

surface is open ocean or arid or semi-arid land, and is thus in the low production category. Unless powerful limiting factors can be removed, net productivity and potential "yield to man" are sharply limited geographically. Secondly, basic primary productivity is not necessarily a function of the kind of producer organisms nor the kind of media (whether air, fresh water or salt water), but is controlled by the local supply of raw materials, sun energy and the ability of local communities *as a whole* (man included!) to utilize and *regenerate* materials for continuous reuse. "Rich" and "poor" may exist side by side depending on the local environmental situation. Terrestrial systems are not inherently different from aquatic systems if light, water and nutrient conditions are similar; however, as previously pointed out, productivity in large bodies of water may be limited by light penetration. Likewise, cultivated crops seem to have a gross productivity of the same order of magnitude as natural "crops" growing on comparable sites. As a matter of fact, annual production by average or "ordinary" agriculture is rather low, because the light energy which is available throughout the year is actually utilized for only less than half the year. Many natural communities, even in relatively cold regions, achieve a longer "production season" by "rotation" of producer organisms adapted to different seasons. It is especially important to note that the maximum production rate achieved by man in intensive agriculture is no greater than that found in certain fertile natural systems. For example, certain coral reefs have been recently shown to be beautifully adapted systems with symbiosis between plants and animals, efficient nutrient circulating (i.e., "self-fertilizing") mechanisms and an annual gross productivity much greater than that of most agricultural efforts (Odum and Odum, 1955; Kohn and Helfrich, 1957). The difference, of course, between a coral reef and a productive rice paddy is that a large portion of the resultant net production in the latter is consumed by man, whereas, on the coral reef, consumption is divided among a large variety of organisms with man usually a minor consumer. In other words, it is one thing to channel primary productivity into specific secondary levels of direct use to man, as does efficient agriculture; and quite a different thing initially to increase primary productivity. One should be careful not to confuse "yield to man," which is what many people mean when they speak of productivity, with basic primary productivity. So far as we can see from data now available, man has not increased maximum primary productivity beyond that which occurs in the absence of man. By supplying water and fertilizers he has, of course, made considerable progress in increasing primary productivity in situations where these materials were limiting in the original state. Unfortunately, man has also greatly reduced the productivity (and especially the "yield to man") of millions of acres of semi-arid lands through exploitation harvest (or in less kind words by being too "greedy") and through the failure to realize that biogeochemical cycles dictate that natural ecosystems must receive the same kind of "loving care and understanding" as cultivated ecosystems if they are to continue to be productive to man.

Since Figure 18 represents a transect of the world at one latitude, one may well ask about the north-south distribution of primary production. The daily rate of production in arctic land areas may be quite respectable for brief periods, but annual rates are bound to be low, thus placing most arctic situations in the same category of deserts or grasslands. On the other hand, Arctic and Antarctic seas are among the most productive deeper waters. In the tropics, even more than in temperate regions, a very large percentage of the area is either arid or deep ocean (with poor nutrient circulation) and hence virtually desert. As we have already seen, certain tropical ecosystems of limited size, such as coral reefs, can be extremely productive. Mangrove forests and other semi-aquatic communities in tropical estuaries and marshes are probably also in this category. The most extensive ecosystems in which one might expect a high productivity are, of course, the tropical rain forests where light, temperature and water are favorable throughout the year. Certainly the standing crop of plants and animals is impressive, but, as we have already seen, this can be misleading. Actually, when man removes the rain forest and attempts to cultivate the area, he is greatly disappointed; yields are lower than in cultivated temperate forest areas and the situation quickly deteriorates as a result of leaching, erosion and other losses of materials. Close symbiosis between numerous organisms may be necessary in rain forests and coral reefs to maintain high productivity by preventing losses of materials from the system. Man's attempt to "simplify" such complex, adapted systems is certainly difficult.

Selected figures on fish harvest from all over the world, as shown in Table 9, illustrate certain aspects of secondary productivity in

Table 9. *Secondary productivity as measured in fish production*

Ecosystem and Trophic Level	Man's Harvest Gms per M² per Year		Lb. per Acre per Year	
I Unfertilized natural waters				
Herbivore-carnivore composition				
North Sea[1]		1.68	15	
World Marine Fishery (average)[2]		0.05	0.45	
Great Lakes[3]	0.09 –	0.82	0.80 –	7.3
African Lakes[1]	0.16 –	25.2	1.40 –	225
U.S. small lakes (sports fishery)[4]	0.21 –	18.1	1.90 –	162
Stocked carnivores				
U.S. fish ponds (sports fishery)[1]	4.5 –	16.8	40 –	150
Stocked herbivores				
German fish ponds (carp)[6]	11.2 –	39.0	100 –	348
II Fertilized waters				
Stocked carnivores				
U.S. fish ponds (sports fishery)[1, 5]	22.4 –	56.0	200 –	500
Stocked herbivores				
Philippine marine ponds[1]	50.4 –	101.0	450 –	900
German fish ponds (carp)[6]	99.7 –	157.0	890 –	1,400
III Fertilized waters *and outside food added*				
Carnivores				
One acre pond, U.S.[6]		227.0	2,027	
Herbivores				
Hongkong[1]	224.0 –	448.0	2,000 –	4,000
South China[1, 6]	112.0 –	1,540.0	1,000 –	13,500
			(average 4,000)	
Malaya[1]		392	3,500	

[1] Hickling (1948).   [4] Rounsefell (1946).
[2] Cutting (1952).   [5] Swingle and Smith (1947).
[3] Rawson (1952).   [6] Viosca (1935).

terms of "yield to man." Since fishery statistics are "wet weights," these values should be reduced by about half in making comparisons with the data on "dry weight" primary productivity in Tables 5-8. Trophic level, primary productivity and the intensity of harvest all contribute to the wide range of values in Table 9. Note that production of herbivores is greater than that of "sport" or carnivorous fish in comparable waters. Large lakes and the sea yield much less on an acre basis than do small fertilized and intensively managed ponds, not only because primary productivity is less but also because man harvests only a part of the available consumer production in large bodies of water. As we have seen in the discussion of trophic efficiencies and ecological pyramids, about 10 per cent of gross and perhaps 20 per cent of net primary productivity is the maximum yield to be expected at the primary consumer level, with perhaps 10 per cent of this at the secondary consumer level. When we compare Table 6 and Table 9, it is evident that only in the intensively managed German and Oriental fish ponds is a harvest even approaching 10 per cent of gross primary production obtained. The very high yields in Section III of Table 9 should not be compared in this way because they were obtained by adding food from *outside* the ecosystem, that is, food (plant or animal products) which represents energy fixed somewhere else. Actually, these yields should be adjusted to include the acres of land from which the food was obtained. Many writers have misinterpreted these high yields obtained in the Orient, thinking that they could be compared directly with fish pond harvests in the United States.

In the final analysis, increasing the amount of food available for the growing human population of the world involves two basic problems: (1) increasing basic productivity, and (2) channeling the available energy into usable food form. The latter involves some of the principles in population ecology which will be discussed in Chapter 7.

Measurement of primary productivity

Because of its great importance, brief attention should be given to the methods of measuring productivity in ecological systems. Although detailed consideration of methods is outside the scope of this text, a discussion of methods at this point will help clarify the principles outlined in this chapter. As already indicated, the ideal way to measure productivity would be to measure the energy flow through the system, but this has so far proved difficult to do. Most measurements have been based on some indirect quantity, such as the amount of substance produced, the amount of raw material used or the amount of by-product released. The simplified equation for photosynthesis given in Chapter 1 gives the over-all reaction which takes place during the production of carbohy‑drates from raw materials as the result of light energy acting through chlorophyll. Since most kinds of production in nature result in new protoplasm, a more inclusive equation of productivity is as follows:

1,300,000 Cal. radiant energy +
$$106\ CO_2 + 90\ H_2O + 16\ NO_3 + 1\ PO_4 + \text{mineral elements}$$
equals

13,000 Cal. potential energy in
3258 gms. protoplasm (106 C, 180 H, 46 O, 16 N, 1 P, 815 gms. mineral ash) + 154 O_2 + 1,287,000 Cal. heat energy dispersed (99%)

This equation is based on the ratios of elements in, and the energy content of, plankton protoplasm (Sverdrup et al., 1942; Clarke, 1948). It is evident that productivity can be measured, theoretically at least, by determining the amount of any one of the above items over the period of time that productivity is being measured. Equations such as this one can be used to convert (and to check against one another) productivity measurements between units of energy, carbon dioxide, nitrate or phosphate utilization, protoplasm weight (or the amount of carbon put in the form of food), and the amount of oxygen used. This is the theory; now let us see about the practice of measurement.

One of the greatest difficulties in determining the productivity of a particular ecological system is determining whether or not the system is in dynamic equilibrium or a *steady state.* In a "steady state" inflows balance outflows of material and energy. The rate of production is in equilibrium with the supply or the rate of inflow of the minimum limiting constituent (in other words, the law of the minimum is applying, see Chapter 3). For example, let us assume that carbon dioxide was the major limiting factor in a lake, and productivity was therefore in equilibrium with the rate of supply of carbon dioxide coming from the decay of organic matter. We shall assume that light, nitrogen, phosphorus, etc., were available in excess of use in this steady state equilibrium (and hence not limiting factors at the moment). If a storm brought more carbon dioxide into the lake, the rate of production would change, and be dependent upon the other factors as well. While the rate is changing there is no steady state and no minimum constituent; instead, the reaction depends on the concentration of *all* constituents present, which in this transitional period differs from the rate at which the least plentiful is being added. The rate of production would change rapidly as various constituents were used until some constituent, perhaps carbon dioxide again, became limiting, and the lake system would once again be operating at the rate controlled by the law of the minimum. In most natural systems the production rate passes from one temporary steady state equilibrium to another because of changes imposed on the system from the outside.

Some of the actual methods used to measure productivity may be briefly summarized as follows:

1. *The Harvest Method.* In situations where herbivore ani-

mals are not important and where a steady state condition is never reached, the harvest method can be used. This is the usual situation in regard to cultivated crops since efforts are made to prevent insects and other animals from removing material, and the rate of production starts from zero at the time of planting seeds and reaches a maximum by the time of harvest. Weighing the growth produced by cultivated crops is straightforward; the productivity of the crops, as given in Table 7, were determined in this manner. The harvest method can be used also in noncultivated terrestrial situations where annual plants predominate (as in a ragweed field) or where plants are little consumed until growth has been completed. In these cases it is best to take harvest samples at intervals during the season rather than to rely on a single terminal harvest (see Penfound, 1956; E. P. Odum, 1959). Such a method could not be used where the food produced is being removed as it is produced, as in many natural communities. If the consumers are large, long-lived animals one might determine productivity in these cases by harvesting the consumers, which are removing the food at a consistent rate, and thus estimate primary productivity from secondary productivity. A method of this sort, of course, is used frequently by animal husbandry men or range managers. The productivity of a western winter range, for example, may be expressed in terms of the number of cattle that can be supported by so many acres (or number of acres per one "animal unit"). The possible pitfalls in this procedure have already been suggested. Since food used by the plants themselves is not included, the harvest method always measures *net production*.

2. *Oxygen Measurement.*   Since there is a definite equivalence between oxygen and food produced, oxygen production might be a basis for determining productivity. However, in most situations animals and bacteria (as well as plants themselves) are rapidly using up the oxygen; and often there is gas exchange with other environments (this is especially true of terrestrial situations). However, oxygen production can be measured in aquatic areas as follows: A bottle is filled with water containing an average concentration of phytoplankton or other production units and suspended at the level from which the water came. Another bottle with an opaque black cover (to exclude all light) is similarly placed. In the first bottle, oxygen is produced by photosynthesis, and some of it is used in respiration; in the black bottle no new

oxygen is produced, but some of the oxygen in the water is used up. Therefore, the sum of the oxygen produced in the light bottle and oxygen used in the dark bottle is the total oxygen production. If respiration by either plants or bacteria should differ in the dark and in the light, a source of error would be introduced since respiration in the dark bottle is assumed to be the same as respiration in the light bottle (where, of course, respiration and production are indistinguishable). By adding a heavy isotope of oxygen, which could be distinguished from ordinary oxygen, Brown (1953) found that the heavy isotope was used up at the same rate in the dark, at least for a number of hours, as in the light, thus indicating that respiration should be the same in both light and dark bottles during experiments of short duration. Whether this is applicable to all plants is a controversial matter. The "light and dark bottle method," pioneered by Gaarder and Gran in 1927, is now very widely used in both marine and fresh-water environments. Dissolved oxygen is usually measured titrametrically by the Winkler method and a given experiment is limited to one 24-hour cycle or less. Since plant respiration is included, this method measures *gross primary production*. It does not, however, measure the metabolism of the part of the community on the bottom; also, the effects of enclosing the community in a bottle have not been clearly delimited.

Oxygen production may also be measured in certain aquatic ecosystems by the "diurnal curve method." In this case, measurements of dissolved oxygen in the water at large are made at intervals throughout the day and night so that production of oxygen during the day and its use during the night may be estimated by determining the area under the diurnal curves. This method is particularly applicable to flowing water systems such as streams or estuaries (H. T. Odum, 1956). If oxygen diffuses out of the body of water or into it from the atmosphere at an appreciable rate, a source of error is introduced; however, reasonable corrections can be made since diffusion is dependent on well defined physical laws. The "diurnal curve method" measures *gross primary production* since O_2 used at night is added to that produced during the day (thus automatically including the respiration of the whole community).

In specialized situations, such as deep temperate lakes, productivity has been measured by a sort of reverse procedure, that is, by measuring the rate of oxygen disappearance in the deep waters (hypolimnion) which are producing no oxygen and are not in circulation with the upper waters during a major part of the production (summer) season (see Chapter 9). Thus, the greater the production in the upper, lighted waters (epilimnion), the more dead cells, bodies, feces, and other organic matter fall to the bottom where they decay under the action of bacteria and fungi with the use of oxygen. The rate of oxygen depletion is, therefore, proportional to productivity. Since decay of both plants and animals uses up oxygen, the "hypolimnetic method" measures the *net production of the whole community* (that is, both primary and secondary production) of the epilimnion. Edmondson and Anderson (1956) have made good use of this method in following changes in productivity which have taken place over a period of years in Lake Washington, a large lake in the middle of the city of Seattle. As the city has grown, the volume of sewage released into the lake has increased with the result that the oxygen deficit in the hypolimnion increased from 1.18 $mg/cm^2/month$ in 1930 to 3.13 in 1956, indicating a 2.7-fold increase in net productivity of the upper waters. As will be indicated more fully in Chapter 9, some fish which require cold water environment, as, for evample, the cisco of the Great Lakes region, can live only in relatively unproductive lakes where cold bottom waters do not become depleted of oxygen during the summer.

3. *Carbon Dioxide Methods.*   In terrestrial situations it is more practical to measure CO_2 rather than O_2 changes. Plant physiologists have long used CO_2 uptake to measure photosynthesis in leaves or single plants, and ecologists have made various attempts to measure production in whole intact communities in this way, beginning with the pioneer experiments of Transeau (1926). A large bell jar or plastic bag is placed over the community; air is drawn through the enclosure and bubbled througn a column of KOH or other CO_2 absorbent. An infra-red gas analyzer may also be used. The amount of CO_2 obtained in a given time period is compared with a similar sample from the community, covered by a dark jar or bag, and with a sample from the ambient air. As in the "light and dark bottle" aquatic method, the dark enclosure measures respiration and the lighted enclosure measures gross minus respiration or net production. Therefore, the CO_2 method measures *gross primary production* if both dark and light enclosures are used.

4. *Disappearance of Raw Materials.*   As indicated by the

above equation, productivity can be measured not only by the rate of formation of materials (food, protoplasm, minerals) and by measuring gaseous exchange but also by the rate of the disappearance of raw material minerals. In a steady state equilibrium, however, the amount used might be balanced by the amount being released or entering the system, and there would be no way of determining the actual rate of use by organisms. Where constituents such as nitrogen or phosphorus are not being supplied steadily, but perhaps once a year or at intervals, the rate at which their concentration decreases becomes a very good measure of productivity during the period in question. This method has been used in certain ocean situations where phosphorus and nitrogen accumulate in the water during the winter and the rate of use can be measured during the period of spring growth of phytoplankton. The method must be used with caution since non-living forces may also cause the disappearance of materials. The disappearance method measures the *net production of the whole community.*

5. *Productivity Determinations with Radioactive Materials.* As with many other fields of science, the use of radioactive tracers in ecology opens new possibilities in determining productivity. With a known amount of "marked material," which can be identified by its radiations, the rate of transfer can be followed even in the steady state system as mentioned above, with the added advantage of less disturbance to the system.

One of the most sensitive methods for measuring aquatic plant production is done in bottles with radioactive carbon (C^{14}) added as carbonate. After a short period of time, the plankton or other plants are separated from the water, dried and placed in a counting device. With suitable calculations, the amount of carbon dioxide fixed in photosynthesis can be determined from the radioactive counts made. When Steeman-Nielsen (1952), who first developed the method, made a series of measurements in the tropical oceans of the world, he found lower values than reported in many previous studies based on oxygen changes in bottled water (light and dark bottle method). If Ryther (1954a) is correct, the radioactive carbon method measures *net production* and not gross, as does the O_2 method; it apparently measures that excess organic matter which is stored over and beyond the simultaneous needs for respiration. Ryther's experiments suggest that tropical waters have a high respiration rate which results in very little net production, thus explaining the low values obtained by Steeman-Nielsen.

When radioactive phosphorus or P^{32} became generally available, it appeared to be a promising tool for applying the "disappearance" method in steady-state communities. While a great deal has been learned about the turnover rates in the phosphorus cycle, as described in Chapter 2, P^{32} has not proved to be very satisfactory in the measurement of short-term productivity, because phosphorus in any form is readily "adsorbed" by sediments and by organisms without being immediately incorporated into protoplasm. Thus, while P^{32} added to a lake may be removed from the water at a rate perhaps proportional to primary productivity, it has been difficult to distinguish between biological assimilation and physical "uptake." Short-term uptake rate, however, may prove to be a good index to potential productivity since it seems to be proportional to the surface area in the ecosystem (see E. P. Odum, et al., 1958).

Radioactive isotopes other than C^{14} and P^{32} offer many possibilities which are yet to be investigated. It is likely that the next ten years will see the development of many new techniques (for additional discussion of radioisotopes in the environment see Chapter 14).

6. *The Chlorophyll Method.*   The possibilities of using the chlorophyll content of whole natural communities as a measure of productivity are now being actively investigated. Offhand it might appear that chlorophyll would be a better measure of standing crop of plants than of productivity, but apparently the opposite is often the case. While Willstatter and Stoll (1918) and others early reported a close relationship between photosynthesis and chlorophyll content of land plants of the same physiological state, ecologists were discouraged from studying chlorophyll in communities by the numerous reports in the plant physiological literature which demonstrated that a variety of factors such as age and light intensity can alter markedly the amount of chlorophyll in leaves and other plant parts. Then, Gessner (1949) made the remarkable observation that the chlorophyll which actually develops on a "per square meter" basis tends to be similar in diverse communities, strongly suggesting that the content of the green pigment in whole communities is more uniform than in individual plants or plant parts. We apparently have here another striking example of "community homeostasis" where the whole is not only different from, but can not be explained by, the parts alone. In intact communities various plants, young and old, sun-

lit and shaded, are apparently integrated and adjust, as fully as local limiting factors allow, to the incoming sun energy, which, of course, impinges on the ecosystem on a "square meter" basis.

Actual data on the chlorophyll content in grams per square meter of fresh-water, marine and terrestrial ecosystems are given in Table 10. Shown also for some of the examples is the *assimilation ratio,* which is the ratio of photosynthetic (gross) production to chlorophyll, expressed as gm O_2/gms. chlorophyll/hour. The similarity of diverse communities is very surprising. It does not seem to matter much whether the photosynthetic zone is very "thin" as in an algal film or grassland, or very "thick" as in a lake or forest; the concentration of chlorophyll per square meter tends to adjust to about one gram when conditions are reasonably favorable for production. Even more significant is the similar order of magnitude of the assimilation ratios; the range of 0.5 to 6.3 is in sharp contrast to the range of 0.1 to 100, which is found when young and old leaves, or young and old cultures, are compared. Thus, de-

Table 10.   *Chlorophyll content of communities on a unit area basis and its relation to primary production*

Ecosystem	Chlorophyll Gms/M^2	Assimilation ratio Gms O_2/gms chlor/hr
SEA		
Long Island Sound (phytoplankton)[1]	0.1 — 0.6	0.5
Woods Hole, rocky shore intertidal zones (seaweed, etc.)[2]	0.5 — 1.5	
Estuaries, Texas[3]	0.1 — 0.6	0.7 — 4.4
CORAL REEF[4]	0.5	4.0
AQUATIC GRASS		
Silver Springs, Fla. (eelgrass beds)[5]	3.0	0.5
LAKES		
Lake Suwa, Japan[e]		
winter	0.006	6.3
summer	0.2	1.4
Wisconsin lakes[7]	0.05 — 1.0	0.8 — 4.0
ROCKY STREAM, Utah[8]	0.3 — 1.6	0.7 — 2.0
FORESTS[9]	1.2	
GRASSLANDS[9]	1.0	
ALGAL CULTURES, steady state		
Sewage[10]		2.0
Chlorella film, dense[11]	0.5	3.0
SINGLE LAND PLANTS[12]	1.0	2.0

[1] Riley, 1956.
[2] E. P. Odum and Gifford (unpublished).
[3] H. T. Odum and McConnell (unpublished).
[4] Odum and Odum, 1955.
[5] H. T. Odum, 1956.
[6] Ichimura, 1954.

[7] Manning and Juday, 1941.
[8] McConnell (unpublished).
[9] Gessner, 1949.
[10] Ludwig et al., 1956.
[11] Myers, 1954.
[12] Rabinowitch, 1951.

spite taxonomic diversity, the relationship between production and chlorophyll in intact ecosystems appears to be more consistent than is the case in "even aged" cultures or individual leaves. Therefore, chlorophyll content should be an index to potential primary productivity.

Manning and Juday (1941), Harvey (1950), Edmondson (1955) and Ryther and Yentsch (1957) have discussed practical procedures for estimating primary production by measuring existing chlorophyll. The latter authors found that 3.7 gms of carbon were assimilated per hour per gram of chlorophyll in marine phytoplankton at light saturation. By determining the amount of chlorophyll and the amount of light under a unit of sea surface, Ryther and Yentsch calculated production rates, finding that the values were very similar to those obtained by simultaneous use of the light-and-dark bottle oxygen method.

While much work yet remains to be done, especially to determine the applicability of the method to terrestrial situations, the chlorophyll method is a most promising one for survey work since it is not necessary to enclose the community in an artificial container or make time lapse measurements. Light data may be obtained from tables which show average solar radiation for various seasons and latitudes. Chlorophyll itself is easy to measure. One needs only to extract the pigment from plant material with acetone and determine the concentration of chlorophyll "A" (and other types, if important) in a spectrophotometer (see Richards and Thompson, 1952; Duxbury and Yentsch, 1956). The yellow or carotenoid pigments can also be determined at the same time. Since carotenoids increase as plants age and slow down, the chlorophyll-carotenoid ratio in whole communities might prove to be a useful index to fluctuations in the vigor of the primary trophic level, which probably occur even in steady-state communities. In algal cultures, at least, the ratio declines from about three to about one as cultures age, and the ratio of net to gross production declines in a parallel manner. That is, a greater percentage of the photosynthate is used up by plant respiration in old cultures, paralleling the increase in the yellow pigments. As has been indicated several times in this chapter, the extent of "respiratory losses" (that is, gap between gross and net production) in natural communities is almost totally unknown.

4 · Principles pertaining to limiting factors

1. Liebig's "law" of the minimum

Statement

To occur and thrive in a given situation, an organism must have essential materials which are necessary for growth and reproduction. These basic requirements vary with the species and with the situation. The essential material available in amounts most closely approaching the critical minimum needed will tend to be the limiting one.

Explanation

The idea that an organism is no stronger than the weakest link in its ecological chain of requirements was first clearly expressed by Justus Liebig in 1840. Liebig was a pioneer in the study of the effect of various factors on the growth of plants. He found, as do agriculturists today, that the yield of crops was often limited not by nutrients needed in large quantities, such as carbon dioxide and water, since these were often abundant in the environment, but by some raw material, as boron, for example, needed in minute quantities but very scarce in the soil. His statement that "growth of a plant is dependent on the amount of foodstuff which is presented to it in minimum quantity" has come to be known as Liebig's "law" of the minimum. Many authors (see, for example, Taylor, 1934) have expanded the statement to include factors other than nutrients (temperature, etc.) and to include the time element. To avoid confusion it seems best to restrict the concept of the minimum to chemical materials (oxygen, phosphorus, etc.) necessary for physiological growth and reproduction, as was originally intended, and to include other factors and the limiting effect of the maximum in the "law" of tolerance. Both concepts can then be united in a broad principle of limiting factors, as outlined below. Thus, the "law" of the minimum is but one aspect of the concept of limiting factors which in turn is but one aspect of the environmental control of organisms.

Extensive work since the time of Liebig has shown that a subsidiary principle, that of *factor interaction*, should be added to the concept. Thus, high concentration or availability of some substance, or the action of some factor other than the minimum one, may modify the rate of utilization of the latter. Sometimes organisms are able to substitute, in part at least, a chemically closely related substance for one that is deficient in the environment. Thus, where strontium is abundant mollusks are able to substitute strontium for calcium to a partial extent in their shells. Some plants have been shown to require less zinc when growing in the shade than when growing in full sunlight; thus a given amount of zinc in the soil would be less limiting to plants in the shade than under the same conditions in sunlight.

2. Shelford's "law" of tolerance

Statement

The presence and success of an organism depend upon the completeness of a complex of conditions. Absence or failure of an organism can be controlled by the qualitative or quantitative deficiency or excess with respect to any one of several factors which may approach the limits of tolerance for that organism.

Explanation

Not only may too little of something be a limiting factor, as proposed by Liebig, but also too much, as in the case of such factors as heat, light, and water. Thus, organisms have an ecological minimum and maximum, with a range in between which represents the *limits of tolerance*. The concept of the limiting effect of maximum as well as minimum was incorporated into the "law" of tolerance by V. E. Shelford in 1913. From about 1910, much work has been done in "toleration ecology," so that the limits within which various plants and animals can exist are known, and this knowledge has helped us to understand the distribution of organisms in nature; however, we should hasten to say, it is only part of the story. All physical requirements may be well within the limits of tolerance for an organism and the organism may still fail as a result of biological interrelations. There are other principles of ecology, as we shall see.

Some subsidiary principles to the "law" of tolerance may be stated as follows:

1. Organisms may have a wide range of tolerance for one factor and a narrow range for another.

2. Organisms with wide ranges of tolerance for all factors are likely to be most widely distributed.

3. When conditions are not optimum for a species with respect to one ecological factor, the limits of tolerance may be reduced with respect to other ecological factors. For example, Penman (1956) reports that when soil nitrogen is limiting, the resistance of grass to drought is reduced. In other words, he found that more water was required to prevent wilting at low nitrogen levels than at high levels.

4. The limits of tolerance and the optimum range for a physical factor often vary geographically (and also seasonally) within the same species; that is to say, organisms often adjust their rate functions to local conditions. McMillan (1956), for example, found that prairie grasses of the same species (and to all appearances identical) transplanted into experimental gardens from different parts of the range responded quite differently to light. In each case the timing of growth and reproduction was adapted to the area from which the grasses were transplanted. A good example of temperature compensation is shown in Figure 19. Northern individuals of the marine jellyfish, *Aurelia,* are able to swim at an optimum rate at temperatures which would completely inhibit southern individuals. This sort of temperature compensation is apparently widespread, although some species show a much greater ability to acclimate than others (Bullock, 1955). Compensatory mechanisms help to explain how northern seas can be equally productive (as was discussed in the previous chapter) as southern seas even when it would appear that low temperatures should be limiting to the whole ecosystem. Sometimes a given individual is able to acclimate if conditions are changed slowly, but frequently limits of tolerance have become genetically fixed in local races or strains (with or without morphological manifes-

tations). This important possibility has often been overlooked in applied ecology with the result that restocking attempts have often failed simply because individuals from remote regions were used, and these proved unable to adapt to conditions in the area to which they were transplanted. It would seem logical to expect that racial differences in transplants would likely be more critical under the competitive conditions of nature as compared with the semiprotection of agriculture, horticulture or animal husbandry, but even in the latter it is often necessary to choose or breed strains adapted to the particular climatic region in question. In ecology, locally adapted variants are often called *ecotypes*.

5. Sometimes it is discovered that organisms in nature are not actually living at the optimum range (as determined experimentally) with regard to a particular physical factor. In such cases some other factor or factors are found to have greater importance. Certain tropical orchids, for example, actually grow better in full sunlight than in shade provided they are kept cool (see Went, 1957); in nature they grow only in the shade because they cannot tolerate the heating effect of direct sunlight. In many cases of this sort biological factors (competition, predators, parasites, etc.) apparently prevent organisms from taking advantage of optimum

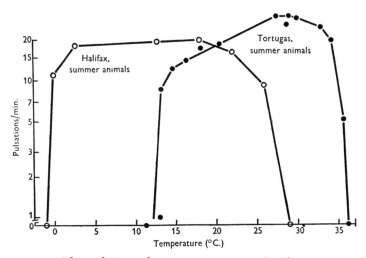

Figure 19. The relation of temperature to swimming movement in northern (Halifax) and southern (Tortugas) individuals of the same species of jellyfish *Aurelia aurita*. The habitat temperatures were 14° and 29° C., respectively. Note that each population is acclimated to swim at a maximum rate at the temperature of its local environment. The cold-adapted form shows an especially high degree of temperature independence. (From Bullock, 1955, after Mayer.)

physical conditions (examples of this are described in the next section of this chapter).

6. The period of reproduction is usually a critical period when environmental factors are most likely to be limiting. The limits of tolerance for reproductive individuals, seeds, eggs, embryos, seedlings, larvae, etc., are usually narrower than for non-reproducing adult plants or animals. Thus, an adult cypress tree will grow on dry upland or continually submerged in water, but it cannot reproduce unless there is moist unflooded ground for seedling development. Adult blue crabs and many other marine animals can tolerate brackish water, or fresh water which has a high chloride content; thus, individuals are often found for some distance up rivers. The larvae, however, cannot live in such waters; therefore, the species cannot reproduce in the river environment and never become established permanently. An interesting case which has not yet been fully worked out is that of the ring-necked pheasant, a game bird introduced into North America. Successfully established in many parts of the United States and Canada, the bird has failed to take hold in southern United States despite large-scale introductions. The adults appear to survive well enough, but reproduction fails. Some experimental evidence (Yeatter, 1950) indicated that the eggs are unable to tolerate high temperatures during the egg-laying period, when they lie unattended in the nest before the beginning of incubation. The problem is not settled and is a good one for further ecological work. The search for real limiting factors is rarely a simple or easy job.

To express the relative degree of tolerance, a series of terms have come into general use in ecology utilizing the prefixes "steno-" meaning narrow, and "eury-" meaning wide. Thus,

stenothermal	— eurythermal	refers to temperature
stenohydric	— euryhydric	refers to water
stenohaline	— euryhaline	refers to salinity
stenophagic	— euryphagic	refers to food
stenoecious	— euryecious	refers to habitat selection

As an example, let us compare the conditions under which brook trout (*Salvelinus*) eggs and leopard frog (*Rana pipiens*) eggs will develop and hatch. Trout eggs develop between 0° and 12° C with optimum at about 4° C. Frog eggs will develop between 0° and 30° C with optimum at about 22°. Thus, trout eggs are stenothermal, low temperature tolerant, compared with frog eggs, which are eurythermal, both low and high temperature tolerant. Trout in general, both eggs and adults, are relatively stenothermal, but some species are more eurythermal than is the brook trout. Likewise, of course, species of frogs differ. These concepts, and the use of terms in regard to temperature, are illustrated in Figure 20. In a way, the evolution of narrow limits of tolerance might be considered a form of specialization, as discussed in the ecosystem chapter, which results in greater efficiency at the expense of adaptability. "Steno" organisms often become very abundant when their conditions are favorable and stable.

3. Combined concept of limiting factors

Statement

The presence and success of an organism or a group of organisms depends upon a complex of conditions. Any condition which approaches or exceeds the limits of tolerance is said to be a limiting condition or a limiting factor.

Explanation

By combining the idea of the minimum and the concept of limits of tolerance we arrive at a more general and useful concept of limiting factors. Thus, organisms are controlled in nature by

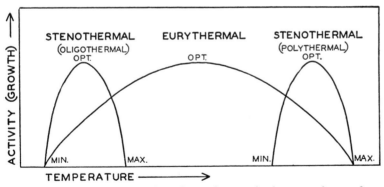

Figure 20. Comparison of the relative limits of tolerance of stenothermal and eurythermal organisms. Minimum, optimum and maximum lie close together for a stenothermal species, so that a small difference in temperature, which might have little effect on a eurythermal species, is often critical. Note that stenothermal organisms may be either low-temperature tolerant (oligothermal) or high-temperature tolerant (polythermal). (After Ruttner, 1953.)

(1) the quantity and variability of materials for which there is a minimum requirement and physical factors which are critical, and (2) the limits of tolerance of the organisms themselves to these and other components of the environment.

The chief value of the concept of limiting factors lies in the fact that it gives the ecologist an "entering wedge" into the study of complex situations. Environmental relations of organisms are apt to be complex, so that it is fortunate that not all possible factors are of equal importance in a given situation or for a given organism. Some strands of the rope guiding the organism are weaker than others. In a study of a particular situation the ecologist can usually discover the probable weak links and focus his attention, initially at least, on those environmental conditions most likely to be critical or "limiting." If an organism has a wide limit of tolerance for a factor which is relatively constant and in moderate quantity in the environment, that factor is not likely to be limiting. Conversely, if an organism is known to have definite limits of tolerance for a factor which also is variable in the environment, then that factor merits careful study, since it might be limiting. For example, oxygen is so abundant, constant and readily available in the terrestrial environment that it is rarely limiting to land organisms (except parasites or those living in soil or at high altitudes). On the other hand, oxygen is relatively scarce and often extremely variable in water and is thus often an important limiting factor to aquatic organisms, especially animals. Therefore, the aquatic ecologist has his oxygen determination apparatus in readiness and takes measurements as one of his procedures in the study of an unknown situation. The terrestrial ecologist, on the other hand, would rarely need to measure oxygen. Oxygen, of course, is just as vital a physiological requirement for most land organisms as for most water organisms, but from the ecological point of view it is rarely limiting on land.

Physical environmental phenomena may exert important controlling influences not only by limiting but also by "triggering" the activities of organisms. Environmental "triggers" or "clocks" are especially important in timing reproduction to coincide with the most favorable conditions. In the desert, where water is almost always far and away the major limiting factor, many seeds of annual plants contain a water soluble inhibitor, which must be washed away before germination can occur. Often a shower of at least 15 mm. is required to remove the inhibitor, thus insuring enough water to complete the life cycle even though no more rain falls. Went (1957) reports that even though such seeds are placed in very moist soil, they often will not germinate until watered with a sprinkler which simulates rain. Light is an especially important environmental "clock," as will be discussed later.

One may carry these concepts one step further and come up with a practical delimitation of "environment." As suggested by Mason and Langenhein (1957), a phenomenon need not be classed as an environmental phenomenon unless it is "operationally significant" to the organism at some time during its life cycle. In other words, not all of the numerous phenomena in the surroundings need be considered in a specific situation. It is particularly important for the beginning ecologist to realize that the aims of environmental analysis are not to make long uncritical lists of possible "factors" but rather to achieve these more significant objectives: (1) to discover, by means of observation, analysis and experiment, which factors are "operationally significant" and (2) to determine how these factors bring about their effects on the individual, population or community, as the case may be.

Examples

A series of examples will serve to illustrate both the importance of the concept of limiting factors and the limitations of the concept itself.

1. As one drives along the broad highways of America from the Mississippi River to the Colorado Rockies, rainfall decreases gradually as one goes west. Water becomes the all-important limiting factor to plants, animals and man. Trees give way to grassland as the amount of available water drops below the limits of tolerance for forests. Likewise, with increasing aridity, tall grass gives way to short grass species. Thus, an annual rainfall of 16 inches (40 cm.) is below the limit necessary for the little blue-stem grass, *Andropogon scoparius,* but adequate for grama grass, *Bouteloua gracilis* (see Figure 127, page 399). However, under certain soil conditions which increase the availability of water to the plant, blue-stem grass is able to survive and compete locally in regions of 16 inches of rainfall (Rübel, 1935).

2. Ecosystems developing on unusual geological formations often provide instructive sites for limiting factor analysis since one or more of the important chemical elements may be unusually scarce or unusually abundant. Such a situation is provided by

serpentine soils (derived from magnesium-iron-silicate rocks) which are low in major nutrients (Ca, P, N) and high in magnesium, chromium and nickel, with concentrations of the latter two approaching toxic levels for organisms. Vegetation growing on such soils has a characteristic stunted appearance, which contrasts sharply with adjacent vegetation on non-serpentine soils, and comprises an unusual flora with many endemic species (see the symposium edited by Whittaker, 1954). In attempting to single out the significant limiting factors Tadros (1957) experimented with two species of shrubs of the genus *Emmeranthe*, one restricted to serpentine soils in western United States and the other never found on such soils. He found that the non-serpentine species would not grow on serpentine soils, but that the serpentine species would grow quite well on normal garden soil provided that the soil was first sterilized. It would appear that the non-serpentine species is prevented from invading serpentine soils by the unusual chemical conditions, but the serpentine species is restricted to the peculiar soils by its inability to tolerate biotic factors, probably substances ("ectocrines") which are produced by microorganisms in normal soils. Although evolving a tolerance for chemical conditions, serpentine species have perhaps lost their ability to tolerate certain biological conditions found in ordinary soils.

3. Great South Bay in Long Island Sound, New York, provides a dramatic example of how too much of a good thing can completely change an ecosystem, to the detriment of man's interest in this case. This story, which might be titled: "The Ducks vs. the Oysters," has now been well documented and the cause and effect relations verified by experiment (Ryther, 1954). The establishment of large duck farms along the tributaries leading into the bay resulted in extensive fertilization of the waters by duck manure and a consequent great increase in phytoplankton density. (The low circulating rate in the bay allowed the nutrients to accumulate rather than to be flushed out to sea.) The increase in primary productivity might have been beneficial were it not for the fact that the organic form of the added nutrients and the low nitrogen-phosphorus ratio produced a complete change in the type of producers; the normal mixed phytoplankton of the area consisting of diatoms, green flagellates and dinoflagellates was almost completely replaced by very small, little-known green flagellates of genera *Nannochloris* and *Stichococcus*. (The most common species was so little known to marine botanists that it had to be described

as a new species.) The famous "blue-point" oysters, which had been thriving for years on a diet of the normal phytoplankton and supporting a profitable industry, were unable to utilize the newcomers as food and gradually disappeared; oysters were found starving to death with a gut full of undigested green flagellates. Other shellfish were also eliminated and all attempts to reintroduce them have failed. Culture experiments demonstrated that the green flagellates grow well when nitrogen is in the form of urea, uric acid and ammonia, while the diatom *Nitzschia*, a "normal" phytoplankter, requires inorganic nitrogen (nitrate). It was clear that the flagellates could "short-circuit" the nitrogen cycle, that is, they did not have to wait for organic material to be reduced to nitrate (see Figure 7, page 32). This case is perhaps a good example of how a "specialist" which is normally rare in the usual fluctuating environment "takes over" when unusual conditions are stabilized.

4. *Cordylophora caspa* is apparently an example of a euryhaline organism which does not actually live in waters of a salinity which is optimum for its growth. Kinne (1956) has made a detailed study of this species of marine hydroid (coelenterate) under laboratory conditions of controlled salinity and temperature. He found that the hydroid could grow under a wide range of conditions although the growth form of the colonies varied somewhat according to conditions (in other words, "ecotypes" could be produced which were adapted to different conditions). A salinity of 16 parts per thousand resulted in the best growth, yet the organism was never found at this salinity in nature, but always at a much lower salinity. The reason for this has not yet been discovered, but it was presumed that some "habitat" factor must be responsible.

As this point it would be well to comment upon the importance of combining field observation and analysis with laboratory experimentation, since the value of this approach is evident from the last three examples listed above. In the case of the serpentine soils, for example, detailed field analysis uncovered some of the probable limiting factors, but experimental work revealed a possibility which would not be uncovered by field observation alone. In the duck-oyster case, laboratory experiments verified the findings of the field analysis; these findings, of course, could not have been proved by field study alone. In case of the hydroid, the experimental approach revealed a degree of tolerance which would not have been suspected from field observation; in this case it is clear that the experimentation must be followed by field analysis if the natural situation is to be understood. In fact, it seems probable that no situation in nature can be really understood from either observation or experimentation alone, since each approach has obvious limitations. In ecology, the development of field experimentation involving use of laboratory techniques in the field can be especially revealing. Whitehead (1957) and Varley (1957) list numerous interesting examples demonstrating how the experimental approach aids the descriptive approach in the study of plant and animal distribution in England. In the training of biologists during the past 40 years, there has been an unfortunate cleavage between the laboratory and the field, with the result that one group tended to be trained entirely in laboratory philosophy (which developed little appreciation or tolerance for field work), while another group tended to be trained quite as narrowly in field techniques. The modern ecologist must break through this barrier. Atomic bombs and other powerful forces make it especially important that scientists who would have been strange bedfellows but a few years ago work together to insure that the over-enthusiastic experimental physicist does not mess up his own environment! We shall discuss this more fully in Chapter 14.

5. Not only do the naturally scarce materials (phosphorus, water in deserts) act as important limiting factors, but sometimes even the abundant materials become limiting because of local scarcity or unavailability. As was brought out in Chapter 2 (see especially page 19), a large portion of the total pool of nutrients is often "bound" in a form not available to living portion of the ecosystem; the rate at which the bound material is "released," and not the total amount present, determines whether or not the particular material is limiting. This is particularly true of calcium, which, as we have seen, is one of the most abundant elements in the sedimentary cycle, yet is often "unavailable." Many mollusks, of course, require larger amounts of calcium than most organisms because of their bulky calcareous shells. In a series of Michigan lakes the number of species of snails and clams and the number of individuals decreased markedly as the available calcium of the water decreased, until only a few individuals of the small clam, *Pisidium*, could be found in the waters containing the least calcium (Jewell and Brown, 1929).

Incidentally, the study of a series of situations in which environmental factors vary along a gradient is a good way to determine which factors are actually the limiting ones (see pages 140 and 255). One may be easily fooled or may jump to a premature conclusion as the result of a limited observation of a single situation. Hunters, fishermen, amateur naturalists, and laymen who are much interested in nature's complexes, and who are often keen observers, nevertheless are too often guilty of "jumping to conclusions" in regard to limiting factors. Thus, a sportsman may see an osprey catch a fish or a hawk catch a quail, and conclude that predators are the principal limiting factors in fish and quail populations. Actually, when the situation is well studied, more basic but less spectacular factors are generally found to be more important than large predators. Unfortunately, much time and money is wasted on predator control without the real limiting factors ever being discovered or the situation improved from the standpoint of increased yield.

6. Shelford (1911) formulated his ideas regarding the "law of tolerance" while making a study of tiger beetles. Tiger beetles are metallic-colored, active beetles which frequent beaches, sandy places, roadsides, and other places with bare soil. As one walks along such places, the adults fly along just ahead of one's footsteps. The eggs are laid in little tunnels in the soil, in which the larvae develop. Shelford found that the period of reproduction was the critical period when the requirements of the species were most exacting. He found that five important conditions were necessary for egg-laying and for subsequent survival of the young: (1) moist soil, neither too dry nor too wet, (2) warm soil, neither too hot nor too cold, (3) reduced light (the eggs must be deposited in partial shade—as under the shadow of a stick lying on the ground), (4) porous soil, sandy with little humus, and (5) well drained soil, as on sloping ground. Shelford pointed out that the female tiger beetle showed a positive response to all of these conditions; she searched actively until situations with the above requirements were found, and then deposited her eggs. The negative reaction, that is, failure to lay or failure of the larvae to survive, could be due to either a deficiency or an excess of any one of the above factors. Thus, it could be too wet or too dry. As far as the occurrence and distribution of the tiger beetle in the region was concerned, the soil conditions would be a primary limiting factor. Given proper soil conditions, the abundance of beetles and their success in any given year or over a given period of time would depend on the temperature and moisture, since these vary consider-

ably. Thus, these latter factors may be said to limit the abundance of the organism.

The case of the tiger beetles illustrates several important points mentioned in the general discussion, namely, the importance of the reproductive period (hence the importance of studying the life history of the organism), the fact that one condition may limit the distribution while another may limit the abundance, and the fact that one condition may be limiting at one time or during one season and another may be more limiting at another time or another season.

7. That certain vital nutrient materials may be limiting, not only to a particular species or class of organisms, but to entire communities of organisms, is well illustrated by a study of a small lake in Connecticut made by Hutchinson (1944). He concluded that all inorganic nutrients were present in great excess (and hence not limiting factors) except for nitrogen and phosphorus (which were thus determined to be the chief limiting factors, as far as nutrients were concerned). Hutchinson found that, although the interrelations were complicated, the seasonal abundance of phytoplankton (and hence all organisms which depend on the phytoplankton) could be pretty well correlated with the seasonal changes in the availability of nitrates and phosphates (see page 305 and Figure 90 in Part II for further details).

8. Oftentimes a good way to determine which factors are limiting to organisms is to study their distribution and behavior at the edges of their ranges. In such marginal situations one or more environmental factors may undergo sudden or drastic change, thus setting up a natural experiment which is often superior to a laboratory experiment, because factors other than the one under consideration continue to vary in a normal manner instead of being "controlled" in an abnormal, constant manner. Perhaps several examples will illustrate this situation. The pale western cutworm, an agricultural pest, is distributed westward through the plains region and survives in the marginal parts of its range during years of normal rainfall. Cooke (1924) found that during a series of dry years, which reduces the atmospheric humidity, the area inhabited by the cutworm is decreased by hundreds of square miles. Thus, humidity was shown to be a limiting factor. It is well to point out that one factor is quite often limiting along one margin of the range and another factor along another margin.

Certain birds which have extended their breeding ranges within the last 50 to 100 years provide other examples of fortuitous field tests which aid in the determination of limiting factors. The horned lark (*Eremophila alpestris*), for example, is a species which was originally widely distributed throughout the grassland, tundra and desert region of central and western North America, but which did not breed in the eastern part of the continent. Following the establishment of extensive grassland communities (pastures, airports, cultivated fields, etc.) by white man, the horned lark has spread eastward to New York and Georgia. Since the east-west climate remained virtually the same during this period it is evident that "biotic factors," i.e., the vegetation and not the climate, were the primary factors limiting the original eastward distribution. Species of birds which have extended their ranges southward as a result of biotic rather than climatic changes include the American robin (*Turdus migratorius*), the song sparrow (*Melospiza melodia*), the chestnut-sided warbler (*Dendroica pennsylvanica*), and (Fig. 21) the house wren (*Troglodytes aedon*) (Odum and Burleigh, 1946; Odum and Johnston, 1951). In most cases, an appreciable lag occurs between the time of widespread

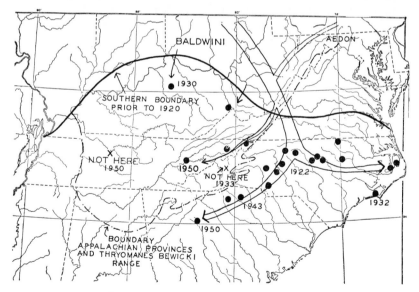

Figure 21.   Southward extension of the breeding range of the house wren (*Troglodytes aedon baldwini*) between 1920 and 1950, believed to be the result of habitat changes produced by man rather than of climatic changes. Southward invasion has been most rapid east of the dotted line where the Bewick wren (*Thryomanes bewicki*), a competitor, is absent. (After Odum and Johnston, 1951.)

change and the actual occupation of new territory because it takes time for population increase to occur. Once begun, however, invasion sometimes is very rapid, almost explosive in nature.

In both North America and Europe other range extensions by birds, particularly gradual northward extensions, seem clearly related to climatic changes. In Finland, for example, weather records show a gradual increase in mean temperatures since 1880, which is correlated with a gradual northward extension of the breeding range of the common lapwing (*Vanellus vanellus*) and other species (Kalela, 1949). Since there were no widespread changes in the biotic environment during this period, climate would appear to be a true limiting factor.

A parallel situation exists in waters off Woods Hole, Mass., where biologists have carried on observations for a long period of years. Since 1900 a general warming trend has been associated with marked changes in abundance of some fish and little or no change in others, thus revealing which species are particularly sensitive to temperature (see Taylor, et al., 1957). The changes in the composition of grasslands during wet and dry cycles have provided another natural "experimental" situation from which much is being learned about the limiting effects of moisture (see Weaver and Albertson, 1956; Albertson, et al., 1957). Thus, extensions and retractions of ranges often give us clues to the interaction of climatic and biotic factors and to the relative importance of each as limiting factors.

9. The principle of limiting factors is often of great practical importance, as will be illustrated in the final example. If the limits of tolerance of agricultural pests are sufficiently well known, it is often possible to manipulate the environment so as to control the pest. For example, wireworms of genus *Limonius* are often destructive to sugar beets and other crops in irrigated regions of the west coast. Field studies "indicated that moisture was the main limiting factor in the ecology of irrigated land wireworms" (Jones, 1951). Either flooding or drying the soil was found to produce conditions exceeding the limits of tolerance of the species. Laboratory studies showed that larvae and prepupae had a narrower range of tolerance for moisture than eggs or adults. Thus, the best time to apply controls was determined. In irrigated lands, flooding was found to be the most practical means of control. On non-irrigated land the planting of alfalfa or wheat was effective because these crops dried out the soil to a point beyond the tolerance of the larvae. Thus, in one situation (irrigated lands) it was prac-

tical to exceed the maximum, and in the other situation (non-irrigated lands) it was practical to exceed the minimum, bringing about effective control in both cases. This example again illustrates the value of careful field observations followed by laboratory experiments.

4. The quantitative expression of limiting factors

If a principle is to become firmly established and to prove useful in practice, it must eventually be subject to quantitative as well as qualitative analysis. Klages (1942) has developed a simple method of determining the optimum regions for agricultural crops. He considers not only the average yield over a period of years but also the coefficients of variation of the yields. The region with the highest average yield and the lowest coefficient of variation (hence the fewest crop failures) is the optimum region. As shown in Figure 22, Wisconsin and Ohio proved to be the optimum states for barley, as determined by this method. Wisconsin had the largest yield; Ohio had the least variation in yield from year to year.

Riley (1943) has shown that the limiting effects of various nutrients on the growth of marine algae can be translated into quantitative terms by means of culture experiments. If adding a substance to normal sea-water medium results in an increase in

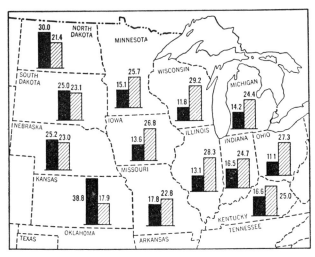

Figure 22.   A method of determining the optimum regions for agricultural crops by comparing average yields and variability in yields from year to year. Cross-hatched columns indicate average yields in bushels/acre, and solid columns the coefficient of variation in the yields of barley in the states of the upper Mississippi valley. (After Klages, 1942.)

growth, then that substance was limiting in the original medium. Differences in the rate of growth or differences in the maximum population of cells obtained can be used as a quantitative measure of the degree of limitation.

Potash (1956) used a similar method to compare the potential productivity of two ponds with the actual productivity as measured in the field. The "carrying capacity" of filtered water was quantitatively determined from growth curves of a single test organism (a green alga, *Kirchneriella subsolitaria*) grown in the water under controlled conditions. Nitrates and phosphates proved to be the major limiting nutrients with the latter more limiting in the winter and the former more limiting in spring and summer. Pond number one was potentially more productive than pond number two, but the greater potential was not realized because of higher turbidity (which reduced light penetration); consequently, pond number two, where turbidity was less limiting, actually was more productive according to field measurements.

For demonstration of quantitative application of limiting factors to a complex field situation, see Chapter 10, Section 4 (pp. 337–338).

5. Brief review of physical factors of importance as limiting factors

As emphasized several times in the preceding discussions, the broad concept of limiting factors is not restricted to physical factors, since biological interrelations ("coactions" or "biological factors") are just as important in controlling the actual distribution and abundance of organisms in nature. However, the latter are best considered in subsequent chapters dealing with populations and communities, leaving the physical and chemical aspects of the environment to be reviewed in this section. To present all that is known in this field would require a book in itself, and is beyond the scope of the present outline of ecological principles. Also, if we should become involved with the details we would become sidetracked from our objective of obtaining an over-all picture of the subject matter of ecology. Therefore, we need only to make a brief roll call of the items which ecologists have found important and worth studying. We shall have more to say about some of these factors in subsequent discussions and illustrations.

1. *Temperature.*   Compared with the range of thousands of degrees known to occur in our universe, life in any form can exist only within a tiny range of about 300 degrees centigrade—from

about —200° to 100° C. Actually, most species and most activity are restricted to an even narrower band of temperatures. Some organisms, especially in a resting stage, can exist at very low temperatures at least for brief periods, whereas a few microorganisms, chiefly bacteria and algae, are able to live and reproduce in hot springs where the temperature is close to the boiling point (85–88° C—see page 326). In general the upper limits are more quickly critical than the lower limits, despite the fact that many organisms appear to function more efficiently toward the upper limits of their tolerance ranges. The range of temperature variation tends to be less in water than on land, and aquatic organisms generally have a narrower limit of tolerance to temperature than equivalent land animals. Temperature, therefore, is universally important and is very often a limiting factor. Temperature rhythms, along with rhythms of light, moisture, and tides, largely control the seasonal and daily activities of plants and animals. Temperature is often responsible for the zonation and stratification which occur in both water and land environments (as will be described in Part II). It is also one of the easiest of environmental factors to measure. The mercury thermometer, one of the first and most widely used precision scientific instruments, has more recently been supplemented by electrical "sensing" devices, such as platinum resistance thermometers, thermocouples (bimetallic junctions) and thermistors (metallic oxide thermally sensitive resistors), which not only permit measurement in "hard-to-get-at" places but also permit continuous and automatic recording of measurements. On land, data from weather stations which have been set up all over the world are a valuable source of information and are much used by ecologists.

Temperature variability is extremely important ecologically. A temperature fluctuating between 10 and 20° C and averaging 15° does not necessarily have the same effect on organisms as a constant temperature of 15° C. It has been found that organisms which are normally subjected to variable temperatures in nature (as in most temperate regions) tend to be depressed, inhibited or slowed down by constant temperature. Thus, to give the results of one of many studies, Shelford (1929) found that eggs and larval or pupal stages of the codling moth developed 7 or 8 per cent faster under conditions of variable temperature than under a constant temperature having the same mean. In another experiment (Parker, 1930), grasshopper eggs kept at a variable temperature showed an average acceleration of 38.6 per cent and nymphs an

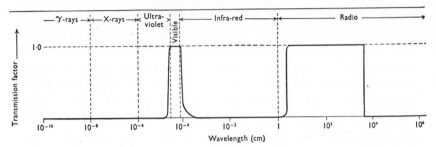

Figure 23. The transmission coefficient of the earth's atmosphere for electromagnetic waves of different lengths. Solar radiations which penetrate the atmosphere consist of a band of visible (to man) light and a small portion of the ultraviolet and infra-red radiations. (By courtesy of The Physical Society.)

acceleration of 12 per cent, over development at comparable constant temperature.

It is not certain whether variation in itself is responsible for the accelerating effect, or whether the higher temperature causes more growth than is balanced by the low temperature. In any event, the stimulating effect of variable temperature, in the temperate zone at least, may be accepted as a well defined ecological principle, and one that might be emphasized, since the tendency has been to conduct experimental work in the laboratory under constant temperature conditions.

Because organisms are sensitive to temperature changes and because temperature is so easy to measure, it is sometimes overrated as a limiting factor. One must guard against assuming that temperature is limiting when other, unmeasured factors may be more important. The ability of plants and animals to compensate or acclimate to temperature has already been mentioned. Good advice for the beginning ecologist might be something as follows: In the study of a particular organism or problem, by all means consider temperature, but do not stop there.

2. *Radiation: Light.*   As aptly expressed by Pearse (1939), organisms are on the horns of a dilemma in regard to light. Direct exposure of protoplasm to light results in death, yet light is the ultimate source of energy, without which life could not exist. Consequently, much of the structural and behavioral characteristics of organisms are concerned with the solution of this problem. Light, therefore, is not only a vital factor but also a limiting one, both at the maximum and minimum levels.

Radiation consists of electromagnetic waves of a wide range in length. As shown in Figure 23, two bands of wave lengths readily penetrate the earth's atmosphere. It is not known whether the long radio waves have ecological significance, despite assertions in the popular press regarding positive effects on migrating birds. The solar radiations which penetrate the upper atmosphere and reach the biosphere consist of electromagnetic waves ranging from about 290 to 5000 millimicrons* in length. To the human eye, visible light lies in the range of 400 to 750 mμ. Ultraviolet is below 390 mμ and infrared above 750. Photochemical activity is greatest at the violet end, ultraviolet thus having the greatest killing effect on protoplasm. Microorganisms which have been injured by ultraviolet are often rejuvenated by exposure to visible light. The role which the high-energy, very short wave gamma radiation, as well as other types of ionizing radiation, may play as ecological limiting factors in the atomic age involves many special and complex considerations, which are best treated separately (see Chapter 14).

Ecologically, the quality of light (wave length or color), the intensity (actual energy measured in gram-calories or foot candles), and the duration (length of day) are known to be important. Both animals and plants are known to respond to different wave lengths of light. Color vision in animals has an interesting "spotty" occurrence in different taxonomic groups, apparently being well developed in certain species of arthropods, fish, birds and mammals but not in other species of the same groups (among mammals, for example, color vision is well developed only in primates). The rate of photosynthesis varies somewhat with different wave lengths. In terrestrial ecosystems the quality of sunlight does not vary enough to have an important differential effect on the rate of photosynthesis, but, as light penetrates water, the reds and blues are filtered out and the resultant greenish light is poorly absorbed by chlorophyll. The red algae, however, have supplementary pigments (phycoerythrins) enabling them to utilize this energy and to live at greater depths than would be possible for the green algae.

As was discussed in the previous chapter, the intensity of light impinging on a given surface area controls the entire ecosystem through its influence on primary production. The relationship of intensity to photosynthesis in both terrestrial and aquatic plants follows the same general pattern of a linear increase up to an

---

* A millimicron or mμ is $1/1000$ of a micron; since a micron is $1/1000$ of a millimeter, a millimicron is 0.000001 mm., or 10^{-7} cm.; 10^{-4} cm. in Figure 23 equals 1000 mμ. In working with ultraviolet and shorter wave lengths, Ångström units are used; 1 Å $= 0.1$ mμ.

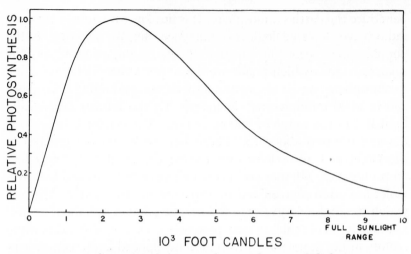

Figure 24. Relationship between photosynthesis and light intensity in marine phytoplankton composed of mixed species of diatoms, dinoflagellates and green algae. A similar pattern might be expected in photosynthesis-light intensity curves for terrestrial vegetation except that the optimum or saturation zone would likely be shifted considerably to the right. (After Ryther, 1956.)

optimum or saturation intensity (which varies from a few hundred foot candles for some species to several thousand f.c. for most species) followed by a decrease at very high intensities (Rabinowitch, 1951; Thomas, 1955). Whole communities may show characteristic patterns with a rather smooth trend resulting from the integration of species located at several different levels. Low light intensity is very often limiting not only for plants in the shade but for those in sun and for whole communities, since there are daily and seasonal periods of considerable length when intensity is below saturation. Bormann (1956) describes an interesting situation in certain species of pine in which young seedlings are shade adapted (i.e., reach saturation at low intensities), while older seedlings and young trees are unable to survive under a canopy. It is not so generally recognized that normal sunlight can be limiting when at full intensity. At high intensities, photo-oxidation of enzymes apparently reduces synthesis. Protein synthesis is especially reduced so that high percentages of carbohydrates are produced at high intensities (Thomas, 1955). As shown in Figure 24, "full sunlight" is definitely inhibitory to marine phytoplankton and this results in a definite mid-day depression in production at the water surface (Ryther, 1956). While terrestrial vegetation has a higher saturation zone (than that shown in Figure 24), the inhibitory effect of high intensity may nonetheless be marked. Where high temperatures accompany intense light, as in mid-summer, net production may be reduced as a result of both reduced photosynthesis and increased respiratory losses.

Duration is very important. Daily rhythms of light and darkness largely control the movements of animals both on land and in water (see Chapter 8, Section 7, Figs. 80, 81). Furthermore, the actual duration or length of day has been shown to be an important factor for a wide variety of plants and animals. The controlling effect of the length of day, known as *photoperiodicity,* is currently an active field of research in physiological ecology. So important is the length of day in their reproductive cycle that plants may be classified into three categories: (1) long-day plants, which bloom when the light duration is more than 12 hours per day, (2) short-day plants, which bloom with less than 12 hours duration of light per day, and (3) plants which have wide tolerance to day length and for which, therefore, day length is not the controlling or limiting factor. Elongation of certain seedling structures is also influenced by length of day. Reproductive cycles of animals, migration, diapause in insects, and seasonal change in feather and hair coats of some species of birds and mammals have also been shown to be photoperiodic. In fact, length of day is probably an important "environmental clock" in all except equatorial regions. It is one of the few environmental factors which is absolutely precise and predictable for any given locality! In temperate regions light tends to gear the reproduction of the whole

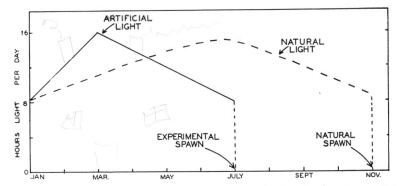

Figure 25. Control of the breeding season of the brook trout by artificial manipulation of the photoperiod. Trout, which normally breed in the autumn, spawn in summer when length of day is increased artificially in the spring and then decreased in the summer to simulate autumn conditions. (Redrawn from Hazard and Eddy, 1950.)

community to the time of maximum food due to maximum productivity. In Silver Springs, Florida, for example, where temperature is constant the year around, many of the important herbivores
are photoperiodic and breed at a time of increasing length of day
which is also, of course, a time of increasing primary productivity
(H. T. Odum, 1957).

The results of experiments on the effect of artificial manipulation of day length in the brook trout are shown in Figure 25. These
trout are autumn breeders and respond to short days. If the day
length is first increased and then decreased artificially, the trout
will spawn several months earlier than normal. Young trout
hatched in hatcheries in mid-summer reach stocking size by the
following spring, whereas fall-hatched fry must be held over
winter before growth can begin. Since trout, unlike pond fish, must
reach a fairly large size for successful stocking of streams, artificial control of day length may have practical applications.

The mechanism by which changes in photoperiods bring about
responses is not yet fully known. Recent work with both plants
and animals indicates that the length of the dark period is actually
more critical than the length of the light period (Hamner, 1940;
Parker, Hendricks, Borthwick and Jenner, 1952). Hormone mechanisms are certainly involved in both plants and animals. In fact,
the similarity in photoperiodic response in organisms as diverse as
seed plants, snails and mammals is little short of amazing. For
reviews on photoperiodicity see Murneek and Whyte (1948) for
plants and Farner (1955) for animals.

3. *Water.*   A physiological necessity for all protoplasm,
water, from the ecological viewpoint, is chiefly a limiting factor
in land environments or in water environments where the amount
is subject to great fluctuation, or where high salinity fosters water
loss from organisms by osmosis. Rainfall, humidity, the evapo-
rating power of the air, and the available surface water supply
are the principal factors measured. A brief résumé of each of these
aspects follows.

Rainfall is largely determined by geography and the pattern of
large air movements or "weather systems." A relatively simple
case is shown in Figure 26. Moisture-laden winds blowing off the
ocean deposit most of their moisture on the ocean-facing slopes,
with a resulting "rain shadow" producing a desert on the other
side; the higher the mountains the greater the effect, in general.
As the air continues beyond the mountains, some moisture is

picked up and rainfall may again increase somewhat. Thus deserts are usually found "behind" high mountain ranges or along the coast where winds blow from large, interior dry land areas rather than off the ocean as shown in Figure 26. Pendleton (1949) reports that even on relatively small islands in the South Pacific, mountains produce local "rain shadows" in which relatively arid grasslands occur in the midst of the generally forested vegetation of the islands. Rainfall distribution over the year is an extremely important limiting factor for organisms. The situation provided by a 35-inch rainfall evenly distributed is entirely different from that provided by a 35-inch rainfall which falls largely during a restricted part of the year. In the latter case, plants and animals must be able to survive long periods of drought. In general, rainfall tends to be unevenly distributed over the seasons in the tropics and subtropics, often with well defined wet and dry seasons resulting. In the tropics, this seasonal rhythm in moisture regulates the seasonal activities (reproduction, especially) of organisms in much the same manner as the seasonal rhythm of temperature and light regulates temperate zone organisms. In temperate climates, rainfall tends to be more evenly distributed throughout the year, with many exceptions. The following tabulation gives a rough approximation of the climax biotic communities (see Chapter 11, Section 4) that may be expected with different annual amounts of rainfall evenly distributed in temperate latitudes:

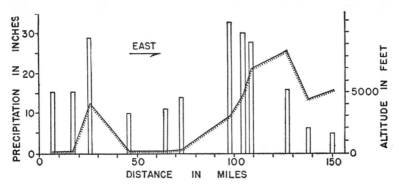

Figure 26.   Mean annual rainfall (vertical columns) in relation to altitude (ornamented line) at a series of stations extending from Palo Alto in the Pacific coast eastward across the Coast Range and the Sierra Nevada to Oasis Ranch in the Nevada desert. The diagram shows (1) the approach effect on the west edge of the Sierra, (2) the zone of maximum rainfall on the middle western slope of the Sierra, and (3) rain shadows to the landward of the two mountain ranges. (Daubenmire, "Plants and Environment," John Wiley & Sons, Inc., 1947.)

0–10 inches per year.... Desert
10–30 inches per year.... Grassland, savanna,* or open
woodland
30–50 inches per year.... Dry forest
over 50 inches per year... Wet forest

Actually, the biotic situation is not determined by rainfall alone but by the balance between rainfall and potential evapo-transpiration, the latter being loss of water by evaporation from the ecosystem, as will be discussed below.

Humidity represents the amount of water vapor in the air. Absolute humidity is the actual amount of water in the air expressed as weight of water per unit of air (grams per kilograms of air, for example). Since the amount of water vapor air can hold (at saturation) varies with the temperature and pressure, *relative humidity* represents the percentage of vapor actually present compared with saturation under existing temperature-pressure conditions. Relative humidity is usually measured by noting the difference between a wet and a dry bulb thermometer mounted on an instrument called a psychrometer. If both thermometers read the same, the relative humidity is 100 per cent; if the wet bulb thermometer reads less than the dry bulb one, as is usually the case, the relative humidity is less than 100 per cent, the exact value being determined by consulting prepared tables. Relative humidity may also be conveniently measured by means of a hygrograph which provides a continuous record. Human hair, especially long blond hair, expands and contracts in proportion to relative humidity, and strands of it can thus be made to operate a lever writing on a moving drum. Another method utilizes the ability of a hygroscopic film of lithium chloride to change its electrical resistance instantly with micro changes in moisture content (relative humidity).

In general, relative humidity has been the measurement most used in ecological work, although the converse of relative humidity, or vapor pressure deficit (the difference between partial pressure of water vapor at saturation and the actual vapor pressure), is often preferred as a measure of moisture relations, because evaporation tends to be proportional to vapor pressure deficit rather than to relative humidity.

Since there is generally a daily rhythm in humidity in nature

* A savanna is a grassland with scattered trees or scattered clumps of trees, a community type intermediate between grassland and forest.

(high at night, low in day, for example), as well as vertical and horizontal differences, humidity along with temperature and light has an important role in regulating the activities of organisms and in limiting their distribution. Humidity has an especially important role in modifying the effects of temperature, as will be noted in the next section.

The evaporative power of the air is an important ecological factor, especially for land plants, and is usually measured by evaporimeters, which measure evaporation from pans, or atmometers, which measure evaporation from the surface of a porous bulb filled with water. Animals may often regulate their activities so as to avoid dehydration by moving to protected places or becoming active at night; plants, however, have to "stand and take it." From 97 to 99 per cent of water which enters plants from the soil is lost by evaporation from the leaves, this evaporation being called transpiration. When water and nutrients are non-limiting, growth of land plants is closely proportional to the total energy supply at the ground surface, as we have already indicated. Since most of the energy is heat and since the fraction providing latent heat for transpiration is nearly constant, then growth is also proportional to transpiration (Penman, 1956). The ratio of growth (net production) and water transpired is called the *transpiration efficiency*, and is usually expressed as grams of dry matter produced per 1000 grams of water transpired. Most agricultural crop species, as well as a wide range of non-cultivated species, have a transpiration efficiency of 2 or less, that is, 500 grams or more of water are lost for every gram of dry matter produced (Briggs and Shantz, 1914; Norman, 1957). Drought resistant crops, such as sorghum and millet, may have efficiencies of 4. Strangely enough, desert plants can do little, if any, better; their unique adaptation involves not the ability to grow without transpiration but the ability to become dormant when water is not available (instead of wilting and dying as would be the case in non-desert plants). It should be emphasized that desert plants, like all organisms, have upper as well as lower limits of tolerance, and each species may have a somewhat different range. When moisture is greatly increased in arid areas, as by irrigation, the primary productivity of the whole ecosystem is increased, but most, if not all, of the desert species of plants die and are replaced by other species whose lower limit for moisture begins where the upper limit of the desert species ends.

The available surface water supply is, of course, related to the rainfall of the area, but there are often great discrepancies. Thus, due to underground sources or supplies coming from nearby regions, animals and plants may have access to more water than that which falls as rain. Likewise, rain water may quickly become unavailable to organisms. Wells (1928) has spoken of the North Carolina sandhills as "deserts in the rain," because abundant rain of the region sinks so quickly through the porous soil that plants, especially herbaceous ones, find very little available in the surface layer. The plant and the small animal life of such areas resemble those of much dryer regions. Other soils in the western plains retain water so tenaciously that crops can be raised without a single drop of rain falling during the growing season, the plants being able to utilize the water stored from winter rains.

Man has done very little, as yet, to change the pattern of rainfall and the climate in general, although recent experiments in rainmaking may indicate that this may not always be the case. Although rainfall in various areas is thus remaining largely undisturbed, man has really played havoc with the surface water relations, or water resources, speaking in broad terms. Ecologists are in general agreement that we need to know more about water resources and to do a better job of managing them before we seriously consider manipulation of rainfall, if and when this becomes technically possible. We could really get ourselves into a mess by bungling both rainfall and surface water control! As it is, too severe removal of vegetative cover and poor land-use practices, with resultant destruction of soil texture and increased erosion, have often increased run-off to such an extent that local deserts are produced in regions of adequate rainfall. On the more positive side, irrigation and artificial impoundment of streams have aided in increasing local water supplies. However, these mechanical engineering devices, useful though they usually are, should never be regarded as substitutes for sound agricultural and forestry land-use practices, which trap the water at or near its sources for maximum usefulness to plants, animals, and man. The ecological viewpoint, considering water as a cyclic commodity within the whole biotic community and ecosystem, is very important. People who think all our floods and erosion and water-use problems can be solved by building big dams or any other mechanical device alone may have a good appreciation of engineering, but they need to brush up on their ecology (see Chapter 12, Section 6). Certainly the water problem is one of the most important problems facing man, because man requires large quantities of water for physiological and cultural needs. In this connection, research at the Coweeta Experimental Forest in western North Carolina is outstanding (Hursh, 1948). Here, in a region of high rainfall, watersheds are being given every sort of treatment, and the amounts of water and soil escaping by way of the stream draining each watershed are accurately measured by means of special weirs (Fig. 27). Some rather surprising results are being obtained, results which are not necessarily what were expected. For example, it was found that logging access roads, rather than logging itself, resulted in the chief damage by erosion. If logging roads were planned and built properly, no damage occurred, and the operation was more profitable as well. In another experiment it was found that typical mountain slope agriculture resulted in very little erosion or excessive run-off the first year, because the soil retained its healthy, porous, biological structure. During the second or third year, however, the soil "collapsed," failed to hold water, and was washed away. Other experiments showed that soil

Figure 27. Special weirs used to measure water run-off and soil erosion at the Coweeta Experimental Forest in western North Carolina. In the picture, a pastured watershed is being compared with a forested watershed seen on the right (the weir for the forested watershed is not visible in this picture). (U. S. Forest Service Photo.)

texture was preserved and more high quality water obtained by stream run-off when the watershed was covered with grass or shrub vegetation rather than forest, because of the high rate of transpiration in forest. All of the work has shown that the important thing is not to destroy the vigorous interaction of plants, animals and microorganisms which maintain the surface of the ground as a "living sponge," able to hold water and release it gradually without excessive loss of valuable materials. Thus, the natural forest community can be modified in various ways to yield desirable products or to serve useful purposes without destroying the essential health of the biotic community, which is necessary for future productivity. A similar research program is under way in more arid, non-forested regions of Arizona.

Dew may make an appreciable, and, in areas of low rainfall, a very vital contribution to precipitation. Dew and "ground fog" may be important not only in coastal forests, where more total water may be precipitated in these forms than in rainfall (see page 393) but also in deserts. Recent development of better dew gauges and automatic-weighing lysimeters, which give the actual water uptake of vegetation, have resulted in better measurements. In many cases, the annual amount and the ability of plants to utilize the water have been greater than was thought formerly.

4. *Temperature and Moisture Acting Together.*   By considering the ecosystem concept first among ecological concepts we have avoided creating the impression that environmental factors operate independently of one another. In this chapter we are attempting to show that consideration of individual factors is a means of getting at complex ecological problems but not the ultimate objective of ecological study, which is to evaluate the relative importance of various factors as they operate together in actual ecosystems. Temperature and moisture are so generally important in terrestrial environments and so closely interacting that they are usually conceded to be the most important part of climate. Thus, it may be well to consider them together before proceeding to other factors.

The interaction of temperature and moisture, as in the case of the interaction of most factors, depends on the *relative* as well as the *absolute* values of each factor. Thus, temperature exerts a more severe limiting effect on organisms when moisture conditions are extreme, that is, either very high or very low, than when such conditions are moderate. Likewise, moisture plays a more critical role in the extremes of temperature. In a sense, this is another aspect of the principle of factor interaction, which was discussed earlier in the chapter. For example, the boll weevil can tolerate higher temperatures when the humidity is low or moderate than when it is very high. Hot, dry weather in the cotton belt is a signal for the cotton farmers to have their spray guns ready and to be on the lookout for an increase in the weevil population. Hot, humid weather is less favorable for the weevil, but, unfortunately, not so good for the cotton plant! In aquatic environments water itself greatly reduces temperature extremes because of its high latent heat of evaporation and melting (that is, water absorbs large quantities of heat and releases it slowly). Large bodies of water greatly moderate land climates. In fact, we may speak of two basic types of climate, the continental climates characterized by extremes of temperature and moisture, and the marine climates characterized by less extreme fluctuation due to the moderating effect of large bodies of water (large lakes thus produce local "marine climates").

Modern classifications of climate, such as those of Köppen or Thornthwaite (1931, 1948), are based largely on quantitative measures of temperature and moisture, taking into consideration the effectiveness of precipitation and temperature (as determined by growing seasons) and seasonal distribution, as well as the mean values. The comparison of precipitation and potential evapo-transpiration (which is dependent on temperature) provides a particularly good picture of climates, as shown in Figure 28, which contrasts climates of three distinctly different biological regions or biomes (see Figures 120 and 121 for maps of the geographical extent of these biomes). The period of "soil moisture utilization" represents the principal period of primary production for the community as a whole and thus determines the supply of food available to the consumers and decomposers for the entire annual cycle. Note that in the deciduous forest region, water is likely to be severely limiting only in late summer, more so in the southern than in the northern portion of the region. Native vegetation is adapted to withstand the periodic summer droughts but most agricultural crops grown in the region are not. After bitter experiences with many late summer crop failures, farmers in the southern United States, for example, are finally beginning to provide for late summer irrigation. In the winter rain region, the main season of production is late winter and spring (see also page 409), while in the

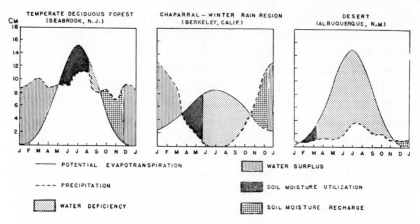

Figure 28. Relationship between rainfall and potential evapo-transpiration (evaporation from soil plus transpiration from vegetation) in three localities representing three distinctly different ecological regions. The dotted area in the charts ("water deficiency") indicates the season when water may be expected to be a limiting factor, whereas the vertical extent of this area indicates the relative severity of this limitation. (After Thornthwaite, 1955.)

desert the effective growing season is much reduced. Here again, native vegetation is adapted to long droughts, but irrigation is an absolute necessity for most agricultural crops in these regions.

In general, the classification of climatic types based on temperature-moisture indices correlates well with crop zones (Klages, 1942). However, the objective climatic types set up by climatologists are often too broad to be useful to the ecologist in local situations. Daubenmire (1956), for example, found that often two distinctly different zones of mountain vegetation (see Figure 135 for examples of such zones), which by all evidence were climatically controlled, would be included within a single one of Thornthwaite's (1931) categories. Climographic analysis, as described below, indicated that the zones did indeed differ markedly in climate as well as in vegetation. Climatic classifications which lean heavily on the vegetation as an indicator of temperature-moisture interaction are, in general, favored by ecologists who find that a good vegetation map is a very practical map of climates. Thornthwaite (1933) has also used this approach in recognizing five humidity zones (from high to low humidity)—(1) rain forest, (2) forest, (3) grassland, (4) steppe, and (5) desert; and six temperature zones (from high to low)—(1) tropical rain forest, (2) temperate rain forest, (3) microthermal rain forest, (4) taiga (coniferous forest), (5) tundra, and (6) perpetual frost (no vegetation). When these zones are combined, thirty basic climatic types are possible, each of which might be expected to exert different limiting effects on organisms.

Climographs, or charts in which one major climatic factor is plotted against another, represent another useful method of graphic representation of temperature and moisture in combination. In temperature-rainfall or temperature-humidity charts mean monthly values are plotted with the temperature scale on the vertical axis and either humidity or rainfall on the horizontal axis, as shown in Figure 30. Months are indicated by numbers, starting with January. The resulting 12-sided polygon gives a "picture" of the temperature-moisture conditions and makes possible graphic comparison of one set of conditions with another. Climographs have been useful in the comparison of one area with another and as an aid in testing the importance of temperature-moisture combinations as limiting factors. Plots of other pairs of factors may also be instructive, for example, of temperature and salinity in marine environments (see Figure 96, page 332).

One use of climographs is illustrated by Figure 29, which compares sagebrush desert with grassland in the Pacific northwest. In this figure, one of several prepared by Daubenmire (1956) in his study of the relation of climate to vegetative zonation, the climographs are divided into two halves, the "warming curves" (i.e., spring and summer) being shown on the left, and the "cooling curves" (i.e., fall and winter) on the right. The greater extremes of temperature on the desert and the much greater precipitation during the spring growing season in the grassland are evident from the figure. Graphic analysis of this sort help bring out climatic divergencies and convergencies which would be less apparent in tabular data. Climograph polygons may not only be studied visually but they also can provide a basis for quantitative analysis. Hocker (1956), for example, used climographs in conjunction with discriminant equations to determine which factors were different outside as compared to inside the range of the loblolly pine (*Pinus taeda*). Winter temperature was singled out by this method as being a factor limiting the range of this pine.

Other uses of climographs relate to the problem of introduced animals and the prediction of insect outbreaks. Two examples will suffice to illustrate the methods. The Hungarian partridge (*Perdix perdix*), a common game bird of central Europe, has been introduced widely in North America. In some localities it has become

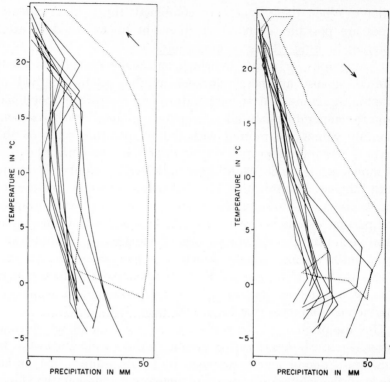

Figure 29. Climographs showing mean monthly temperature and mean median precipitation for a number of weather stations in the sagebrush (*Artemisia*) desert (solid lines), with the pattern of similar data from grassland superimposed. Climograph polygons are separated into two halves with the warming curves shown on the left and the cooling curves on the right. (After Daubenmire, 1956.)

established, and in many others it has failed. In Figure 30 A, a climograph (from Twomey, 1936) has been constructed, picturing the average conditions in the most favorable part of the original range in Europe, each monthly point being an average of data from localities scattered within the favorable range. Superimposed upon this polygon are climographs of two specific localities in North America, Havre, Montana and Columbia, Missouri. It will be seen that the temperature-moisture points for the spring and summer months in Montana fall within the polygon of central Europe, which presumably represents the limits of temperature-moisture tolerance of the species. Conditions for the winter months, however, do not "fit," temperature being much lower in Montana. In Missouri the opposite situation holds: the fall and winter months are within the range, and the spring and summer months are well out of range. Since, as we have already emphasized, conditions during the breeding season are most likely to be limiting, we might infer that, of the two localities, temperature-moisture conditions would be *less* limiting in Montana than in Missouri, the question being whether or not the bird could tolerate the cold winter in the former locality. As a matter of fact, the Hungarian partridge has actually thrived in Montana* and failed completely when it was stocked in Missouri. Climograph tests of this type resemble blood tests which attempt to determine human parentage, in that *negative results—failure of fit in this instance— are likely to be more convincing or to have more predictive value than positive results—goodness of fit in this instance.* Thus, positive correlation simply indicates that the two factors, temperature and moisture, are not likely to be limiting, but it does not mean that other factors, especially biotic ones, may not be limiting. Wide divergence of climograph polygons, on the other hand, gives a strong indication that temperature and moisture conditions may be sufficiently different to have limiting effects; the organism might still succeed under both conditions if compensation factors (reduced predation, or local water or microclimate conditions) are powerful enough. In the present example, of course, the assumption was made that the basic polygon in Figure 30 A does represent the limits of tolerance and that some other factor did not limit the European range short of the full climatic tolerance of the species (as in the case of the horned lark previously mentioned). The problem of introduced organisms is complicated and important and will be discussed in Part III. We merely wish to indicate here that climographic analysis is one method of getting a start on the problem.

Climographs are useful in analyzing annual differences within a given locality, and this involves a much less complex situation than that described in the previous example. Comparison of climographs for different years and of the annual population levels of the organism often provide excellent information on the limiting effect of temperature-moisture combinations. Such information may be of great value in predicting outbreaks, such as outbreaks of insects which respond quickly to favorable conditions. An example will be taken from the extensive work of Bodenheimer

---

* An interesting sequel to this story is that the Hungarian partridge has slowly declined in a number of localities in the northwestern states where it had been well established for a long time. Whether the decline might be due to cold winters or to changes in agricultural practices which affect habitat and food has not been determined.

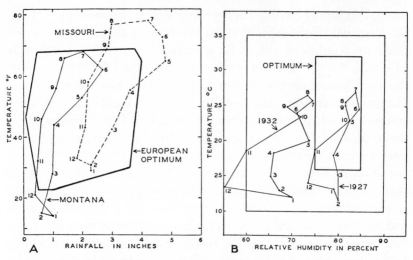

Figure 30. Temperature-moisture climographs. A: Temperature-rainfall monthly averages for Havre, Montana, where Hungarian partridge has been successfully introduced, and Columbia, Missouri, where it has failed, compared with average conditions in the European breeding range. (Redrawn from Twomey, 1936.) B: Temperature-humidity conditions at Tel Aviv, Palestine, for two different years, compared with optimum (inner rectangle) and favorable (outer rectangle) conditions for Mediterranean fruit fly. Damage to oranges was much greater in 1927. (After Bodenheimer, 1938.)

(1938) in Palestine. In Figure 30 B the inner rectangle represents the most favorable temperature-humidity conditions for the Mediterranean fruit fly (*Ceratitis capitata*), as determined by both field and laboratory observation. The outer rectangle represents less favorable conditions which, however, are well within the limits of tolerance. Actual climographs of two different years, 1927 and 1932, are shown for Tel Aviv where the organism is well established. Higher populations of fruit flies and more damage to oranges occurred at Tel Aviv in 1927, when conditions were more favorable. Here again, note that although the winter months are somewhat outside the "most favorable" area, in 1927 all the breeding season months were extremely favorable. In 1932 not only were the winter months bordering limits of the outer rectangle but the critical breeding months were too dry for great success.

Bodenheimer speaks of the climatic "bonitation" being more favorable in 1927, "bonitation" being defined as the condition of well-being for the species as indicated by the numerical development of the population. He has further developed a numerical index for indicating the relative "bonitation" for a particular season or year and has used this to determine the likelihood of outbreaks of agricultural and medical pests.

Climate chambers provide another useful approach to the study of combinations of physical factors. These vary from simple temperature-humidity cabinets in use in many laboratories to large controlled greenhouses, such as the "phytotron" in which any desired combination of temperature, moisture and light can be maintained (see Went, 1957). These chambers are often designed to control environmental conditions in order that other variables (genetic, for example) can be studied, but they are equally useful in the study of limiting factors. As already stressed, experiments of this sort help single out factors which may be "operationally significant," but they can reveal only part of the story since many significant aspects of the ecosystem can not be duplicated indoors, but must be studied or experimented with outdoors (for an outdoor environmental laboratory, see Figure 37).

5. *Atmospheric Gases.*   Except for the large variations in water vapor already discussed under the heading of water, the atmosphere of the major part of the biosphere is remarkably constant. Therefore, atmospheric gases such as oxygen, carbon dioxide, and nitrogen, as well as the biologically inert trace gases (argon, neon, helium, krypton, etc.), are not generally limiting factors on land environments. There are some exceptions, of course. Deep in soil, high on mountains, and within the bodies of large animals the oxygen supply may be less and thus be a definite limiting factor, at least for animals. Many animals living in such situations have developed special adaptations for coping with the limited supply. Many microorganisms can get along without free oxygen in the media, and others can switch from aerobic to anaerobic respiration. In the latter case, however, the rate of decomposition may be reduced, as illustrated by the example given in Chapter 2 (Fig. 5, page 23). Consequently, in bogs and other environments where the concentration of oxygen in the substrate is low, organic products accumulate, and these may not only tie up materials but also may be inhibitory to other organisms. For some microorganisms such as the tetanus bacillus (*Clostridium tetani*), too much oxygen is a limiting factor.

Likewise the concentration of carbon dioxide is remarkably constant in the atmosphere, as a result of the efficient self-regulatory mechanisms of the carbon cycle (see Chapter 2). There are a few places where carbon dioxide escapes from vents (fumaroles) in the earth surface to such an extent that a pure carbon dioxide atmosphere replaces air near the vents. The famous death valley of the Dieng plateau of Java is an example; animal life is completely absent in such places. Industrial developments have increased the carbon dioxide concentration locally to a slight extent, but this has had no demonstrable effect on organisms, although other volatile products of the industrial age do have marked effects (see discussion of "smog," page 451). Experimentally, the rate of photosynthesis can be increased in many plants as a result of a moderate increase in the carbon dioxide concentration in the air (recall that CO_2 is a basic raw material in photosynthesis and that its concentration in the atmosphere is very low, about 0.03 per cent by volume). In the geological and physiological sense, the low concentration of carbon dioxide now existing is limiting to all land plants in that it appears that photosynthesis in nature is not always proceeding as rapidly as it might if more CO_2 were available. However, from the present-day ecological viewpoint, carbon dioxide does not generally limit one organism more than another, since it does not vary enough to affect distribution and behavior, or the productivity of large terrestrial ecosystems.

The situation in aquatic environments is quite different, because amounts of oxygen, carbon dioxide and other atmospheric gases dissolved in water and thus available to organisms are quite variable. Oxygen is an A-1 limiting factor, especially in lakes and in waters with a heavy load of organic material. Despite the fact that oxygen is more soluble in water than is nitrogen, the actual quantity of oxygen that water can hold under the most favorable conditions is much less than that constantly present in the atmosphere. Thus, if 21 per cent by volume of a liter of air is oxygen, there will be 210 cc. of oxygen per liter. By contrast, the amount of oxygen per liter of water does not exceed 10 cc. Temperature and dissolved salts greatly affect the ability of water to hold oxygen, the solubility of oxygen being increased by low temperatures and decreased by high salinities. The oxygen supply in water comes chiefly from two sources, by diffusion from the air and from photosynthesis by aquatic plants. Oxygen diffuses into water very slowly unless helped along by wind and water movements, while light penetration is an all-important factor in the photosynthetic production of oxygen. Therefore, important daily seasonal and spatial variations may be expected in the oxygen concentration of aquatic environments. The details of oxygen distribution and its relation to aquatic communities will be covered in Part II.

Carbon dioxide, like oxygen, may be present in water in highly variable amounts, but its behavior in water is rather different and its ecology is not yet well known. It is therefore difficult to make general statements as to its role as a limiting factor. Although present in low concentrations in the air, carbon dioxide is extremely soluble in water, which also obtains large supplies from respiration, decay, and soil or underground sources. Thus, the "minimum" is less likely to be of importance than is the case with oxygen. Furthermore, unlike oxygen, carbon dioxide enters into chemical combination with water to form H_2CO_3, which in turn reacts with available limestones to form carbonates ($-CO_3$) and bicarbonates ($-HCO_3$). These compounds not only provide a source of nutrients but also act as buffers, helping to keep the hydrogen ion concentration of aquatic environments near the neutral point. Moderate increases in CO_2 in water seem to speed up photosynthesis and the developmental processes of many organisms, but high concentrations may be definitely limiting to animals, especially since such high carbon dioxide concentrations are associated with low oxygen concentrations. Fishes respond vigorously to high concentrations and may be killed if the water is too heavily charged with unbound CO_2.

Hydrogen ion concentration, or pH, is closely related to the carbon dioxide complex, and, being relatively easy to measure, it has been much studied in natural aquatic environments. During the revival of interest in organized ecological study at the beginning of the twentieth century, pH was considered to be an important limiting factor and thus to be a promising indicator tool for determining the general ecological condition of aquatic environments, but this has not proved to be the case. The picture of the ecologist faring forth armed only with a pH kit was quite common. The physiologist, looking out of his laboratory window, probably smiled tolerantly, because the early interest in pH in ecological work was due to the discovery by the physiologist that pH was very important in regulating respiration and enzyme systems within the body, very small differences being critical. Unless values are extreme, which is unusual, most organisms (some microorganisms, especially bacteria, may be exceptions) in nature seem to have a wide tolerance for the naturally occurring range. Thus, measurement of pH alone has not proved as instructive as had been hoped. However, when the total alkalinity is constant, pH change is proportional to CO_2 change, and therefore is a useful measure of the latter. Soils and waters of low pH (i.e., "acid" soils and waters) are quite frequently deficient in nutrients and low in productivity.

6. *Biogenic Salts: Macronutrients and Micronutrients.*   Dissolved salts vital to life may be conveniently termed *biogenic salts*. We have already presented several examples of their importance as limiting factors in soil and water. In fact, Liebig's original "law" of the minimum was based largely on the limiting action of vital raw materials which are scarce and variable in the environment. As already indicated, nitrogen and phosphorus salts are of major importance, and the ecologist may do well to consider these first as a matter of routine. Following closely on the heels of these two elements, potassium, calcium, sulfur and magnesium merit high consideration. Calcium is needed in especially large quantities by the mollusks and the vertebrates, and magnesium is a necessary constituent of chlorophyll, without which no ecosystem could operate. Elements and their compounds needed in relatively large amounts are often known as *macronutrients*.

In recent years great interest has developed in the study of elements and their compounds which are necessary for the operation of living systems, but which are required only in extremely minute quantities (see the review by Vallee, 1951). These elements are generally called trace elements or *micronutrients*. Since minute requirements seem to be associated with an equal or even greater minuteness in environmental occurrence, the micronutrients have importance as limiting factors. One difficulty in working with micronutrients is that the amounts concerned are so small as to defy measurement. However, with the development of modern methods of microchemistry, spectrography, x-ray diffraction, and biological assay, rapid progress is being made. Also, the availability of radioactive isotopes of many of the trace elements has greatly stimulated experimental studies (see Comar, 1957). Deficiency diseases due to the absence of trace elements have been known, in a general way at least, for a long time. Pathological symptoms have been observed in laboratory, domestic, and wild plants and animals. Under natural conditions deficiency symptoms of this sort are sometimes associated with peculiar geological history and sometimes with a deteriorated environment of some sort, often a direct result of man's poor management. An example of peculiar geologic history is found in southern Florida. The potentially productive organic soils of the Everglades did not come up to expectation (for crops and cattle) until it was discovered that this sedimentary region lacked copper and cobalt which are usually present in most regions. In any event, the ecologist is much interested in the trace elements as possible indicators of "unhealthy" or unbalanced ecosystems.

Hewitt (1957) lists ten micronutrients which are definitely known to be essential to plants. These are: iron, manganese, copper, zinc, boron, sodium, molybdenum, chlorine, vanadium and cobalt. Most of these are also essential for animals, and a few others, such as iodine, are essential for certain animals, such as vertebrates. The dividing line between macro- and micronutrients, of course, is not sharp nor the same for all groups of organisms; sodium and chlorine, for example, would be needed in larger amounts by vertebrates than by plants. Many of the micronutrients resemble vitamins in that they act as catalysts. The trace metals often combine with organic compounds to form "metalloactivators"; cobalt, for example, is a vital constituent of vitamin B_{12}. Recently, molybdenum has been shown to be essential for nitrogen-fixing microorganisms; this element is deficient in certain tropical soils, and is apparently a limiting factor of major importance in parts of Java and Australia. As with most factors, there are upper as well as lower limits of tolerance, so that we can even have too much of a micronutrient (as perhaps is the case with magnesium in serpentine soils referred to earlier in this chapter)!

7. *Currents and Pressures.*   The atmospheric and hydrospheric media in which organisms live are not often completely still for any period of time. Currents in water not only greatly influence the concentration of gases and nutrients, but act directly as limiting factors. Thus, the differences between a stream and a small pond community (see Chapter 9, Section 7) may be due in large part to the big difference in the current factor. Many stream plants and animals are specifically adapted morphologically and physiologically to maintaining their position in the current and are known to have very definite limits of tolerance to this specific factor. On land, wind exerts a limiting effect on the activities and even the distribution of organisms in the same manner. Birds, for example, remain quiet in protected places on windy days, which are, therefore, poor times for the ecologist to attempt to census a bird population. Plants may be modified structurally by

the wind, especially when other factors are also limiting, as in alpine regions. Whitehead (1956) has demonstrated experimentally that wind limits the growth of plants in exposed mountain locations. When he erected a wall to protect the vegetation from wind, the height of plants increased. Storms are of major importance, even though they may be only local in extent. Hurricanes (as well as ordinary winds) transport animals and plants for great distances and, when they strike land, the winds may change the composition of the forest communities for many years to come. It has been observed that insects spread faster in the direction of the prevailing winds than in other directions to areas which seem to offer equal opportunity for the establishment of the species. In dry regions, wind is an especially important limiting factor for plants, since it increases the rate of water loss by transpiration. Good critical studies of the effect of wind are needed. In their preoccupation with temperature and moisture, ecologists have neglected this important factor.

Barometric pressure has not been shown to be an important direct limiting factor for organisms, although some animals appear able to detect differences, and, of course, barometric pressure has much to do with weather and climate, which are directly limiting to organisms. In the ocean, however, hydrostatic pressure is of importance because of the tremendous gradient from the surface to the depths. In water the pressure increases one atmosphere for every 10 meters. In the deepest part of the ocean the pressure reaches 1000 atmospheres. Many animals can tolerate wide changes in pressure, especially if the body does not contain free air or gas. When it does, gas embolism may develop. In general, great pressures such as are found in the depth of the ocean exert a depressing effect, so that the pace of life is slower.

8. *Soil.*   It is sometimes convenient to think of the biosphere as being made up of the atmosphere, the hydrosphere, and the pedosphere, the latter being the soil. Each of these divisions owes many of its characteristic features to the ecological reactions and coactions of organisms and to the interplay of ecosystems and basic cycles between them. Each is composed of a living and a nonliving component more easily separated on theoretical than on practical grounds. Biotic and abiotic components are especially intimate in soil, which by definition consists of the weathered layer of the earth's crust with living organisms and products of their decay intermingled. Without life, the earth would have a

crust and might have air and water, but the air and water, and especially the "soil," would be entirely different from these components as we know them. Thus, soil not only is a "factor" of the environment of organisms but is produced by them as well. In general we may think of soil as the net result of the action of climate and organisms, especially vegetation, on the parent material of the earth's surface. Soil thus is composed of a parent material, the underlying geologic or mineral substrate, and an organic increment in which organisms and their products are intermingled with the finely divided particles of the modified parent material. Spaces between the particles are filled with gases and water. The texture and porosity of the soil are highly important characteristics and largely determine the availability of nutrients to plants and soil animals.

If we examine the cut edge of a bank or a trench (Fig. 31), it will be found that soil is composed of distinct layers, which often differ in color. These layers are called soil horizons, and the sequence of horizons from the surface down is called a soil pro-

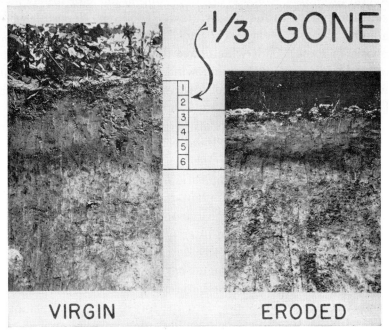

VIRGIN   ERODED

Figure 31.   Soil profile of a virgin area compared with that of an eroded area in the deciduous forest region. In the left picture, 1–2 represents the A_1 horizon, 3–4 the A_2 horizon, and 5–6 the B_1 layer (accumulation of leached material). Compare with Figure 32. (U. S. Soil Conservation Service Photo.)

file. The upper horizon, or *A horizon* ("top soil"), is composed of the bodies of plants and animals which are being reduced to finely divided organic material by the process known as *humification* (see page 19). In a mature soil this horizon is usually subdivided into distinct layers representing progressive stages of humification. These layers (Fig. 31) are designated (from the surface downward) as A_{01}, A_{02}, A_{03}, A_1, and A_2, or, less technically, as litter, duff, leaf-mold, humus (A_1), and leached (light-colored) zone (A_2). The next major horizon, or *B horizon,* is composed of mineral soil in which the organic compounds have been converted by decomposers into inorganic compounds by the process of *mineralization,* and thoroughly mixed with finely divided parent material. The soluble materials of B horizon are often formed in the A horizon and deposited, or leached by downward flow of water, in B horizon. The dark band in Figure 31 represents the upper part of B horizon where materials have accumulated. The third horizon, or *C horizon,* represents the more or less unmodified parent material. This parent material may represent the original mineral formation which is disintegrating in place or it may have been transported to the site by gravity (colluvial deposit), water (alluvial deposit), glaciers (glacial deposit), or wind (eolian deposit, or loess). Soils which have developed on material transported by glaciers, water, and wind are often extremely fertile (witness the deep loess soils of Iowa and the rich soils of the deltas of large rivers).

The soil profile and the relative thickness of the horizons are generally characteristic for different climatic regions and for topographic situations (Figs. 32 and 33). Thus, grassland soils differ from forest soils in that humification is rapid, but mineralization is slow. Since the entire grass plant, including roots, is short-lived, with each year are added large amounts of organic material which decays rapidly, leaving little litter or duff, but much humus. In the forest litter and roots decay slowly and, since mineralization is rapid, the humus layer remains narrow (Fig. 32). The average humus content of grassland soil, for example, is 600 tons per acre, compared with 50 tons per acre for forest soils (Daubenmire, 1947). In the forest-grassland buffer zone (see Figure 33) in Illinois, one can easily tell by the color of the soil which cornfield was once prairie and which was forest: the prairie soil is much blacker, due to its high humus content. Given adequate rainfall, it is no accident that the "granaries of the world" are located in grassland regions.

Topographic conditions greatly influence the soil profile within a given climatic region. Hilly or well-drained land, especially if misused by man, will tend to have thin A and B horizons due to erosion (Fig. 31). In flat land water may leach materials rapidly into the deeper layers, sometimes forming a "hardpan" through which roots of plants, animals, and water cannot penetrate. Poorly drained situations such as bogs favor the accumulation of humus, since poor aeration slows down decay. The lack of oxygen and the accumulation of carbon dioxide and other toxic products become severe limiting factors. Sometimes soils developing on poorly drained sites are extremely productive if they are properly drained —witness the muck soils of the Everglades of Florida which rate as some of the most productive soils in the world, when properly handled. The catch is that "proper handling" involves difficult ecological, as well as engineering, problems.

In tropical climates, the rate of decay is so rapid that little humus accumulates. Thus, although other growing conditions are favorable, cleared land is often "worn out" in a couple of years and has to be abandoned. The problem of fertility of tropical soils is primarily an ecological one and needs further study.

Classification of soil types has become a highly empirical sub-

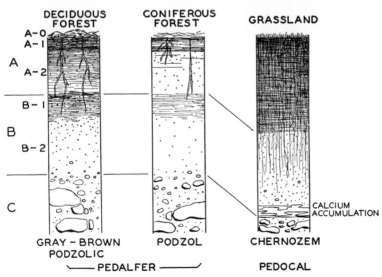

Figure 32. Simplified diagrams of three major soil types which are characteristic of three major biotic regions. See legend of Figure 34.

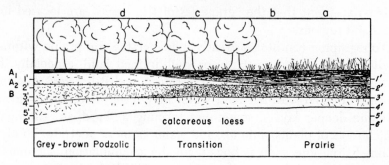

Figure 33. Soil-vegetation relationships in a prairie-forest transition zone. Distinctly different soils develop from the same parent material (calcareous loess, or wind-transported "C" horizon in this case) under influence of different vegetation and climate. The decrease in organic matter, the development of a podzolic A horizon (with narrow humus layer, see Figure 32), and increased structural development of the B horizon are the main features differentiating the forest soils from the prairie soils. (After Crocker, 1952.)

ject. The soil scientist may recognize dozens of soil types as occurring within a county or state. Type names for local soils, for example, Norfolk Sandy-Loam, usually include the geographical locality where the series was described and an indication of the texture. The ecologist, of course, should do more than merely name the soil on his study area. At the very minimum, measurements should be made of three important attributes in at least the A and B horizons as follows: (1) texture, that is, the per cent of sand, silt and clay (or more detailed determination of particle size), (2) per cent organic matter and (3) exchange capacity, that is, an estimate of the amount of exchangeable nutrients; as emphasized in Chapter 2, the "available" minerals rather than the total amount determine potential fertility, other conditions being favorable. Variation in texture, organic content and exchange capacity in a series of soils, and the effect which these attributes have on the uptake of radiostrontium by plants is shown in Figure 156 (page 482).

Since soil is the product of climate and vegetation, a map of major (zonal) soil types of the world (Fig. 34) becomes a composite map of climate and vegetation (Fig. 35). Given a favorable parent material the action of organisms and climate will tend to build up a soil characteristic of the region (compare Figure 34 with map of biotic communities, Fig. 120, page 384). From a broad ecological viewpoint, the soils of a given region may be lumped into two groups, those which are largely controlled by climate and vegetation of the region and those which are largely

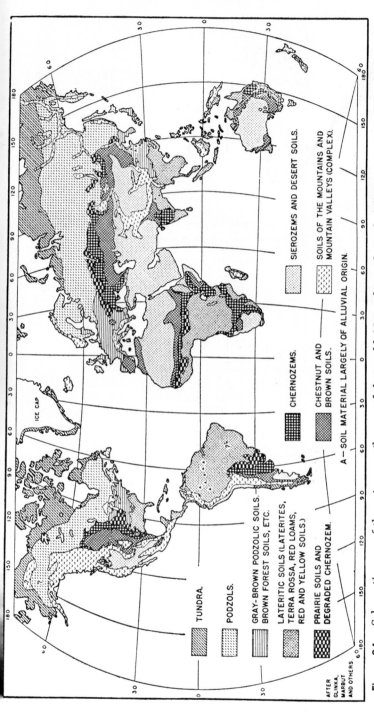

Figure 34. Schematic map of the primary soil types of the world. Not only north-south differences are evident but also east-west differences which are related to rainfall. Podzolic and lateritic soils of humid regions are often known as "pedalfers" because of the accumulation of iron and aluminum in the B horizons, while the chernozems and other soils of more arid regions are "pedocals," because of the accumulation of calcium (see Figure 32). (Map from U. S. Department of Agriculture Yearbook, 1938.)

TUNDRA.

PODZOLS.

GRAY-BROWN PODZOLIC SOILS.
BROWN FOREST SOILS, ETC.

LATERITIC SOILS (LATERITES,
TERRA ROSSA, RED LOAMS,
RED AND YELLOW SOILS.)

PRAIRIE SOILS AND
DEGRADED CHERNOZEM.

CHERNOZEMS.

CHESTNUT AND
BROWN SOILS.

A—SOIL MATERIAL LARGELY OF ALLUVIAL ORIGIN.

SIEROZEMS AND DESERT SOILS.

SOILS OF THE MOUNTAINS AND
MOUNTAIN VALLEYS (COMPLEX).

AFTER
GLINKA,
MARBUT
AND OTHERS.

ICE CAP

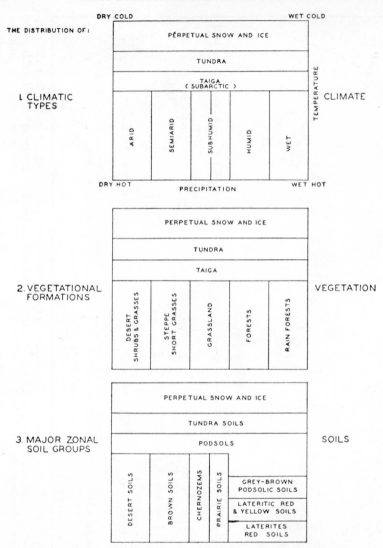

Figure 35. Schematic representation showing the interrelation of climate, vegetational formations and zonal soil groups. (From Oosting, 1952 (2nd Ed.), after Blumenstock and Thornthwaite.)

controlled by local or edaphic conditions of extreme or unusual topography, water level or type of parent material. Thus, the local climate might favor a grassland community which in turn "builds" a grassland type of soil, wherever conditions are not so extreme as to retard or prevent characteristic ecological action and reaction. Where some condition is extreme or limiting, as, for example, poor surface drainage, an entirely different soil may develop, which in turn supports a different biotic community. The extent to which local or edaphic factors influence soil development varies with the region. In general, edaphic conditions are more important (1) in regions which are geologically young and in which climate and vegetation have not yet been able to "build" a uniform soil cover, and (2) in regions where the climate is extreme, as in deserts, for example, where small differences in soil may make big differences in the resulting biotic community. Thus, ecologists working in the Middle West where soils are well developed find that virtually the same sort of biotic community will, if given time, develop on a variety of soil types. Thus, these ecologists tend to look upon the soil, unless very extreme in type, as not being a critical limiting factor in the long run. On the other hand, ecologists working on the coastal plain of southeastern United States, where the sandy soils are relatively undeveloped or "geologically young," are very soil-conscious because they find that climate and vegetation have not yet been able to build a characteristic soil; more or less permanent differences in biotic communities are directly correlated with differences in soil types.* This difference in viewpoint in regard to soil as an over-all limiting factor is, of course, inherent in the principle of limiting factors in general. Both groups of workers are right as far as their respective localities are concerned. The particular aspects of the environment which function as primary limiting factors will vary with the region and the organisms being studied. The ecologist should not carry into a new region stereotyped ideas based on experience in another region.

For good general discussions of soil, reference may be made to Wolfanger (1930), Kellogg (1948), Russell and Russell (1950), Simonson (1951) and Russell (1957).

9. *Fire as an Ecological Factor.*   Research during the last twenty or thirty years has made necessary a rather drastic reorientation of our ideas about fire as an ecological factor. It is now evident that fire should be considered not a minor or abnormal factor, but a major factor which in many regions is, and has been for centuries, almost a part of the normal "climate." As with most ecological factors, man has greatly modified its effect, increasing its influence in many cases and decreasing it in others. Also, it has

---

* Translated into quantitative terms, 83 per cent of the soils of Marshall County, Iowa, are mature, compared with only 15 per cent in Bertie County, N. C., on the coastal plain, according to Wolfanger (1930).

become clear that fire is not always detrimental to man s interest. Properly used, fire can be an ecological tool of great value. Fire is thus an extremely important limiting factor if for no other reason than that mankind is able to control it to a far greater extent than he can many other limiting factors.

Fire is most important in forest and grassland regions of temperate zones and in tropical areas with dry seasons. In many parts of western or southeastern United States, it would be difficult to find a sizable area which does not give evidence of fire having occurred on it during the last fifty years at least. In many sections fires are started naturally by lightning. Primitive man, the North American Indian, for example, regularly burned woods and prairies for practical reasons. Fire thus was a limiting factor long before the white man began to drastically modify his environment in an attempt to improve his status. Inadvertently, through careless behavior white man has often so increased the effect of fire that the very thing he is seeking—a productive environment—is destroyed or injured. On the other hand, complete protection from fire has not always resulted in what was expected, namely, a more productive environment for man's purposes. Thus, it has become clear that fire should be considered an ecological factor along with such other factors as temperature, rainfall and soil, and should be studied with an open mind. Whether fire is a friend or a foe of civilization will depend on intelligent knowledge and control.

In speaking of fire as an ecological factor, the first thing to emphasize is that there are several types of fire in nature which are different in effect (Fig. 36). For example, *crown fires* often destroy all of the vegetation, whereas *surface fires* have entirely different effects. The former is limiting to most organisms; the biotic community must start to develop all over again, more or less from scratch, and it may be many years before the area is productive from man's viewpoint. Surface fires, on the other hand, exert a selective effect; they are more limiting to some organisms than to others and thus favor the development of organisms with high tolerance to the fire factor. Also, light surface fires aid bacteria in breaking down the bodies of plants and in making mineral nutrients more quickly available to new plant growth. Nitrogen-fixing legumes often thrive after a light burn. In regions especially subject to fire, occasional light surface fires greatly reduce the danger of severe crown fires by keeping the combustible litter to a minimum. In examining an area in regions where fire is a factor, the

Figure 36. The two extremes of fire. Upper: Result of a severe crown fire in Idaho. Lower: A controlled burning operation on the Alapaha Experimental Range, Georgia, which removes hardwood competition, stimulates growth of legumes, and improves the reproduction of valuable pine timber. Burning is done under damp conditions in afternoon (fire is stopped at night by dewfall). Note that smoke is *white* and thin line of fire can be stepped over at almost any point. Insert: Long-leaf pine seedling; the terminal bud is well protected by long needles, which explains why this species is especially resistant to fire. (U. S. Forest Service Photos; insert by the author.)

ecologist usually finds some evidence of the past influence of fire. Whether fire should be excluded in the future (assuming that it is practical) or should be used as a management tool will depend entirely on the type of community that is desired or seems best from the standpoint of regional land use.

A single example taken from a well studied situation will illustrate how fire acts as a limiting factor, and how fire is not necessarily "bad" from the human viewpoint. On the coastal plain of southeastern United States the long-leaf pine is more resistant to fire than any other tree species. The terminal bud of seedling long-leaf pines is well protected by a bunch of long, fire-resistant needles (Fig. 36, insert). Thus, ground fires selectively favor this species. In the complete absence of fire, scrub hardwoods grow rapidly and choke out the long-leaf pines. Grasses and legumes are also eliminated, and the bob-white and other animals dependent on legumes do not thrive in the complete absence of fire in forested lands. Ecologists are generally agreed that the magnificent virgin, open stands of long-leaf pine of the coastal plain (Fig. 125, page 394) are fire-controlled, or a "fire climax," and that long-leaf pine and its associated animals cannot be maintained in the complete absence of fire. Since the long-leaf pine is one of the world's best timber trees and bob-white are generally considered more valuable than blue jays (which might thrive in the scrub oaks), it is obvious that "controlled burning" or the right use of fire is desirable from the economic standpoint. To put it another way, fire is a major limiting factor in the coastal plains pine region.*

Among the best places to observe the long-term effects of intelligent use of fire are the plantations of southwestern Georgia where for many years Herbert Stoddard and E. V. Komarek have been studying the relation of fire to the entire ecological complex. As a result of these studies, Stoddard was one of the first to advocate the use of controlled or "prescribed" burning for increasing both timber and game production. For years he has maintained high densities of both quail and wild turkeys on land devoted to highly profitable timber crops through the use of a system of "spot" burning aided by a diversification in the land use (Stoddard, 1936). All ecologists should visit one of these areas to see firsthand the "good" side of fire.

We emphasized that the example of the long-leaf pine men-

* For additional details, see Heyward (1939), Heyward and Barnette (1934), Stoddard (1936), and Garren (1943).

tioned above is well studied. In other regions fire-resistant species might be undesirable or lead to an unproductive environment. Thus, conclusions regarding fire should be restricted to situations where study has been adequate. Sweeping statements should be avoided, at least until more information is available. Certainly there is no more fascinating and important field for ecological research.

10. *Microenvironment.*[*]   Not only are regional differences in temperature, moisture and other factors important, but also local horizontal and vertical differences. Organisms occupying the same general habitat may actually be living under very different conditions. The concept of microenvironment, the environment of small areas in contrast to large ones, has been developed only within the last decade. Other terms, commonly applied to this concept but much more restrictive in scope, are microclimate and bioclimate. Since the term microenvironment is a relative one, it may signify the immediate environmental area occupied by a pine stand, or equally well of that occupied by a lichen within the stand. Critical studies at the microenvironmental level have significantly sharpened our approach to the study of individual organisms as well as to communities of organisms; the data are especially valuable in calculating energy flow of various populations within the community.

Basic considerations and safeguards which have now come into fairly common use, but which were not well understood or generally accepted a decade or more ago include: (1) the environment of a particular organism at a particular time is not the same as that some distance removed, either by millimeters or by miles; (2) data cannot be transposed in time any better than in space; (3) environmental effects observed on an individual cannot be applied without question to the population or the species; (4) data obtained in greenhouses under unnatural conditions cannot be used for interpretation of the same organism when living in its natural environment and (5) vertical as well as horizontal gradients are of far greater significance than point measurements of environmental conditions.

Figure 37 illustrates a microenvironmental laboratory located in southern Georgia, which consists basically of two fifty-foot wooden towers located at the ecological extremes of a dense woodland and an open field. These towers have been equipped with

[*] This section has been prepared in collaboration with Dr. Robert B. Platt, Emory University, Atlanta, Georgia.

Figure 37. A field installation for the study of correlations of micro-environmental conditions with the distribution and abundance in space and time of a wide variety of plants and animals. The installation consists of fifty foot wooden towers erected at ecological extremes of a dense woodland (left) and an adjacent open field (right) in southwestern Georgia. Facilities are provided for obtaining biological data simultaneously with automatically recorded environmental data through various vegetational levels from the ground to the tree crowns. The mature forest of the region (left picture) contains a mixture of both deciduous and broad-leaved evergreen trees festooned with long streamers of the epiphytic Spanish "moss" (*Tillandsia*). The tower in the right picture is equipped for the study of mosquito activity in relation to vertical temperature-humidity gradients. Automatic sweep nets may be seen on the left, and light traps are placed at each platform. The temperature-humidity recording instruments are housed in the box on the first platform, and one of the shelters containing the sensing elements may be seen to the right of the first platform. (After Platt, 1957.)

instruments for automatic recording of microenvironmental gradients, vertically from ground level to various elevations above the ground and horizontally between the two towers. For detailed studies of the distribution and abundance of local mosquito populations, both attractant and non-attractant collection devices have been installed at the ground, 3, 6, 15, 25, and 50 foot levels, corresponding to those for which environmental data are obtained. Results obtained over a two year period clearly demonstrate that not only do various species of mosquitoes have their own patterns of distribution and abundance, which may vary from night to night, but also that these patterns shift through the night both vertically and horizontally. An analysis of both environmental and mosquito data obtained simultaneously at hourly intervals through the night demonstrated a positive correlation between relative humidity and the distribution and abundance of one of the more common species, *Aedes vexans*. This correlation held, regardless of elevation, time of night or habitat (woods or field)— the optimum humidity being around 70 per cent (Platt, 1957).

An unusual example of the microenvironment of a very small area, that of a single leaf, is illustrated in Figure 38. An oak leaf was oriented with its upper side facing the sun. The temperature then of the upper side was determined at frequent intervals over a five minute interval by the use of a highly sensitive temperature sensing element (a thermistor), which would provide leaf surface temperatures with an accuracy of one hundredth of one degree centigrade. With such simple environmental changes as shading

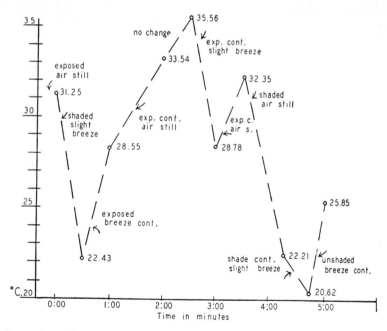

Figure 38.   Temperature changes in an oak leaf caused by changes in air movement and exposure. The leaf was oriented with the upper side to the sun. Circles denote temperature determinations. Arrows denote time of indicated changes in air movement and exposure. Thermistors were used to detect temperature changes. (After Platt and Wolfe, 1950.)

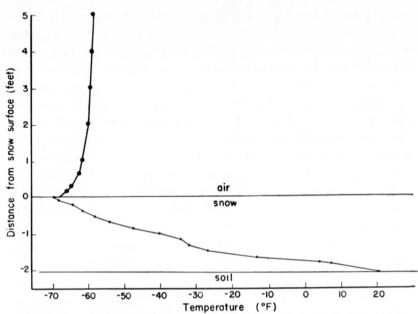

Figure 39. Vertical temperature gradient during a cold snap in central Alaska, an extreme case of microclimatic differences above and below the snow. Measurements were made simultaneously by the use of small copper-constantan thermocouples so arranged that conduction and radiation errors were minimized and the snow cover was undisturbed. (Data of H. McClure Johnson obtained during contract research between Cornell University and Alaskan Air Command Arctic Aero Medical Laboratory, Ladd AFB, Alaska.)

and slight differences in air movement a variation of 10 to 15 C. degrees occurred several times within the five minute period. An understanding of this kind of microenvironmental influence on leaf temperature, for example, makes it easier to understand the wide physiological and anatomical differences which occur between sun and shade leaves, and also the various modifications which leaves have evolved to adverse heat and drought, such as changing the angle of incidence of the leaf to the sun by rolling of the leaf blade or by change of position.

Figure 39 rather spectacularly illustrates the microenvironmental variation on the tundra, showing differences in temperature recorded simultaneously at different points above and below the snow during a winter cold snap in central Alaska. Note that although temperatures were between 60 and 70 degrees below zero above the snow, the temperature at the surface of the soil below the snow was some 80 degrees higher! Animals living above the snow, such as the caribou or the arctic fox, would be subjected to the low temperatures, whereas animals living under the snow would virtually be living in a more southerly climatic zone! At the station where the measurements graphed in Figure 39 were made, voles of the genus *Microtus* were quite active in the two-inch air space between the snow and soil. These voles have rather thin fur and are not especially well adapted for extreme cold (compared with the arctic hare, for example); yet they are able to survive in a region of very cold winter climate because of the favorable subnivean microenvironment.

For an example of the effect on vegetation of horizontal micro-environmental differences in soil and climate see Figure 77, page 268. For a comparison of macro- and micro-climatic variables, reference may be made to the study of Wolfe, Wareham and Scofield (1949). Geiger's book, *The Climate Near the Ground* (revised edition, 1957), contains much of interest to ecologists.

6. Ecological indicators

Since, as we have seen, specific factors often determine rather precisely what kinds of organisms will be present, we can turn the situation around and judge the kind of physical environment from the organisms present. Often it is useful to employ a biological assay of this sort, particularly if we have something specific in mind, and the factor or factors in question are difficult or inconvenient to measure directly. In fact, the ecologist constantly employs organisms as indicators in exploring new situations or evaluating large areas. Terrestrial plants are especially useful in this regard. In western United States, for example, plants have been much used as indicators of water and soil conditions (especially as they affect grazing and agricultural potentials) since the early work of Shantz (1911) and Clements (1916). The use of vertebrate animals, as well as plants, as indicators of temperature zones (developed by Merriam (1894, 1899)), has also been much studied. More recently, the use of functional assay methods, described in Section 4 of this chapter, has received attention.

Some of the important considerations which should be borne in mind in dealing with ecological indicators follow:

1. In general, "steno" species make much better indicators than "eury," for reasons which should be obvious. Such species are often not the most abundant ones in the community. Additional discussion along this line and the concept of "fidelity" are included in Chapter 11 (page 383).

2. Large species usually make better indicators than small species because, as demonstrated in Chapter 3, a larger and more stable biomass or standing crop can be supported with a given energy flow. The turnover rate of small organisms may be so great (here today, gone tomorrow) that the particular species present at any one moment may not be very instructive as an ecological indicator. Rawson (1956), for example, found no species of algae which could serve as an indicator of lake types.

3. Before relying on single species or groups of species as indicators, there should be abundant field evidence, and, if possible, experimental evidence that the factor in question is limiting. Also, ability to compensate or adapt should be known; if marked ecotypes exist, the occurrence of the same series of taxa in different localities does not necessarily mean that the same conditions exist (see McMillan, 1956).

4. Numerical relationships between species, populations and whole communities often provide more reliable indicators than single species, since a better integration of conditions is reflected by the whole than by the part. This has been particularly well brought out in the search for biological indicators of various sorts of pollution (see page 440). Recent work in Europe has demonstrated that the floristic makeup of weed communities provide excellent quantitative indicators of potential agricultural productivity of land (Ellenberg, 1950).

An interesting atomic age slant on the subject of indicators is provided by the discovery that certain plants are useful in prospecting for uranium (Cannon, 1952, 1953, 1954). When deep rooted plants such as pines and junipers grow over uranium deposits, the above-ground plant parts contain a higher concentration of uranium than normal. Foliage may be easily collected, ashed and examined fluorimetrically; over two ppm uranium in the ash is considered indicative of commercially usable deposits underground. Since selenium is often associated with uranium ore, selenium indicating plants, for example, species of *Astragalus* in the Rocky Mountain Region, may also be useful in locating deposits. Likewise, where sulfur and uranium are associated, the sulfur accumulating members of the mustard and lily family provide useful indicators.

5 · Introduction to population and community ecology

In the preceding three chapters we have been concerned with the interaction of the living and the nonliving. We have considered the broad concept of the ecosystem and energy relationships within it; and we have outlined the relation of various physical and chemical factors to organisms. We now come to a discussion of the more purely biological aspects of ecology, that is, the relationships of organism to organism. Organisms do not live alone, nor do they ever have an entirely private autecology. Organisms living in any given area, whether large or small, are associated together in what are known as biotic communities. The biotic community is rather loosely but definitely held together as a unit by the interdependence of its members. The community is primarily a functional unit; it has definite structure, to be sure, but the structural pattern is often more variable than the community metabolism pattern because the species components of the community are to some extent interchangeable in time and space. (This will be discussed more fully.) The biotic community is composed of smaller groups, the members of which are more intimately associated with each other, and hence these groups form a cohesive unit. Such groups within the community are called populations. The word population is derived from the Latin word *populus,* meaning people, and originally referred to a group of people occupying a particular space. In ecology the definition is broadened to include groups of organisms occupying a particular space. In general, a population is considered to be composed of individuals of the same species. However, the term

need not be tied rigidly to the species concept since varieties, ecotypes or other groups may have ecological unity. Also, of course,
we may use the plural in referring to groups which contain several species.

Obviously, there is no hard and fast line between population
and the community. Both are to some extent abstractions which
help us get our mental teeth into complex subjects. Both represent
what we may consider levels of organization above that of the
individual. Some have suggested that the community be considered a sort of "super-organism," and its populations be considered the organs and organ systems of the super-organism.
Although there are some similarities between communities and
organisms in an abstract way, populations and communities are
not actually put together in the same way that tissues and organs
are put together to form the organism. Therefore, the super-organism concept is probably a useful analogy but not a true homology.
Nevertheless, the important point to stress is that the population
and community are *real entities,* even though one cannot usually
pick them up and put them in the collecting kit as one would
collect an organism. They are real things, because these group
units have *characteristics additional to the characteristics of the
individuals composing them.* The forest is more than a collection
of trees. (These points were fully discussed in Chapter 2.)

Community and population ecology, group ecology, or synecology—however one wishes to express it—is both the heart and the
unique part of modern ecology. Its importance can hardly be
overstressed. For example, the temperature and the nutrient and
other physical and chemical requirements of a hemlock tree or a
tiger beetle might be known, but the ecology of the organism cannot be complete until population and community relations have
also been studied. The occurrence and survival of organisms in
nature often is due as much to competition or other population
and community relationships as to the direct action of physical
and chemical factors.

There is good reason for considering population and community ecology the unique part of ecology. Some, at least, of the
principles considered in the preceding chapters might be considered as being a part of chemistry or physics, or an extension of
physiology. The study of group organization, however, is exclusively in the realm of ecology and could hardly be considered a
part of any other field as now conceived.

Up to this point we have stressed the similarities and interrelations between plants and animals, pointing out that many of the most important principles of ecology apply equally well to, or must include both groups of organisms as well as the great stem group of microorganisms. We now come to the point where some differences, at least in viewpoint and methods, should be mentioned. With terrestrial plants, most synecological work has dealt with the community level. Plants "stay put" and respond to environmental conditions by growth and structural changes rather than by behavior changes, as do animals. All the important species in a community can usually be counted and studied with precision. The animal portion of the community is harder to get at, and as a consequence there is more emphasis on discrete populations which can be measured with more precision. Also, animals have more direct dealings with each other and with plants than do plants. Likewise, ecological work in aquatic habitats, where direct observation by air-breathing man is often limited, has tended to stress the community level. Thus, population ecology has developed to a greater extent on the land animal side, and community ecology to a greater degree on the terrestrial plant and aquatic side. Obviously, all approaches contribute to our understanding of the biotic community as a whole, which, of course, is the ultimate goal.

From a practical standpoint it is not necessary, nor indeed is it often possible, to consider all the species to be found in a community. As we shall see, most communities are composed of a few very common species and numerous relatively rare species (certain tropical communities are exceptions). Thus, the major part of the energy flow involves a comparatively small number of kinds of organisms at any one point in time and space. Therefore, we can learn a lot about communities, as well as specific populations in which we have a special interest, by concentrating on dominant populations in the major trophic levels. For example, if we wish to study a lake and have a special interest in the game fish, we would first consider the basic producer plants, their distribution and abundance, and the physical and chemical factors which might prove to be limiting factors. We would next study the game fish population in order to work out food-chain relationships with other animals and plants, and to determine reproductive rate, mortality rate, age distribution, and other population characteristics. We would hope that such studies would lead to the clarification of the basic energy relationships of the ecosystem as a whole and to the determination of how efficiently energy is being channeled into usable fish flesh. Such knowledge might then be "applied" to the management of the lake for the purpose of increasing productivity for man's benefit. We should hasten to say that rare species are by no means unimportant or uninteresting ecologically. Often a principle is more clearly brought out by the study of a rare species. As we shall see, the relationship between numbers of species and numbers of individuals is of very great interest. The very question why some species are rare and others common is a central problem in community study (Preston, 1948; Elton, 1949; Braun-Blanquet, 1951).

6 · Principles and concepts pertaining to organization at the species population level

1. Population group properties

Statement

The population, which has been defined as a collective group of organisms of the same species occupying a particular space, has various characteristics which, although best expressed as statistical functions, are the unique possession of the group and are not characteristic of the individuals in the group. Some of these properties are: density, natality (birth rate), mortality (death rate), age distribution, biotic potential, dispersion, and growth form.

Explanation

As has been well expressed by Thomas Park (in Allee et al., 1949), a population has characteristics or "biological attributes" which it shares with its component organisms, and it has characteristics or "group attributes" unique to the group. Among the former, the population has a life history in that it grows, differentiates, and maintains itself as does the organism. It has a definite organization and structure which can be described. On the other hand, group attributes, such as birth rate, death rate and age ratio, apply only to the population. Thus, an individual is born and dies and has age, but it does not have a birth rate, death rate, or an age ratio. These latter attributes are meaningful only at the group level. In the following sections the important group attributes will be considered and examples given.

In simple laboratory populations observed under controlled conditions many of the above-mentioned group attributes can be measured, and the effect of various factors on them studied. In natural populations, however, it is often difficult or impossible to measure all of the attributes. Some of this difficulty is being overcome as methods of population study improve. The development of better methods for measuring the population of various important organisms is thus a very fruitful line of ecological research today. Even with great improvement in methods, it is doubtful if all population attributes can be measured with equal accuracy in nature. Fortunately, it is often not necessary actually to measure all these in order to obtain a useful picture of the population. Frequently one characteristic of a population can be calculated from data on another characteristic. Thus, accurate measurement of one or two properties may be more valuable than poor measurement of several.

2. Population density and indices of relative abundance

Statement

Population density is population size in relation to some unit of space. It is generally assayed and expressed as the number of individuals, or the population biomass, per unit area or volume—for example, 200 trees per acre, 5 million diatoms per cubic meter of water, or 200 pounds of fish per acre of water surface. Sometimes it is important to distinguish between *crude density*—the number (or biomass) per unit total space, and *specific or ecological density**—the number (or biomass) per unit of habitat space (available area or volume that can actually be colonized by the population). Often it is more important to know whether a population is changing (increasing or decreasing) in size at any one moment. Also, population size often changes so rapidly (especially among lower plant and animal taxonomic groups) or is so difficult to measure accurately (perhaps because of the large size of the area to be censused or because of the irregular distribution of individuals) that density per unit space has little meaning. In such cases, indices of *relative abundance* are useful; these may be "time-relative," as, for example, the number of birds seen per

* Also called *economic density* by Elton (1933).

hour, or they may be percentages of various kinds, such as the percentage of sample plots occupied by a species of plant.

Explanation

In undertaking a study of a population, density would often be the first population attribute to receive attention. It might be said that natural history becomes ecology when "how many" as well as "what kinds" are considered. The effect which a population exerts on the community and the ecosystem depends not only on what kind of organism is involved but also on how many—in other words, on population density. Thus, one crow in a 100-acre corn-field would have little effect on the ultimate yield and cause the farmer no concern, but 1,000 crows per 100 acres would be something else!

As with some of the other population attributes, population density is quite variable. However, it is by no means infinitely variable; there are definite upper and lower limits to species population sizes that are observed in nature or that theoretically could exist for any length of time. Thus, a large area of forest might show an average of 10 birds per hectare and 2,000 soil arthropods per square meter, but there would never be as many as 2,000 birds per square meter or as few as 10 arthropods per hectare! As has been brought out in Chapters 3 and 4, the upper limit of density is determined by the energy flow (productivity) in the ecosystem, the trophic level to which the organism belongs and the size and rate of metabolism of the organism. The lower limit may not be so well defined, but in stable ecosystems, at least, homeostatic mechanisms operate to keep density of the common or dominant organisms within rather definite limits. Within these broad limits, density will vary according to interaction with other species (competition) and action of physical limiting factors.

In Figure 40 the range of density reported for common mammals is shown. Density (expressed as biomass per hectare) is that of the species within its normal geographical range, in its preferred habitat (i.e., ecological density) and under conditions where man or other "outside" forces are not unduly restrictive. Species are arranged in the chart according to trophic level, and within the four levels according to individual size. We see that while density of mammals as a class may range over nearly five orders of magnitude, the range for any given species or trophic

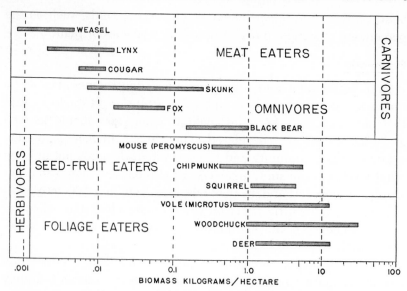

Figure 40. The range of population density (as biomass per hectare) of various species of mammals as reported from preferred habitat of the species in localities where man is not unduly restrictive. Species are arranged according to trophic levels and according to individual size within the four levels to illustrate the limits imposed by trophic position and size of organism on the expected standing crop. (Graph prepared from data collected by Mohr (1940) plus results of later studies.)

group is much less. The influence of trophic level is, of course, striking, and the effect of size is also indicated since larger mammals in each level tend to maintain a larger biomass than the small mammals. The point to emphasize is that the first order of population control is the energy flow—physical factor complex; the second order of control involves the subject matter of this and the subsequent two chapters.

When the size of individuals in the population is relatively uniform, density expressed in terms of number of individuals is quite satisfactory as a measure. On the other hand, when individual size is variable, as is true of fish, trees, or mixed populations generally, some sort of biomass measure may be more satisfactory as a measure of density. Live (or wet) weight, dry weight, volume, and carbon or nitrogen weight can be used as a measure of biomass density. Special measures and terms are used for special groups. With trees, for example, the population can be divided into size classes and the number in each determined, or the "basal area" could be calculated. Basal area is the sum total of cross section area of tree trunks (determined from measurements of "d.b.h.," or "diameter breast high"). Foresters, of course, determine "board feet" or other measures of the commercially usable part of the tree. These and many others are density measures as we have broadly defined the concept, since they express in some manner the size of the "standing crop" per unit area.

One of the greatest difficulties in measuring and expressing density arises from the fact that individuals in populations are often unevenly distributed in space, i.e., show a "clumped" distribution (see Figure 62). Therefore, care must be exercised in choice of size and number of samples used to determine density. This problem is discussed in detail in Sections 13 to 15 of this chapter.

As was indicated in the statement at the beginning of this section, relative abundance is often a useful measure when density cannot be determined. The terms "abundant," "common," "rare," etc., are common, and are most useful when tied to something that is measured or estimated in a manner that makes comparison meaningful. Such population "indices," as might be imagined, are widely used not only with rapidly changing populations but with populations of larger animals and terrestrial plants, where it is imperative that a measure applicable to large areas be obtained without excessive expenditure of time and money. Percentage indices are widely used in the study of vegetation, and specially defined terms have come into general use, for example: Frequency = per cent of sample plots in which the species occurs. Abundance = per cent of individuals in a sample. Cover = per cent of ground surface covered as determined by projection of areal parts. Other such indices are discussed in Chapter 11. One should be careful not to confuse indices of relative abundance with true density, which is always in terms of a definite amount of space. Relating the indices of relative abundance to actual abundance on an area basis is an important job that generally is yet to be done.

Many different techniques for measuring population density have been tried, and methodology comprises an important field of research in itself. There would be little point in going into detail on methods here, because the man in the field will generally find that he will first have to review the original literature applying to his situation and then develop modifications and improvements of existing methods to fit his specific case. It can be pointed out, however, that methods fall into several broad categories: (1)

total counts, sometimes possible with large or conspicuous organisms or with those which aggregate into colonies; (2) sampling methods (involving plots, quadrats, transects, or sampling devices of various sorts), by necessity often the most widely used (see Sections 13 to 15); (3) marking-recapture methods (for animals), in which a sample of population is captured, marked, and released, and proportion of marked individuals in a later sample used to determine total populations* (with proper precautions and a knowledge of life history and population attributes this can be a very good method); (4) indirect methods, involving "signs"; hunting, fishing, and trapping take; food or oxygen consumption, etc.

Examples

Samples of observed range in densities of selected populations (and various units of measurement) listed in Table 11 illustrate many of the points discussed and give some idea of the order of magnitude to be expected in dealing with different kinds of organisms. Also, some examples of relative abundance indices are given. These data are largely self-explanatory; only a few spot comments need be made. Example I-3 illustrates "specific density," which is more meaningful than "crude density" in cases where the habitat of the organism in question is specialized or sufficiently well known to be delimited from unsuitable areas. Example II-2 illustrates the tendency (by no means universal) for mixed populations to be larger in areas of mixed habitat; this is because there are generally more niches available in mixed habitat than in an equal area comprising uniform habitats. Examples II-1 and 3 call attention to the tremendous number of organisms that exist in soil and water. (See also Tables 21, 22 in Chapter 11.) Example III provides another illustration of operation of food chain and ecological pyramid principles. Bass and other game fish are higher on the pyramid than "rough fish," and biomass density is correspondingly less. Example V illustrates how density in terms of individuals alone may be misleading when individual size varies greatly.

In the case of measures of relative abundance, it is highly de-

---

* If 100 individuals were marked and released and 10 out of a second sample of 100 were found to be marked, then population would be figured as follows: $100/P = 10/100$, or $P = 1000$.

sirable to have more than one "index" applicable to the same population as shown in example VI-2, where combination of two indices gives a better picture of the relative importance of species in a grassland than does either index alone. Experimentation with various combinations of indices is an active field of interest at the present time. When seasonal or annual changes are being investigated, it is also desirable to have more than one measure of relative abundance, as illustrated by VI-3. One is inclined to put more confidence in such measures of relative abundance if several indices all show the same trend.

All in all, the subject of numbers is a fascinating one. The examples shown in Table 11, it is hoped, will whet the appetite of the reader for further explorations in this direction.

Table 11. *Examples of population densities, their variation in time, and different units of measurement*

I. Species populations, individuals per unit area; with indication of variation in density found in long-range intensive studies in restricted geographical areas:

    1. Loblolly pine (*Pinus taeda*), Piedmont, North Carolina (data from Oosting, 1942).

Age of stand in years	11	22	31	34	42	75
Density, trees per 100 m.^{2}	27	18	15	12	12	3

    2. Bob-white quail, fall population density in two regions.

	Wisconsin; at edge of range, unfavorable winter climate (Data from Errington, 1945)	*Southern Georgia estates; favorable climate (Data from Stoddard, 1932)*
Observed range of density over a period of years	2.7 to 9.6 per 100 acres	20 to 100 per 100 acres

    3. Specific density, knapweed gallfly (*Urophora jaceana*), at Madingley, England, peak season (July-August); number per square meter of knapweed (data from Varley, 1947).

	1934	*1935*	*1936*
Adult flies emerging	—	6.9	2.0
Larvae forming galls	43	147.6	28.0

II. Mixed populations, individuals per unit area or volume:

    1. Zooplankton (mostly copepods), various stations in western Atlantic from Tortugas to Long Island Sound (data from Riley, 1939).

        380 to 224,000 per cubic meter water

    2. Breeding birds in three biotic communities, United States (data from Hickey, 1943, Appendix B).

Table 11 *(continued)*

Community	Number areas censused	Population density, adults per 100 acres Average	Extremes
Grasslands (Central U. S.)	11	144	20– 591
Maple-beech and oak-hickory forests (Eastern U. S.)	10	465	232– 634
Diversified man-made habitats (campuses, estates, and parks) (East and Pacific Coast, U. S.)	11	827	140–2,020

3. Macroscopic soil invertebrates, Treelease Woods, Urbana, Illinois, samples at all seasons over a period of 6 years (data from Shelford, 1951).

50 to 2,200 per square meter

III. Mixed populations, biomass per unit area:

Fish in artificial ponds in Illinois (data from Thompson and Bennett, 1939). Fish groups arranged in approximate order of food chain relations with "rough fish" occupying the lowest trophic level and "game fish" the highest.

	Fish in pounds per acre Pond No. 1	Pond No. 2	Pond No. 3
Game and pan fish (bass, bluegills, etc.)	232	46	9
Catfish (bullheads and channel cats)	0	40	62
Forage fish (shiners, gizzard shad, etc.)	0	236	3
Rough fish (suckers, carp, etc.)	0	87	1,143
Totals	232	409	1,217

IV. Comparison of individual and biomass density where size of organism undergoes pronounced change with age:

Fingerling sockeye salmon in a British Columbia lake. The salmon hatch in streams and in April enter the lake, where they remain until mature. Note that between May and October the fish grew rapidly in size, with the result that biomass increased three times, even though the number of fish was greatly reduced. From October to the next April very little growth occurred, and continued death of fish reduced the total biomass. (Data from Ricker and Forester, 1948.)

	May	October	April
Individuals, thousands in the lake	4,000	500	250
Biomass, metric tons in the lake	1.0	3.3	2.0

V. Estimates of total population size of large areas:

1. World population of the gannet (*Sula bassana*), a large sea bird which nests in a few densely populated colonies on northern Atlantic shores of North America and Europe (data from Fisher and Vevers, 1944).

Date	Total number breeding individuals
1834	334,000
1894 (after considerable persecution by man)	106,000
1939 (following protection by man)	165,600±9,500

Table 11.   (*continued*)

2. Estimated number of pronghorn antelope on approximately 50,000 square miles of the desert plains region at junction of California, Nevada, Oregon, and Idaho, determined by aerial censuses made from slow, low-flying planes. Number in large herds determined from enlarged aerial photographs. (Data from Springer, 1950.)

   Total in 1949 29,940

VI. Example of indices of relative abundance:

1. Colombia (South America) jungle mosquitoes. See Figure 52 (page 191).

2. Relative importance of species of grasses and forbs in a Texas grassland (data from Dyksterhuis, 1946).

Species	Cover (%)	Frequency (%)	Cover times frequency
Andropogon scoparius	64.66	100	64.66
Perennial forbs	8.21	100	8.21
Bouteloua curtipendula	8.11	100	8.11
Sorghastrum nutans	5.12	83	4.25
Sporobolus asper	2.10	92	1.93
Bouteloua hirsuta	2.50	67	1.68
Annual forbs	2.30	50	1.15
Andropogon furcatus	2.20	50	1.10
Stipa leucotricha	0.70	42	0.29

3. Relative abundance of mourning doves, as determined by two different seasonal indices, in southeastern states (unpublished data, U. S. Fish and Wildlife Service, noted with permission).

	1950	1951
Breeding season index. Average number doves calling per 20-mile sample route (3 minute listening station each mile in early morning)	15.65 ± 1.02	21.20 ± 1.03
Fall index. Doves killed by hunters, number per gun hour	1.44	1.55

3. Basic concepts regarding rates

Statement

Since a population is a changing entity, we are interested not only in its size and composition at any one moment, but also in how it is changing. A number of important population characteristics are concerned with rates. A rate is always obtained by dividing the change by the period of time elapsed during the change; it is the rapidity with which something changes with time. Thus, the number of miles traveled by a car per hour is the speed rate, and the number of births per year is the birth rate. The "per" means "divided by." For example, the growth rate of a population is the number of organisms added to the population per time and

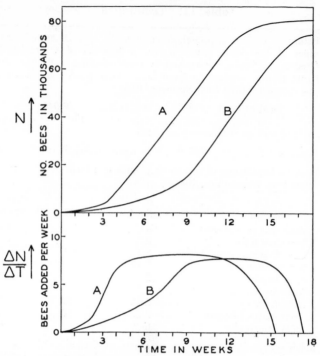

Figure 41. A population growth curve (upper) and growth rate curve (lower) for two bee colonies in the same apiary. A—Italian bees; B—Cyprian bees. (Redrawn from Bodenheimer, 1937.)

is obtained by dividing the population increase by the time elapsed.

If time is plotted on the horizontal axis (x-axis, or abscissa) and the number of organisms on the vertical axis (y-axis, or ordinate) of a graph, a population growth curve is obtained. In Figure 41, growth curves for colonies of two kinds of honeybees raised in the same apiary are shown. Also, the approximate growth rate at weekly intervals is plotted against time. Note that growth rate increases and decreases as the slope of the growth curve increases and decreases. Population B's growth rate is considerably less than A's during the first eight weeks or so, but eventually population B grows as rapidly as A. Not only do population growth curves provide a means of summarizing time phenomena, but the type of curve may give hints as to the underlying processes controlling population changes. Certain types of processes give characteristic types of population curves. As we shall see in Section 8, S-shaped growth curves and "humped-backed" growth rate curves are often characteristic of populations in the pioneer stage.

For convenience, it is customary to abbreviate "the change in" something by writing the symbol Δ (delta) in front of the letter representing the thing changing. Thus, if N represents the number of organisms and t the time, then:

ΔN = the change in the number of organisms.

$\dfrac{\Delta N}{\Delta t}$ = the average rate of change in the number of organisms per (divided by, or with respect to) time. This is the growth rate.

$\dfrac{\dfrac{\Delta N}{\Delta t}}{N}$ or $\dfrac{\Delta N}{N\ \Delta t}$ = the average rate of change in the number of organisms per time per organism (the growth rate divided by the average number of organisms during the period of time). This is often called the per cent growth rate or the specific growth rate.

Often we are interested not only in the average rate over a period of time but in the theoretical instantaneous rate at particular times; in other words, the rate of change when Δt approaches zero. In the language of calculus, which is the branch of mathematics dealing (in part) with the study of rates, the letter d (for derivative) replaces the Δ when instantaneous rates are being considered. In this case the above notations become:

$\dfrac{dN}{dt}$ = the rate of change in the number of organisms per time at a particular instant.

$\dfrac{\dfrac{dN}{dt}}{N}$ = the rate of change in the number of organisms per time per individual at a particular instant.

In terms of the growth curve the slope (straight line tangent) at any point is the growth rate.

For the purposes of this book and for the usual purposes of measurement in ecology, the calculus notation is not necessary. Calculus formulations are mainly used in ecology in theoretical mathematical derivations by which the quantitative consequences of various assumptions are computed. In this and the next chapter we are interested in using simple mathematical models to illustrate principles and provide a more precise meaning to terms and concepts, leaving the derivation of models for advanced studies. For this reason we shall use the $\Delta N/\Delta t$ notation. The dN/dt notation can be substituted in any of the models, and this would be necessary in many types of actual mathematical manipulations.

Example

Suppose a population of 50 protozoa in a pool is increasing by division. Suppose the population of 50 has increased to 150 after an hour has passed. Then

ΔN (change in number) $= 100$

$\dfrac{\Delta N}{\Delta t}$ (average rate of change per time) $= 100$ per hour

$\dfrac{\dfrac{\Delta N}{\Delta t}}{N}$ (average rate of change per time per individual, or per cent growth rate) $= 2$ per hour per individual

The instantaneous rate, dN/dt, cannot be measured directly. We would need to know the type of population growth curve exhibited by the population and then calculate the instantaneous rate. We cannot attach a "speedometer" to a population and determine its instantaneous speed rate as we can with a car. An approximation could be obtained, of course, by making a census of the population at very short intervals. We would likely discover that the rate of growth varies from time to time, something that the value for the average rate gives no hint. In the above example, the per cent growth rate is in terms of the original population present at the beginning of the measurement (i.e., 50 protozoa). In other words the 50 protozoa gave rise in some manner or other to 2 additional protozoa for each of the 50 original ones. There are various ways in which this could come about; some individuals could have divided twice, some not at all and some could have disappeared from the population. Our measurement does not tell us just what happened, but we could theoretically calculate the possibilities. The per cent growth rate could also be expressed in terms of average population during the hour; assuming that this was 100, the per cent growth rate would be 1. While this form of expression has theoretical usefulness, the average density would often be difficult to determine. Consequently, in our consideration of rate functions we shall think in terms of the initial density.

4. Natality

Statement

Natality is the inherent ability of a population to increase. Natality rate is equivalent to the "birth rate" in the terminology of human population study (demography); in fact, it is simply a broader term covering the production of new individuals of any organism whether such new individuals are "born," "hatched," "germinated," "arise by division," or what not. *Maximum* (some-

times called absolute or physiological) *natality* is the theoretical
maximum production of new individuals under ideal conditions
(i.e., no ecological limiting factors, reproduction being limited
only by physiological factors); it is a constant for a given population. *Ecological* or *realized natality* (or just plain "natality," without qualifying adjective) refers to population increase under an
actual or specific environmental condition. It is not a constant for
a population but may vary with the size and composition of the
population and the physical environmental conditions. Natality is
generally expressed as a rate determined by dividing the number
of new individuals produced by time ($\Delta N_n/\Delta t$, the absolute natality rate) or as the number of new individuals per unit of time per
unit of population [$(\Delta N_n/\Delta t)/N$, the per cent natality rate].

Explanation

Natality can be measured and expressed in a number of ways.
Following the notation in the preceding section we have:

$$\Delta N_n = natality, -production\,of\,new\,individuals\,in\,the\,population. \quad (1)$$

$$\frac{\Delta N_n}{\Delta t} = B \text{ or natality rate per unit time.} \quad (2)$$

$$\frac{\Delta N_n}{N\Delta t} = b \text{ or natality rate per unit time per individual.} \quad (3)$$

N may represent the total population or only the reproductive part
of the population. With higher organisms, for example, it is customary to express natality rate per female. With all the different
"kinds" of birth rates it is clear that confusion can easily result unless the concept used is clearly defined, preferably by using standard mathematical notations as above. Which concept is used
will depend on the available data and the type of comparisons or
predictions which one wishes to make.

Although the same notations may be used in referring to natality
rate and population growth rate, the two are not the same because
ΔN represents somewhat different quantities in the two cases.
With respect to natality, ΔN_n represents *new individuals* added to
the population. Natality rate is zero, or always positive. With respect to growth rate ΔN represents *the net increase or decrease* in
the population, which is the result not only of natality but of
mortality, emigration, immigration, etc. Growth rate may be
either negative or positive, since the population may be either in-

creasing or decreasing. Population growth rate will be considered in Sections 7 and 8.

Maximum natality, as indicated in the above statement, is the theoretical upper limit which the population, or the reproductive portion of the population, would be capable of producing under ideal conditions. As might be imagined, it is difficult to determine but is of interest for two reasons. (1) It provides a yardstick for comparison with the realized natality. Thus, a statement that natality of a population of mice was 6 young per female per year would mean more if it was known to what extent this might be higher if conditions were less limiting. (2) Being a constant, maximum natality is useful in setting up equations to determine or to predict the rate of increase in a population, as we shall see in subsequent sections. For practical purposes maximum natality can be approximated by experimental methods. For example, the highest average seed production achieved in a series of experiments with alfalfa, in which the most favorable known conditions of moisture, temperature, and fertilizer were combined, could be taken as maximum natality for that particular population. Another method of establishing a base is to observe the reproductive rate of a population when it is placed in a favorable environment, or when major limiting factors are temporarily nonoperative. If a small group of paramecia, for example, is placed in a new batch of favorable media, the maximum reproductive rate achieved would be a good measure of maximum natality rate. This method can often be used in the field, if the ecologist is alert, since in nature there are often fortuitous circumstances when limiting factors are temporarily relaxed. As we shall point out later, many natural populations regularly exhibit maximum natality for brief seasonal or other periods. Reproductive performance during such favorable periods would be a practical approximation of maximum natality. *Since the value of maximum natality concept lies in its use as a constant against which variable observed natalities may be compared, any reasonable estimate could be used so long as conditions under which it was made are defined.*

It should be repeated that natality, and the other concepts discussed in this section, refer to the population and not to isolated individuals. The average reproductive capacity should be taken as the measure of natality, and not the capacity of the most productive or least productive individual. It is well known that occasional individuals in a population will exhibit unusual reproductive rates, but the performance of such individuals would not be a fair measure of the maximum possibilities of the population as a whole. Furthermore, in some populations the highest reproductive rate may occur when the population density is low, but in others —some of the higher vertebrates with complicated reproductive patterns, for example—the highest rate may occur when the population is medium sized or even relatively large (Allee effect, see Section 14 and Figure 64). Thus, the best estimate of the maximum natality should be made not only when physical factors are not limiting but also when population size is optimum. We shall see more about this business of a population acting as a limiting factor on itself in the next few sections.

Examples

In Table 12 two examples are worked out, one from field and one from laboratory data, to illustrate concepts of maximum-realized natality and absolute-specific natality rate. Maximum natality is based on somewhat arbitrary conditions, as must always be the case, but these conditions are clearly defined in the table. The ecological natalities are actual measurements. From these examples we see that the insect considered here has an enormously greater natality than does the vertebrate, but the latter realizes a greater percentage of its potential under the conditions listed. For comparisons, it is more satisfactory to use the specific rate (i.e., so many eggs, young, etc., per female per time unit). In the case of the bluebird, the exact number of females in the population was not known so that rate calculations shown in Part III of the table are approximations. It should also be pointed out that bluebird females may actually lay more than 15 eggs per season, if one or more of her sets are destroyed. Under ideal conditions, however, no eggs would be lost and three broods of 5 each would theoretically be all that a female could physiologically manage during a season. The bluebird data also demonstrate a striking seasonal variation in natality; fewer eggs are laid in late broods and more of the eggs laid are infertile, fail to hatch, or are lost in other ways. Seasonal variation in natality is almost a universal phenomenon, as is also variation due to differences in the age and sex distribution in the population.

One problem in comparing the natality of different species populations rests in the difficulty of measuring natality at comparable stages in the life history; this is especially true of organisms such as insects and birds which have complicated life his-

Table 12. *Comparison of maximum and realized natality of two species*

Expressed as natality rate per time (B) and natality rate per time per female (b)

I. Field population of bluebirds (*Sialia sialis*) in city park, Nashville, Tenn., 1938 (from Laskey, 1939):

	Max. natality Total eggs laid	Ecological or realized natality rate			
		Eggs produced		Young fledged	
		No.	% max.	No.	% max.
1st brood	170[1]	170	100	123	72
2nd brood	175[1]	163	93	90	51
3rd brood	165[1]	122	74	52	32
Total for year	510[1]	455	89	265	52

[1] Calculated by multiplying 5 times number nests attempted; five eggs per set is average number which the population is able to produce in the most favorable part of the season.

II. Laboratory population of flour beetles (*Tribolium confusum*), 18 pairs for 60 days (approx. one generation) (from Park, 1934):

	Max. natality Total eggs laid	Ecological or realized natality rate			
		Eggs produced		Larvae produced	
		No.	% max.	No.	% max.
Fresh flour	11,988[1]	2,617	22	773	6
Old or "conditioned" flour[2]	11,988[1]	839	7	205	2

[1] Determined by average rate of 11.1 eggs per female per day which is average of two 60 day cultures held under optimum conditions (see Table 4, in Park, Ginsburg, and Horwitz, 1945).

[2] Flour in which a previous culture has been living; contains metabolic or "waste products." This situation might be similar to one in nature where the organism does not continually have the benefit of "unused" environment.

III. Natality of bluebird and flour beetle populations expressed as specific rates ($\Delta N_n / N \Delta t$):

Bluebird: Maximum specific natality rate eggs per female per year	Realized specific natality per female	
	Eggs	Fledged young
15	13.4	7.8

Flour beetle: Maximum natality rate eggs per female per day		Realized natality per female	
		Eggs	Larvae
Fresh flour	11.1	2.40	0.61
Condition flour	11.1	0.73	0.19

tories. Thus, in one case the number of eggs might be known whereas in another case only the number of larvae or independent young could be determined. In comparing one species and population with another, it is, therefore, important to be sure there is a comparable basis.

5. Mortality

Statement

Mortality refers to death of individuals in the population. It is more or less the antithesis of natality with some parallel subconcepts. Mortality rate is equivalent to "death rate" in human demography. Like natality, mortality may be expressed as the number of individuals dying in a given period (deaths per time), or as a specific rate in terms of the percentage of the total population or any part thereof. *Ecological or realized mortality*—the loss of individuals under a given environmental condition—is, like ecological natality, not a constant but varies with population and environmental conditions. There is a theoretical *minimum mortality*, a constant for a population, which represents the loss under ideal or nonlimiting conditions. That is, even under the best conditions individuals would die of "old age" determined by their *physiological longevity* which, of course, is often far greater than the average *ecological longevity*.

Explanation and examples

Natality and mortality are complex population characteristics which may be expressed in a number of ways. To prevent confusion, therefore, the general term "mortality" needs to be qualified and, wherever possible, expressed by definite mathematical symbols, as indicated in previous sections. Generally, *specific mortality* is expressed as a percentage of the initial population dying within a given time.* Since we are often more interested in organisms that survive than in those that do not, it is often more meaningful to express mortality in terms of the reciprocal survival rate. As with natality, both the minimum mortality rate (theoretical constant) and the actual or ecological mortality rate (variable) are of interest, the former to serve as a base or "measuring stick" for comparisons. Since even under ideal conditions individuals of any population die of "old age," there is a minimum mortality which would occur under the best possible conditions that could be devised, and this would be determined by the average physiological longevity of the individuals. In most populations in nature the average longevity is far less than the physiologically inherent life span, and, therefore, actual mortality rates are far greater than the minimum. However, in some populations or for brief periods in others, mortality may, for all practical purposes, reach a minimum, and thus provide opportunity for practical measurement under population conditions.

* As with other rates we have been discussing, mortality rate can be expressed as a per cent of average population instead of the initial population; this would be of interest in situations where density changed greatly during the period of measurement.

Table 13.   *Life table for the Dall Mountain sheep (Ovis D. Dalli)**
Based on known age at death of 608 sheep dying before 1937 (both sexes combined).† Mean length of life 7.09 years.

x	x'	d_x	l_x	$1000\,q_x$	e_x
Age (Years)	Age as per cent deviation from mean length of life	Number dying in age interval out of 1000 born	Number surviving at beginning of age interval out of 1000 born	Mortality rate per thousand alive at beginning of age interval	Expectation of life, or mean life-time remaining to those attaining age interval (years)
0–0.5	−100	54	1000	54.0	7.06
0.5–1	−93.0	145	946	153.0	—
1–2	−85.9	12	801	15.0	7.7
2–3	−71.8	13	789	16.5	6.8
3–4	−57.7	12	776	15.5	5.9
4–5	−43.5	30	764	39.3	5.0
5–6	−29.5	46	734	62.6	4.2
6–7	−15.4	48	688	69.9	3.4
7–8	−1.1	69	640	108.0	2.6
8–9	+13.0	132	571	231.0	1.9
9–10	+27.0	187	439	426.0	1.3
10–11	+41.0	156	252	619.0	0.9
11–12	+55.0	90	96	937.0	0.6
12–13	+69.0	3	6	500.0	1.2
13–14	+84.0	3	3	1000	0.7

* From Deevey (1947); data from Murie (1944).
† A small number of skulls without horns, but judged by their osteology to belong to sheep nine years old or older, have been apportioned *pro rata* among the older age classes.

Since mortality varies greatly with age, especially in the higher organisms, specific mortalities at as many different ages or life history stages as possible are of great interest inasmuch as they enable us to determine the forces underlying the crude, overall population mortality. A complete picture of mortality in a population is given in a systematic way by the *life table*, a statistical device developed by students of human populations. Raymond Pearl first introduced the life table into general biology by applying it to data obtained from laboratory studies of the fruit fly, *Drosophila* (Pearl and Parker, 1921). Deevey (1947) has assembled data for the construction of life tables for a number of natural populations, ranging from rotifers to mountain sheep. As a result of improved methods of marking and censusing of natural populations, it is often possible to determine at regular intervals the individuals surviving out of an initial population of known size. Such data are then comparable with data obtained from laboratory populations living in a simplified environment. Approximate life tables may also be constructed for natural populations if the age at death is known or if the age structure (that is, proportion of different ages) can be determined at intervals.

As an example, let us take the Dall mountain sheep (Table 13). The age of these sheep can be determined from the horns. When a sheep is killed by a wolf or dies for any other reason, its horns remain preserved for a long period. Adolph Murie spent several years in intensive field study of the relation between wolves and mountain sheep in Mt. McKinley National Park, Alaska. During this period he picked up a large series of horns, thus providing admirable data on the age at which sheep die in an environment subject to all the natural hazards, including wolf predation (but not including predation by man, as sheep were not hunted in the McKinley National Park). As shown in Table 13, the life table consists of several columns, headed by standard notations, giving l_x the number of individuals out of a given population (1,000 or any other convenient number) which survive after regular time intervals (day, month, year, etc.—see column x); (d_x) the number dying during successive time intervals; (q_x) the death or mortality rate during successive intervals (in terms of initial population at beginning of period); and (e_x) the life expectancy at the end of each interval. As may be seen from Table 13, the average age is better than seven years, and if a sheep can survive the first year

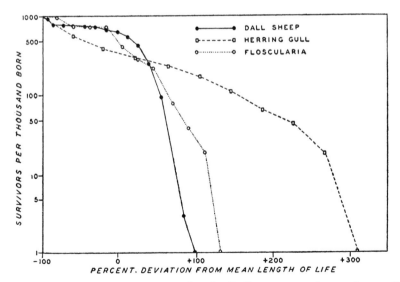

Figure 42. Survivorship curves for the Dall mountain sheep, the sessile rotifer (*Floscularia conifera*) and the herring gull, age being expressed as percentage deviation from the mean length of life. (After Deevey, 1947.)

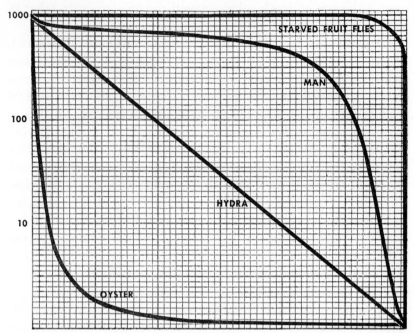

Figure 43. Several types of survivorship curves plotted on the basis of survivors per thousand log scale (vertical coordinate) and age in relative units of mean life span (horizontal coordinate). (After Deevey, 1950.)

or so, its chances of survival are good until relative old age, despite the abundance of wolves and the other vicissitudes of the environment.

Curves plotted from life-table data may be very instructive. When data from column l_x are plotted with the time interval on the horizontal coordinate and the number of survivors on the vertical coordinate, the resulting curve is called a *survivorship curve*. If a semilogarithmic plot is used (as in Figure 42), with the time interval on the horizontal coordinate expressed as a percentage of the mean length of life (see column x^1, Table 13), species of widely different life spans may be compared. Furthermore, a straight line on a semilogarithmic plot indicates a constant specific rate of survival. In Figure 42 the survivorship curve for the mountain sheep is highly convex. A rather different situation is seen in the case of the herring gull, for which a survivorship curve is also plotted. Here we see that mean length of life is short in proportion to maximum length. The survival rate in the gull is more nearly constant for middle age groups.

The three basic types of survivorship curves are shown in Figure 43. If the average physiological longevity were to be realized, the curve would be highly convex and sharp-angled, all individuals living out their inherited life span and dying more or less all at once. A close approach to this has been obtained by Pearl with "starved fruit flies." That is, when flies of a genetically homozygous strain were given no food on emerging from the pupa, they all lived out their inherited span and all died within a very short time (Fig. 43). If the specific mortality rate at all ages is constant, the survivorship curve will be a straight, diagonal line (on semi-log plot), as shown for hydra (Fig. 43). Finally, a concave curve indicates a high mortality during the young stages. In the oyster, for example, mortality is extremely high during the free-swimming larval stage; once the individual is attached to a favorable substrate, the life expectancy improves considerably!

The shape of the survivorship curve may vary with the density of the population, as shown in Figure 44. Data on age structure were used by Taber and Dasmann (1957) to construct the curves for two stable deer populations living in the chaparral region of California. As may be seen in the figure, the survivorship curve

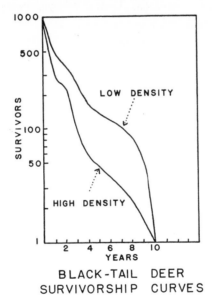

BLACK-TAIL   DEER
SURVIVORSHIP   CURVES

Figure 44. Survivorship curves for two deer stable populations living in the chaparral region of California. The high density population (about 64 deer per square mile) is in a managed area where an open shrub and herbaceous cover is maintained by controlled burning, thus providing a greater quantity of browse in the form of new growth. The low density population (about 27/sq. mi.) is in an unmanaged area of old bushes unburned for 10 years. Recently burned areas may support up to 86 deer/sq. mi. but the population is unstable and hence survivorship curves can not be constructed from age distribution data. (After Taber and Dasmann, 1957.)

of the denser population is quite concave. In other words, deer living in the managed area, where the food supply was increased by controlled burning, have a shorter life expectancy than deer in the unmanaged area, presumedly because of increased hunting pressure, intraspecific competition, etc. From the viewpoint of the hunter, the managed area is most favorable, but from the viewpoint of the individual deer, the less crowded area offers a better chance for a long life. History records a number of parallels to this situation in human populations where high density was not always favorable to the individual.

Civilized man has greatly increased his own "ecological" longevity as a result of modern medical knowledge, better nutrition, etc., so that man's curve (Fig. 43) approaches the sharp-angled minimum mortality curve. However, man apparently has not increased his maximum or "physiological" longevity, since no more people live now to be 100 years old than did in past centuries. Most animal populations in nature will probably exhibit a survivorship curve which is moderately concave, somewhere between the curves of the oyster and the hydra, whereas most plant populations probably would plot out rather nearer the oyster type curve, although few data are available.

From this brief discussion it is evident that survivorship curves are of great value in understanding the dynamics of the population. Such curves tell us at what age periods the organism is most vulnerable; reducing or increasing the mortality during these critical periods might have marked effects on the population and on its future size. For wild organisms one difficulty is the lack of knowledge of the survival of the young stages; ecologists need to study the problems of youth in nature!

Where a large proportion of the mortality occurs in successive, relatively brief early life history stages of varying lengths, as in many birds and insects, the life-table tabulation, with its equal time intervals, is not always satisfactory. In such cases survival or mortality percentages can be determined for the critical stages irrespective of their time lengths. For ruffed grouse in New York state, for example, the average survival is 50 per cent in the egg stage and 37 per cent from hatching to fall hunting season four months later (Bump, Darrow, Edminster, and Crissey, 1947). In other words, out of every 100 eggs, 50 will hatch on the average. Of these, 37 per cent or only about 19 birds will be alive after four months. The average 19 per cent survival or 81 per cent mortality provides a good index for comparing grouse seasons and regions where the fall hunting population is of special interest.

It is self-evident that neither population size nor trend (whether increase or decrease) to be expected can be determined from knowledge of mortality alone. Natality and other population characteristics must also be considered. On the basis of studies so far made, however, many ecologists are inclined to believe that for many important economic species mortality is generally more variable and more affected by various environmental changes within and outside the population than is natality. Consequently, mortality plays a leading role in population control, and systematic study of this factor becomes very important to the population ecologist.

6. Population age distribution

Statement

Age distribution is an important population characteristic which influences both natality and mortality. Mortality usually varies with age, and reproduction is quite often restricted to certain age groups, for example, the middle age groups in the higher animals and plants. Consequently, the ratio of the various age groups in a population determines the current reproductive status of the population and indicates what may be expected in the future. Usually a rapidly expanding population will contain a large proportion of young individuals, a stationary population a more even distribution of age classes, and a declining population a large proportion of old individuals. However, a population may pass through changes in age structure without changing in size. There is evidence that populations have a "normal" or stable age distribution toward which actual age distributions are tending. Once a stable age distribution is achieved, unusual increases in natality or mortality result in temporary changes, with spontaneous return to the stable situation.

Explanation

In so far as the population is concerned, there are three ecological ages, which have been listed by Bodenheimer (1938) as *prereproductive, reproductive,* and *postreproductive.* The relative duration of these ages in proportion to the life span varies greatly with different organisms. In modern man, the three "ages" are relatively equal in length, about a third of his life falling in each class. Primitive man, by comparison, had a much shorter post-reproductive period. Many plants and animals have a very long prereproductive period. Some animals, notably insects, have extremely long prereproductive periods, a very short reproductive period, and no postreproductive period. The May fly (or *Ephe-meridae*) and the seventeen-year locust are classic examples. The former requires from one to several years to develop in the larval stage in the water and lives but a few days as an adult; the latter has an extremely long developmental history (not necessarily seventeen years, however), with adult life lasting less than a single season. It is obvious, therefore, that the duration of the ecological ages needs to be considered in interpreting data on age distribution.

Lotka (1925) has shown on theoretical grounds that a population tends to develop a stable age distribution, that is, a more or less constant proportion of individuals of different ages, and that if this stable situation is disrupted by temporary changes in the environment or by temporary influx from or egress to another population, the age distribution will tend to return to the previous situation upon restoration of normal conditions. More permanent changes, of course, would result in development of a new stable distribution. A direct quotation from Lotka is perhaps the best way to clarify the important concept of stable age distribution: ". . . the force of mortality varies very decidedly with age, and it might therefore be supposed that any discussion of the rate of increase of a population of organisms must fully take into account the age distribution. This supposition, however, involves an assumption, namely, the assumption that age distribution itself is variable. Now in point of fact, age distribution is indeed variable, but only within certain restricted limits. Certain age distributions will practically never occur, and if by arbitrary interference or by a catastrophe of nature, some altogether unusual form were impressed upon the age distribution of an isolated population, the irregularities would tend shortly to become smoothed over. There is, in fact, a certain stable type of age distribution about which the actual age distribution varies and toward which it returns if through any agency disturbed therefrom. The form of this distribution in an isolated population (i.e., with immigration and emigration negligible) is easily deduced. . . ." The mathematical proof of this parameter and the method of calculating the theoretical stable age distribution is beyond the scope of this presentation (see Lotka, 1925, Chapter IX, pages 110–115). Suffice it to say that life-table data and knowledge of the specific growth rate (see Sections 2 and 7) are needed to determine the stable age distribution.

The idea of a stable age distribution is an important one. Again, as in the case of the maximum natality constant, it furnishes a base for evaluating actual age distributions as they may occur. It is one more constant that may help us untangle the seemingly bewildering array of variables that occur in nature. The whole theory of a population, of course, is that it is a real biological unit with definite biological constants and definite limits to variations that may occur around or away from these constants.

Examples

A convenient way to picture age distribution in a population is to arrange the data in the form of a polygon or age pyramid (not to be confused with the ecological pyramids discussed in Chapter 3), the number of individuals or the percentage in the different age classes being shown by the relative widths of successive horizontal bars. The upper pyramids in Figure 45 illustrate three hypothetical cases: (left) a pyramid with broad base, indicating a high percentage of young individuals; (middle) a bell-shaped polygon, indicating a moderate proportion of young to old; and (right) an urn-shaped figure, indicating a low percentage of young individuals. The latter would generally be characteristic of a senile or declining population. The other pyramids in Figure 45 are based on actual and theoretical populations. Those in the middle of the figure show age distribution of a population of meadow voles (left) under conditions of maximum rate of population increase with a stable age distribution, and (right) same population with natality equaling mortality and rate of increase equaling zero. The rapidly growing population has the much greater proportion of young individuals.

In many warm-blooded vertebrates often only two age classes can be distinguished during the non-breeding season—immatures and adults. Even so, age-distribution data are instructive. In game and fur-bearing vertebrates, the ratio of first year animals to older animals determined during the season of harvest (fall or winter) may aid in estimating natality and survival of young from the previous breeding season and thus provide an index to the popu-

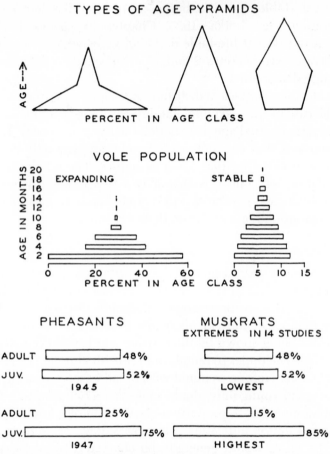

Figure 45. Age pyramids. Upper: Three types of age pyramids representing a large, moderate, and small percentage of young individuals in the population. Middle: Age pyramids for laboratory populations of the vole, *Microtus agrestis*, (left) when expanding at an exponential rate in an unlimited environment, and (right) when birth rates and death rates are equal (data from Leslie and Ransom, 1940). Lower: Extremes in juvenile-adult ratios in pheasants in North Dakota (data from Kimball, 1948) and in muskrats in eastern United States (data from Petrides, 1950).

lation trends. The diagrams at the lower left in Figure 45 show the age distribution of ring-necked pheasants in the Dakotas for two specific years. In 1945 the pheasant population was declining. Since adult mortality was not known to have been excessive, the low proportion of juveniles definitely indicated a poor production and/or survival of young hatched during the preceding breeding season. In 1947, the ratio of juvenile birds was much higher. If the latter pattern continued and adult mortality did not increase, it would be safe to predict a rising population level. The diagrams at the lower right in Figure 45 show the highest and lowest ratio of immature to adult muskrats found in studies of 14 different populations scattered in seven states and representing a span of years (data from Petrides, 1950). Thus we see that muskrat popu-

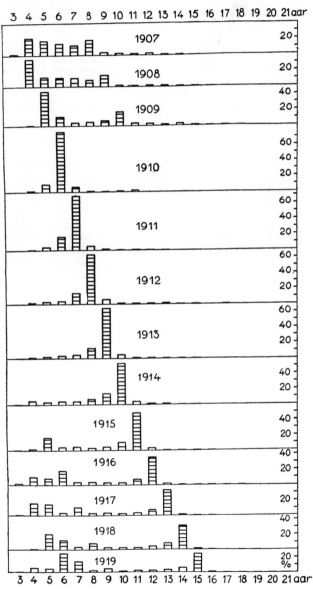

Figure 46. Age distribution in the commercial catch of herring in the North Sea between 1907 and 1919. The 1904 year class was very large and dominated the population for many years. (After Hjort, 1926.)

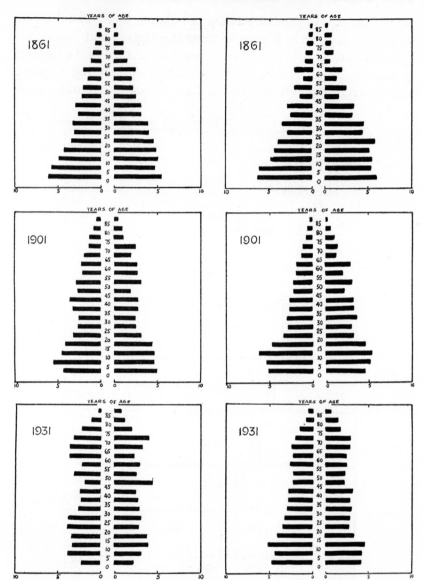

Figure 47. Age pyramids for man in two localities in Scotland. Series at the left is for a parish with top-heavy age structure by 1931 in a deteriorated habitat. Series at right is for a population in a somewhat healthier environment. Age classes have been reduced to percentage of total population, with males represented at left and females at right of each pyramid. (After Darling, 1951.)

lations at season of trapping varied from 52 to 85 per cent young of the year. The highest figure, 85 per cent, occurred in a population which had been heavily trapped for the previous few years;

reduction in total population in this manner had apparently resulted in increased natality for those individuals surviving. Thus,
as Lotka would say, the population was "spontaneously" returning
to a more stable age distribution which would presumedly lie
somewhere between the extremes shown.

Fish are good forms for the study of age distribution, because
the age of individuals can often be determined from growth rings
on the scales or other hard parts. For the herring of the North Sea
it has been determined that the scale method is reliable. Figure 46
shows the percentage of the total commercial catch of herring
belonging to different year classes (horizontal axis) for a series
of years (from Hjort, 1926). Since young fish are not taken in the
commercial nets, only fish older than 5 or 6 years are adequately
sampled. Despite the fact that the number of young fish was not
known, it is evident from the graph that there was an extremely
successful hatch and survival in 1904. Fish of this year dominated
the population until 1918 when, at 14 years old, they still out-
numbered fish in younger age groups! This phenomenon of a
"dominant age class" has been repeatedly observed in fish populations which have a very high potential natality rate. When a
large year class occurs, reproduction is suppressed for the next
several years. Fishery ecologists are currently trying to find out
what environmental conditions result in the unusual survival
which occurs every now and then.

As final examples, Figure 47 shows a series of interesting age
pyramids for human populations in two localities in Scotland. Both
populations in 1861 were young and vigorous, and by 1901 they
had assumed an age distribution of a stationary population. By
1931 one population had assumed a top-heavy age structure (relatively few children, large proportion of old people) as a result of
a deteriorated habitat. These figures are interesting, also, in that
they show how sex distribution can be pictured along with age
distribution.

7. Optimum rates of natural increase and concept of biotic potential and environmental resistance

Statement

When the environment is unlimited (space, food, other organisms not exerting a limiting effect), the per cent growth rate (i.e.,
the population growth rate per individual) becomes constant and

maximum for the existing microclimatic conditions. The value of the growth rate under these favorable population conditions is maximal, is characteristic of a particular population age structure, and is a single index of the inherent power of a population to grow. It may be designated by the symbol r, which is the exponent in the equation for population growth in an *unlimited environment* under specified physical conditions:

$$\frac{\Delta N}{\Delta t} = rN; \quad r = \frac{\frac{\Delta N}{\Delta t}}{N} \quad \text{(in an unlimited environment)}$$

for short intervals of time, or for cumulative effects over longer periods of time (the exponential integrated form follows automatically from the short time rate form by calculus manipulation):

$$N_t = N_o e^{rt}$$

N_o represents the number at time zero, N_t the number at time t and e the base of natural logarithms. The index r is actually the difference between the instantaneous specific natality rate (i.e., rate per time per individual) and the instantaneous specific death rate, and may thus be simply expressed:

$$r = b - d$$

The overall population growth rate under unlimited environmental conditions (r) depends on the age composition and the specific growth rates due to reproduction of component age groups. Thus, there may be several values of r for a species depending upon population structure. When a stationary and stable age distribution exists, the specific growth rate is called the *intrinsic rate of natural increase* or r_i. The maximum value of r is often called by the less specific but widely used expression *biotic potential,* or reproductive potential. The difference between the maximum r or biotic potential and the rate of increase which occurs in an actual laboratory or field condition is often taken as a measure of the *environmental resistance,* which is the sum total of environmental limiting factors which prevent the biotic potential from being realized.

Explanation

We have now come to the point where we wish to put together natality, mortality, and age distribution—each important but each admittedly incapable of telling us very much by itself—and come out with what we really want to know, namely, how is the population growing as a whole and what would it do if conditions were different, and what is its best possible performance against which we may judge its everyday performances? Chapman (1928) proposed the term *biotic potential* to designate maximum reproductive power. He defined it as "the inherent property of an organism to reproduce, to survive, i.e., to increase in numbers. It is sort of the algebraic sum of the number of young produced at each reproduction, the number of reproductions in a given period of time, the sex ratio and their general ability to survive under given physical conditions." The concept of biotic potential, or *reproductive potential*, suggested by some as more descriptive (see Graham, 1952), has gained wide usage. However, as might be imagined from the very generalized definition given above, biotic potential came to mean different things to different people. To some it came to mean a sort of nebulous reproductive power lurking in the population, terrible to behold, but fortunately never allowed to come forth because of the forthright action of the environment (i.e., "if unchecked the descendants of a pair of flies would weigh more than the earth in a few years"). To others it came to mean simply and more concretely the maximum number of eggs, seeds, spores, etc., the most fecund individual was known to produce, despite the fact that this would have little meaning in the population sense in most cases, since most populations do not contain individuals all of which are continually capable of peak production.

It remained for Lotka (1925), Dublin and Lotka (1925), Leslie and Ranson (1940), Birch (1948), and others to translate the rather broad idea of biotic potential into mathematical terms that can be understood in any language (with, sometimes, the help of a good mathematician!). Birch (1948) expressed it well when he said: "If the 'biotic potential' of Chapman is to be given quantitative expression in a single index, the parameter r_i would seem to be the best measure to adopt since it gives the intrinsic capacity of the animal to increase in an unlimited environment."

At this point the reader may well raise the question: How can there possibly be a single index to reproductive potential when natality and mortality vary so much with different-age individuals? The single index concept stands or falls on two assumptions, (1) that average natality and mortality remain the same for any specific age group when environmental conditions are optimum, and (2) that a population with constant age schedules of natality and mortality in an unlimited environment assumes a fixed age distribution, as was explained in the previous section. At the moment these assumptions seem well grounded, so, until someone proves them wrong, we may play with the intriguing idea of a single index representing the inherent power of increase and the ultimate biotic potential.

The question that now arises is: What kind of data do we need to work out such an index as r or r_i, and can we apply this concept to natural populations, or is it only good for highly simplified laboratory populations? Although natural populations must be approached with caution, if we can estimate natality, the essential data needed to calculate r are found in the life table. As we have seen, at least approximate life tables may be constructed for such very wild populations as mountain sheep living in rugged Alaska country.

Environmental resistance is another very useful concept first proposed by Chapman. It represents the difference between the potential ability of a population to increase and the actual observed performance. If the biotic potential can be nailed down as a specific quantity, then differences between biotic potential or maximum r and the observed rate of increase could be considered a measure of the environmental resistance, since failure of the population to measure up would be the result of non-optimum factors in the environment decreasing natality or increasing mortality somewhere along the line. In terms of our models, environmental resistance can be indicated by adding limiting factors to the exponential growth equation. When a population is stationary or is oscillating back and forth around a mean size, natality rate equals mortality on the average, and the specific growth rate is zero.

In terms of the growth curves discussed in Section 3, the specific growth rate ($\Delta N/N\Delta t$) may be obtained graphically when population growth is exponential. If growth is plotted as logarithms or on semi-logarithmic paper, the log of population number plotted against time will give a straight line if growth is exponential; r is the slope of this line. The unlimited specific growth rate is selected as a measure for comparing populations because it has been observed many times in a variety of organisms that populations exhibit logarithmic growth at least for a time when there is ample food and no crowding effects, enemies, etc. Under such conditions the population as a whole is expanding at a terrific rate even though each organism is reproducing at the same rate as before, i.e., the specific growth rate is constant. Many other phenomena such as absorption of light, monomolecular chemical reactions, and compound interest behave in the same manner.

It is obvious that this unlimited rate of increase cannot continue indefinitely; often it is never realized. The role of environmental resistance in shaping population growth form will be considered next.

Examples

Table 14 gives the unlimited rate of natural increase for two insects, two rodents, and man. The values for the rodents and for the insects at 29° C are presumed to be "maximum r" (biotic potential), since populations on which calculations were based

Table 14. *Unlimited rate of natural increase of certain species of insects, rodents and man*

Organism and condition	r, or instantaneous rate per female		Finite rate (e^r): number times population would multiply in	
	week	year	week	year
Calandra[1] (rice weevil) at optimum temp. 29° C	0.76	39.6	2.14	1.58×10^{16}
Calandra[1] at 23° C	0.43	22.4	1.54	5.34×10^8
Calandra[1] at 33.5° C	0.12	6.2	1.13	493
Tribolium castaneum[2] (flour beetle) at 28.5°C and 65 per cent relative humidity	0.71	36.8	2.03	1.06×10^{15}
Microtus agrestis[3] (English vole)[4] optimum laboratory	0.088	4.5	1.09	90
Rattus norvegicus[5] (brown rat) optimum laboratory	0.104	5.4	1.11	221
Man,[6] white population USA in 1920	—	0.0055	—	1.0055

[1] From Birch (1948).

[2] From Leslie and Park (1949).

[3] From Leslie and Ranson (1940).

[4] From data presented by Hamilton (1937), it seems likely that the American vole, *Microtus pennsylvanicus*, has a higher biotic potential than its English counterpart, although the value of maximum *r* has not been calculated.

[5] From Leslie (1945).

[6] From Dublin and Lotka (1925).

were living under as nearly optimum conditions as could be devised experimentally. The extremely wide differences in potential ability of different populations to increase are especially emphasized in the last column, which shows the number of times the population would multiply itself if the exponential rate continued. In the case of the rice weevil it will be noted that varying the temperature above and below the optimum has marked effects on the ability of the population to increase. The difference between maximum r and that found at non-optimum temperature (but still within limits of tolerance) is an example of environmental control in the absence of crowding. Even under these less favorable temperatures, it will be noted, the population is still able to increase several hundred fold in the course of a year, *if* biotic conditions remain non-limiting. Since insects are often considered man's most serious competitors, it is indeed fortunate that we do not have to depend solely on physical factors (or spray guns!) to keep insects in check; population and other biological factors offer powerful checks also. The more we can learn about these "living environmental resistances," the better equipped we should be in the "war" with insects.

8. Population growth form and concept of carrying capacity

Statement

Populations have characteristic patterns of increase which are called population growth forms. For the purposes of comparison we may designate two basic patterns, the *J-shaped growth form* and the *S-shaped* or *sigmoid growth form,* which may be combined and/or modified in various ways according to the peculiarities of different organisms and environments. In the J-shaped form density increases rapidly in exponential or compound interest fashion and then stops abruptly as environmental resistance becomes effective more or less suddenly. This form may be represented by the simple model:

$$\frac{\Delta N}{\Delta t} = rN \quad \textit{with a definite limit on N}$$

In the sigmoid form, population growth is slow at first (establishment or positive acceleration phase), becomes rapid (the logarithmic phase) as in the other type, but soon slows down gradually as the environmental resistance increases percentage wise (the negative acceleration phase), until a more or less equilibrium level is reached and maintained. This form may be represented by the simple logistic model:

$$\frac{\Delta N}{\Delta t} = rN \frac{(K-N)}{K}$$

The upper level, beyond which no major increase can occur, as represented by the constant K, is the *upper asymptote* of the sigmoid curve and has been aptly called the *carrying capacity*. In the J-form there may be no equilibrium level, but the limit on N represents the upper limit imposed by the environment. The two growth forms and certain variants are shown schematically in Figure 48.

Explanation

When a few individuals are introduced into or enter an unoccupied area (for example, at the beginning of a season) characteristic patterns of population increase have often been observed. When time is plotted on the horizontal axis and the number of individuals (or other measurement of density) on the vertical axis, the part of the growth curve which represents population increase often takes the form of an S or a J, as shown in Figures 48, 49, 50 and 51. It is interesting to note that these two basic growth forms are similar to the two metabolic or growth types that have been described in the case of individual organisms (Bertalanffy, 1957). However, it is not known if there is a causal relationship between growth of individuals and growth of populations; it is not safe at this point to do more than call attention to the fact that there are some similarities in patterns.

It will be noted that the equation given above as a simple model for the J-shaped form is the same as the exponential equation discussed in the previous section, except that a limit is imposed on N; that is, the relatively unrestricted growth is suddenly halted when the population runs out of some resource (such as food or space) or when frost or any other seasonal factor intervenes. When the upper limit of N is reached, the density may remain at this level for a time, or, as is often the case, an immediate decline occurs, producing a "relaxation oscillation" pattern in density, as shown in Figure 48. This type of pattern, which Nicholson (1954) has called "density triggered" seems to be char-

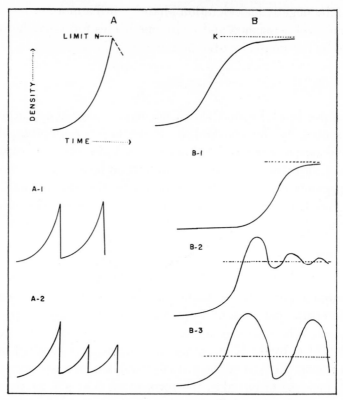

Figure 48. Some aspects of population growth form, showing the J-shaped (exponential) (A) and the S-shaped (sigmoid) (B) forms and some variants. A-1 and A-2 show oscillations which would be inherent in the J-shaped form. B-1, B-2 and B-3 show some possibilities (but by no means all) where there is a delay in density effect, which occurs when time elapses between production of young individuals and full influence of the individuals (the case in higher plants and animals). When nutrients or other requisites accumulate prior to population growth, an "overshoot" may occur as shown in A-2 and B-2. (This explains why new ponds or lakes often provide better fishing than old ones!) (Curves adapted from Nicholson, 1954.)

acteristic of many populations in nature such as algal blooms, annual plants, some insects and perhaps lemmings on the tundra.

A type of growth form which is observed frequently follows an S-shaped or sigmoid curve. The sigmoid curve is the result of greater and greater action of detrimental factors (environmental resistance) as the density of the population increases, in contrast to the previous model where environmental resistance was delayed until near the end of the increase. For this reason Nicholson (1954) has spoken of the sigmoid type as "density conditioned." The simplest case which can be conceived is the one in which detrimental factors are linearly proportional to the density. Such simple or "ideal" growth form is said to be logistic and conforms to the logistic equation which we have used as a basis for our model of the sigmoid pattern. The equation may be written as follows (three forms are shown above and the integrated form below):

$$\frac{\Delta N}{\Delta t} = rN\frac{(K-N)}{K} \text{ or } = rN - \frac{r}{K}N^2 \text{ or } = rN\left(1 - \frac{N}{K}\right)$$

$$N = \frac{K}{1 + e^{a-rt}}$$

where $\Delta N/\Delta t$ is the rate of population growth (change in number in time), r the specific growth rate, as discussed in Section 6, N the population size (number), K the maximum population size possible, or "upper asymptote," e the base of natural logarithm and a equals r/K.

As will be noted, this is the same equation as the exponential one written in the previous section with the addition of the expression $(K-N)/K$ or $(r/K)N^2$. The latter expressions are two ways of indicating the environmental resistance created by the growing population itself, which brings about an increasing reduction in the potential reproduction rate as population size approaches the carrying capacity. In word form, these equations simply mean:

$$\begin{bmatrix} \text{Rate of} \\ \text{population} \\ \text{increase} \end{bmatrix} \text{ equals } \begin{bmatrix} \text{maximum possible} \\ \text{rate of increase} \\ \text{(unlimited specific} \\ \text{growth rate times} \\ \text{numbers in the} \\ \text{population)} \end{bmatrix} \begin{array}{c} \text{times} \\ \\ \text{or} \\ \\ \text{minus} \end{array} \begin{bmatrix} \text{degree of real-} \\ \text{ization of max-} \\ \text{imum rate} \end{bmatrix} \\ \begin{bmatrix} \text{unrealized} \\ \text{increase} \end{bmatrix}$$

It should now be emphasized that although the growth of a great variety of populations—representing microorganisms, plants, and animals—including both laboratory and natural populations, have been shown to follow the sigmoid pattern, it does not follow necessarily that such populations increase according to the logistic equation. There are many mathematical equations which will produce a sigmoid curve. Almost any equation in which the negative factors increase in some manner with density will produce sigmoid curves. Mere curve-fitting is to be avoided. One needs to have evidence that the factors in the equation are actually operating to control the population before an attempt is made to compare

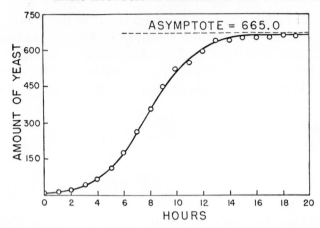

Figure 49.   Growth of yeast in a culture. A simple case of the sigmoid growth form in which environmental resistance (in this case, detrimental factors produced by organisms themselves) is linearly proportional to the density. This type of population growth pattern is said to be logistic (because it corresponds to the logistic equation) and is characteristic of organisms with simple life histories. (From Allee et al., 1949, after Pearl.)

actual data with a theoretical curve. The simple situation where environmental resistance increases linearly with density seems to hold for populations of organisms which have very simple life histories (for example, yeasts, see Fig. 49) and which are growing in a limited space (as in a culture). Populations often "overshoot" the upper asymptote and undergo mild oscillations before settling down at the carrying capacity level (see Fig. 48). In populations of higher plants and animals, which have complicated life histories and long periods of individual development, there are likely to be delayed responses which greatly modify the growth form, producing what Nicholson (1954) has called "tardy density conditioned" patterns. In such cases a more concave growth curve may result (longer period required for natality to become effective) or definite oscillations may be produced. For a discussion of some of these possibilities and how they are related to the basic models reference may be made to Andrewartha and Birch (1954) and Nicholson's paper cited above.

As can well be imagined, data on population growth of field populations are few, incomplete, and hard to come by. One reason, aside from the difficulty of determining numbers, is that many natural populations are in the "adult" stage when studied. The best opportunity to observe the fundamental growth form occurs when the population enters or is introduced into a new, unoccupied environment. One of the important and little understood aspects of population growth concerns "time lag" effects of the environment. Environmental action with time lag tends to produce fluctuations (as in curves B-2 and B-3, Fig. 48). (For a theoretical discussion of time lag effects see Wangersky and Cunningham, 1957.)

Examples

Figure 49 illustrates the sigmoid growth form in its simplest form; Figure 50 illustrates the J-shaped pattern. In the latter the thrips (small insects) increase rapidly during favorable years until the end of the season calls a halt, after which an equally rapid decline in density occurs. In less favorable years the growth form is more sigmoid. Broadly speaking, the J-shaped form may be considered an incomplete sigmoid curve since a sudden limiting effect is brought to bear before the self-limiting effects within the population become important.

The sigmoid growth form is by no means restricted to small organisms or those with simple life histories but may be observed in birds and mammals. A good example of growth of a population

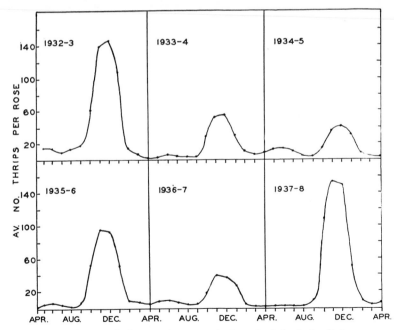

Figure 50.   Seasonal changes in a population of adult thrips living on roses (graph constructed from data by Davidson and Andrewartha, 1948).

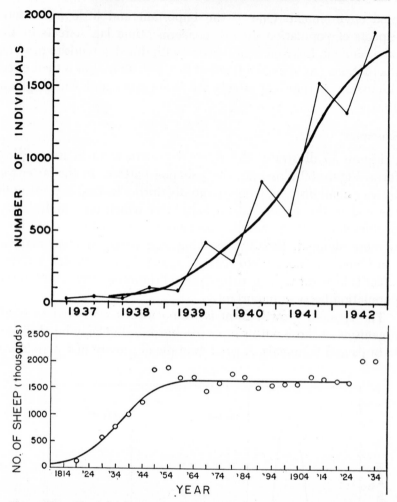

Figure 51. Growth of two populations introduced into new environments. Upper: Pheasants (*Phasianus colchicus*) on Protection Island, Washington; points represent numbers found during censuses each spring and fall, heavy line connects averages at end of each year. (Data from Einarsen, 1945.) Lower: Sheep populations in Tasmania; circles are averages for 5-year periods. (From Davidson, 1938.)

introduced into a new environment is shown in the lower diagram in Figure 51. Sheep were introduced on the island of Tasmania near Australia about 1800 and reasonably good records were kept of the number present. The number of sheep followed the sigmoid curve and the population reached the asymptote about 1850. Since then the population has fluctuated irregularly above and below 1,700,000 sheep, the fluctuations being presumed to be due to variations in climatic factors which limit the number of sheep that could be maintained profitably.

In 1937, two males and six female ring-necked pheasants were introduced on an island off the coast of Washington state, and censuses were made each spring and fall for the next five years. The results are shown in the upper diagram in Figure 51. Unfortunately, World War II interrupted the study, and servicemen stationed on the island applied rather excessive "environmental resistance," so that the population was not able completely to "express" its growth form. Nevertheless, a sigmoid growth form is evident with the almost exponential rate of increase beginning to "slack off" at about the fifth year. Note that the mortality between breeding seasons (fall to spring) was small, compared with the natality in this temporarily unlimited environment.

9. Population fluctuations and so-called "cyclic" oscillations

Statement

Even in those populations which tend to reach and maintain an upper asymptote or carrying capacity level, population density tends to fluctuate above and below this level. Such fluctuations may result from changes in the physical environment which, in effect, raise and lower the asymptotic level, and/or interactions within the population or between closely interacting populations. Thus, fluctuations may occur even in a constant environment such as might be maintained in the laboratory. In nature, it is important to distinguish between (1) seasonal changes in population size, largely controlled by seasonal changes in environmental factors, and (2) annual fluctuations. For the purposes of analysis the latter may be considered under two headings: (a) fluctuations controlled primarily by annual differences in the physical environment of the population, or extrinsic factors (i.e., outside sphere of population interactions), and (b) oscillations primarily controlled by population dynamics, or intrinsic factors (i.e., factors within populations). In general, the former tend to be irregular and clearly correlated with the variation in one or more major physical limiting factors (such as temperature, rainfall, etc.) while the latter often exhibits such regularity that the terms "oscillations" or "cycles" seem appropriate (and species exhibiting such regular variation in population size are often known as "cyclic" species). As we have seen in the previous section, oscillations would be inherent in populations exhibiting the J-shaped growth form especially if the life cycle is short. It is, of course, understood that both extrinsic and intrinsic factors influence all fluctuations;

the fundamental problem is to evaluate the importance of each, or at least to determine which is the major cause of variation in specific cases. In the terrestrial environment it has been repeatedly observed that animal species population density fluctuates from year to year most violently in relatively simple ecosystems where communities are composed of a relatively few species populations, as, for example, in arctic communities and artificial pine forest communities.

Explanation and examples

1. *Samples of Various Types of Population Density Variations.* The mechanism behind the ebb and flow of population size is a fascinating and largely unsolved problem in ecology. As indicated in the preceding paragraph, fluctuations could logically result from variations in the external physical environment, as, for example, climatic variations. We would classify such fluctuations as being extrinsic in nature, because they were caused by factors outside the population, or nonbiological factors. On the other hand, it is also logical that pronounced fluctuations could be the result of intrinsic factors, that is, of events partly within the population, such as predation, disease, inherent type of growth form, etc. So far, ecologists have not been able to distinguish quantitatively between these possibilities. We can only state that certain definite types of fluctuations or oscillations are characteristic of certain populations in certain regions. In some cases, the causes seem clear. In other cases there is little agreement among those who have studied the situation.

We are all familiar with seasonal variations in population size. We come to expect that at certain times of the year mosquitoes or gnats will be abundant, or the woods will be full of birds, or the fields full of ragweed; at other seasons populations of these organisms may dwindle to the vanishing point. Although it would be difficult to find in nature populations of animals, microorganisms, and herbaceous plants that do not exhibit some seasonal change in size, the most pronounced fluctuations occur with organisms which have limited breeding seasons, and especially those with short life cycles. Despite the widespread occurrence of seasonal variations very few cases have been intensively studied and causal relations are often assumed without real proof. Perhaps this is because the commonest and most familiar phenomena are apt to be studied last, or perhaps it is because it takes a great deal of time and patience to follow any population for long periods of time! Figure 50, already referred to, illustrates not only J-shaped growth form (no equilibrium level at higher densities) but also seasonal fluctuations. A pattern of this sort is probably typical of most insects and of most "annuals" among plants and animals.

One of the most spectacular types of seasonal fluctuations which occurs in aquatic situations, both fresh-water and ocean, is the phytoplankton "bloom." One or more times a year sudden but brief increases occur, with population density being many times that generally found (see Figures 90 and 98).

Pronounced seasonal variations in population density are as characteristic of the tropics as of temperate and arctic regions. For example, Bates (1945) found that the relative abundance of only one out of seven tropical species of mosquitoes failed to show seasonal variations (Fig. 52). Fluctuations in the tropics are often related to rainfall.

To return to the thrips, Figure 50 also illustrates annual variations. The maximum population achieved varied quite a bit from year to year. In some years the specific growth rate was less than in others, as shown by the differences in the slopes of the steep

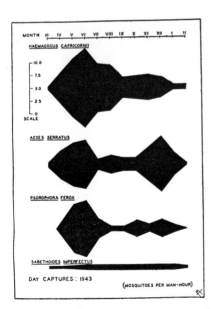
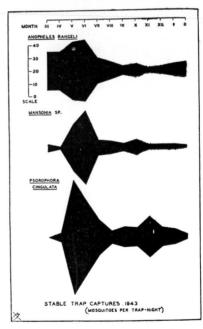

Figure 52. Seasonal changes in the abundance of seven species of mosquitoes in the tropical environment of eastern Colombia. (After Bates, 1945.)

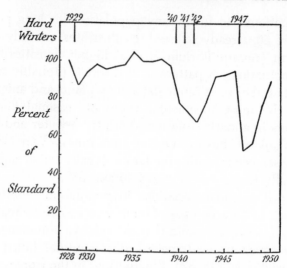

Figure 53. Changes in the abundance of the heron, *Ardea cinerea,* in Great Britain between 1928 and 1950. A relation betweeen cold winters and a decline in relative abundance is indicated. (After Lack, 1951.)

part of the curves. Peak density did occur at about the same time each year, but in general it would not be safe to base an estimate of annual population size on one or two determinations taken at the same date each year; enough determinations must be made during the suspected peak season to make certain that the same relative points on the population growth curve are being compared. Applied ecologists who are called upon to determine relative population levels of economically important species from year to year should take special note of this potential source of error.

A typical example of a rather irregular variation in population size which appears to be correlated with climate is shown in Figure 53. During most years the heron population in Great Britain remains relatively constant, Great Britain apparently providing an environment having a rather stable carrying capacity for herons. However, a sharp decrease in density with subsequent recovery occasionally occurs following a severe winter. This correlation looks good, but, as with all correlations, it should be followed up with an actual demonstration that severe winters do increase the mortality rate sufficiently to produce the observed breeding population decrease. The irregular variations in the sheep population which followed the reaching of the asymptotic level as diagrammed in Figure 51 are another example of logical correlation with weather, in this case rainfall (Davidson, 1938).

That is, in arid areas rainfall is the chief limiting factor determining the amount of grass and thereby the number of sheep that can profitably be raised in any particular year.

The most interesting and the least understood density variations are those which apparently are not related to seasonal or obvious annual changes, but which involve regular oscillations or cycles of abundance with peaks and depressions every few years, often occurring with such regularity that population size may be predicted in advance. The best known cases concern the mammals, although regular oscillations are known for certain birds, insects, and fish, and for seed production in plants. The best-studied examples exhibit either a 9–10 year or a 3–4 year periodicity. A classic case of a 10-year oscillation is that of the snowshoe hare and the lynx (Fig. 54). Since about 1800 the Hudson Bay Company of Canada has kept records of pelts of fur-bearers trapped each year. When plotted, these records show that the lynx, for example, has reached a population peak every 9–10 years, averaging 9.6 years, throughout this long stretch of time. Peaks of abundance often are followed by "crashes," or rapid declines, the lynx becoming exceedingly scarce for several years. The snowshoe hare follows the same cycle, with a peak abundance generally preceding that of the lynx by a year or more. Since the lynx is largely dependent on the hare for food, it is obvious that the cycle of the predator is related to that of the prey, but whether the two cycles are cause and effect is another thing. The shorter, or 3–4 year cycle, is characteristic of many northern murids—lemmings, mice,

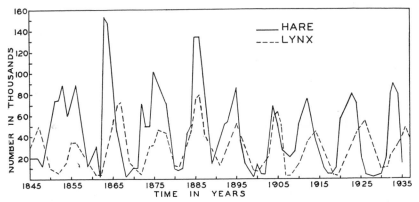

Figure 54. Changes in the abundance of the lynx and the snowshoe hare, as indicated by the number of pelts received by the Hudson Bay Company. This is a classic case of cyclic oscillation in population density. (Redrawn from MacLulich, 1937.)

Figure 55. The snowshoe or varying hare, famous in ecological annals for its spectacular cyclic abundance (see Figure 54). The individual shown is in its white winter pelage. The change from the brown summer pelage to the white one of winter has been shown to be controlled by photoperiodicity (see page 109). (U. S. Soil Conservation Service Photo.)

voles, and their predators, especially the snowy owl and foxes. The cycle of the lemming of the tundra and the arctic fox and the snowy owl are well documented classic instances (Elton, 1942). Every three or four years, over enormous areas of the northern tundra of two continents, the lemmings (two species in Eurasia and one in North America of genus *Lemmus*, and one species of *Dicrostonyx* in North America) become extremely abundant only to "crash," often within a single season. Foxes and owls, which increase in numbers as their food increases, decrease very soon afterward. Foxes starve in large numbers, and owls migrate south into the United States (sometimes as far south as North Carolina) in search of food. This eruptive migration of surplus birds is apparently a one-way movement; few if any owls ever return. The owl population thus "crashes" as a result of the dispersal movement. So regular is this oscillation that bird students in the United States can count on a snowy owl invasion every 3 or 4 years. Since the birds are conspicuous and appear everywhere about cities, they attract a lot of attention and get their pictures in the paper or their skins mounted in local taxidermy shops. In years between invasions, few or no owls are seen in the United States or southern Canada. Gross (1947) and Shelford (1943) have analyzed the invasion records and have shown that they are correlated with the periodic decrease in abundance of the lemming, their chief food item. In Europe, but apparently not in North America, the lemmings themselves become so abundant at the crest of the cycle that they may emigrate from their overcrowded haunts. Elton (1942) vividly describes the famous lemming "migrations" in Norway. The animals pass through villages in such numbers that dogs and cats get tired of killing them and just ignore the horde. On reaching the sea, many drown. Thus, as in the owl eruption, the lemming movement is one-way. These spectacular emigrations do not occur at every 4-year peak in density, but only during exceptionally high peaks. Often the population subsides without the animals leaving the tundra or mountains.

The population fluctuations of four species of moths in German artificial pine (*Pinus sylvestris*) forests recorded in a 60-year period are plotted in Figure 56. The moth caterpillars feed on the pine needles during the growing season and pupate or hibernate in the soil over the winter; thus counts of pupae or larvae in the soil in winter provide a good means of comparing different years. Under the German system of artificial forest management the forests remained relatively constant as to stand density, age ratios, etc., over the 60 years. Thus, we have here a superb set of long-term population data suitable for analysis of annual variations. So great is the fluctuation in population density that a log scale is necessary if the data for the four species are to be plotted on the same graph. Thus, in the case of *Bupalus*, the density of pupae varied from less than one per 1,000 square meters to over 10,000 per 1,000 square meters (0.001 to 10 per square meter). One can well imagine that with 10,000 potential moths emerging for every 1,000 square meters, and several generations in a season,

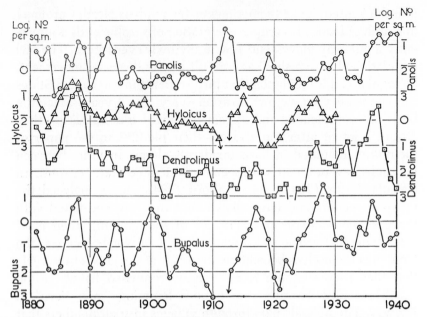

Figure 56.   Fluctuations in numbers of four species of moths whose larvae feed upon foliage of pines in German-managed (pure stand) forests (at Letzlingen). The points on the graphs represent the results of 60 successive winter census counts of pupae (or hibernating larvae in the case of *Dendrolimus*) per square meter of forest floor plotted on a log scale. (After Varley, 1949.)

enough caterpillars could be produced, if not seriously checked, to eat all the needles off the trees (complete defoliation) in a season. This sometimes actually happened! It will be noted that peaks for the four species coincided between 1880 and 1890, but after that the cycles show no real correlation. It would seem that each population is oscillating independently, with maxima and minima of two or more populations coinciding occasionally.

Finally, it will be noted from Figure 56 that oscillations of forest insect pests do not exhibit the regularity of the mammal periodicities discussed previously. There are no clear-cut 3–4- or 10-year cycles, the average apparently being somewhere in between.

Probably the most famous of all insect population oscillations are those involving locusts or grasshoppers. In Eurasia records of outbreaks of the migratory locust (*Locusta migratoria*) go back to antiquity (Carpenter, 1940a). The locusts live in desert or semi-arid country and in most years are non-migratory, eat no crops, and attract no attention. At intervals, however, population density increases to an enormous extent; the locusts actually become morphologically different (develop longer wings, etc.) under effects of crowding,* and emigrate into cultivated lands, consuming everything in their path. Uvarov (1957) points out that activities of man, such as shifting cultivation and overgrazing by his cattle, tend to increase rather than decrease the chance of an outbreak because a patchwork or mosaic of vegetation and bare ground (in which 'hoppers lay eggs) is favorable for population buildup in the exponential or J-shaped manner. As in the case of the lemming, it is probable that not every population maxima is accompanied by an emigration; therefore, the frequency of the plagues does not necessarily represent true periodicity of the density oscillations. Even so, outbreaks have been recorded at least once every 40 years between 1695 and 1895. In all these cases we are dealing with violent oscillations generated in environments which support relatively simplified communities parallel to the previously discussed instances furnished by the tundra and pine forest. It seems probable that emigration has been evolved as a safety valve, or sort of homeostatic mechanism, which prevents the population from destroying its environment in those ecosystems where factors do not operate to produce the sigmoid growth form.

An interesting type of "predator-prey" oscillation involves plants and animals. Seed production in conifers is often "cyclic," and seed-eating birds and other animals show corresponding oscillations.

2. *Theories as to Mechanism of the Violent Oscillatory Type of Population Fluctuations.*   As previously indicated, fluctuations above and below an equilibrium level appear to be characteristic of most populations, and this would indeed be expected under nature's varied influence, but the mechanism behind the regular periodicities which we have just described is but little understood. Such regularity is almost paradoxical in the face of nature's notorious irregularity! Two striking features of these oscillations are: (1) they are most pronounced in the less complex ecosystems of northern regions, as occur, for example, in the tundra, in northern waters, in deserts, or in coniferous forests; if regular cycles of abundance occur in species populations in complex communities of southern or tropical regions, they either are much less pronounced or have not been demonstrated; and (2) although peaks

---

* Solitary and migratory forms occur in a number of species of locusts and often were described as separate species, before their true relations were known.

of abundance may occur simultaneously over wide areas, peaks in the same species or in different species in different regions do not always coincide by any means.

Attempts to relate these regular oscillations to climatic factors have so far been unsuccessful. At one time the cycle of sunspots, which cause major weather changes, was considered by many as an adequate explanation for the cycle of the lynx and other 10-year cycles. However, MacLulich (1937) and others have demonstrated that, actually, there is no correlation. So far, no widespread climatic periodicities which would fit the 3–4-year interval (which, as indicated above, may be the fundamental interval) have been demonstrated. Even if there were good correlations, the problem would still not be settled until it could be demonstrated just how sunspots or ultraviolet or other climatic factors affect natality, mortality, dispersal, or other population characteristics. As indicated before in our discussion, correlations (or "cycle-fitting") without evidence of mechanism are dangerous indeed.

If climatic factors should prove not to be the major cause of the violent oscillations (although undoubtedly they have important modifying effects), then we would naturally look for causes within the populations themselves (i.e., for "intrinsic factors"). Here we have some evidence of possible mechanisms which might operate in conjunction with weather or other changes in physical factors. As already indicated in the discussion of population growth form, populations which undergo more or less unrestricted exponential growth for a time may be expected to oscillate in density since such populations may exceed the bounds of some limiting factor rather than achieve a steady state. The simpler the ecosystem, that is, the fewer the species and major limiting factors, the greater the likelihood of temporary imbalances. As will be discussed in the next chapter, Lotka, Volterra and Gause early demonstrated mathematically and, to a limited extent, experimentally that a system containing a single prey and a single predator specialized to feed upon it can oscillate even in a constant physical environment. The most extensive experimental data have been obtained by Utida (1957) who has kept together in a constant environment populations of bean weevils and parasitic wasps for many generations over periods of time up to several years. Regardless of the number of individuals with which the cultures were started, the density of host and parasite continued to rise and fall reciprocally for long periods of time. In some experiments the parasite became extinct and occasionally both species became extinct, but usually both survived. Figure 57 shows the results of one of the longest experiments. Interestingly enough, oscillations were very violent for the first few generations then diminished as host and parasite achieved a better adjustment to each other. However, violent oscillation soon occurred again followed by a damping of the fluctuations. In the particular experiment shown in Figure 57 there were three periods of violent oscillations.

The oscillation of the German forest pests, as shown in Figure 56, would seem to represent a field situation which was similar to that of Utida's experiments. Varley (1949) points out that food supply for foliage insects is abundant and general predators or competitors lacking in the restricted fauna of artificial pine forests; the chief biological "environmental resistances" are specialized parasitic insects whose larvae consume host eggs or larvae. Thus, if the pest population is low, parasites are unable to find prey and

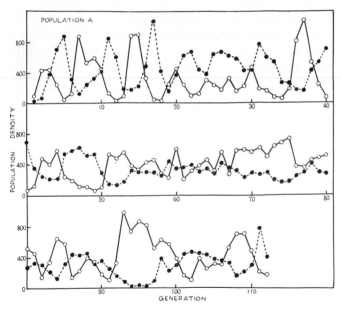

Figure 57. Long-term trend in density fluctuations in interacting populations of a host (solid line) and a parasite (broken line) in a constant environment (constant temperature, light, humidity, kind and amount of food for host, and size of container). The host is the bean weevil, *Callosobruchus chinensis,* and the parasite is a braconid wasp, *Heterospilus prosopidis,* whose larvae parasitizes the weevil larvae. The experiment shown continued uninterrupted through 110 generations, or a little over six and a half years. (After Utida, 1957.)

drop to an even lower level. With temporary removal of restric-
tions the prey species multiply so rapidly that they exceed the
carrying capacity and may defoliate the trees before the parasites
can "catch up"; at this point limiting factors in the form of parasites, diminished food and/or weather could cause sudden decline.
In mixed forests this sort of violent oscillation is less often reported, presumedly because a variety of unspecialized predators
and competitors would be "ready" to nip population increase in
the bud; likewise, food supply for any one kind of insect would
not be so abundant as to encourage exponential increase (Voute,
1946). It is for this reason that many foresters are now advocating
mixed rather than pure stands on the theory that serious insect or
disease outbreaks would be less likely in the former. Man must,
of course, simplify many ecosystems in order to obtain maximum
yield for himself, but he often needlessly destroys the biological
mechanisms which produce stability and thereby a better yield in
the long run.

When populations exceed or approach carrying capacity, predators, parasites and disease are not the only check mechanisms
which have evolved; intraspecific factors may be equally important. Thus, populations of snowshoe hares may continue to oscillate even in the absence of predators, hunting by man or disease.
During the rapid decline or "crash" phase, rabbits in large numbers may die of a functional disorder called "shock disease," which
appears to be identical with the Selye stress syndrome resulting
from a breakdown of the adrenopituitary system. There seems to
be good experimental and field evidence (enlarged adrenals, etc.)
indicating that crowding, added to other environmental pressures,
does produce sufficient physiological stress to bring about wholesale die-offs in populations of cyclic mammals (Christian, 1950,
1956).

Another situation where increase in density causes physiological changes in the individuals of the population has been described
for tent caterpillars (*Malacosoma*) by Wellington (1957). These
insects, which build the familiar silken webs among the branches
of trees, fluctuate violently in numbers in many parts of North
America, reaching peaks of abundance at approximately eight-
year intervals. On the upswing of the cycle the colonies build
elongated tents which are shifted about, and the individuals are
active in moving out into the foliage to feed. At peak density, the
colonies become inactive, build compact tents and are more sub-

ject to disease. Adults reared from the sluggish larvae are also sluggish and do not move far. Thus, further spread or increase in density is checked by the change in the vigor and behavior of the population. It should be emphasized that intrapopulation check mechanisms, as illustrated by the mammal and insect examples, are not necessarily the primary cause of oscillations, but rather may be devices to prevent even greater oscillation, which could endanger the survival of the species.

Palmgren (1949) and Cole (1951) have pointed out that the peaks of some population fluctuations are random; this does not mean that the oscillations are not causal, but that the causes are varying in a random manner. That is, random distribution may be expected when numerous factors, rather than one of several dominant factors, are interacting. Cole (1957) believes that in most cases "natural populations are not subject to alteration only by two or three interacting factors but are affected by a large enough number to encourage us to look for secondary simplicity; the highly acclaimed regularity of population cycles seems to be no greater than that which is encountered in a sequence of random numbers." The problem of cyclic oscillation in any specific case may well boil down to determining whether one to several factors are primarily responsible or whether causes are so numerous as to be difficult to untangle even though the total interaction may be understood. As we have already indicated, the former is certainly possible in simple ecosystems, whether experimental or natural; the latter may be more likely in complex ecosystems.

10. Population dispersal

Statement

Population dispersal* is the movement of individuals or their disseminules (seeds, spores, larvae, etc.) into or out of the population or population area. It takes three forms: *emigration*—one-way outward movement; *immigration*—one-way inward movement; and *migration*—periodic departure and return.

Dispersal supplements natality and mortality in shaping population growth form and density. In most cases some individuals or their reproductive products are constantly entering or leaving the

---

* Dispersion should not be confused with dispersal. Dispersion, especially as used in statistics, refers to the internal pattern of a population, e.g., the distribution of items around the mean.

population. Often this gradual type of dispersal has little effect on the total population (especially if the unit of population size is large), either because emigrations balance immigrations or because gains and losses are compensated for by changes in natality and mortality. In other cases, however, mass dispersal occurs involving rapid changes with corresponding effect on the population. Dispersal is greatly influenced by barriers, and by the inherent power of movement of individuals (or disseminules), which is indicated by the term *vagility*.

Explanation and examples

In much of our discussion so far in this chapter we have considered the population as if it were a unit isolated from other populations. Although this is not usually true (in nature, at least), it is true that exchanges between populations are often less important than some of the "internal" processes that we have been discussing. Since there are many popular misconceptions about "stocking" (i.e., artificial immigration) in natural populations, it is important to determine the part dispersal really plays in specific cases.

The effect which dispersal will have on a population depends first on the status of the growth form of the population (whether it is at or near the carrying-capacity level, or is actively growing or declining), and second on the rate of dispersal. Let us consider these in order.

If a population is "well stocked" and in balance with the limiting factors of the environment (i.e., at asymptotic level), moderate immigration or emigration will have little general or permanent effect; gains or losses by dispersal simply result in compensating changes in natality and mortality. If a population is well above or below carrying capacity, dispersal may have more pronounced effects. Immigration, for example, may speed up population growth or, in case of extreme reduction, prevent extinction. We have already seen how emigration of lemmings or snowy owls from overcrowded regions is a factor in bringing about the sharp decline or "crash" characteristic of the population fluctuations of those species. Gause (1934) produced predator-prey oscillations in protozoa by regular introduction of "immigrants" in cultures that exhibited no oscillations in the absence of immigrations.

Rapid or large scale immigrations or emigrations obviously are more likely to have pronounced effects than are gradual or small

dispersal movements. Mass dispersal may even change the structure of a balanced population. Thus, the introduction of a large
number of bluegill fingerlings into a pond where the bluegill population has reached or is approaching carrying capacity may result
in decreased growth throughout the population and a smaller
average size of fish. Even though the biomass density remains
unchanged, individual size of fish may be so reduced that fishing
is poor, probably to the disappointment of the person who thought
that additional "stocking" would improve fishing!

Dispersal is much influenced by the presence or absence of
barriers, and the vagility or inherent power of movement. Vagility
is often greater than is commonly realized. Although birds and
insects are noted for their ability to "get around," many plants and
lesser forms of animals actually have greater dispersal powers.
Recent studies of the life found floating in the air, or "aerial
plankton," have revealed a surprising number of organisms, not
only spores, seeds, and microorganisms, but animals such as
spiders which float for miles attached to threadlike parachutes of
their own making.

Wolfenbarger (1946) has summarized a large volume of literature on dispersal. He found that most small organisms or disseminules, regardless of whether movement was passive (produced by
currents of air or water) or active (flying, swimming, etc.), tended
to disperse as the logarithm of the distance from the source. That
is, if the distance from the source was plotted on the x-axis and
the number or relative abundance on the y-axis, a concave curve
was usually obtained (like the first half of the sigmoid curve in
reverse). Several examples are shown in Figure 58, including both
light and heavy "objects," and showing both horizontal and vertical dispersal. When distance units were placed logarithmically
and incidence units (y-axis) uniformly (semi-logarithmic plot),
then a straight line was often obtained (thus demonstrating a
true logarithmic decrease). The slope of this regression line then
becomes a quantitative measure of dispersal useful for comparing
different populations (comparing, for example, the rate of decrease in bacteria and insects, or spores and mosquitoes). Knowledge of relative vagility is often of great practical importance, as,
for example, in determining how far from human habitations control measures for mosquitoes would need to be undertaken.

Organisms with well developed nervous systems and directed
movement, of course, may not follow the pattern of logarithmic

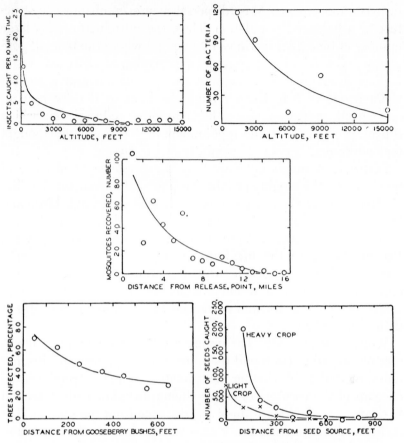

Figure 58. Both vertical and horizontal dispersal of small organisms or disseminules exhibit a similar pattern. The upper graphs show the vertical dispersal of insects (left) and bacteria (right) in the air. In the middle graph the number of marked mosquitoes recovered at various distances from the release point are plotted. In the lower graphs dispersal of minute spores of white pine blister rust, which are produced by the fungus on gooseberry bushes and infect white pines (left), is compared with dispersal of seeds of the Douglas fir (right). (After Wolfenbarger, 1946.)

decrease from the source. Bees and birds, for example, may pass by food near the hive or nest in favor of food at greater distances. Likewise, migrations and other movements directed along specific pathways or to specific points will result in population dispersal patterns characteristic for each species.

Migration, as defined above, is a special and very remarkable type of population dispersion often involving the mass movement of entire populations. This can occur, of course, only in motile organisms, and is best developed in arthropods and vertebrates.

Seasonal and diurnal migrations not only make possible occupation of regions which would be unfavorable in the absence of migration but also enable animals to maintain a higher average density and activity rate. Non-migratory populations often must undergo considerable reduction in density or assume some form of dormancy during unfavorable periods. The orientation and navigation of long-distance migrants (birds, fish, etc.) constitute a popular field for experiments and theories, but are little understood, as yet. It seems fairly certain that animals do not respond to magnetic forces of the earth, but there is much evidence that both birds and insects do make use of a "light compass" or "sun compass" (see von Frisch, 1950; Matthews, 1955).

Figure 59 is a good illustration of emigration and migration

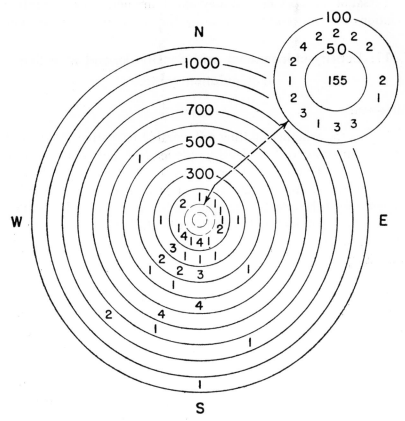

Figure 59. Dispersal of banded barn owls in relation to their hatching places. Distance of movement in terms of miles is indicated by concentric circles. The number of birds recovered in any given direction is indicated by the numbers between the circles. Within 100 miles dispersal is non-directional; beyond this distance dispersal is definitely directional. (After Stewart, 1952.)

as it affects a single species population. The barn owl is migratory in northern United States but non-migratory in the southern part of the country. In both regions young birds tend to disperse from the nesting site. As shown in Figure 59, this dispersal of young is random in all directions, but is restricted to about 100 miles, which figure would be a measure of the emigration vagility. Migratory movement, however, is definitely directional (southward) and involves longer distances.

Quite apart from its effect on population size and composition, dispersal brings about gene exchange between populations and hence is important from the standpoint of population genetics and speciation. Finally, we are not concerned here with effects of immigration of a new species into a community or the effect of dispersal of one species as it may affect another. These important relations are best considered under the heading of competition.

11. Density-independent and density-dependent action in population control

Statement

Any factor, whether limiting or favorable (negative or positive) to a population, is (1) *density-independent* (in terms of total population), if the effect or action is constant regardless of the number of individuals in the population, or (2) *density-dependent*, if the effect on the population varies with the density. Density-dependent action is often direct, that is, it begins to act well below the carrying capacity level and intensifies as the upper limit is approached, but it may also be inverse (decrease in intensity as density increases). Density-dependent factors act like governors on an engine, and for this reason are considered one of the chief agents preventing over-population and thereby responsible for the achievement of a steady state (asymptotic or carrying-capacity) density level where such is observed. Climatic factors often, but by no means always, act in a density-independent manner, whereas biotic factors (competition, parasites, pathogens, etc.) often, but not always, act in a density-dependent manner.

Explanation

Ecologists working with small organisms (such as insects or plankton which have short life cycles, high biotic potentials and high rates of metabolism per gram and, hence, relatively small standing crop per unit space at any one time) have been impressed with the following: (1) the importance of the period of time when the unlimited rate of increase (r) is positive; (2) the importance of density-independent factors such as weather in determining the length of favorable periods; (3) the secondary rather than primary importance of self-limiting forces within the population (as in J-shaped growth form) and (4) the general lack of stability in the density of any one species even when the ecosystem is stable. These points have been particularly well brought out by Andrewartha and Birch (1954). Ecologists working with larger organisms, such as birds, mammals or forest trees, where life cycles are longer and numbers and biomass more clearly reflect energy flow have been impressed with the following: (1) the importance of density-dependent factors especially intraspecific competition (as in sigmoid growth equation) and interspecific checks of various sorts (predators, etc.), and (2) the stability or at least consistency (as in the "cyclic" species) in the density pattern in situations where the ecosystem is stable. Interestingly enough, persons working with confined populations of small organisms, such as bacteria or flour beetles in culture, are also impressed with these two aspects, which is perhaps not surprising since standing crop per unit space in cultures is greater than would be usual in nature. For an analysis of some of the factors which act in a density-dependent manner, see Lack (1954).

Above all, when we become interested in intensive study of specific populations we must not forget the integration which occurs at the community and ecosystem level, because (as emphasized in Chapter 2) the part (population) can never be completely explained without considering the whole (ecosystem), or vice versa. Where there are a large number of species occupying a trophic level (herbiverous insects in a forest, for example) the population ecology of any one species may make little sense unless we know what the "co-workers" in the community are doing at the same time.

Strictly speaking, an effect would be density-independent only if a constant influence were exerted on the population regardless of its size. For example, if the same number of hunters are allowed two deer per season and they hunt until they obtain their deer, then the same number of deer would be removed each year, regardless of the total number of deer. It has been customary, however, also to speak of a factor as "density-independent" if the effect *percentagewise* is the same regardless of density, as would be the case, for example, if 10 per cent of the deer were removed each year, even though the number affected (removed) would depend on density! If we wish to make a distinction we may speak of the constant percentage effect as density-proportional.

One way to clear up these matters is to think in terms of the growth equations previously given (another example of usefulness of mathematical models). A constant added to the equation, of course, represents absolute density-independent action. A constant multiplied by N (the number in the population) represents a constant percentage density-independent effect. Any factor (such as $(K\text{-}N)/K$) that increases or decreases percentagewise as the number increases would be density-dependent.

Predators, parasites, and pathogens often act in a direct density-dependent manner because, as the population of prey or host increases, a relatively greater number can be located and attacked, especially since numbers of victims are being forced into less favorable situations. However, if there is a wide difference in the specific reproductiveness (r) of the interacting populations, as in predator birds and prey insects, predation may become essentially density-independent or inverse density-dependent, at least for a while. Thus, an insect population might increase greatly within a few months while the bird population could not increase so quickly. The result would be (assuming no immigration) that the stationary bird population would eat a smaller percentage of the insect population as the latter increased.

One of the most important of density-dependent actions is that of competition. As population density increases, competition for nutrients, food, and living space usually intensifies, providing one of the most effective controls of both plant and animal populations. As the number of plants increases in a forest, competition for light, water, and nutrients becomes increasingly severe, with resulting elimination of many individuals and a great reduction in reproduction. Forest density is therefore controlled as much by this density-dependent factor as by temperature, etc. At the other extreme, natality increases with density in some colonial animals. Thus, Darling (1938) found that many sea birds failed entirely to nest unless the colony had a certain minimum density of adults (see also page 220).

To summarize, density-independent aspects of the environment tend to bring about variations, sometimes drastic, in population density and to cause a shifting of upper asymptotic or carrying-capacity levels, while density-dependent natality and mortality tend to maintain a population in a "steady-state" or to hasten the return to such a level. In most natural populations density tends toward a varying level (Solomon, 1949) because of the varying combinations of density-independent, and density-dependent action.

Examples

Severe storms, sudden drops in temperature, and other drastic changes in physical factors generally provide the most clear-cut examples of density-independent action. For example, a sudden severe cold spell in January, 1940, on the Texas coast resulted in the large scale death of fishes. The following tabulation (from Gunter, 1941) of the 3 months' catch of flounders (the species hardest hit by cold) before and after the cold snap shows that the percentage loss was the same regardless of locality or size of original population:

| | Commercial catch | | Per cent |
Locality	Before	After	decline
Matagorda	16,919	1,089	93.6
Aransas	55,224	2,552	95.4
Laguna Madre	2,016	149	92.6

In sharp contrast to the above, data from Varley's (1947) intensive study of the knapweed gallfly show that the action of a major parasitic insect, *Eurytoma curta*, can be density-dependent, since it killed a much greater percentage as well as a larger total number of the host when the population of the host was high:

Year and population level	Larval population at beginning of season (No./m.²)	Larvae killed by parasite (No./m.²)	Per cent population killed by parasite
1934 (low population)	43	6	14
1935 (high population)	148	66	45

In another study Varley and Edwards (1957) report that when the "area of discovery" is low as was the case with the parasitic wasp, *Mormoniella*, the action of the parasite on its dipteran hosts was not necessarily density-dependent. Thus, differences in behavior can be important.

That natality as well as mortality may vary with density is shown by the two final examples, one taken from the laboratory

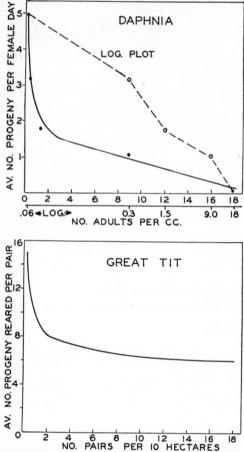

Figure 60. Density-dependent natality in a laboratory population of cladocera (upper graph) and a wild population of great tits (lower graph). The curve showing the decline in production of young with increasing density is strikingly similar in these two dissimilar populations. (Upper graph redrawn from Frank, 1952; lower graph redrawn from Kluijver, 1951.)

and one from the field, illustrated in Figure 60. From these graphs we see that the production of eggs and young per female decreased with increasing density in laboratory cultures of cladocera ("water fleas") and in wild populations of great tits (small birds).

12. Population energy flow

Statement

Energy flow (= rate of assimilation) in a population provides the most reliable basis for (1) evaluating observed fluctuations in density and (2) determining the role of a population within its community.

Explanation and example

Many of the concepts of energy flow and productivity outlined in Chapter 3 apply to the population level as well as to the ecosystem level. As was brought out on page 56, numbers (numerical density) overemphasize, and weights (biomass density) underemphasize the importance of small organisms, while the reverse is true with large organisms. If data on numbers and biomass can be used to calculate rates of change and energy flow, then a more reliable estimate of the importance of a population in its community can be obtained. Figure 61 illustrates a study in which this was done for a population of grasshoppers living in a salt marsh

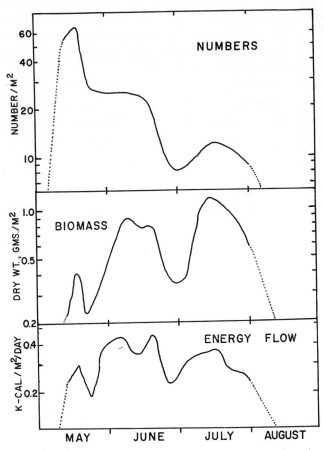

Figure 61. Numbers, biomass (dry weight), and energy flow (population assimilation rate) per square meter in a population of salt marsh grasshoppers (*Orchelimum fidicinium*) living in a *Spartina alterniflora* marsh near the University of Georgia's Marine Institute, Sapelo Island, Georgia. (After E. P. Odum and Alfred E. Smalley, 1959.)

community. In this relatively simple case, the animal is a strict herbivore, is sedentary, has but one generation per year and lives in a rather uniform stand composed of one species of plant which provides its sole source of food and shelter. The numbers and biomass per square meter were determined at 3 to 4 day intervals. From these data, population growth, or production, was determined by adding the increase in weight of the living population to the growth of individuals which died during the census interval. Production was then converted to calories/M^2/day. Oxygen consumption (respiration) of adults and different sized nymphs in relation to temperature was then determined in the laboratory. From these data population respiration of the average standing crop during each interval was calculated and adjusted to the actual temperature of the environment. Oxygen consumption was converted to calories by means of an oxycaloric coefficient (see Ivlev, 1934). The total population assimilation rate was then obtained by adding production to respiration.

As may be seen from Figure 61, numbers were at a peak in mid-May, when numerous very small nymphs hatched out from over-wintering eggs, and then declined rapidly during the season. In the particular year of the study there were two periods of heavy mortality, each of which was followed by accelerated growth of survivors, and also by a small amount of recruitment (new eggs hatching in early summer, immigration during late summer). Thus, biomass fluctuated rather violently, reaching a peak in late summer when the population was composed mostly of large adults. Note that the peak of energy flow did not correspond with either the peak in numbers or the peak in biomass, but occurred during the period when the population was composed of a medium number of medium sized nymphs, all growing very rapidly. In other words, the greatest impact of the population on the marsh (in terms of consumption of the grass) did not coincide with maximum numbers or biomass, although more nearly with the latter than the former. Also, note that, while numbers and biomass varied and fluctuated five to six fold, energy flow varied only two fold. Since metabolism-per-gram of small nymphs was several times greater than that of adults, the high number but small biomass population of the spring was about equal to the low number but large biomass population of late summer. From the bottom graph in Figure 61 we see that approximately one-third of a kilo-calorie/day/M^2 was assimilated by the population for about 2½ months. The total energy flow per M^2 for the season was approximately 28 calories or about 7 grams dry weight of grass (4 Calories/gram). Since these grasshoppers assimilate only about a third of what they eat (assimilation efficiency about 33 per cent, see Table 2, page 54), then about 21 grams/M^2 were probably removed from the growing plants. It should be emphasized that the 14 grams not assimilated did not change trophic levels but were available as food for other primary consumers, such as bacteria, fungi or detritus-feeding animals.

From this example we see that even within the same species density or "standing crop" data can be misleading if used as a measure of importance; only by integrating numbers and biomass and adding respiration (which is 50 per cent or more of energy flow in many situations) can a true picture be obtained, especially if we wish to compare populations in which individuals differ greatly in size (as ants and deer, for example). Finally, it should be emphasized that although an animal was used in the above example, the energy flow approach is equally applicable to all populations (plant, animal or microbe) in all environments.

13. Population structure: internal distribution patterns (dispersion)

Statement

Individuals in a population may be distributed according to three broad patterns (Fig. 62): (1) random, (2) uniform (more regular than random), and (3) clumped (irregular, non-random). Random distribution is relatively rare in nature, occurring where the environment is very uniform and there is no tendency to aggregate. Uniform distribution may occur where competition between individuals is severe or where there is positive antagonism which promotes even spacing. Clumping of varying degree represents by far the commonest pattern, almost the rule, when individuals are considered. However, if individuals of a population tend to form groups of a certain size—for example, pairs in animals, or vegetative clones in plants—the distribution of the *groups* may more nearly approach random. Determination of the type of distribution, of the degree of clumping (if any), and of the size and permanence of groups are necessary if a real understanding of the nature of a population is to be obtained, and especially if density is to be correctly measured. Thus, sample methods and statistical analyses which would be quite sound for random or uniform distribution might be entirely inadequate or misleading when applied to strongly clumped distributions.

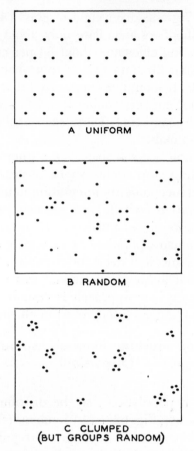

Figure 62. Three basic patterns of the distribution of individuals, pairs or other units, in a population.

Explanation

The three patterns of distribution or "intrapopulation disper-sion" are shown in a simplified manner in Figure 62. Each rec-tangle contains approximately the same number of individuals. In the case of clumped distribution (C), the groups could be the same or of varying size (as shown), and they could be randomly distributed (as shown), uniformly distributed, or themselves aggregated or clumped, with large unoccupied spaces. In other words, we might consider that there are five types of distribution: (1) uniform, (2) random, (3) random clumped, (4) uniform clumped, and (5) aggregated clumped. All these types are un-doubtedly found in nature. It is obvious from examining Figure

62 that a small sample drawn from the three populations could yield very different results. A small sample from a population with a clumped distribution would tend to give either too high or too low a density when the number in the sample is multiplied to obtain the total population. Thus "clumped" populations require larger and more carefully planned sample techniques than non-clumped ones.

It should be recalled that random distribution is one that follows the so-called "normal" or bell-shaped curve on which standard statistical methods are based. This type of distribution is to be expected in nature when many small factors are acting together on the population. When a few major factors are dominating, as is the usual case (recall principle of limiting factors), there is no reason to expect a completely random distribution in nature.

The problem of intrapopulation dispersion has been well stated by Cole (1946), as follows: "Some of the most persistent difficulties encountered in ecological field work stem from the fact that populations of living organisms are rarely distributed at random over the space available to them. Nor is random distribution, implying that the individual organisms are scattered by chance, to be expected in most biological material. When plants reproduce vegetatively or by means of seeds there is a tendency for the offspring to be concentrated near the parent plant. The same is true of animals which produce their young in litters and especially of the many forms which deposit masses of eggs thus temporarily leading to a heavy concentration of individuals within a small area. Most animals furthermore show some tendency toward active congregation. Even the sexual attraction which brings pairs of animals together is a departure from the theoretical conditions necessary to produce a randomly distributed population, while the social instincts which induce the formation of flocks in birds, herds in mammals, and colonies in social insects depart so radically from random processes that no one would expect the density of ants or deer to exhibit any uniformity over a wide area. . . . To a greater or lesser extent the investigator can circumvent intersample variability by selecting as homogeneous an area as possible for sampling, but there is always the possibility that the organisms under investigation were responding to local factors of which the investigator was unaware."

Cole goes on to suggest that non-random or "contagious" distributions of organisms be considered to be made up of intermingled random distributions of groups containing various numbers of individuals (see Figure 62). In other words, to take an extreme case, it would be much better to determine the number of ant colonies (i.e., using the colony as the population unit) by a sample method and then determine the average number of individuals per colony, than it would be to try to measure the number of individuals directly by random samples.

A number of methods have been suggested that may be used to determine the type of spacing and degree of clumping between individuals in a population (where it is not self-evident), but there is much that must still be done in solving this important problem. Two methods may be mentioned as examples. One method is to compare the actual frequency of occurrence of different sized groups obtained in a series of samples with a "Poisson" series that gives the frequency with which groups of 0, 1, 2, 3, 4, etc., individuals will be encountered together if the distribution is random. Thus, if the occurrence of small sized groups (including blanks) and large sized groups is more frequent and the occurrence of middle sized groups less frequent than expected, then the distribution is clumped. The opposite is found in uniform distribution. Statistical tests can be used to determine whether the observed deviation from the Poisson curve is significant, but this general method has the disadvantage that sample size may influence the results.

Another method, suggested by Dice (1952), involves actually measuring the distance between individuals in some standardized way. When the square root of the distance is plotted against frequency, the shape of the resulting frequency polygon indicates the distribution pattern. A symmetrical polygon (a normal bell-shaped curve, in other words) indicates random distribution, a polygon skewed to the right a uniform distribution, and one skewed to the left a clumped distribution (individuals coming closer together than expected). A numerical measure of the degree of "skewness" may be computed. This method, of course, would be most applicable to plants or stationary animals, but it could be used to determine spacing between animal colonies or domiciles (fox dens, rodent burrows, bird nests, etc.).

Examples

Park (1934) found that flour beetle larvae were usually distributed throughout their very uniform environment in a random manner, since observed distribution corresponded with the Poisson distribution. Forest trees which have reached sufficient height to form a part of the forest crown may show a uniform distribution according to Dice (1952), because competition for sunlight is so great that the trees tend to be spaced at very regular intervals, "more regular than random." A cornfield, of course, would be another good example. Desert shrub vegetation often are very regularly spaced almost as if planted in rows, apparently because of the intense competition (which may include root antibiotics) in the low moisture environment (see Figure 130, page 404). As for clumped distributions, the reader will not have to look far to find ample examples! Of several forest floor invertebrates studied by Cole, only spiders showed a random distribution, while he reports on another study in which only 4 out of 44 plants showed a random distribution. All the rest showed varying degrees of clumping. This gives us something of an idea of what to expect in natural situations. Further attention will be given to aggregations in the next section.

14. Population structure: aggregation and Allee's principle

Statement

As indicated in the previous section, varying degrees of "clumping" are characteristic of the internal structure of most populations at one time or another. Such clumping is the result of the aggregation of individuals (1) in response to local habitat differences, (2) in response to daily and seasonal weather changes, (3) as the result of reproductive processes, or (4) as the result of social attractions (in higher animals). The degree of aggregation to be found in a given species population, therefore, depends on the specific nature of the habitat (whether uniform or discontinuous), the weather or other physical factors, the type of reproductive pattern characteristic of the species, and the degree of sociality. Aggregation may increase competition between individuals for nutrients, food, or space, but this is often more than counterbalanced by increased survival of the group. Individuals in groups often experience a lower mortality rate during unfavorable periods or during attacks by other organisms than do isolated individuals, because the surface area exposed to the environment is less in proportion to the mass and because the group may be able to favorably modify microclimate or microhabitat. The degree of aggregation, as well as the over-all density which results in optimum population growth and survival, varies with species and conditions; therefore, undercrowding (or lack of aggregation), as well as overcrowding, may be limiting. This is Allee's principle.

Explanation and examples

In plants, aggregation may occur in response to the first three factors listed above, whereas in higher animals spectacular aggregations may be the result of all four factors as illustrated, for example, by the great herds of reindeer or caribou which occur in the very uneven arctic habitat. Figure 63 is a map of location of all individuals of three species of plants in an old field in Michigan. Much the same sort of pattern of animals would often be obtained if it were possible to photograph them from above. Looking at the map we first note that part of the area, a minor part in this case, is not suitable for any of the three species (because it is too damp); thus the nature of the habitat accounts for the first deviation from random distribution (in this case, a minor deviation). Next, we note that the three species vary in the degree of aggregation, the goldenrod (*Solidago*) showing almost a random distribution, whereas the *Lespedeza* plants are highly clumped. The latter commonly reproduce vegetatively, new individuals coming up from the root stocks; thus the pattern of reproduction, in part at least, accounts for the aggregation.

In plants in general, and probably in some of the lower animal groups, it is a rather well defined ecological principle that aggregation is inversely related to the mobility of disseminules (seeds, spores, etc.) (Weaver and Clements, 1929). For example, in driving about the country all of us have frequently observed that in old fields cedars, persimmons, and other plants with non-mobile seeds are nearly always clumped near a parent or along fences and other places where birds or other animals have deposited the seeds in groups. On the other hand, ragweeds and grasses, and even pine trees which have light seeds widely distributed by the wind, are, by comparison, much more evenly distributed over the old fields.

Group survival value is an important characteristic that may result from aggregation. A group of plants may be able to withstand the action of wind better than isolated individuals or be able to reduce water loss more effectively. With green plants, however, the deleterious effects of competition for light and

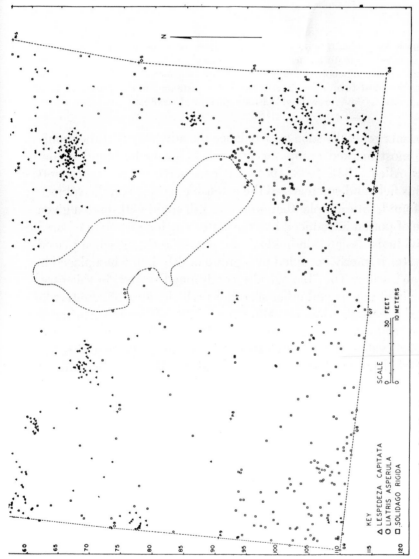

Figure 63. The distribution of three species of plants in an old field in Michigan. The distribution of individuals of Solidago approached random, while that of Lespedeza is highly "clumped." (After Cain and Evans, 1952.)

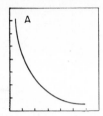 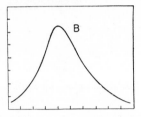

Figure 64. Illustration of Allee's principle. In some populations growth and survival is greatest when population size is small (A), whereas in others intraspecific protocooperation results in an intermediate sized population being the most favorable (B). In the latter instance "undercrowding" is as detrimental as "overcrowding." (From Allee et al., 1949.)

nutrients generally soon over-balance the advantages of the group. The most marked group survival values are to be found in animals. Allee (1931, 1938, 1951) has conducted many experiments in this field and summarized the extensive writings on the subject. He found, for example, that groups of fish could withstand a given dose of poison introduced into the water much better than isolated individuals. Isolated individuals were more resistant when placed in water formerly occupied by a group of fish than when placed in "clean" water. The "biologically conditioned" water, in this case, contained mucus and other secretions which aided in counteracting the poisons, thus revealing something of the mechanism of group action in this case. Bees provide another example of group survival value; a hive or cluster of bees can generate and retain enough heat in the mass for survival of all the individuals at temperatures low enough to kill all the bees if each were isolated. Darling's results with colonial birds were mentioned in the previous section. Allee points out that these types of primitive cooperation (protocooperation) found even in very primitive phyla are the beginning of social organization, which shows varying degrees of development in the animal kingdom, culminating in the intelligent group behavior of human beings (which, we hope, has great survival value!). Allee's principle is diagrammatically illustrated in Figure 64.

Actual social aggregations as seen in the social insects and vertebrates (as contrasted with passive aggregation in response to some common environmental factor) have a definite organization involving social hierarchies and individual specializations. A social hierarchy may take the form of a "peck-order" (so-called because the phenomena were first described in chickens) with clear-cut dominance-subordinance between individuals often in linear order (like a military order of command from general to private!), or it may take the form of a more complicated pattern of leadership, dominance, and cooperation as occurs in well-knit groups of birds and insects that behave almost as a single unit. In such units there may be a definite leader, but as often as not no one individual actually leads; individuals in the group follow whichever individual acts forthrightly as if it "knew what it was about." Social organization in animals is summarized by Scott (1956).

The remarkable organizations of social insects are in a class by themselves and have been much studied (especially by W. M. Wheeler and A. E. Emerson; see Allee et al., 1949, Chapter 24). The most highly developed insect societies are found among the termites (order *Isoptera*) and ants, bees, etc. (order *Hymenoptera*). A division of labor is accomplished in the most specialized species by three castes—reproductive (queens and kings), workers, and soldiers, each morphologically specialized to perform the functions of reproduction, food getting, and protection.

15. Population structure: isolation and territoriality

Statement

Forces which bring about isolation or the spacing of individuals, pairs, or small groups in a population are perhaps not as widespread as those favoring aggregation but they are nevertheless important, especially in populations of higher animals. Isolation usually is the result of (1) interindividual competition, or (2) actual directed antagonism. In the first instance nearby individuals are eliminated by the most vigorous, and in the second instance individuals avoid or are driven out of the immediate area already occupied. In both cases a random or a uniform distribution may result, as outlined in Section 13. Individuals, pairs, or family groups of vertebrates and the higher invertebrates commonly restrict their activities to a definite area, called the *home range*. If this area is actively defended, it is called a *territory*. Territoriality is most pronounced in vertebrates and certain arthropods which have complicated reproductive behavior patterns involving nest building, egg laying, and care and protection of young. Territorial behavior is most often restricted to the breeding season.

Isolation of this sort reduces competition, conserves energy during critical periods, and, in some cases at least, prevents overcrowding and exhaustion of food supply.

Explanation and examples

Just as aggregation may increase competition, but has other advantages, so spacing of individuals in a population may reduce the competition for the necessities of life, but perhaps at the expense of the advantages of cooperative group action. Presumably, which pattern survives in a long-term evolutionary sense in a particular case depends on which gives the greatest long-time advantage. In any event, we find both patterns to be frequent in nature; in fact, some species populations alternate from one to the other (robins, for example, isolate into territories during the breeding season and aggregate into flocks in the winter), and thus obtain advantages from both arrangements! Again, different ages and sexes may show opposite patterns at the same time (adults isolate, young aggregate, for example).

The role of intraspecific competition in bringing about spacing, as in forest trees and desert shrubs, has already been discussed (Section 11). We need only to call attention to the spacing which results from active antagonism as exhibited in higher animals. Many animals isolate themselves and restrict their major activities to definite areas or home ranges, which may vary from a few square inches to many square miles in the case of a puma. Since home ranges often overlap, only partial spacing is achieved (Fig. 65). Territoriality achieves the ultimate in spacing (Fig. 65, right); best known in birds, it is also characteristic of other animals, especially fish, reptiles, and social insects. Territories have been classified by Nice (1941) into several basic types: A, entire mating, feeding, and breeding area defended; B, mating and nesting but not feeding area defended; C, mating area only defended; D, nest only defended; E, non-breeding areas defended. In most territorial behavior actual fighting over boundaries is held to a minimum. Owners advertise their land or location in space by song or displays and potential intruders generally avoid entering an established domain. The fact that the area defended by birds is often larger at the beginning of the nesting cycle than later when the demand for food is greatest, and the fact that many territorial species of birds, fish, and reptiles do not defend the feeding area at all give support to the idea that reproductive isolation for the nest builder has greater survival value than the isolation of a food supply.

A good place to observe territorial behavior in the spring is in the shallow water of a pond containing bass or sunfish. Males may

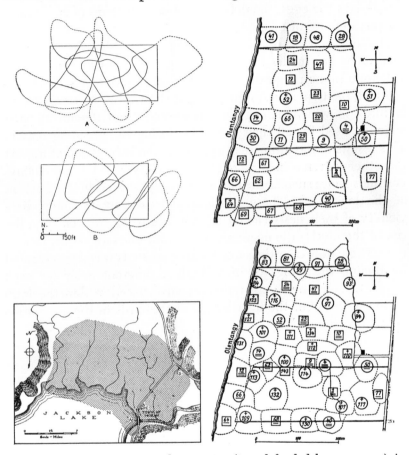

Figure 65.   Home ranges and territories (i.e., defended home ranges) in various animals. Upper left: Home ranges of 15 box turtles (*Terrapene carolina*) occupying parts of a five-acre plot; A—males, B—females. In this species there is no defense of the home ranges, which overlap. (From Stickel, 1950.) Right: Territories of song sparrows (*Melospiza melodia*) during two successive years on the same tract of land. Each territory is occupied by a pair and is vigorously defended by the male so that little or no overlap occurs. One line under number in a territory indicates that male occupied that territory the previous season, two lines indicate two seasons, etc. Territoriality of type "A" (see text), as illustrated here, results in relatively even spacing (uniform type of distribution, see Figure 62) if the habitat is uniform. (From Nice, 1937.) Lower left: Type "D" territory in the cliff swallow in which birds of four colonies (A, B, C, D) share a common feeding area (shaded area) and isolate themselves only in the immediate vicinity of the nest. (From Emlen, 1952.)

be observed defending a "nest" or "bed" (a scooped-out place on the bottom) and its vicinity. When another individual approaches the male displays his bright fin colors and charges toward the intruder. Since the male defends the area before as well as after the female lays the eggs, the defense is clearly in terms of space, and not just defense of offspring.

The diagram at upper left in Figure 65, showing the area covered by box turtles, is a good example of a solitary animal with a definite home range that overlaps that of other individuals. In contrast, the two diagrams at the right show type "A" territoriality in birds in which pairs isolate themselves and defend an area which is used for all their activities during the breeding season. This results in the ultimate of spacing if the habitat is uniform. At the other extreme in bird territorialism (type "D") are colony-nesting species such as the cliff swallow, illustrated in the diagram at the lower left. These swallows defend only the immediate vicinity of their nests (as far as they can reach to peck from the rim of the nest!); the members of the four colonies shown ranged indiscriminately over the same feeding area (as was demonstrated by dyeing the wings of birds with a different color for each colony). Thus, nests are rather evenly spaced within the individual colony, but the distribution of the birds in the population is highly "clumped"!

7 · Principles and concepts pertaining to organization at the interspecies population level

1. Types of interaction between two species

Statement

Theoretically, populations of two species may interact in six basic ways, corresponding to the six combinations of 0, +, and —, as follows: 0 0, — —, ++, +0, —0, and +—.* Two of these combinations (++ and +—) are commonly subdivided, resulting in eight important interactions which have been demonstrated. These (see Table 15) are as follows: (1) *neutralism,* in which neither population is affected by association with the other; (2) *competition,* in which each population adversely affects the other in the struggle for food, nutrients, living space, or other common need; (3) *mutualism,* in which growth and survival of both populations is benefited and neither can survive under natural conditions without the other; (4) *protocooperation,* in which both populations benefit by the association but relations are not obligatory; (5) *commensalism,* in which one population is benefited but the other is not affected; (6) *amensalism,* in which one population is inhibited and the other not affected; (7) *parasitism* and (8) *predation,* in which one population adversely affects the other by direct attack but is dependent on the other. In terms of

* Burkholder (1952), following the scheme of Haskell (1949), lists nine possible combinations by considering — + different from + —, etc.

Table 15.   *Analysis of two-species population interactions*

	Effect on population growth and survival of two populations, A and B				
	When not interacting		When interacting		General result of
Type of interaction	A	B	A	B	interaction
1. Neutralism (A and B independent)	0	0	0	0	Neither population affects the other
2. Competition (A and B competitors)	0	0	—	—	Population most affected eliminated from niche
3. Mutualism (A and B partners or symbionts)	—	—	+	+	Interaction obligatory for both
4. Protocooperation (A and B cooperators)	0	0	+	+	Interaction favorable to both, but not obligatory
5. Commensalism (A commensal; B host)	—	0	+	0	Obligatory for A; B not affected
6. Amensalism (A amensal; B inhibitor or antibiotic)	0	0	—	0	A inhibited B not affected
7. Parasitism (A parasite; B host) 8. Predation (A predator; B prey)	—	0	+	—	Obligatory for A; B inhibited

+ Population growth increased (positive term added to growth equation).
− Population growth decreased (negative term added to growth equation).
0 Population growth not affected (no additional term in growth equation).

population growth and survival, these interactions involve adding positive, negative, or zero terms to basic population growth equations as written in Chapter 6, Section 8.

All these population interactions are likely to occur in the average community and may be readily recognized and studied, at least qualitatively, even in complex communities. For a given species pair the type of interaction may change under different conditions or during successive stages in their life histories. Thus, two species might exhibit parasitism at one time, commensalism at another, and be completely neutral at still another time. Simplified communities and laboratory experiments provide means for singling out and studying quantitatively the various interactions. Also, deductive mathematical models derived from such studies enable us to analyze factors not ordinarily separable from the others.

Explanation

A familiar situation is the action of one population affecting the growth or death rate of another population. Thus, the members of one population may eat members of the other population, compete for foods, excrete harmful wastes, or otherwise interfere with the other population. Likewise, populations may help one another, the interaction being either one-way or reciprocal. Interactions of these sorts fall into several definite categories as listed in the above statement and shown in Table 15. Before discussing actual cases, it will be helpful to diagram hypothetical and somewhat simplified cases in order to see how these interactions can operate to influence the growth and survival of populations. As previously pointed out, growth equation "models" make definitions more precise, clarify thinking, and enable us to determine how factors may operate in complex natural situations.

If the simplified growth of one population can be diagrammed and described by an equation (see Chapter 6, Section 8), the influence of another population may be expressed by a term that modifies the unrestricted growth of the first population. Various terms can be substituted according to the type of interaction. For example, in competition the growth rate of each population is equal to the unlimited (specific) rate minus its own self-crowding effects (which increase as its population increases) minus the detrimental effects of the other species, N_2 (which also increase as the numbers of both species, N and N_2, increase), or

$$\underset{\left[\begin{array}{c}\text{growth}\\\text{rate}\end{array}\right]}{\frac{\Delta N}{\Delta t}} = \underset{\left[\begin{array}{c}\text{unlimited}\\\text{rate}\end{array}\right]}{rN} - \underset{\left[\begin{array}{c}\text{self-crowding}\\\text{effects}\end{array}\right]}{\left(\frac{r}{K}N^2\right)} - \underset{\left[\begin{array}{c}\text{detrimental effects}\\\text{of the other species}\end{array}\right]}{CN_2N}$$

This equation is the same as that given in the section on population growth form (Chapter 6, Section 8), except for the addition of the last term, "minus detrimental effects of the other species." There are several possible results of this kind of interaction. If "C" is small for both species so that the interspecific depressing effects are less than intraspecific (self-limiting) effects, the growth rate and perhaps the final density of both species would be depressed slightly; but both species would probably be able to live together. In other words, the depressing effects of the other species would be less important than the competition within the species. Also, if the species exhibit exponential growth (with self-limiting factor absent from the equation) then interspecific competition might result in the leveling off of growth in a sigmoid manner. However, if "C" is large, the species exerting the largest effect will eliminate its competitor or force it into another niche. Thus, theoretically, species which have similar requirements cannot live together in exactly the same niche, because strong competition will likely develop, causing one of them to be eliminated from the niche. Our models point up some of the possibilities; we shall see in the next section how these possibilities actually work out.

When both species of interacting populations have beneficial effects on each other instead of detrimental ones, a positive term is added to the growth equations. In such cases both populations grow and prosper, reaching equilibrium levels that are mutually beneficial. If beneficial effects of the other population (the positive term in the equation) are necessary for growth and survival of both populations, the relation is known as mutualism. If, on the other hand, the beneficial effects only increase the size or growth rate of the population but are not necessary for growth or survival, the relationship comes under the heading of cooperation or protocooperation. (Since the cooperation indicated is not the result of conscious or "intelligent" reasoning that is the basis of cooperation between individual human beings, the latter term is probably to be preferred.) In both protocooperation and mutualism the outcome is similar, i.e., the growth of either population is less or zero without the presence of the other population. When an equilibrium level is reached the two populations exist together stably, usually in a definite proportion.

That type of relationship in which one species benefits but not the other is very common and is known as commensalism. The organism benefiting is the commensal. In this case the interaction is usually obligatory for the commensal, but growth and survival of the other or "host" population is not affected, at least not in any measurable manner. The opposite of commensalism is amensalism; one population (the amensal) is inhibited, whereas the other is not affected. The bread mold, *Penicillium,* which secretes a substance (which we call penicillin) that inhibits the growth of bacteria, is a good example of this type of interaction. So far as is now known, the bacteria have no effect on the mold. In nature, the mold presumably obtains more food when the competing bacteria are removed from its immediate vicinity. Man, of course, is making good use of this type of interaction by extracting the inhibiting substance and using it to combat pathogenic microorganisms. Metabolites, such as penicillin, which are produced by lower plant organisms are commonly called antibiotics, which, unfortunately, is a broad term being used in a restricted sense. Antibiosis is not always an amensal type of interaction. Sometimes the victim (bacterium) fights back, producing an anti-fungus substance, in which case the relation is one of competition (– –). In other cases, the interaction appears to be parasitism. There is much to be learned about the ecology of antibiosis. The possibility that both growth and inhibitory substances secreted by organisms may act as "environmental hormones" in the ecosystem was mentioned in Chapter 2.

There is no sharp distinction between predators and parasites, as has already been indicated in Chapter 4. As shown in Table 15, the theoretical interaction is the same. If the organism exerting adverse effect is larger than the victim species, the relation is generally classed as that of predator-prey. In a simplified case where there is but one predator (or parasite) and one prey (or host), the populations of the two may tend to oscillate, as was discussed in Chapter 6, Section 9.

A parasite is often broadly defined as an organism which lives on or within another organism, whether it harms the host or not. Thus, for convenience we may quite commonly call a specific organism a "parasite" even though it interacts in a commensal manner part of the time, or for part of the life cycle, and as a detrimental parasite under other conditions. In terms of the basic equations, new terms are added and various constants change as the type and degree of interaction change. What we are attempting to classify with some precision in Table 15 is *types of interactions*, not species; any given species may exhibit any or all of the types of interactions.

It may be pointed out that consideration of population interactions as shown in Table 15 or in terms of growth equation avoids confusion which often results when terms and definitions alone are considered. Thus, the term "symbiosis" is sometimes used in the same sense as mutualism; sometimes the term is used to cover commensalism and parasitism as well. Various nouns have been proposed for the same type of interaction, adding to the confusion. When relations are diagrammed, however, there is little doubt as to the type of interaction being considered; the word or "label" then becomes secondary to the mechanism and its result. Even if we were never able to apply equations to actual situations, these "mathematical models" are still highly useful in clarifying one's thinking, in opening the way for quantitative expression, and in helping to avoid cumbersomely worded definitions which have plagued the early history of ecology!

, One final point. Note that the word "harmful" was not used in describing negative interactions. Competition and predation decrease the growth rate of affected populations, but this does not necessarily mean that the interaction is harmful from the long-time survival or evolutionary standpoint. For example, competition might increase the rate of natural selection, resulting in adaptation to a new niche and an ultimate increase in the "success" of the species. We have rather good evidence that predators are often beneficial to populations as a whole, in that they may prevent overpopulation which might result in self-destruction (see example in Section 3).

2. Competition, and the number of species in a niche

Statement

Competition refers to the interaction of two organisms striving for the same thing. In ecology, interspecific competition is any interaction between two or more species populations which adversely affects their growth and survival. As outlined in the previous section, any case in which negative terms are substituted in the population equations of both populations due to action of the other population is a case of competition. In terms of observed growth curves, if the curves of two populations are both steeper when they are separate than when they are interacting, competition of some sort is operating. Because of competition, only one species tends to occur in an ecological niche at the same time or place.

Explanation

A great deal has been written about competition by ecologists, geneticists and evolutionists. Some writers (see, for example, Birch, 1957; Williamson, 1957) have objected to the broad use of the word competition as we have delimited it in Table 15, and have suggested that the term be restricted to situations where negative influences are due to a shortage of materials used by both, leaving out other types of reciprocal effects such as the secretion of harmful substances. The author is of the firm opinion that words such as competition, community, population, which are not only widely used in science but in the general language as well, should be precisely defined (as we have done), but should remain broad in scope. It is much less confusing to everyone to leave the basic term broad, and then "subclassify" by means of adjectives or modifying phrases where a more restrictive meaning is in order. For example, we can speak of competition for resources, antibiotic competition, competition for light, etc. Or we could subdivide quantitatively according to the severity of the depressing effect as Philip (1955) has done with the use of models.

The competitive interaction may involve common space, food, or nutrients, light, waste material action, mutual predation, susceptibility to carnivores, disease, etc., and many other types of mutual interactions. Competition, at least under hypothetical conditions, as we have seen in the preceding paragraph, can result in equilibrium adjustments by two species, or it can result in one species population replacing another or forcing it to occupy another space or to use another food, whatever the object of competitive action. It is often observed that closely related organisms having similar habits or life forms often do not occur in the same places. If they do occur in the same places, they use different food, are active at different times, or are otherwise occupying somewhat different niches. Recall that an ecological niche, as defined in Chapter 2, involves not only the physical space occupied by an organism but also its place in the community, including its energy source, period of activity, etc. No two species can have exactly the same niche, of course, and still be different, but species, especially if they are closely related (and hence have similar morphological and physiological characteristics), are often so similar as to have virtually the same niche requirements. Also, competition occurs wherever niches overlap even to a partial extent. It is not known how great the overlap must be before one species pushes out the other. In any event, experimental and observational research has shown that the rule of one species to a niche is true in a high proportion of cases. This idea was first clearly demonstrated experimentally by Gause in 1934, and is often known as *Gause's principle*.

Some of the most widely debated theoretical aspects of com-

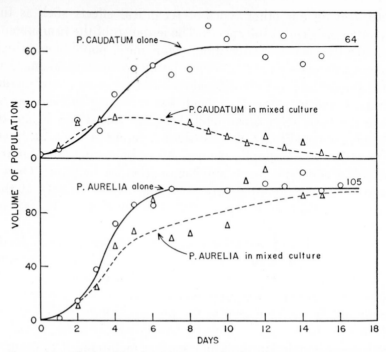

Figure 66. Competition between two closely related species of protozoa which have identical niches. When separate, *Paramecium caudatum* and *Paramecium aurelia* exhibit normal sigmoid growth in controlled cultures with constant food supply; when together, *P. caudatum* is eliminated. (From Allee et al., 1949, after Gause.)

petition theory revolve around what have become known as the Lotka-Volterra equations (so-called because the equations were proposed as models by Lotka and Volterra in separate publications in 1925-26). These equations consist of a pair of differential equations similar to the one outlined in the preceding section. Despite differences of opinion (see, for example, the opposite opinion of Andrewartha and Birch, 1953 and Philip, 1955), the equations seem theoretically sound as models so long as they are not applied beyond the scope for which they are intended. We come back again to the desirability of having some kind of definite base from which to work; if a particular situation does not conform to the model, we know we should look for other factors that might account for the phenomena.

Examples

The results of one of Gause's original experiments are illustrated in Figure 66. This is, we might say, a "classic" example of the action of competition and its relation to niche in simple laboratory populations. Two closely related ciliate protozoans, *Paramecium caudatum* and *Paramecium aurelia,* when in separate culture, exhibited typical sigmoid population growth and maintained a constant population level in culture medium which was maintained constant with a fixed density of food items (bacteria which did not themselves multiply in the media and thus could be added at frequent intervals to keep food density constant). When both protozoans were placed in the same culture, however, *P. aurelia* alone survived after 16 days. In this case neither organism attacked the other or secreted harmful substances; *P. aurelia* popu-

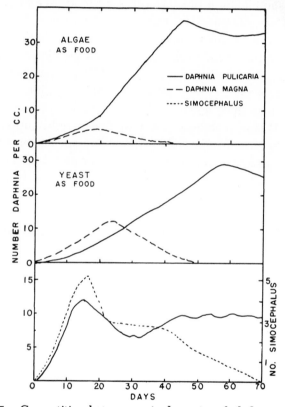

Figure 67.   Competition between paired species of cladocera in cultures. *Daphnia pulicaria* eliminates the closely related *D. magna* but, with yeast as food for both, *D. magna* persists for a longer period since this food is less favorable for the dominant species. Competition is less severe between *Daphnia* and *Simocephalus,* which have overlapping niches. In mixed culture both species population undergo normal growth form and persist together for 40 days, but eventually *Simocephalus* is eliminated. (For a picture of Cladocera, see page 304.) (Upper two graphs redrawn from Frank, 1957; lower graph redrawn from Frank, 1952.)

lations simply had more rapid growth rate (higher intrinsic rate of increase) and thus "out-competed" *P. caudatum* for the limited amount of food under the existing conditions. On the other hand, *Paramecium caudatum* and *Paramecium bursaria* were both able to survive and reach a stable equilibrium in the same culture medium because, although they were competing for the same food, *P. bursaria* occupied a different part of the culture where it could feed on bacteria without competing with *P. caudatum*. Thus, the habitat feature of the niche of these two species proved to be sufficiently different, even though their food was identical. Other examples could be cited where two closely related species exist in the same habitat but take different food (see Fig. 69), thus resulting in equally effective separation of niches.

A much more extensive series of experiments have been completed by Frank (1952, 1957), who used species of *Cladocera* (water fleas). As may be seen in Figure 67 one species eliminated the other when very closely related forms belonging to the same genus were matched; however, the pattern of interaction varied with food. When yeast was used (which would support either species when grown separately), the losing species had a temporary advantage and was able to increase for about 20 days. When less similar species were compared, such as those belonging to different genera, both populations underwent more or less normal sigmoid growth in mixed culture and maintained an upper asymptote level for about 40 days (Fig. 67, lower graph). Gradually, thereafter, the *Simocephalus* population declined and disappeared from the culture. This case appears to be a good example of overlapping niches. In nature, where competition would not likely be as severe, or as long continued, as in the small laboratory cultures, the two species would have less difficulty coexisting in the same habitat.

Studies on competition in flour beetles have been instructive. Crombie (1947), for example, found that *Tribolium* exterminates *Oryzaephilus* when both live in flour, because *Tribolium* is more active in destroying immature stages of other species. However, if glass tubes are placed in the flour where immature stages of *Oryzaephilus* may escape, then both populations survive. Thus, when a simple "one-niche" environment is changed to a "two-niche" environment competition is reduced sufficiently for the support of two species. It can be readily seen from experiments of this sort that the more niches that are present in nature the greater the number of species that may be potentially able to survive. In other experiments with flour beetles, it was found that the presence of a parasite attacking the dominant species could turn the tables and result in survival of the species which is normally eliminated in the two-species culture.

An especially long series of experiments with flour beetles have been carried out by Park (1948; 1954). Extinction of one of the two competing species invariably resulted when they were placed in the same uniform flour habitat, but no a priori prediction as to which survived could be made. Differences in population growth rates of single species populations were not alone sufficient to predict which species would win out when a given two species were grown together.* In other words, the general result of severe competition, as suggested by the simple growth equation models, was verified in this case, but it was obvious that factors other than rate of population growth or intrinsic rate of increase were involved.

So much for laboratory examples. It is readily conceded that crowding may be greater in laboratory experiments and, hence, competition exaggerated. Interspecific competition in plants in the field has been much studied, and is generally believed to be an important factor in bringing about a succession of species (as will be described in the next chapter). Keever (1955) describes an interesting situation where a species of tall weed which occupies first year fallow fields in almost pure stands was gradually replaced in these fields by another species previously unknown in the region. The two species, although belonging to different genera, have very similar life histories (time of flowering, seeding) and life forms and were thus brought into intense competition in the same niche.

Griggs (1956) has made an interesting study of plant competition on a rocky mountain fellfield where most of the species grew in isolated tussocks. Tussocks of one species were often invaded by other species. Griggs was able to prepare a list of species in the order of their ability to invade other tussocks. This "competitive ladder" did not prove to be the same as the order of succession because ability to invade and ability to completely replace were not entirely correlated.

We have already noted that competition between individuals

* In contrast, Frank (1957) was able to predict the outcome of competition in *Daphnia* from growth curves.

of the same species is one of the most important density-dependent factors in nature, and the same can be said of interspecific competition. Competition appears to be extremely important in determining the distribution of closely related species, and Gause's rule of no two species in the same niche seems to hold as well for field as for laboratory although much of the evidence is circumstantial. In nature, closely related species, or species which have very similar requirements, usually occupy different geographical areas or different habitats in the same area or otherwise avoid competition by differences in daily or seasonal activity or in food. For example, the common black-capped chickadee (*Parus atricapillus*) over much of its range in eastern North America has no competition from closely related birds. It occupies a wide variety of forests. In Europe, however, this species is associated with a number of very similar forms belonging to the same genus. As a result, the black-cap has become restricted during the breeding season to swamp forests, other species of tits occupying other types of forests, the same types, incidentally, that in the United States would be occupied by the blackcap.

An example which is perhaps less circumstantial is provided by the distribution of two species of sessile invertebrates on the Australian coast. In the intertidal area of rocky shores *Tetraclita,* a barnacle, and *Galeolaria,* a serpulid worm, occupy adjacent zones, one above the other. The range of the barnacle extends farther northward than does the range of the tubeworm. As one goes northward, the barnacle zone extends downward to fill the intertidal region vacated by the worm (Erdean, Kerry, and Stephenson, 1956). In other words, the vertical area occupied by the barnacle is greater when its presumed competitor is absent.

The important role which competition plays in habitat selection is summarized in Figure 68. The curves represent the range of habitat which can be tolerated by the species, with optimum and marginal conditions indicated. Where there is competition with other closely related or ecologically similar species the range of habitat conditions which the species occupies generally becomes restricted to the optimum (i.e., to the most favorable conditions where the species has an advantage in some manner over its competitors). Where interspecific competition is less severe, then intraspecific competition generally brings about a wider habitat choice. The same principle applies to geographical as well as to habitat distribution. It also often accounts for differences in habitat selection by the same species in different geographical regions, since a competitor may be present in one part of the range and absent in another.

There are many cases which seem at first to be exceptions to Gause's rule but which, on careful study, prove otherwise. A good example of this is the case of two similar fish-eating birds of Britain, the cormorant (*Phalacrocorax carbo*) and the shag (*P. aristotelis*) studied by Lack (1945). These two species commonly feed in the same waters and nest on the same cliffs, yet close study showed that actual nest sites were different and, as shown in Figure 69, the food was basically different. Thus the shag feeds in the upper waters on free-swimming fish and eels, whereas the cormorant is more of a bottom feeder, taking flat fish (flounders) and bottom invertebrates (shrimp, etc.).

Just because closely related species are sharply separated in nature does not, of course, mean that competition is actually operating continuously to keep them separated; the two species may have evolved different requirements or preferences which effectively keep them out of competition. A single example each from the plant and animal kingdom will suffice to illustrate. In Europe, one species of *Rhododendron*, namely, *hirsutum* is found on calcareous soils while another species, *R. ferrugineum* is found on acid soils. The requirements of the two species are such that neither can live at all in the opposite type of soil so that there

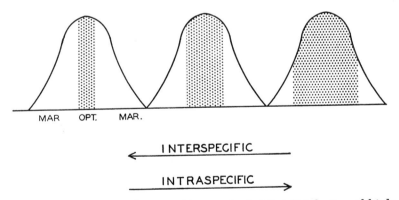

Figure 68.   The effect of competition on the habitat distribution of birds. When intraspecific competition dominates, the species spreads out and occupies less favorable (marginal) areas; where interspecific competition is intense the species tends to be restricted to a narrower range comprising the optimum conditions. (Modified from Svardson, 1949.)

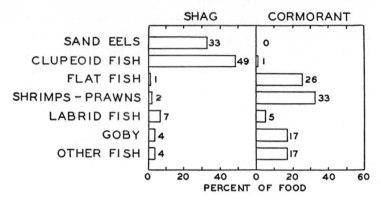

Figure 69.   Food habits of two closely related species of aquatic birds, the cormorant (*Phalacrocorax carbo*) and the shag (*P. aristotelis*), which are found together during the breeding season. Food habits indicate that although the habitat is similar the food is different; therefore, the niche of the two species is different and they are not actually in direct competition. (Data from Lack, 1945.)

is never any actual competition between them (see Braun-Blan-quet, 1932). Teal (1958) has made an experimental study of habi-tat selection of species of fidler crabs (*Uca*) which are usually separated in their occurence in salt marshes. One species, *U. pugilator*, is found on open sandy flats, while another, *U. pugnax*, is found on muddy substrates covered with marsh grass. Teal found that one species would tend not to invade the habitat of the other even in the absence of the other, because each species would dig burrows only in its preferred substrate. The absence of active competition, of course, does not mean that competition in the past is to be ruled out as a factor in bringing about the isolating behavior.

We may do well to close out this discussion of examples by adopting the three tentative models proposed by Philip (1955) as a basis for future observation, analysis and experimentation. These are: (1) imperfect competition, where interspecific effects are less than intraspecific effects; interspecific competition is a limiting factor but not to the extent of complete elimination of one species; (2) perfect competition as in the unmodified Gause or Lotka-Volterra model in which one species is invariably eliminated from the niche by a gradual process as crowding occurs; (3) hyperperfect competition in which the depressing effects are great and immediately effective, as in the production of antibiotics.

3. Negative interactions: predation and parasitism

Statement

As already indicated, predation and parasitism are examples of interactions between two populations which result in negative effects on the growth and survival of one of the populations (negative term in growth equation of one of the populations, see Table 15). A cardinal principle is that the negative effects tend to be quantitatively small where the interacting populations have had a common evolutionary history in a relatively stable ecosystem. In other words, natural selection tends to lead to reduction in detrimental effects or to the elimination of the interaction altogether, since continued severe depression of a prey or host population by the predator or parasite population can only lead to the extinction of one or both populations. Consequently, severe interaction is most frequently observed where the interaction is of recent origin (when two populations first become associated) or when there have been large scale or sudden changes (perhaps temporary) in the ecosystem (as might be produced by man).

Explanation and examples

It is difficult to approach the subject of parasitism and predation objectively. We all have a natural aversion to parasitic organisms, whether bacteria or tapeworms. Likewise, although man himself is the greatest predator the world has known, he tends to condemn all other predators without bothering to find out if they are really detrimental to his interests or not. The idea that "the only good hawk is a dead hawk" is widely held, but, as we shall see, it is by no means a true generalization.

The best way to be objective is to consider predation and parasitism from the population rather than from the individual standpoint. Predators and parasites certainly kill and injure individuals, and they depress in some measure at least the growth rate of populations or reduce the total population size. But does this always mean that populations would be better off without predators or parasites? From the long term view, are predators and parasites the sole beneficiaries of the association? Let us look at some specific cases and see what sort of answers we might get.

Prior to 1907 there were estimated to be about 4,000 deer and a good population of predators—pumas and wolves—on the Kaibab plateau, an area of about 700,000 acres on the north side of the

Grand Canyon of Arizona. Between 1907 and 1923 a concerted effort was made to remove the predators. By 1925 the deer population had increased to 100,000, which was far beyond the carrying capacity of the vegetation. Everything in reach—grass, tree seedlings, shrubs—was eaten and the whole area gave the appearance of a huge over-grazed and over-browsed pasture. In two winters 40 per cent of the enormous herd starved to death, and decline continued to about 10,000. The range continues to be depleted, and damage to forest reproduction will be evident for a long time. It has been estimated that the original range could have supported no more than 30,000 deer. Thus, the predator-prey interaction was maintaining a relatively stable equilibrium, with the deer population being held well below the point where its own food supply would be depleted.

The story of the chestnut blight in America is a case where a new parasite was introduced rather than an old one removed. Originally, the American chestnut was an important member of the forests of the Appalachian region of eastern North America. It had its share of parasites, diseases, and predators. Likewise, the oriental chestnut trees in China—different but related species— had their share of parasites, etc., including the fungus, *Endothia parasitica*, which attacks the bark of the stems. In 1904 the fungus was accidentally introduced into the United States. The American chestnut proved to be unresistant to this new parasite; finally, by 1952 all the large chestnuts had been killed, their gaunt gray trunks being a characteristic feature of Appalachian forests (Fig. 70). Both blight and chestnut sprout growths still exist, and no one can say whether the ultimate outcome will be complete extinction or adaptation. For all practical purposes the chestnut has been removed, for the time being at least, as a major influence in the forest.

The above examples are not just cases hand-picked to "prove a point." If the student will do a little reading in the library, he can find hundreds of similar examples which show: (1) that where parasites and predators have long been associated with their respective hosts and prey, the effect is moderate, neutral, or even beneficial from the long term view, as indicated in the case of the deer on the Kaibab plateau; and (2) that newly acquired parasites or predators are the most damaging. In fact, if one makes a list of the diseases, parasites, and insect pests which cause the greatest loss to agriculture or are most pathogenic to man himself, the list will include a large number of species which have recently been introduced into a new area, as in the case of the chestnut blight, or acquired a new host or prey.

The lesson for man, of course, is to beware of new negative interactions and to avoid sponsoring new ones any faster than is absolutely necessary.

Although predation and parasitism are similar from the ecological standpoint, the extremes in the series, the large predator and the small internal parasite, do exhibit important differences other than size. Parasitic or pathogenic organisms usually have a higher biotic potential than do predators. They are often more specialized in structure, metabolism, host specificity, and life history, as is necessitated by their special environment and the problem of dispersal from one host to another.

Of special interest are organisms which are intermediate between predators and parasites, for example, the so-called parasitic insects. These forms often have the ability of consuming the entire prey individual, as does the predator, and yet they have the host

Figure 70. Results of the chestnut blight in the southern Appalachian region (Georgia), an example of the extreme effect which a parasitic organism (fungus) introduced from the Old World may have on a newly acquired host (American chestnut tree).

specificity and high biotic potential of the parasite. Man has been able to propagate some of these organisms artificially and utilize them in the control of insect pests. In general, attempts to make similar use of large unspecialized predators have not been successful. Can you give reasons why this has been the case?

4. Positive interactions: commensalism, cooperation, and mutualism

Statement

Associations between two species populations which result in positive effects are exceedingly widespread and probably as important as competition, parasitism, etc., in determining the nature of populations and communities. Positive interactions may be conveniently considered in an evolutionary series as follows: commensalism—one population benefited; protocooperation—both populations benefited; and mutualism—both populations benefit and have become completely dependent on each other.

Explanation and examples

The widespread acceptance of Darwin's idea of "survival of the fittest" as an important means of bringing about natural selection has directed attention to the competitive aspects of nature. As a result, the importance of cooperation between species in nature has perhaps been underestimated. At least, positive interactions have not been subjected to as much quantitative study as have negative interactions. Like a balanced equation, it seems reasonable to assume that negative and positive relations between populations eventually tend to balance one another if the ecosystem is to achieve any kind of stability.

Commensalism represents a simple type of positive interaction and perhaps represents the first step toward the development of beneficial relations. It is especially common between sessile plants and animals on the one hand and motile organisms on the other. The ocean is an especially good place to observe commensalism. Practically every worm burrow, shellfish, or sponge contains various "uninvited guests," organisms which require the shelter of the host but do neither harm nor good in return. Perhaps you have opened oysters, or been served oysters on the half shell, and observed a small delicate crab in the mantle cavity. These are usually "commensal crabs," although sometimes they overdo their "guest" status by partaking of the host's tissues (Christensen and McDermott, 1958).

It is but a short step to a situation where both organisms gain by an association or interaction of some kind, in which case we have protocooperation. Crabs, for example, often "have" various coelenterates on the dorsal side of their bodies. The coelenterates provide protection and camouflage. In turn, the coelenterates are transported about and obtain particles of food when the crab captures and eats another animal.

In the above instance the crab is not absolutely dependent on the coelenterate, or vice versa. A further step in the process of cooperation results when each population becomes completely dependent on the other. Such cases have been called mutualism, or symbiosis. Often quite diverse kinds of organism are associated. In fact, instances of mutualism are most likely to develop between organisms with widely different requirements. (As we have seen, organisms with similar requirements are more likely to get involved in negative interactions.) An interesting and important case of mutualism is that between forest trees (producers) and mycorrhizal fungi (consumers) which "infect" the roots. The intimate association between the organisms results in composite fungus-root structures which have a morphology different from roots which have no mycorrhiza. The fungi require soluble carbohydrates and growth substances which they get from root secretions, while, in turn, the composite fungal-root structure is more efficient in extracting minerals from the soil than is the root alone, especially in humic soils which are very low in nutrients. Thus, pine seedlings grow much better and contain a higher percentage of phosphorus, nitrogen, etc., in their tissues if mycorrhiza are present (Harley, 1956). The following additional examples will give some idea of the variety of remarkable associations which have been discovered and studied:

1. Bacteria—seed plant: nitrogen-fixing bacteria and legumes (Fig. 7).
2. Algae—fungi: the lichen (the algae produce food, the fungi provide protection—both so closely associated that botanists consider the lichen as a single species; neither the fungus nor the alga exists alone in nature).
3. Plant—animal: yucca plant and yucca moth (the latter is the sole agent of pollination of the flowers).

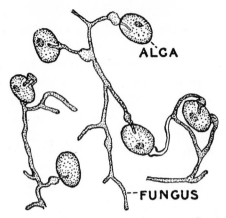

Figure 71. In some simple lichens (such as *Epigloea*), the fungus filaments penetrate and parasitize the algal cells. In most species, however, the
fungus and algae form a true partnership with mutual benefit. It appears
that parasitism may be a primitive trait in the evolution of lichens toward a
balanced symbiosis. (From Burkholder, 1952, after Jaog and Thomas.)

4. Protozoa—insect: intestinal flagellates and termites (the
   former digest wood, the latter provide the habitat; termites
   starve to death when deprived of their intestinal protozoa).

It is possible that protocooperation and mutualism may have
evolved not only through commensalism, but also through parasitism (as was hinted in the preceding section). In some primitive
lichens, for example, the fungi actually penetrate the algal cells
(see Figure 71) and thus are essentially parasites on the algae. In
the more "advanced" species this is not the case. The fungal
mycelia do not break into the algae cells, but the two live in close
harmony with mutual benefit.

8 · Principles and concepts pertaining to organization at the community level

1. The biotic community concept

Statement

A biotic community is any assemblage of populations living in a prescribed area or physical habitat; it is a loosely organized unit to the extent that it has characteristics additional to its individual and population components (see Chapter 5). It is the living part of the ecosystem, as indicated in Chapter 2. "Biotic community" is, and should remain, a broad term which may be used to designate natural assemblages of various sizes, from the biota of a log to that of a vast forest. *Major communities* are those which are of sufficient size and completeness of organization that they are relatively independent of adjoining communities (that is, they need only to receive sun energy from the outside). *Minor communities* are those which are more or less dependent on neighboring aggregations. Communities have a definite functional unity with characteristic trophic structures and patterns of energy flow (see Figure 11, page 47). They also have taxonomic unity in that there is a certain probability that certain species will occur together. However, species are to some extent replaceable in time and space so that functionally similar communities may have different species compositions.

Explanation

The community concept is one of the most important principles in ecological thought and in ecological practice. It is important in ecological theory because it emphasizes the fact that diverse organisms usually live together in an orderly manner, not just haphazardly strewn over the earth as independent beings. Like an ameba, the biotic community is constantly changing its appearance (visualize the forest in autumn and in spring), but it has structures and functions which can be studied and described, and which are unique attributes of the group. Victor E. Shelford, a pioneer in the field of biotic community ecology, has defined the community as an "assemblage with unity of taxonomic composition and a relatively uniform appearance." To this we might add: "and with a definite trophic organization and metabolic pattern." Communities may be sharply defined and separated from each other; this would be the case, of course, when the community habitat exhibits abrupt changes, but relatively sharp boundaries may also be the result of community interaction itself. Very frequently, however, communities blend gradually into one another so that there are no sharply defined boundaries. This in no way negates the community concept. Integrating communities are analogous to a colony of sponge organisms in which the limits of the individual are not sharply marked. Both a blending series of communities and a blending colony of sponges are, nevertheless, composed of units which might under other conditions exist separately. Just how many units are to be recognized, like all classification conceived by the human mind, depends on practical considerations.

The community concept is important in the practice of ecology because "as the community goes, so goes the organism." Thus, often the best way to "control" a particular organism, whether we wish to encourage or discourage it, is to modify the community, rather than to make a direct "attack" on the organism. For example, it has been demonstrated time and again that we have a better quail population by maintaining the particular biotic community in which the quail is most successful than by raising and releasing birds or manipulating any one set of limiting factors (such as predators, for example). Mosquitoes can often be controlled more efficiently and cheaply by modifying the entire aquatic community (as by fluctuating the water levels, for example) than by attempting to poison the organisms directly. Man's welfare, like that of the quail or mosquito, depends ultimately on the nature of the communities and ecosystems upon which he superimposes his culture.

Example

Perhaps the best way to illustrate the community concept is to give two examples of specific community studies, one made primarily from the descriptive or "standing crop" standpoint and the other made from the functional or "community metabolism" standpoint. For the descriptive study I have selected a study of the biotic communities of the northern desert shrub region in western Utah made by R. W. Fautin (1946). Dry regions are favorable places for beginning the study of whole communities, because the kinds of organisms are fewer and the resulting interrelations are much simpler than in less limiting regions. Study of such simple communities (relatively, that is; no natural community is actually "simple") should eventually provide a basis for understanding the more complex communities where practical problems of measurement are at present rather overwhelming for the young science of ecology.

In the Utah research Fautin selected for intensive investigation a number of "study areas," that is, areas large enough to be characteristic of the region but small enough to facilitate quantitative study. The density and frequency of plants, the numbers and kinds of vertebrate animals (birds, mammals, and reptiles) and the invertebrate populations were carefully measured by the best sample methods which, from past experience, Fautin knew to be practical under the conditions in the field. Of the major constituents, only the microorganisms were not studied and measured directly. Quantitative measurements were made throughout the year but especially during the growing season, for a period of about three years. From these data it was possible not only to describe the community "structure" at any one time but also to determine seasonal and annual variations. Finally, the data on the biota were correlated with the large amount of data available on the communities' physical habitat, that is, climate, soil–water relations, etc. The study revealed that there were two major communities (see definition in the statement above). These were the sagebrush community and the shad scale community, each named after its most conspicuous organism, a plant. Temperatures were the same for both communities, the chief community limiting factor being water. The sagebrush community occupied areas where "the precipitation is greater (about twice as great) and/or where the soil is deep, more permeable, and relatively saline free." The shad scale community, on the other hand, occurred where it was drier and where the soil was often impregnated with mineral salts. Within the shad scale major community there were a number of well developed minor communities determined by differences in the availability of soil moisture. All communities, major and minor, had rather sharp boundaries. Large animals, especially predators, were found to range throughout major communities and from one major community to another. Smaller animals and many plants, on the other hand, were restricted to or had their greatest abundance in particular major or minor communities. Birds, rodents, lizards, ants, spiders, and tenebrionid beetles showed particular adaptations for living under dry conditions and consequently comprised the bulk of the animal population. Rodents were particularly important to the community as a whole because of their "grazing" and burrowing activities. Many other important relations of stand ing crop units were clarified by the study. After examination ot the 62 pages comprising the technical report, it is not difficult to conclude that a thoroughgoing description of a community is not for the lazy or the impatient! (For a picture of sagebrush desert country, see Figure 130.)

A study by John M. Teal of a small spring community will serve as an excellent example of the community metabolism approach. In this study, not only the composition and size of the standing crop but also the energy transformation by the organisms in the intact ecosystem were determined. The important components of this relatively simple community included algae, imported organic matter (leaves and other debris coming in from surrounding land), insect larvae and other invertebrates which fed on the algae or debris, the planarians (flatworms), which were the chief predators, and microorganisms. Only a few species of macroscopic organisms were abundant enough to make an appreciable contribution to the total community metabolism. The general trophic structure was similar to that diagramed in Figure 12, page 50.

The net production and respiration of the whole community was determined each month by the use of the "light and dark bottle" method described in Chapter 3 (page 81), except that cylinders, instead of bottles, were used so that the bottom (where

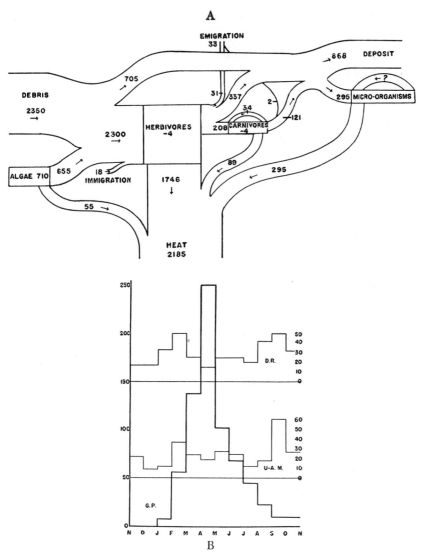

Figure 72. Community metabolism of a small spring in Massachusetts. (A) Energy flow diagram for the entire community; figures are in kilo-calories/M²/ year. Numbers inside boxes (which represent trophic levels) represent changes in the standing crop, arrows indicate direction of energy flow. (B) Month to month comparison of gross production (G.P.), mortality of macroscopic animals not assimilated by predators (U-A.M.), and decomposer respiration (D.R.). The two period of accumulation of dead bodies correspond to period of increased decomposer activity. For the community as a whole, a very large portion of the assimilated energy is "imported" (i.e., debris); primary production is correspondingly small and herbivore production (including detritus consumers) is correspondingly large. Compare this "heterotrophic" type of community with the "autotrophic" spring community shown in Figure 16, page 65. (After Teal, 1957.)

most organisms lived) could be included. The numbers and bio-mass of the consumers were determined at monthly intervals, and respiratory and growth rates measured in the laboratory or in containers placed in the spring. The respiration of decomposers and algae was obtained by subtracting consumer respiration from the total community respiration. To complete the picture, the mortality of consumers, the loss due to emergence of aquatic insects and the input and outgo of organic matter were measured by methods which we need not detail here. The complete picture is shown in Figure 72A in the form of an energy flow diagram (note that this diagram is similar to the one in Figure 11, page 47). Something of the seasonal changes in production and consumption is shown in Figure 72B. For the year as a whole, the "balance sheet" showed that more organic matter was accumulated than was consumed; eventually, the continued accumulation must wash downstream (or else the spring would fill up). Primary production accounted for only one-fourth of the energy transformed by organisms of the community, the rest being "imported." Some other interesting results of this study follow: Energy flow often proved a better measure of importance in the community than biomass; for example, the most conspicuous species of herbivore considered as biomass rated only third in energy flow in its trophic level. About 20 per cent of herbivores which died were not eaten by predators. Only 1 per cent of a year's total energy input emerged as adult insects. A study of community metabolism reveals many things which would never be discovered if we were content merely to list the numbers and kinds of organisms present.

2. Intracommunity classification, and concept of ecological dominance

Statement

Not all organisms in the community are equally important in determining the nature of the whole community. Out of the hundreds or thousands of kinds of organisms that might be present in a community, a relatively few species or species groups generally exert the major controlling influence by virtue of their numbers, size, or activities. Relative importance in the community is not indicated by taxonomic relations, since major controlling or "ruling" organisms often belong to widely different taxonomic

groups (see previous discussion of competition among closely related species, page 230). Intracommunity classification therefore
goes beyond taxonomic (floral and faunal) listing and attempts
to evaluate the actual importance of organisms in the community.
The most logical primary classification from this viewpoint is based
on trophic levels, or major niches, as discussed in Chapter 2,
pages 10-11. Communities, at least major ones, have producers,
consumers, and decomposers. Within these groups species or species groups which largely control the energy flow are known as
ecological dominants.

Explanation

The problem of classification within the biotic community may
be clarified by taking a simplified example. Suppose we took a
walk over a pasture and made a note of the important organisms
which we observed. After such a "census" we might list:

bluegrass	beef cattle	turkeys
white clover	dairy cattle	sheep
oak trees	chickens	horses

Such a "taxonomic" listing alone would not give a very good
picture of the pasture. Adding a quantitative estimate would help:

bluegrass	48 acres	chickens	6 individuals
white clover	2 acres	turkeys	2 individuals
oak trees	2 individuals	sheep	1 individual
beef cattle	2 individuals	horses	1 individual
dairy cattle	48 individuals		

From this it would be clear that bluegrass is the "dominant" among
the "producers," and dairy cattle among the "consumers." The
community is essentially a dairy cattle pasture. A more complete
picture, of course, would be obtained if we learned from the
farmer the seasonal variation in use, the annual hay and milk
production, etc., and if we knew something about the activities
of microorganisms in the soil.

Actually, of course, there are many other kinds of organisms in
a pasture, but the bluegrass and the cattle and the soil microorganisms are the most important from the viewpoint of controlling influence (aside from man, the ultimate dominant in this
case). Natural communities may have an even larger number of
species. Even so, a relatively few species often control the community and are said to be dominant. An ecological dominant,
therefore, is an organism which exerts a major controlling influence

on the community. Removal of the dominant would result in important changes in the community, whereas removal of a non-dominant species would produce much less change. Generally, dominants are those species in their trophic groups which have the largest productivity (i.e., energy fixation per unit time). For large organisms, but not necessarily for small organisms, biomass may be an indicator of dominance, as we have had occasion to emphasize previously.

In land communities, plants usually are major dominants because not only are they producers but they provide shelter for the great bulk of the organisms in the community, and they modify physical factors in various ways. In fact, the term dominant has been largely used by plant ecologists to mean the "overstory" or tallest plants in the community. Clements and Shelford (1939) have pointed out that animals (consumers) may also control communities. Where plants are small in size, animals may produce relatively greater changes on the physical habitat. The concept of dominance has not been applied to microorganisms but there is every reason to believe that among the decomposer groups (bacteria, etc.), as among the producers and consumers of the community, some kinds are more important than others. (See Chapter 11, page 374, for an example of how the dominant microbial population changed with a basic change in the type of organic matter in the soil.)

Northern communities almost always have fewer species which may be classed as dominants than have southern communities. Thus, a northern forest may have one or two species of trees which comprise 90 per cent or more of the stand. In a tropical forest, on the other hand, a dozen or more species may be dominant by the same criterion (see page 413). Also, dominants are fewer where physical factors are extreme, as indicated in the previous section. Thus, dominance in all ecological groups is much more clear-cut on deserts, tundras, and other extreme environments. Or, to put it another way, the controlling influence in communities in extreme environments is divided among fewer species.

3. The naming and classification of biotic communities

Statement

Communities may be conveniently named and classified according to (1) major structural features such as dominant species, life forms or indicators, (2) the physical habitat of the community or (3) functional attributes such as the type of community metabolism. No precise rules for naming communities have been formulated, as has been done for naming or classifying organisms, if, indeed such is desirable or possible. Classifications based on structural features are rather specific for certain environments; attempts to set up a universal classification on this basis have largely been unsatisfactory. Functional attributes offer a better basis for the comparison of all communities, whether terrestrial, marine or freshwater.

Explanation and examples

First, let us consider naming and classification on a structural basis. Since the community is composed of organisms, many ecologists feel that communities should always be named for important organisms, generally the dominants. This works well for communities where there are but few dominants which remain conspicuous at all times. In many cases, however, long cumbersome names would result if this method of naming were logically followed. As was pointed out in the very first principle (Chapter 2), the ecosystem, rather than the community, is the real basic unit. Therefore, there is no logical reason why a community cannot be named after some non-living community habitat feature, if this procedure results in conveying a clear picture of the community to someone else. Community names, like names for anything else, should be meaningful but kept as short as possible; otherwise, the names will not be used. The best way to name a community, therefore, is to pick some conspicuous, stable feature, whether living or not, and use that in the name. On land, major plants usually provide the most convenient base for nomenclature. Thus, "sagebrush community" is a good name for the community used as an illustration in Section 1 of this chapter. Sagebrush is far and away the major dominant; it stands out there all the year around and is easily recognized. However, many communities, such as those on the southern Appalachian plateau or in moist tropical regions, have so many dominants that a multiple name would be impractical, and misleading as well. In such cases, a group name or a life-form name for dominant plants may be available. Mixed mesophytic forest, tropical rain forest, or bunch-grass grassland communities are examples which immediately convey to the ecologist the essential structural features of the community

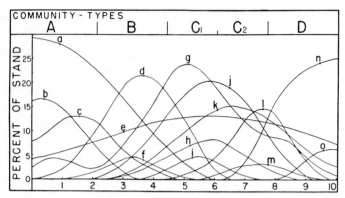

Figure 73. Distribution of populations of dominant trees along a hypothetical gradient, 0 to 10, illustrating the arrangement of component populations within a "continuum" type of community. Each species shows a "bell-
shaped" distribution with a peak of relative abundance (per cent of stand)
at a different point along the gradient; some species show a wider range of
tolerance (and usually a lesser degree of dominance) than other species.
Within the large community, sub-communities may be delimited (as indicated
by A to D above the graph) on the basis of combinations of two or more
dominants, indicators or other features. Such divisions will be somewhat
arbitrary but useful for description and comparison. The curves have been
patterned after data of several studies of tree distribution along an altitude or
other gradient. (After Whittaker, 1954a.)

in question. In aquatic communities, conspicuous large plants are
often lacking and thus not available for convenient names. In such
cases, the physical habitat may serve the purpose, as, for example,
stream–rapids community, mud-flat community, pelagic (open
water) ocean community, or sand-beach community. If animals
are conspicuous and highly characteristic, such as sessile bottom
animals in many marine communities, the community may conveniently be named after them, as, for example, an oyster-bed
community. In general, the inclusion of highly motile animals into
the community name is not satisfactory because the animal component is generally too variable from time to time; rarely is there
clear-cut long-term dominance by one or two species. Shelford
has advocated including animals in the community name in order
to emphasize that animals as well as plants are integral parts of
the biotic community. However, this emphasis is accomplished
by the description of the community which accompanies the name.
Communities, as well as organisms, need to have descriptions as
well as names.

Deciding where to draw boundaries is one of the interesting
problems in community classification, just as it is in any other

kind of classification. As indicated above, sharp changes in habitat often create sharp boundaries between communities, but frequently the habitat changes gradually in space, often along a gradient of moisture, temperature, water depth, altitude, etc. Since species belonging to the same trophic level have evolved somewhat different requirements and limits of tolerance and are "competing" (at least potentially) rather than "cooperating" (as are organisms of different trophic levels) in the functioning of the community, we frequently find that species populations change gradually along a gradient, as shown in Figure 73. The scheme shown here is a hypothetical one, but is based on actual distributions of forest trees along an altitude or other gradient. The pattern of overlapping populations has been called a "continuum" (see Curtis and McIntosh, 1951; Curtis, 1955; Whittaker, 1951, 1954a) which is, in effect, a large community with component populations distributed along a gradient. Typically, some species have narrow and others wide ranges of tolerance. For convenience or purposes of study one may designate subcommunities or "associations" within the continuum (as shown by A, B, etc., in the diagram) based on combinations of dominants or on indicators, but there are no sharp divisions between populations or combinations of populations.

However, a continuum does not continue indefinitely; sooner or later conditions favor ecologically different (rather than ecologically similar) sorts of organisms and a natural discontinuity is produced. For example, if we are following a gradient of decreasing moisture, a point is reached when grass is favored over trees resulting in an entirely different set of plants, animals and microorganisms, which in turn produce a soil quite different from that of the forest (see Figure 33, page 132). Once well established, the grassland may resist the invasion of the forest even should climate become more favorable for trees, as may be seen in the "prairie peninsula" of Illinois, Indiana and Ohio.

An example of communities remaining distinct from one another without marked difference in habitat is given by Buell (1956). At Itasca Park, the Minnesota spruce-fir forest occurs as islands within the maple-basswood forest. Over a period of years the spruce-fir first gained and then lost ground to the maple-basswood, with both units remaining intact with rather sharp boundaries between them. Rocky shores along the seacoast offer good spots to observe rather sharp zonations of communities de-

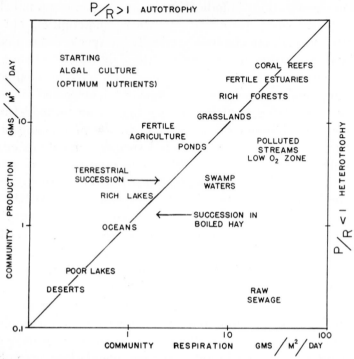

Figure 74. Position of various types of communities in a classification scheme based on community metabolism. Photosynthetic production (P) exceeds the community respiratory consumption (R) in the upper left side of the diagram (P/R is greater than 1; autotrophic types). In the lower left side of the diagram the activities of the respiratory processes exceed photosynthesis. Such communities are importing organic matter or living off previous storage. (P/R is less than 1; heterotrophic type.) Over a year's average, communities along the diagonal line tend to consume about what they make. Such communities often have an autotrophic regime in springtime and an heterotrophic regime in the winter. In general, succession proceeds toward the diagonal line from either extremely autotrophic condition or extremely heterotrophic condition. The diagram emphasizes two kinds of biological fertility, one based on concurrent plant photosynthesis, the other based on accumulations of organic matter from the past. It is possible to have a steady state with any P and R anywhere on the diagram if proper amounts of substances are flowing into and out of the community regularly. The term climax is most often used for the more self sufficient communities along the diagonal line. (Redrawn from H. T. Odum, 1956.)

spite gradual changes in physical factors which characterize the intertidal region.

The possibilities of community classification on a functional basis are beginning to receive the attention of ecologists. Since habitat and kinds of organisms are completely different in aquatic and terrestrial ecosystems, such "structural" features do not provide a satisfactory basis for a general or universal system of community classification. However, all communities, of whatever taxonomic composition or habitat, function in much the same way, as described in Chapter 3 and elsewhere. Although we do not yet know enough about how communities work it seems likely that functional attributes can provide a basis for the comparison of all communities. Figure 74 illustrates one way of making comparisons based on the level and type of community metabolism. The scheme is tentative and suggestive since comparable data are few. We know that communities may change in P/R ratio by the process of succession (to be described in the next section), but we do not know if this is always accompanied by a change in productivity.

4. Ecological succession

Statement

Ecological succession is the orderly process of community change; it is the sequence of communities which replace one another in a given area. Typically, in an ecosystem, community development begins with pioneer stages which are replaced by a series of more mature communities until a relatively stable community is evolved which is in equilibrium with the local conditions. The whole series of communities which develop in a given situation is called the *sere*; the relatively transitory communities are called *seral stages* or seral communities, and the final or mature community is called the *climax*. The concept of climax will be discussed further in the next section. The community sere is analogous to the life history of the organism, the seral stages are suggestive of the life history stages, and the climax represents the "adult" community.

Explanation

The principle of succession is one of the most important in ecology. Systematic study of plant succession in Denmark and on the sand dunes of Lake Michigan at the turn of the century marked the beginning of modern ecology just as the rediscovery of Mendel's laws ushered in the modern era of genetics at about the same time. Also, the realization that natural communities change in an orderly way resulted in the concept of a dynamic balance of nature, which replaced the old idea of a static balance of nature.

The remarkable thing about ecological succession is that it is directional. In situations where the process is well known, the seral stage present at any given time may be recognized and future changes predicted. Thus, pioneer stages may be slow to become established, then successive communities may replace each other rapidly, each year sometimes bringing almost an entirely new set of organisms, then the process slows down with the climax being reached very gradually, often with fluctuations resembling population fluctuations around an asymptote. The rate of change, however, varies widely in different seres. Most if not all of the organisms in the community change, not just some of them. Also, the physical habitat changes.

A very large terminology has been built up around the principle of succession. Many of the terms were proposed by Frederic E. Clements in his pioneer monograph on plant succession (1916) and his subsequent voluminous papers and books. In their zeal for studying succession, ecologists have probably overdone the nomenclature, a not unusual happening when scientists explore an exciting new field. Terminology needs to be critically examined from time to time and the terms which confuse, rather than clarify, thrown into synonymy and discarded, the same fate accorded excess taxonomic names for organisms. Pioneer community, sere, seral stage, and climax are the basic and highly useful terms which are generally accepted. We can leave the host of other terms for the advanced student to discuss and eventually decide on which should be retained.

Two other concepts should be mentioned. If succession begins on an area which has not been previously occupied by a community (such as newly exposed rock or sand surface), the process is known as *primary succession*. If community development is proceeding in an area from which a community was removed (such as a plowed field or cutover forest), the process is called *secondary succession*. Secondary succession is usually more rapid because some organisms, at least, are present already. Furthermore, previously occupied territory is more receptive to community development than are sterile areas. This is the type which we see all around us. In general, when we speak of ecological succession, we refer to changes which occur in the present geological age, while the pattern of climate remains essentially the same. Changes in communities which have occurred in the past will be discussed in Section 10.

What causes the orderly process of community development which we call ecological succession? A complete answer cannot be given as yet. Succession is directed by climate since the final results vary with different climates, but climate does not cause it, since the process proceeds when climatic patterns remain the same year after year. By and large, succession seems to be a characteristic of the community itself; it results from the fact that the action of the community on the habitat tends to make the area less favorable for itself and more favorable for other sets of organisms—that is, until the equilibrium or climax state is reached. As indicated in Figure 74, pioneer communities often produce a great deal more organic matter than they consume; this excess organic matter (if not immediately "exported") may change the habitat physically as well as be a source of food, growth or inhibitory substances which influence the composition of the community. Only after the habitat has been modified as far as possible by organisms is it possible for a community to become stable.

Orderly, unidirectional succession is by no means universal in nature. Where the physical environment is extreme or subject to frequent large-scale changes, organisms may not modify the environment, and thus no succession (as we are here defining it) can occur. Changes, if any, will occur only in response to changes in physical factors. The community itself must play at least some part in controlling the environment if orderly succession is to obtain. On a sand beach, for example, the environment is dominated by tides and other strong physical forces; organisms have little effect in modifying such a physical environment (see also Chapter 9, Section 9).

The discussion of succession may profitably be closed with a final point. It is rather amazing that, in a great many instances, organisms which man most desires to perpetuate are members of early seral rather than of late seral or climax stages. Thus, most game birds, many fresh-water game fish, and many of the most valuable timber trees thrive best in what are, actually, temporary communities. Since a particular organism cannot be maintained in nature without maintaining at least the essential parts of its community, the problem is to learn how to halt succession and keep the desired seral community permanently in existence. This has oftentimes proved easier said than done. An alternative would be to allow succession to proceed normally but to arrange to have a sufficient number of areas continually coming into the desired stage.

Examples

Several examples of ecological succession from field and laboratory are illustrated by Tables 16 and 17 and by Figures 75 and 76. The first example, Table 16, illustrates ecological succession of plant and certain invertebrate components of the community on the Lake Michigan dunes. Lake Michigan was once much larger than it is at present. In retreating to its present boundaries, it left successively younger and younger sand dunes. Because of the sand substrate, succession is slow and a series of communities of various ages are available—pioneer stages at the lake shore and increasingly older seral stages as one proceeds away from the shore. It was in this "natural laboratory of succession" that H. C. Cowles (1899) made his pioneer studies of plants and Shelford (1913) his studies of animal succession. The pioneer communities on the dunes consist of grasses (*Ammophila, Agropyron, Calamovilfa*), willow, cherry, and cottonwood trees, and animals such as tiger beetles, burrowing spiders, and grasshoppers. The pioneer community is followed by forest communities as shown, each of which has changing animal populations. Although it began on a very dry and sterile sort of habitat, development of the community eventually results in a beech–maple forest, moist and cool in contrast with the bare dune. The deep humus-rich soil, with earthworms and snails, contrasts with the dry sand on which it developed. Thus, the original relatively unhospitable pile of sand is eventually transformed completely by the action of a succession of communities. This is an example of primary succession on land.

Succession in the early stages on dunes is often arrested when the wind piles up the sand over the plants and the dune begins to move, entirely covering the vegetation in its path. Eventually, however, as the dune moves inland it becomes stabilized and pioneer grasses and trees again become established.

The second example illustrates how changes in breeding birds (Table 17) parallel that of dominant plants in secondary succession following the abandonment of upland agricultural fields in southeastern United States (Fig. 75). Although plants are the most important organisms which bring about changes, birds are by no means entirely passive agents in the community, since the major plant dominants of the shrub and hardwood stages depend on

Table 16. *Ecological succession of plants and invertebrates on the Lake Michigan dunes**

Invertebrates of ground strata	Cottonwood— beach grass	Seral Stages Jack pine forest	Black oak dry forest	Oak and oak-hickory moist forest	Climax beech- maple forest
White tiger beetle (Cicindela lepida)	• •				
Sand spider (Trochosa cinerea)	• •				
White grasshopper (Trimerotropis maritima)	• •				
Long-horn grasshopper (Psinidia fenestralis)	• •	• •			
Burrowing spider (Geolycosa pikei)	• •	• •			
Digger wasps (Bembex and Microbembex)	• •	• •			
Bronze tiger beetle (C. scutellaris)		• •			
Ant (Lasius niger)		• •			
Migratory locust (Melanoplus)		• •			
Sand locusts (Ageneotettix and Spharagemon)	• •				
Digger wasp (Sphex)	• •		• •		
Ant-lion (Cryptoleon)			• •		
Flatbug (Neuroctenus)			• •		
Grasshoppers (six species not listed above)			• •		
Wireworms (Elateridae)			• •	• •	• •
Snail (Mesodon thyroides)			• •	• •	• •
Green tiger beetle (C. sexguttata)				• •	• •
Millipedes (Fontaria and Spirobolus)				• •	• •
Centipedes (Lithobius, Geophilus, Lysiopetalum)				• •	• •
Camel cricket (Ceuthophilus)				• •	• •
Ants (Camponotus, Lasius umbratus)				• •	• •
Betsy beetle (Passalus)				• •	• •
Sowbugs (Porcellio)				• •	• •
Earthworms (Lumbricidae)				• •	• •
Woodroaches (Blattidae)				• •	• •
Grouse locust (Tettigidae)					• •
Cranefly larvae (Tipulidae)					• •
Wood snails (7 species not found in previous stages)					• •

* From Shelford, 1913. A few species of invertebrates are listed to illustrate the general pattern of change; for more complete listing see his tables L to LV.

Table 17. *Distribution of breeding passerine birds in a secondary upland sere, Piedmont region, Georgia**

Plant Dominants / Age in years of study area / Bird species (having a density of 5 or more in some stage)†	Forbs 1–2	Grass 2–3	Grass-shrub 15	20	25	Pine forest 35	60	100	Oak–hickory climax 150–200
Grasshopper sparrow	10	30	25						
Meadowlark	5	10	15	2					
Field sparrow			35	48	25	8	3		
Yellowthroat			15	18					
Yellow-breasted chat			5	16					
Cardinal			5	4	9	10	14	20	23
Towhee			5	8	13	10	15	15	
Bachman's sparrow				8	6	4			
Prairie warbler				6	6				
White-eyed vireo				8		4	5		
Pine warbler					16	34	43	55	
Summer tanager					6	13	13	15	10
Carolina wren						4	5	20	10
Carolina chickadee						2	5	5	5
Blue-gray gnatcatcher						2	13		13
Brown-headed nuthatch							2	5	
Wood pewee							10	1	3
Hummingbird							9	10	10
Tufted titmouse							6	10	15
Yellow-throated vireo							3	5	7
Hooded warbler							3	30	11
Red-eyed vireo							3	10	43
Hairy woodpecker							1	3	5
Downy woodpecker							1	2	5
Crested flycatcher							1	10	6
Wood thrush							1	5	23
Yellow-billed cuckoo								1	9
Black and white warbler									8
Kentucky warbler									5
Acadian flycatcher									5
Totals: (including rare species not listed above)	15	40	110	136	87	93	158	239	228

* After Johnston and E. P. Odum (1956). Figures are occupied territories or estimated pairs per 100 acres.

† By density, the "dominant" species for each stage are as follows:
1. Forb and grass stage: Grasshopper sparrow and meadowlark.
2. Grass-shrub stage: Field sparrow, yellow throat, and meadowlark.
3. Young pine forest (25–60 years): Pine warbler, towhee, and summer tanager.
4. Old pine forest (with well developed deciduous understory): Pine warbler, Carolina wren, hooded warbler, and cardinal.
5. Oak-hickory climax: Red-eyed vireo, wood thrush, and cardinal.

birds or other animals to disperse seeds into new areas. The final result, or climax, is an oak–hickory forest instead of a beech–maple forest, as in the previous example, because of differences in

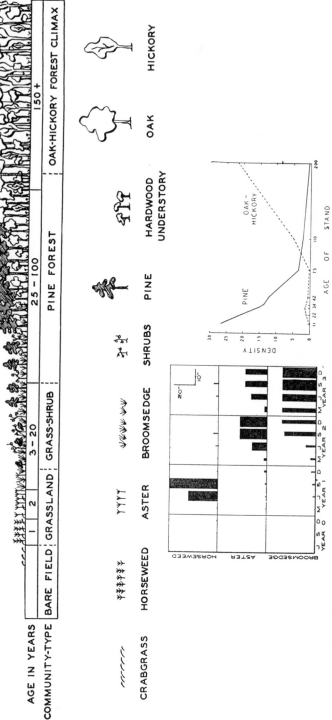

Figure 75. Secondary succession on the piedmont region of southeastern United States. The principal plant dominants of the upland sere which follows abandonment of crop land (cotton, corn, etc.) are shown in pictorial fashion in the upper diagram (after E. P. Odum). The lower charts contain quantitative data. On the left, the relative size of the three pioneer plants which reach dominance in successive years, namely, horseweed (*Leptilon* = *Erigeron*), aster (*Aster*), and broomsedge (*Andropogon*), is depicted (after Keever, 1950), while the gradual change from pine to hardwood dominance is indicated on the right (after Oosting, 1942). In the diagram at left, depicting relative size of the three plants, height of the columns represents average height of plants in inches, and width of columns represents relative diameter of stems. In the diagram at the right, the density figures are number per 100 M².

regional climate. Thus, while climate and other physical factors control the composition of the communities and determine the climax, the communities themselves play the major role in bringing about succession. For a diagram of secondary succession farther north (Canada), see Figure 78.

Secondary plant succession is equally striking in grassland regions as in the forest even though only herbaceous plants are involved. In 1917 Shantz described succession on the abandoned wagon roads used by pioneers crossing the grasslands of central and western United States, and virtually the same sequence has been described many times since. While the species vary geographically the same pattern everywhere holds. This pattern involves four successive stages: (1) annual weed stage (2 to 5 years), (2) short-lived grass stage (3 to 10 years), (3) early perennial grass stage (10 to 20 years) and (4) climax grass stage (reached in 20 to 40 years). Thus, starting from bare or plowed ground, 20 to 40 years are required for nature to "build" a climax grassland, the time depending on the limiting effect of moisture, grazing, etc. A series of dry years or overgrazing causes the succession to go backwards towards the annual weed stage; how far back depends on the severity of the effect.

Succession is also quite apparent in many aquatic habitats. When the retreat of Lake Michigan created the series of land succession stages on the old dunes, water collected in depressions between the dunes, creating a series of lakes and ponds. The ponds nearest the present border of Lake Michigan are, of course, the youngest, and those nearest the original shore are the oldest. We thus have a series of seral stages which can be studied at the same time instead of having to wait around many years for a single pond to change! Shelford (1911b) found that the youngest ponds contained relatively little rooted vegetation and were full of bass and bluegills. Older ponds were more and more choked with vegetation, and smaller and smaller in size as the action of plants and animals filled up the basin with sediments. Bass and bluegills were replaced by golden shiners and catfish (bullheads). Eventually, shrubs and trees invaded; the pond became a swamp and finally dry land, on which a succession of land communities continues.

Not all aquatic successions lead to land communities. Where the body of water is large and deep, or where there is strong wave action or other powerful physical force, succession may lead to a stable aquatic community which undergoes no further change.

Succession is quite evident in artificial ponds as in natural ones. Sometimes man inadvertently speeds up succession by allowing excessive erosion to speed up the filling process, with the result that even large ponds or reservoirs may virtually disappear in a few years. In fish ponds and also in reservoirs of eastern North America, the natural successional trend (if not modified by man) is from bass and other game fish, which thrive when the pond is first constructed, toward catfish, carp, and other fish which we often do not consider so desirable. Failure to recognize that succession is a basic characteristic of many aquatic as well as land situations has resulted in many failures and disappointments in man's attempt to maintain artificial communities of particular compositions which he considers desirable. (See Chapter 12, Section 6.)

The final example, that of succession in a protozoan culture, is taken from the classic experiments of Woodruff (Fig. 76). When a culture medium made by boiling hay is allowed to stand, a thriving culture of bacteria develop. If some pond water (con-

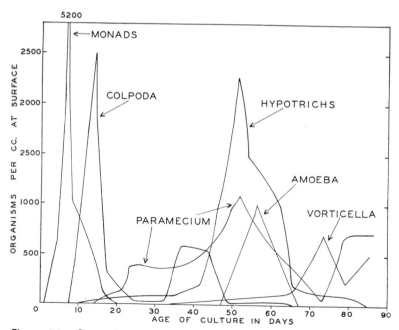

Figure 76. Succession in a protozoan culture with dominance by successive species. (After Woodruff, 1912.)

taining seed stock of various protozoa) is then added, Woodruff found that a definite succession of protozoan populations with successive dominants occurred, as shown in Figure 76. In this situation energy is maximum at the beginning and then declines. Unless new medium is added, the system eventually runs down and the protozoa completely disappear. This is quite different from the "open" system in nature, where energy in the ecosystem is not necessarily reduced as succession occurs.

5. Concept of the climax

Statement

The final or stable community in a successional series (sere) is the climax community; it is self-perpetuating and in equilibrium with the physical habitat. Presumedly, in a climax community, in contrast to a developmental or other unstable community, there is no net annual accumulation of organic matter. That is, the annual production and import is balanced by the annual community consumption and export (see Fig. 74). For a given region it is convenient, although somewhat arbitrary, to recognize (1) a single *climatic climax* which is in equilibrium with the general climate and (2) a varying number of *edaphic climaxes* which are modified by local conditions of the substrate. The former is the theoretical community toward which all successional development in a given region is tending; it is realized where physical conditions of the substrate are not so extreme as to modify the effects of the prevailing regional climate. Succession ends in an edaphic climax where topography, soil, or water are such that the climatic climax cannot develop.

Explanation and examples

The assumption that succession eventually produces a stable community is generally accepted as based on sound observation and theory. However, there have been two schools of interpretation. According to the "mono-climax" idea, any region has only one climax toward which all communities are developing, however slowly. According to the "poly-climax" idea, it is unrealistic to assume that all communities in a given climatic region will end up the same when conditions of physical habitat are by no means uniform. Nor are all habitats capable of being molded to a common level by the community within a reasonable length of time

as measured in terms of the life-span of man (or of a few mul-
tiples thereof!). A good compromise between these viewpoints
is to recognize a single theoretical climatic climax and a variable
number of edaphic climaxes, depending on the variation in the
substrate. As was indicated in Chapter 6, analysis of complex situations in the light of "constants" and "variables" is sound procedure. Thus, the climatic climax is the theoretical constant against
which observed conditions may be compared. The degree of
deviation, if any, from the theoretical climax can be measured and
the factors responsible for the deviation can be more readily determined when there is a basic "yardstick" available for comparison.

These concepts can best be illustrated by a specific example.
Topographic situations in southern Ontario and the stable biotic
communities associated with the various physical situations are
shown in Figure 77. On level or moderately rolling areas where
the soil is well drained but moist, a maple–beech community
(sugar maple and beech being the dominant plants) is found to
be the terminal stage in succession. Since this type of community
is found again and again in the region wherever land configura-
tion and drainage are moderate, the maple–beech community is
judged to be the normal, unmodified climax of the region. Where
the soil remains wetter or drier than normal (despite the action
of communities), a somewhat different end-community occurs,
as indicated. Still greater deviations from the climatic climax
occur on steep south-facing slopes where the microclimate is
warmer, or on north slopes and in deep ravines where the microclimate is colder. These latter climaxes often resemble climatic
climaxes found farther south and north, respectively. Thus, as
shown in Figure 77, we have the climatic climax where local
climate and soils are normal, and various edaphic climaxes associated with different combinations of modified climates and
drainages.

Theoretically, an oak–hickory community on dry soil, for example, would, if given indefinite time, gradually increase the organic content of the soil and raise its moisture-holding properties,
and thus eventually give way to the maple–beech community.
Actually, we do not know whether this would occur or not, since
we can see little evidence of such change and since records of undisturbed areas have not been kept for the many human generations that probably would be required. In contrast, a maple–beech

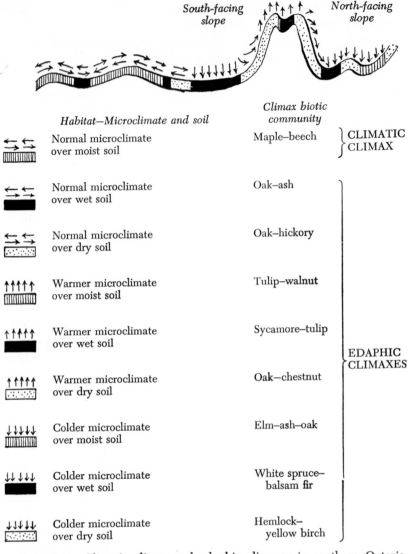

Figure 77. Climatic climax and edaphic climaxes in southern Ontario. (Simplified from Hills, 1952.)

community may develop in favorable situations in 200 years or less, even beginning from a plowed field! Starting with severe physical conditions, such as a steep slope or deep ravine, it seems likely that biotic communities would never be able to overcome the "handicaps" and the climatic climax would not be realized. In any event, it is more practical to consider communities in such situations as edaphic climaxes which will remain quite stable in terms of man's life span, and probably until there is a change in the regional climate or a geological change in the substrate. In other words, the question of climatic and edaphic climaxes comes back to the point emphasized in the section on succession. The orderly process of changes which we define as ecological succession results from the interaction of the organisms themselves which produces conditions favorable for a new set of organisms until the final stage is reached. The more extreme the physical substrate, the more difficult modification of environment becomes and the more likely that community development will stop (or at least slow down to an imperceptible "crawl") without achieving an equilibrium condition with the regional climate.

Land regions vary considerably in the percentage of area that is capable of supporting climatic climax communities. On the deep soils of the central plains early settlers found a large proportion of the land covered with a climax grassland. In contrast, on the sandy, "geologically young" lower coastal plain of the southeast the climatic climax (a broad-leaved evergreen forest) was originally as rare as it is today. Most of the coastal plain is occupied by edaphic climaxes or their seral stages. (See also pages 395-396.)

Usually, species composition has been used as a criterion to determine if a given community is climax or not. It is sometimes difficult to determine if dominant species are maintaining the same average density level since species populations often fluctuate within certain limits. The nature of the community metabolisms as indicated by the P/R ratio (i.e., ratio of primary production and community respiration) may also serve as an indicator of the degree of stability. The assumption is that a climax community should have a P/R ratio close to 1, but not enough data have been obtained to verify this.

Man, of course, has much to say about the progress of succession and the achievement of climaxes. When a stable community, which is not the climatic or edaphic climax for the given site, is maintained by man or his domestic animals, it may conveniently be designated as a *disclimax* (= *dis*turbance *climax*). For example, overgrazing by stock may produce a desert community of creosote bushes, mesquite, and cactus where the local climate actually would allow a grassland to maintain itself. The desert community would be the disclimax, the grassland the climatic climax. In this case the desert community is evidence of poor management by man, whereas the same desert community in a region with a true desert climate would be a natural condition.

On certain topographic sites of the southeastern coastal plain a stable long-leaf pine forest is maintained by periodic fires; without fires the succession proceeds to a broad-leaved forest. In this case the disclimax is more valuable to man than the climatic climax.

6. Community stratification

Statement

Vertical stratification is a characteristic structural feature of biotic communities. Two basic strata are found in both terrestrial and aquatic communities: (1) an upper sunlight or euphotic zone dominated by autotrophic organisms and (2) a lower re-generating–consumer zone dominated by heterotrophic organisms. Within these broad strata, which are generally evident on inspection of the community, populations themselves are usually found to exhibit more or less distinct layering. Population stratification, however, is less constant and often exhibits daily and seasonal changes; frequently more than one major layer of the community is required for completion of the life history of a species. Because of their almost complete interdependence, community strata are best considered subdivisions of the community rather than separate communities. Stratification increases the number of habitats available in a given surface area, thereby reducing interspecific competition, and enables a large number of species of organisms to utilize effectively the solar energy impinging upon the area.

Explanation and examples

Since details of community stratification in land and water habitats are presented in Part Two, it will only be necessary here to illustrate the principle. In Figure 78 stratification in communities of a deciduous forest succession is diagrammed. In the forest community the vegetation comprises one basic layer which is primarily concerned with production metabolism, while the soil is the other basic layer where the excess organic matter not used by vegetation and associated consumers is consumed and decomposed with the release of nutrients. Each of these basic layers is subdivided as indicated. Each of the strata has its characteristic animals, even though many species exhibit considerable vertical movement. Thus, Dowdy (1947) sampled the arthropod populations of five major strata of an oak–hickory forest in Missouri throughout the year. He found that of 240 species of insects, spiders, and myriapods, 181 species (or about 78 per cent) were collected from one stratum only, 32 from two strata, 19 from three, and only 3 to 5 species were found in as many as four or all five of the strata. This indicates a rather remarkable adherence to strata by a highly motile group of organisms.

Even birds, which can easily fly from the ground to the tops of the highest trees in a few seconds if they so desire, often demonstrate close adherence to certain layers, especially during the breeding season. Not only the nests but also the entire feeding areas are often restricted to a surprisingly narrow vertical range. Stratification in highly motile groups such as birds is most marked where there are a number of similar species (often closely related) in potential competition. For example, in the evergreen forests of New England, the magnolia warbler occupies the low levels, the black-throated green warbler the middle levels, and the blackburnian warbler the high levels in the forest. All these species are members of the family Parulidae and have similar feeding

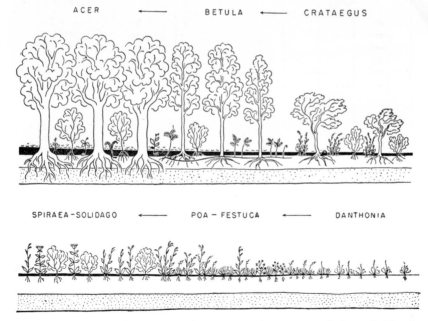

Figure 78. Stratification in a forest sere. Three strata of the soil (A_1, A_2 and B horizons) are shown. The vegetation above the soil forms essentially one layer in the pioneer *Danthonia* community and up to four distinct layers in the climax maple (*Acer*) forest, namely, herbs, shrubs, understory trees, overstory trees. (After Dansereau, 1949.)

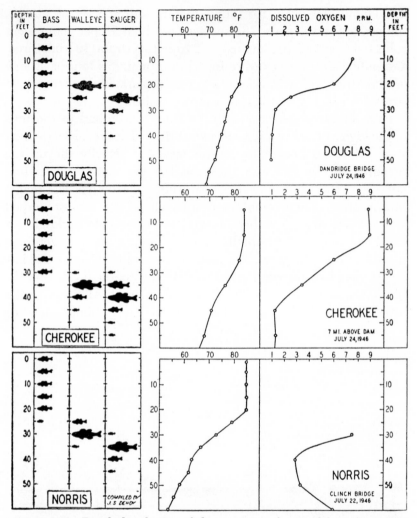

Figure 79. Depth distribution of three species of game fish in three TVA impoundments in midsummer. Oxygen and temperature conditions which determine the level at which different species aggregate are shown on the right. (After Dendy, 1945.)

habits. Other warbler species occupy different horizontal niches. Mention has already been made of relation of competition to horizontal separation of niches in Chapter 7, Section 2.

The fundamental division into "autotrophic" and "heterotrophic" layers is equally characteristic of ponds, lakes and oceans as of forests (see Fig. 2). An interesting example of population stratification in water is illustrated by the depth distribution of three species of game fish in TVA impoundments in midsummer

(Fig. 79). As in many deep lakes in temperate regions, a distinct physical stratification develops during the summer with a layer of warm, oxygen-rich, circulating water lying over a deeper, colder, noncirculating layer which often becomes depleted of oxygen. (See Chapter 9, Section 5, for additional discussion of lake stratification.) As indicated in the figure, the large-mouth bass is the most tolerant of high temperatures (as is also indicated by the fact that it occurs in nature farther south than the other two species) and is found near the surface. The other two species aggregate in deeper waters, the sauger selecting the deepest (and, therefore, the coldest) water which still contains an adequate supply of oxygen. By determining the depth distribution of oxygen and temperature it is thus possible to predict where the fish will be found in greatest numbers. Diagrams such as that in Figure 79 have, in fact, been published in local papers in order to aid the fisherman in deciding how deep he should fish to catch the desired species. As every fisherman knows, however, simply knowing where the fish are does not guarantee success; but it might help!

7. Community periodicity

Statement

Community periodicity* refers to the more or less rhythmic changes in activities or movements of organisms which produce regular recurring changes in the complexion of the community as a whole. Community periodicity results mainly from (1) daily (diel) rhythms; (2) seasonal rhythms in physical factors which directly or indirectly bring about periodicities in many component populations; (3) rhythms associated with lunar changes, especially in marine environments; and (4) rhythms inherent in organisms or populations (not governed by external factors). Finally, there are certain long-range community periodicities, as yet but little understood; some may be linked with climatic or hydrographic cycles with periods of several to many years in length. In individual organisms and populations periodicities may

* In this discussion "rhythm" and "cycle" are used synonymously with "periodicity." There is a general tendency to use "rhythmic" and "cyclic" when recurring events are quite regular but to make a technical distinction between the three terms in regard to ecological phenomena seems undesirable. It is less confusing to use adjectives to qualify these common terms when a restricted meaning is in order.

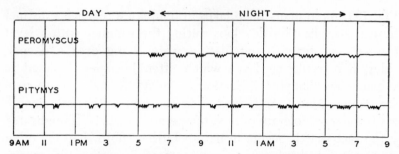

Figure 80. Periodicity in activity of two mice. The white-footed mouse, *Peromyscus*, is strictly nocturnal, the day–night rhythm persisting under experimental conditions of continuous darkness. The pine vole (*Pitymys*), on the other hand, alternates short periods of activity and inactivity irrespective of day or night. The records were made under undisturbed conditions in the laboratory where activity was recorded automatically on a moving drum.

be: (1) extrinsic—entirely dependent on an external environmental stimulus; (2) intrinsic—synchronized with an environmental stimulus but capable of persisting in its absence; and (3) inherent—independent of environmental changes (that is, the rhythmic activity is independent although length and duration of the periods may be modified by environmental changes). The complicated pattern of staggered periodicities often enables different species to occupy the same habitat-niche at different times.

Explanation and examples

Since the daily progression of light, temperature, etc. makes itself felt in all but deep water, soil, or cave communities, it is to be expected that the majority of populations in most communities will exhibit periodicities which are related either directly or indirectly to changes occurring during the 24-hour day–night period. The term *diel periodicity* refers to events which recur at intervals of 24 hours or less. For example, food manufacture, opening of flowers, and other activities of plants exhibit diel rhythms. Likewise, it is well known that many animals in terrestrial communities are active only during the period of darkness (*nocturnal*), others during the day (*diurnal*), and still others only during twilight periods (*crepuscular*). What is not so well known is that some populations have periodicities which are apparently independent of the daily rhythm of physical factors. For example, among the small mammals of the forest community, both the white-footed mouse (*Peromyscus*) and the pine vole (*Pitymys*) have regular periods of activity (spent in search for food, etc.) alternating with periods of inactivity (spent in the nest). However, the periodicity of the former is strictly nocturnal; the latter exhibits alternate short periods of activity and inactivity irrespective of day or night (Fig. 80).

A striking example of diel periodicity in aquatic habitats is to be found in the vertical "migration" of zooplankton organisms which regularly occurs in both lakes and oceans. Copepods, cladocerans, larval forms, etc. which make up the vast floating life in the open waters generally move upward to or toward the surface at night and downward during the daylight hours (Fig. 81). While light is clearly the controlling factor here, these diel movements are complex, and the physiological mechanisms have not yet been fully elucidated. Each species, and sometimes different stages of the same species, respond in a different manner so that all organisms do not attempt to crowd into the same region. Thus, stratification of different populations is maintained at least through most of the 24-hour period, even though the arrangement may vary at different light intensities. (For a discussion of plankton diel periodicity, see Clarke, 1933; Clarke and Backus, 1956.)

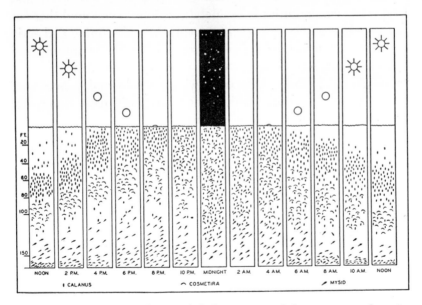

Figure 81. Diagram of vertical diel migration of three species of marine plankters, namely, a copepod (*Calanus finmarchicus*), a small jellyfish (*Cosmetira pilosesella*), and a mysid crustacean (*Leptomysis gracilis*) in the North Atlantic. (From Allee et al., 1949, after Russell and Yonge.)

Seasonal periodicities are likewise nearly universal in communities and often result in almost complete change in the community during the annual cycle. Temperature and photoperiods (relative length of day and night) are prominent factors in temperate land communities, whereas seasonal variation in temperature and salinity are often responsible for seasonal periodicities in marine communities. A regular seasonal difference in rainfall or humidity (i.e., "wet" and "dry" seasons) is a major factor in tropical land areas. The important role which length of day (photoperiodicity) plays in the cyclic flowering of plants and in the reproduction and migration of animals has already been discussed (Chapter 4). Photoperiod is a very handy "time clock," since it is constant from year to year. Generally, temperature interacts with length of day. Thus, Leopold and Jones (1947) found that variation from year to year in the time of flowering of plants and the arrival of migratory birds is greater in early spring when temperatures are critical than in late spring, even though experiments (by other workers) show that the length of day is the controlling factor in many of the cases.

While we conventionally think in terms of four seasons (spring, summer, autumn, winter), ecologists studying terrestrial and freshwater communities in temperate regions have found that (as suggested in the above paragraph) early and late spring and early and late summer are as different from each other as autumn and winter. Hence, six seasons seem more representative of community periodicities: *hibernal* (winter or hiemal), *prevernal* (early spring), *vernal* (late spring), *aestival* (early summer), *serotinal* (late summer), and *autumnal*.

One of the characteristic features of the marine environment which apparently has little or no parallel in fresh water or on land is the tidal rhythm. Tides result from the gravitational pull of the moon supplemented by that of the sun, the normal period from high water to high water being 12½ hours. At intervals of approximately 14 days unusually high and unusually low tides (spring tides) occur when the forces of the moon and sun are completely supplementary. Organisms living in the shallow waters near shore are naturally very much influenced by tides; periodicities in such communities, in fact, are more related to both daily and bi-monthly tides than to the 24-hour cycle of light and temperature. Polychaete worms provide examples of spectacular lunar rhythms. *Nereis*, for example, on the Atlantic coast of North

America spawns twice each lunar month during the summer. The worms normally live in burrows on the bottom and emerge in enormous numbers as actively swimming forms at the full moon and again at the "half-moon" point.

From the foregoing discussion it is evident that community periodicity is the result of the interaction of population periodicities which produce a complex but characteristic pattern of activities and movements. To understand community periodicity, the periodicities of different species, and the factors controlling them, must be understood. When periodicity is examined at the organism and population level, it is found that an almost graded series occurs from periodicities which are entirely dependent on environmental stimulus, i.e., extrinsic, to those which appear to be inherent in the organism or population. Intermediate between these extremes many organisms have rhythms which are coordinated with daily and seasonal changes in physical factors but which will persist in the absence of the stimulus (at least for a time) under experimental conditions. The advantage of such a more or less intrinsic periodicity, of course, is that daily and seasonal changes are "anticipated," and physiological and other adjustments can take place before or immediately at the time of the change. During the past several years there has been a great deal of study of the internal or physiological "time clocks mechanism" and the way in which it enables organisms to more efficiently synchronize their activities with environmental periodicities. For discussion of "clocks" see the work of Brown (1958) and Pittendrigh (1958).

Examples of the three basic types of periodicity may be drawn from examples already given in the above general discussion. Thus, the vertical diel migration of zooplankton is an example of an extrinsic periodicity, "environmentally coupled" with light intensity. The response appears to be direct and does not occur in the absence of light intensity changes, although some persistence may occur in certain cases. The activity of the white-footed mouse (*Peromyscus*) is more definitely intrinsic, since approximately the normal rhythm will persist for some time even when the animal is kept under conditions of constant darkness. Finally, the activity of the pine mouse (*Pitymys*) is an example of an inherent periodicity not associated with an environmental rhythm. (For a good general discussion of periodicity, see Kleitman, 1949.)

As was discussed in Chapter 6, Section 9, there is a possibility that the cyclic variation in population density of some organisms may be the result of events within the population itself. In such a case we would have an inherent periodicity at the population level.

8. Ecotones and the concept of edge effect

Statement

An ecotone is a transition between two or more diverse communities as, for example, between forest and grassland or between a soft bottom and hard bottom marine community. It is a junction zone or tension belt which may have considerable linear extent but is narrower than the adjoining community areas themselves. The ecotonal community commonly contains many of the organisms of each of the overlapping communities and, in addition, organisms which are characteristic of and often restricted to the ecotone. Often, both the number of species and the population density of some of the species are greater in the ecotone than in the communities flanking it. The tendency for increased variety and density at community junctions is known as the *edge effect*.

Explanation

As has already been mentioned, communities frequently change very gradually, as along a gradient, or they may change rather abruptly. In the latter case a tension zone would be expected between two competing communities. What may not be so evident from casual observation is the fact that the transition zone often supports a community with characteristics additional to those of the communities which adjoin the ecotone. Thus, unless the ecotone is very narrow, some niches and, therefore, some organisms are likely to be found in the region of the overlap which are not present in either community alone. Since well developed ecotonal communities may contain organisms characteristic of each of the overlapping communities plus species living only in the ecotone region, we would not be surprised to find the variety and density of life greater in the ecotone (edge effect). Organisms which occur primarily or most abundantly or spend the greatest amount of time in junctional communities are often called "edge" species.

Examples

In terrestrial communities the concept of edge effect has been shown to be especially applicable to bird populations. For example, Beecher (1942) made a thorough attempt to locate all bird nests on a tract of land which contained a number of marsh and upland communities. He found that there were fewer nests in a large block of cattail marsh, for example, as compared with an equivalent acreage composed of numerous small blocks of the same plant community. For the study as a whole it was demonstrated that population density increased with the increase in the number of feet of edge per unit area of community. As shown in Figure 82, the number of nests per quarter-acre sample quadrat was greater when there were two, three, or four communities per quadrat than when there was only a single community present. Not all species were partial to margins of communities but enough so responded to result in a greater nest density in the ecotones. A somewhat similar tendency is indicated by the data in Table 11, item II-2 (p. 155). In this case, density of breeding birds (expressed as adults per 100 acres) was greater on estates, campuses, etc., which had mixed habitat and, consequently, much "edge," as compared with tracts of uniform forest or grassland.

As emphasized in the statement above, ecotones may have characteristic species not found in the communities forming the ecotones. As a concrete demonstration of this we may refer again to the plant–bird succession study mentioned in Section 4. In this study, areas representing the principal seral stages of the upland

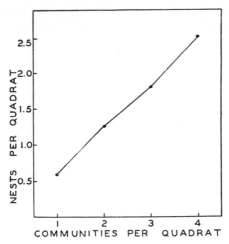

Figure 82. The "edge effect" in nesting birds. The number of nests in quarter-acre quadrats was less when the quadrat contained only one type of vegetation than when the quadrat contained two, three, or four distinct plant communities. (Redrawn from Beecher, 1942.)

sere in northern Georgia were selected so as to minimize the influence of junctions with other communities. As shown in Table 17 (page 262), 30 species of birds were found to have a density of at least 5 pairs per 100 acres in some one of these stages. However, about 20 additional species were known to be common breeding birds of upland communities of the region as a whole; 7 of these were found in small numbers, whereas 13 species were not even recorded on the uniform study areas. Among the latter were included such common species as robin, bluebird, mockingbird, indigo bunting, chipping sparrow, and orchard oriole. Many of these species require trees for nest sites or observation posts, yet feed largely on the ground in grass or other open areas; therefore, their niche requirements are met in ecotones between forest and grass or shrub communities, but not in areas of either alone. Thus, in this case about 40 per cent (20 out of 50) of the common species known to breed in the region may be considered primarily or entirely ecotonal.

One of the most important general types of ecotones as far as man is concerned is the forest edge. A forest edge may be defined as an ecotone between forest and grass or shrub communities. Wherever man settles he tends to maintain forest edge communities in the vicinity of his habitations (see Figure 139, page 432). Thus, if he settles in the forest he reduces the forest to scattered small areas interspersed with grasslands, croplands, and other more open habitats. If he settles on the plains, he plants trees, creating a similar pattern. Some of the original organisms of the forest and plains are able to survive in the man-made forest edge, whereas those organisms especially adapted to the forest edge, notably many species of "weeds," birds, insects, and mammals, often increase in number and expand their ranges as a result of creation by man of vast new habitats (see Fig. 21, page 101).

Before leaving the subject it should be emphasized that an increase in density at ecotones is by no means a universal phenomenon. Many organisms, in fact, may show the reverse. Thus, the density of trees is obviously less in a forest-edge ecotone than in the forest. Although many economic species of animals, such as game animals, are "edge" species, or utilize ecotones to a large extent, Barick (1950) has shown that for deer and grouse in the Adirondack region the edge-effect concept may be overrated. In fact, it seems likely that ecotones assume greater importance where man has greatly modified natural communities, so that a patchwork of small community areas and numerous ecotones result. Species which may originally have been characteristic of large tracts must either become adapted to ecotones or become extinct.

9. Species-numbers relationships in communities

Statement

Of the total number of species in a trophic component, or in a community as a whole, a relatively small per cent are usually abundant (represented by large numbers of individuals) and a large per cent are rare (represented by a small number of individuals). The ratio between the number of species and the number of individuals is the *diversity index*. Either strong physicochemical limiting factors or intense interspecific competition tends to reduce the diversity within a community.

Explanation

The general relationship between species and numbers (or other measure of density) to be expected in most communities is shown in Figure 83A. While the pattern of few species with large numbers of individuals associated with many species with few individuals is characteristic of community structure, the actual ratio between species and individuals varies widely in different kinds of communities. It is often found that if a moderate-sized sample is removed from a given community or component the number of species divided by the log of the number of individuals is a fixed ratio characteristic of that community; such a ratio is one form of diversity index which may be used to compare community or trophic units of equivalent size. An index of this type is shown graphically in Figure 83B. In this example, high productivity resulted (after a period of time) in competition for a limited space and a reduction in the diversity index (or, to put it another way, an increase in the number of individuals per species). Severe physical limiting factors also result in a low diversity index. Thus, arctic tundras and salt lakes have few species but often large numbers of individuals. At the opposite extreme a tropical rain forest, with its numerous niches, may have a very high diversity. When man introduces stringent limiting factors into a natural community, as in stream pollution, diversity is usually reduced even though the total number of individuals or the total productivity remains unchanged or perhaps is increased (see Patrick,

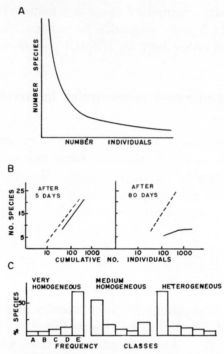

Figure 83. Some aspects of species-numbers relationships in communities. A, General relationship found in most communities which contain a few species, each represented by large numbers of individuals (the common species) and many species, each represented by few individuals (the rare species). B, Species-numbers relationships in diatoms which attached to glass slides placed in a productive (solid line in graph) and an unproductive (broken line) location in Silver Springs, Florida. The number of species found is plotted in a semi-log graph against the cumulative number of individuals counted in successive microscopic fields. The left graph shows the situation after the slides had been in the water for only 5 days, while the right graph shows the situation after 80 days. The diversity index is the slope (number of species per tenfold) increase in the number of individuals counted. This ind ex remained virtually the same in the less productive station but declined in the productive location as competition for limited space on the slide intensified. (After Yount, 1956.) C, Frequency diagrams often are used to determine the homogeneity of a stand of vegetation where numerous quadrats or other equal-sized samples are employed. The frequency classes represent increasing percentage occurrence as follows: A, 0 to 20 per cent; B, 20 to 40 per cent; C, 40 to 60 per cent; D, 60 to 80 per cent; E, 80 to 100 per cent. The middle diagram represents the usual pattern in most temperate forest communities and is often called the "Raunkaier normal" frequency distribution. (See Raunkaier, 1934.)

Hohn and Wallace, 1954; also Figure 142, page 442). Thus, any strong limiting factor whether biotic (competition, etc.) or abiotic will tend to reduce diversity.

It should be emphasized that in speaking of diversity indices we are here concerned with species-numbers relations in communities or functional portions thereof (producers, for example) and not with the biota of geographical areas containing a variety of habitats and mixed communities, although samples from mixed habitats (for example, insects attracted to a light trap) may show similar trends. Regional samples, however, will tend to reflect the variety of habitats present rather than the variety within any one habitat.

A somewhat different way of considering species composition is shown in Figure 83C. In these frequency diagrams Class A represents the species with limited or sporadic distribution and Class E species with individuals widely distributed in the area in question. Frequency diagrams of this sort are often used by plant ecologists to determine the degree of taxonomic homogeneity of a stand of vegetation.

10. Community structure and succession in past ages; paleoecology

Statement

Since it is generally accepted from fossil and other evidence that organisms were different in past ages and have evolved to their present status, it naturally follows that the structure of communities and the nature of environments must have been different also. It is evident that knowledge of past communities and climates will contribute greatly to our understanding of present communities. This is the subject of paleoecology, a borderline field between ecology and paleontology, which has been defined by Stanley Cain (1944) as "the study of past biota on a basis of ecological concepts and methods insofar as they can be applied," or, more broadly, as the study "of the interactions of earth, atmosphere and biosphere in the past." The basic assumptions of paleoecology are: (1) that the operation of ecological principles has been essentially the same throughout various geological periods, and (2) that ecology of fossils may be inferred from what is known about equivalent or related species now living.

Explanation

Since Charles Darwin brought the theory of evolution to the forefront of man's thinking, reconstruction of life in the past through the study of the fossil record has been an absorbing scientific pursuit. The evolutionary history of many species, genera, and higher taxonomic groups has now been pieced together. For example, the story of the skeletal evolution of the horse from a four-toed animal the size of a fox to its present status is pictured in most elementary biology textbooks. But what about the associates of the horse in its developmental stages? What did it eat, and what was its habitat and niche? What were its predators and competitors? What was the climate like at the time? How did these ecological factors contribute to the natural selection which must have had a part to play in shaping the structural evolution? Some of these questions, of course, may never be answered. However, given quantitative information on fossils associated together at the same time and place, it should be possible for scientists to determine something of the nature of communities, and of their dominants, in the past. Likewise, such evidence, together with that of a purely geological nature, may aid in determining climatic and other physical conditions existing at the time.

Until recently little attention was paid to the questions listed in the above paragraph. Paleontologists were busy describing their finds and interpreting them in the light of evolution at the taxonomic level. As such information accumulated, however, it was only natural that interest in the evolution of the group should develop, and thus a new branch of science, paleoecology, was born. In summary, then, the paleoecologist attempts to determine from the fossil record how organisms were associated in the past, how they interacted with existing physical conditions, and how communities have changed in time. The basic assumptions of paleoecology are much the same as for paleontology, that is, that "natural laws" were the same in the past as they are today, and that organisms with structures similar to those organisms living today had similar behavior patterns and ecological characteristics. Thus, if the fossil evidence indicated that a spruce forest once occurred 10,000 years ago where an oak–hickory forest now is climax, we have every reason to think that the climate was colder 10,000 years ago, since species of spruce as we know them today are adapted to colder climates than are oaks and hickories.

One of the difficulties in reconstructing past conditions has been the difficulty of establishing precise dates. In recent years a promising new tool, which may be called "radioactive dating," has been brought to use. Thus, if the rate of decay of a radioactive element is known, the quantity of the element still remaining in strata and fossils may serve as a geological "time clock." Uranium serves as a long-term "clock," since its half-life is 7.6 billion years; that is, half of a chunk of uranium will decay to lead in that amount of time. For more recent events which are more definitely associated with life, "radiocarbon dating" offers seemingly unlimited promise. Radioactive carbon, or C^{14} (carbon of atomic mass 14), is produced apparently at a steady rate in the upper atmosphere by the action of cosmic rays. Plants absorb this radiocarbon along with regular carbon (of atomic mass 12, or C^{12}) in the form of carbon dioxide and it becomes part of their tissues. Animals, of course, get radiocarbon by eating plants. When an organism dies, no further radiocarbon is added, and the "time clock" begins to "run down." The half-life of carbon-14 is about 5,500 years, so that if an organism becomes a fossil, half of its original supply will be gone in that time, while in another 5,500 years half of the remaining amount, or one-fourth of the original amount, will be gone. The amount of radiocarbon possessed by living organisms is known, and, even though the amount is very small, it has been possible to "date" fossil material back to 12,000 years ago; improved techniques may push the measurable time back to 30,000 years. Of special interest to ecologists are communities which existed since the last Pleistocene glaciation, which is now believed to have occurred ten or twelve thousand years ago. Thus radiocarbon dating is applicable to this period. In some cases, at least, radiocarbon dating has shown that events of the ice age were more recent than had been previously thought. (See Libby, 1955, for radiocarbon techniques.)

Illustration

Since many important or dominant animals in the sea have shells, fossils may be numerous in the sediments and provide a record of nature of marine communities of the past. For example, we know that the Baltic sea was warmer about 5,000 years ago than it is now because certain mollusks which were abundant then are now found only further south. Fossil pollen provides excellent material for the reconstruction of terrestrial communities which have existed since the Pleistocene period. Figure 84 is a generalized diagram showing how the nature of post-glacial communities and climates in a glaciated region can be reconstructed by determining the dominant trees. As the glacier re-

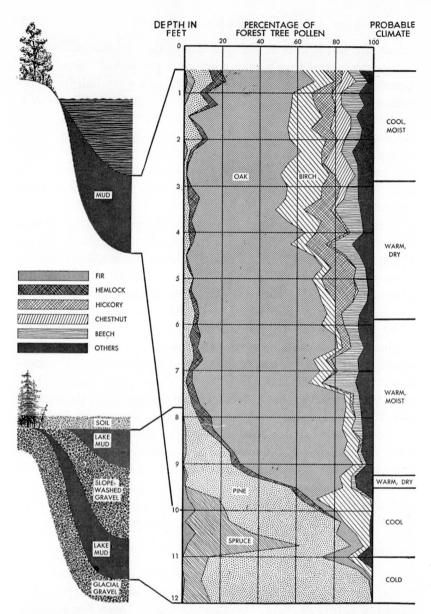

Figure 84. A pollen profile of a Connecticut lake bottom which provides a record of communities and climates since the time of formation of the lake during the last glaciation (10 to 12 thousand years ago). Radiocarbon dating helps to "date" the layers at various depths, the deeper layers, of course, representing the older conditions. It cannot be assumed that the abundance of trees was in direct proportion to the abundance of pollen in the sediments, because some pollen, such as that of pine, is carried by winds to greater distances than others; therefore, the abundance of pine in the deepest layers is probably out of proportion to the importance of pine as a dominant in the immediate vicinity of the lake. (After Deevey, Scientific American, February, 1952.)

treats it often leaves scooped-out places which become lakes. Pollen from plants growing around the lake sinks to the bottom and becomes fossilized in the bottom mud. Such a lake may fill up and become a bog. If a vertical core is taken from the bog or lake bottom, a chronological record is obtained from which the percentage of various kinds of pollen can be determined. Thus, in Figure 84, the "oldest" pollen sample is composed chiefly of spruce and pine, indicating a cold climate. A change to oak, hemlock, and beech indicates a warm moist period several thousand years later, whereas oak and hickory suggest a warm dry period still later. Finally, the pollen "calendar" indicates a return to a somewhat cooler and wetter period, with spruce pollen reappearing. We thus have a picture of climatic changes since the last glaciation and of the climax dominants of terrestrial communities which must have existed during these periods. It is evident, then, that a definite succession of climax communities occurred in this particular region, as illustrated by Figure 84.

II · The habitat
approach

Introduction

In Part I the subject of ecology is organized from the viewpoint of principles and concepts as they apply to different levels of organization. The individual, the population, the community, and the ecosystem are the convenient levels which were used (see Chapter 1, Section 2). This method of presentation brings together the central themes which unify the subject of ecology and establish it as one of the basic biological sciences. Likewise, the "principles" approach provides a sound basis for specific studies and for applications to be made in the interest of mankind.

In becoming acquainted with a subject field, most of us believe that, in addition to a broad basic approach as presented in Part I, attention should be focused on a "first hand" examination of a specific segment. In the case of ecology, a "specific segment" would be a definitely delimited area of the earth's surface, or perhaps specific kinds of organisms. Experience in teaching (and we are here including "self-teaching") has shown that a "lecture–laboratory" or "theory–practice" procedure is sound. Thus, Part I is the "theory," and Part II is the "laboratory" where we meet our subject on intimate terms, learn some of the necessary "jargon," and test the theories on living organisms. In Part I we have strongly emphasized the functional aspects of ecology, that is, how systems of nature "work." Although no sharp distinction can or should be made between function and structure, Part II will emphasize structure, that is, how nature "looks," with appropriate cross references to Part I. In other words we shall point out what the beginning student may see on his field trips as he begins to think in terms of critical studies of nature.

By studying a particular habitat we become acquainted with organisms and physical factors actually associated in a particular ecosystem. This helps mitigate the pitfalls that may follow excessive generalization. Also, we obtain some insight into the methods, instrumentation, and technical difficulties applicable to specific situations!

If Part I has not been read, reference should be made to the sections on the ecosystem (Chapter 2, Section 1), habitat and niche (Chapter 2, Section 2), biogeochemical cycles (Chapter 2, Section 3), energy relations (Chapter 3), principle of limiting factors (Chapter 4, Section 3), and the biotic community (Chapter 8, Section 1), as background for the discussions in Part II. There are three major habitats in the biosphere, namely, marine, fresh-water, and terrestrial. Since most biologists postulate that life began in the ocean, it would be logical to start study with the marine habitat. In actual practice, however, it is best to start with a fresh-water habitat for several reasons. In the first place, examples of fresh-water habitats are available wherever man lives. Many fresh-water habitats are small, and, therefore, are more readily accessible throughout with the use of relatively simple equipment. Finally, there are fewer kinds of organisms in small bodies of fresh water than in the ocean, making it easier for the beginner to comprehend something of the nature of the natural community without an overburden of effort in learning to identify organisms in a large number of classes and phyla. For these reasons, this section begins with the fresh-water environment.

9 · Fresh-water ecology*

1. The fresh-water environment: types and limiting factors

Since water is both an essential and the most abundant substance in protoplasm, it might be said that all life is "aquatic." However, in practice we speak of an aquatic habitat as one in which water is the principal *external* as well as internal medium. Fresh-water habitats may be conveniently considered in two series, as follows:

Standing-water, or lentic (*lenis*, calm), habitats:
> Lake—Pond—Swamp or Bog

Running-water, or lotic (*lotus*, washed), habitats:
> Spring—Stream (brook-creek)—River

There are no sharp boundaries between the two series or between categories within a series. A gradual change or gradient occurs in the direction indicated (see Chapter 8, Section 4). Erosion from land and the activities of organisms (especially plants) in lakes and ponds tend to fill them up, eventually producing terrestrial habitats unless this tendency is countered by strong physical forces such as floods, wind, or solution of underlying substrate. Streams tend to cut down to base level and thus change as a result of the action of the water. When base level is reached, current is reduced, sedimentation occurs, and a base-level meandering river results which represents a more or less unchanging or "climax" state. However, as deltas are built up by deposi-

* The study of natural fresh waters in all their aspects—physical, chemical, geological, and biological—is termed *limnology*. Fresh-water ecology is sometimes interpreted to be synonymous with limnology but is more properly considered as the primarily biological aspect of limnology.

tion of silt, uplifts may eventually occur elsewhere, thus starting the erosion cycle all over again.

Aquatic habitats sometimes change very rapidly, as in the case of a vegetation-choked pond filling up to become a swamp. On the other hand, large lakes and streams change more slowly, and may be relatively stable in terms of a few life spans of man.

Limiting factors which are likely to be especially important in fresh water, and hence which we would wish to measure in any thoroughgoing study of an aquatic ecosystem, are as follows:

Temperature

Water has several unique thermal properties which combine to minimize temperature changes; thus the range of variation is smaller and changes occur more slowly in water than in air. The most important of these thermal properties are: (1) High specific heat, that is, a relatively large amount of heat is involved in changing the temperature of water. One calorie of heat is required to raise one milliliter (or one gram) of water one degree centigrade (between 15° and 16°). Only ammonia and a few other substances have values higher than 1. (2) High latent heat of fusion. Eighty calories are required to change 1 gram of ice into water with no change in temperature (and vice versa). (3) Highest known latent heat of evaporation. Five hundred and thirty-six calories per gram are absorbed during evaporation which occurs more or less continually from both water and ice surfaces. (4) Water has its greatest density at 4° C; it expands and hence becomes lighter both above and below this temperature. This unique property prevents lakes from freezing solid.

Although temperature is thus less variable in water than in air, it is nevertheless a major limiting factor because aquatic organisms often have narrow tolerances (stenothermal, see Chapter 4, Section 2). Also, temperature changes produce characteristic patterns of circulation and stratification (to be described later), which greatly influence aquatic life. Large bodies of water greatly modify the climate of adjacent areas of land (see page 117).

Transparency

Penetration of light is often limited by suspended materials, restricting the photosynthetic zone wherever aquatic habitats have appreciable depth. Turbidity, therefore, is often important as a limiting factor.

Current

Since water is "dense," the direct action of current is a very important limiting factor, especially in streams. Also, currents often largely determine the distribution of vital gases, salts, and small organisms.

Concentration of respiratory gases

Oxygen and carbon dioxide concentration are often limiting (see Chapter 4, Section 5, subdivision 5).

Concentration of biogenic salts

Nitrates and phosphates seem to be limiting to some extent in nearly all fresh-water ecosystems (see Chapter 4, Section 5, subdivision 6; see also Chapter 4, Section 3, example 7). In soft water lakes and streams, calcium and other salts also are likely to be limiting (see Chapter 4, Section 3, example 5). Except for certain mineral springs, even the hardest fresh waters have a salt content or salinity of less than 0.5 part per thousand, compared with 30 to 37 parts per thousand for sea water (see Figure 96).

Two other characteristics of fresh-water habitats may influence the number and distribution of species present (or qualitative richness of biota). Since fresh-water habitats are often isolated from each other by land and sea, organisms with little means of dispersal over these barriers may have failed to become established in places otherwise favorable. Fish are especially subject to this limitation; streams, for example, only a few miles apart by land but isolated by water, may have their niches occupied by different species. On the other hand, most small organisms—algae, crustacea, protozoa, and bacteria, for example—have amazing powers of dispersal (see Chapter 6, Section 10). Thus, one may find the same kind of water flea (*Daphnia*, for example) in a pond in the United States as in England. A manual of freshwater invertebrates written for the British Isles, for example, serves almost as well for the United States. At least, down to the family and generic level, the lower plants and invertebrates of fresh water show a great degree of cosmopolitanism.

Fresh-water organisms have a definite problem "to solve" in regard to osmoregulation. Since the concentration of salts is greater in the internal fluids of the body or cells than in the fresh-water environment, either water tends to enter the body by osmosis if membranes are readily permeable to water (Fig. 85), or salts

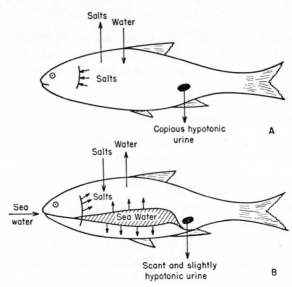

Figure 85. Osmoregulation in fresh water (A), compared with marine (B) bony fish. (From Florkin and Morgulis, 1949, after Baldwin.)

must be concentrated if membranes are relatively impermeable. Fresh-water animals, such as protozoa with their thin cell membranes and fish with their gills (Fig. 85), must have efficient means of excreting water (accomplished by contractile vacuoles in protozoa and by kidneys in fish) or the body would literally swell up and burst! Difficulties of osmoregulation may explain, partially at least, why a great number of marine animals—entire phyla, in fact—have never been able to invade the fresh-water environment.

2. Ecological classification of fresh-water organisms

Since organisms in fresh water (or in any other natural habitat) are not arranged in taxonomic order (such as is usually followed in biology texts or systematic museums), some sort of classification on an ecological basis is useful. First, organisms may be classified as to major niches based on their position in the energy or food chain (see Chapter 2, Section 1, Figure 2, and Chapter 3, Sections 2 and 3) as:

Producers: green plants and chemosynthetic microorganisms.

Consumers: primary, secondary, etc.; herbivores, predators, parasites, etc.

Decomposers: subclassified according to nature of substrate reduced.

Within these trophic levels it is generally instructive to recognize those species which act as major dominants (see Chapter 8, Section 2).

Secondly, organisms in water may be classified as to their *life form* or *life habit,* based on their mode of life, as follows:

Benthos: organisms attached or resting on the bottom or living in the bottom sediments.

Periphyton or *Aufwuchs**:   organisms (both plant and animal) attached or clinging to stems and leaves of rooted plants or other surfaces projecting above the bottom.

Plankton: floating organisms whose movements are more or less dependent on currents. While some of the zoo-plankton exhibit active swimming movements that aid in maintaining vertical position, plankton as a whole is unable to move against appreciable currents. In practice, net plankton is that which is caught in a fine-meshed net which is towed slowly through the water; nannoplankton is too small to be caught in a net and must be extracted from water collected in a bottle or by means of a pump.

Nekton: swimming organisms able to navigate at will (and hence capable of avoiding plankton nets, water bottles, etc.).

Neuston: organisms resting or swimming on the surface.

Finally, organisms may be classified as to region or subhabitat. In the ponds and lakes three zones are generally evident as follows (Fig. 86):

Littoral zone: the shallow water region with light penetration to the bottom; typically occupied by rooted plants.

Limnetic zone: the open water zone to the depth of effective light penetration.† The community in this zone is composed only of plankton, nekton, and sometimes neuston. This zone is absent in small,

---

* The German word, *Aufwuchs,* proposed by Ruttner (1953), is perhaps more appropriate than the English "periphyton."

† Often called compensation level; it is the level where the rate of photosynthesis is just equal to the rate of respiration.

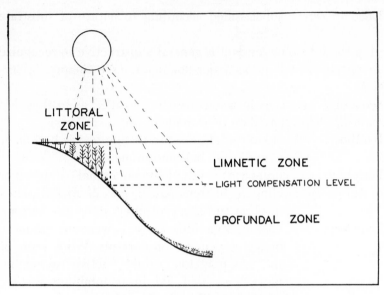

Figure 86.   The three major zones of a lake.

shallow ponds. The term *euphotic zone* refers to the total illuminated stratum including littoral and limnetic.

Profundal zone: the bottom and deep water area which is beyond the depth of effective light penetration. This zone is often absent in ponds.

In small streams two major zones are generally evident:

Rapids zone: shallow water where velocity of current is great enough to keep the bottom clear of silt and other loose materials, thus providing a firm bottom. This zone is occupied largely by specialized benthic or periphytic organisms which become firmly attached or cling to a firm substrate.

Pool zone: deeper water where velocity of current is reduced, and silt and other loose materials tend to settle to bottom, thus providing a soft bottom, unfavorable for surface benthos but favorable for burrowing forms, nekton, and, in some cases, plankton.

Two points should be emphasized. To clarify the ecological role or niche of a given organism, its position in all three classifications should be determined. Thus a diatom which lives suspended in the open water zone would be classified as a plankton producer of the limnetic zone. If, furthermore, it proved to be very abundant during the spring and scarce at other times, we would say that it was a major dominant (see Chapter 8, Section 2) among the producers of the limnetic community during the spring or vernal (see Chapter 8, Section 7) season. A second important point to note is that ecological classification of a particular species may be different at different stages in its life history. Thus, an animal might be a primary consumer while a larva and a secondary consumer as an adult (tadpole–frog, for example); or an animal might be a member of the profundal community during the larval stage (for example, a chironomid larva) and then leave the water entirely as an adult. In this respect ecological classification is quite different from taxonomic classification, which, of course, does not change with changes in life history stages.

3. The fresh-water biota (flora and fauna)

The major divisions of plants and many of the major animal phyla are represented by one or more genera living in fresh-water communities. Considering the fresh-water environment as a whole, the algae are the most important producers, with the aquatic spermatophytes ranking second. Except for the pond weeds and duck weeds, most aquatic higher plants are members of diverse families in which the majority of species are terrestrial.

Among the animal consumers, three groups will likely comprise the bulk of the biomass in most fresh-water ecosystems, namely, aquatic insects, crustacea, and fish. The mollusks, annelids, rotifers, protozoa, and helminths would generally rank lower in importance, although in specific instances any of these groups may loom large in the "economy" of the system.

Among the decomposers, the water bacteria and the aquatic fungi seem to be of equal importance in performing the vital role of reducing organic matter to inorganic form which may then be used again by the producers. The distribution and activities of decomposers in aquatic habitats was discussed in Chapter 2 (pages 16; 20-25). See also Henrici, 1939; Weston, 1941.

In summary, the beginning student should first become familiar with algae, bacteria and fungi, the aquatic spermatophytes, the crustacea, the aquatic insects, and fish.

4. Lentic communities

The general zonation characteristic of ponds and lakes has been diagrammed in Figure 86. Characteristic organisms of the various zones are illustrated in Figures 87 to 89. A brief account, emphasizing community organization in these zones, follows. For aid in identification and for accounts of life histories, reference should be made to standard treatises on fresh-water biology, monographs, and manuals as are available for local use.

Nature of communities in littoral zone

1. *Producers.*   Within the littoral zone producers are of two main types: rooted or benthic plants, belonging mostly to the division Spermatophyta (seed plants), and phytoplankton, or floating green plants, which are mostly algae (see Figure 87). Sometimes the duckweeds, which are neuston spermatophytes, not attached to the bottom, are important; in fact, in some ponds they may form almost a continuous sheet on the surface at certain seasons and virtually "shade out" other green plants. Typically, rooted aquatics form concentric zones within the littoral zone, one group replacing another as the depth of the water changes (either in space or in time). A representative arrangement proceeding from shallow to deeper water may be briefly described as follows (in any given body of water it should not be assumed that all three zones will be present or that they will be arranged in the order listed):

(a) Zone of emergent vegetation: Rooted plants with principal photosynthetic surfaces projecting above the water. Thus, carbon dioxide for food manufacture is obtained from air but other raw materials are obtained from beneath the water surface. Cattails (several species of the genus *Typha*) are a widespread dominant producer, and may be considered a "type" for this niche. Other plants in this category include: bulrushes (*Scirpus*), arrowheads (*Sagittaria*), bur reeds (*Sparganium*), spike rushes (*Eleocharis*), and pickerelweeds (*Pontederia*). The emergent plants, together with those on the moist shore, form an important link between water and land environments. They are used for food and shelter by amphibious animals, muskrats, for example, and provide a convenient means of entry and exit into the water for aquatic insects which spend part of their lives in the water and part on land.

(b) Zone of rooted plants with floating leaves. The water lilies

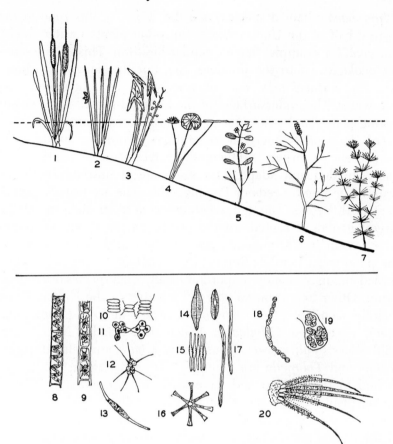

Figure 87. Some producers of lentic communities, including emergent, floating, and submergent rooted littoral plants (1–7), filamentous algae (8–9), and phytoplankton (10–20). The phytoplankton include representative green algae (10–13), diatoms (14–17), and blue-green algae (18–20). Note that phytoplankton exhibit "flotation" adaptations which enable them to remain suspended or at least decrease markedly the rate of sinking (these organisms, of course, have no power of movement of their own)—for example, reduction in integumentary material, flotation process, and colonial life-habit, which increases surface area, and gas vacuoles indicated by black spots in the blue-green algae cells (18–20). Organisms diagrammed are: 1, cattail (*Typha*); 2, bulrush (*Scirpus*); 3, arrowhead (*Sagittaria*); 4, water lily (*Nymphaea*); 5 and 6, two species of pond weeds (*Potamogeton diversifolia, P. pectinatus*); 7, muskgrass (*Chara*); 8, *Spirogyra;* 9, *Zygnema;* 10, *Scenedesmus;* 11, *Coelastrum;* 12, *Richteriella;* 13, *Closterium* (a desmid); 14, *Navicula;* 15, *Fragilaria;* 16, *Asterionella* (which floats in the water like a parachute); 17, *Nitzschia;* 18, *Anabaena;* 19, *Microcystis;* 20, *Gloeotrichia* (19 and 20 represent parts of colonies enclosed in a gelatinous matrix). (8 to 17 redrawn from Needham and Needham, 1941; 18 to 20 redrawn from Ruttner, 1953.)

(*Nymphaea*, about 4 species) are the "type" in this zone in the eastern half of the United States, but other plants (water shield, *Brasenia*, for example) have a similar life form. This zone is similar, ecologically, to the previous one, but the horizontal photosynthetic surfaces may more effectively reduce light penetration into water. The undersurfaces of the lily pads provide convenient resting places and places for egg deposition by animals.

(c) Zone of submergent vegetation: Rooted or fixed plants completely or largely submerged. Leaves tend to be thin and finely divided and adapted for exchange of nutrients with the water. The pond weeds or Potamogetonaceae are usually prominent in this zone. The genus *Potamogeton* is, in fact, one of the largest genera of rooted aquatic plants, having about 65 species which occur in all temperate parts of the world. Other genera in the pond-weed family (*Ruppia, Zannichellia*) are likewise widespread and may be more important locally than species of *Potamogeton*. Other important submerged aquatics in the United States include: coontail (*Ceratophyllum*), water milfoils (*Myriophyllum*), waterweed (*Elodea* or *Anacharis*), naiads (*Najas*), and wild celery (*Vallisneria*). "Muskgrass," *Chara*, and related genera *Nitella* and *Tolypella* are generally classed as algae, yet are attached to the bottom and have a life form resembling that of higher plants. *Chara* may thus be ecologically classed along with the above submerged producers. It often marks the inner boundary of the littoral zone, since it is able to grow in deep water.

The non-rooted producers of the littoral zone comprise numerous species of algae. Many species are found floating throughout both littoral and limnetic zones (plankton), but some, especially those which are attached to or associated with rooted plants, are especially characteristic of the littoral zone. Likewise, many species have special adaptations for increasing buoyancy and hence are characteristic of the limnetic zone. As shown in Figure 87, the principal types of algae are:

(1) Diatoms (*Bacillariaceae*), with box-like silica shells and yellow or brown pigment in the chromatophores masking the green chlorophyll.

(2) Green algae (*Chlorophyta*), which includes single cell forms like desmids, filamentous forms either floating or attached, and various floating colonial forms. In these forms the chlorophyll is not masked by other pigment.

(3) The blue-green algae (*Cyanophyta*), rather simple single-

celled or colonial algae with diffuse chlorophyll (not concentrated into chromatoplasts) masked by blue-green pigment. This group is often of great ecological importance because of the enormous biomass that may develop in ponds and lakes. As was indicated in the legend for Figure 7, some of the blue-green algae are able to fix gaseous nitrogen into nitrates and thus perform the same role in water as is performed by bacteria in the soil.

Filamentous green algae or "pond scums," such as *Spirogyra, Zygnema, Oedogonium,* which are studied in elementary botany courses, are often characteristic of the littoral zone of ponds, where they may form floating masses. Other filamentous forms assume a periphyton life form, each kind of rooted plant often having characteristic algal encrustments, the two organisms apparently being associated in a commensal or mutualistic relationship (see Chapter 7, Section 4). *Chara* seems to form an especially favorable substrate and is nearly always covered with a crust of other algae. A sample of the free-floating phytoplankton of the littoral zone would likely reveal numerous diatoms, desmids, and other green algae and chlorophyll-containing (hence holophytic, or "producing") protozoa, such as the familiar laboratory form, *Euglena,* and its many relatives. Among the blue-green algae might be mentioned *Oscillatoria* and *Rivularia,* which may cover the bottom or be found attached to stems and leaves of submerged spermatophytes.

2. *Consumers.*   The littoral zone is the home of a greater variety of animals than are the other zones. All five "life habits" are well represented, and all phyla which have fresh-water representatives are likely to be present. Some animals, especially the periphyton, exhibit a zonation paralleling that of the rooted plants, but many species occur more or less throughout the littoral zone. Vertical rather than horizontal zonation is more striking in animals. Some of the characteristic animals of littoral regions are shown in Figure 88. Among the periphyton forms, for example, pond snails, damsel fly nymphs and climbing dragonfly nymphs (Odonata), rotifers, flatworms, bryozoa, hydra, etc., and midge larvae rest on or are attached to stems and leaves of the large plants. Snails feed on plants or *Aufwuchs;* midge larvae are also primary consumers but obtain their food as detritus. The dragonfly and damsel fly larvae are exclusively carnivorous, using their hinged labium to good advantage to capture sizable prey which chance to pass by their lookout posts. Another group containing

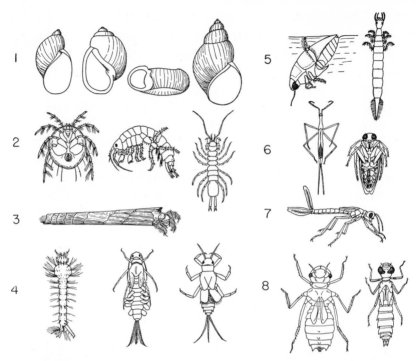

Figure 88.   Some representative animals of the littoral zone of ponds and lakes. Series 1 to 4 are primarily herbivorous forms (primary consumers); series 5 to 8 are predators (secondary consumers). 1. Pond snails (left to right): *Lymnaea* (*pseudosuccinea*) *columella; Physa gyrina; Helisoma trivolvis; Campeloma decisum.* 2. Small arthropods living on or near the bottom or associated with plants or detritus (left to right): a water mite, or Hydracarina (*Mideopsis*); an amphipod (*Gammarus*); an isopod (*Asellus*). 3. A pond caddis fly larva (*Triaenodes*), with its thin, light portable case. 4. (left to right) A mosquito larva (*Culex pipiens*); a clinging or periphytic mayfly nymph (*Cloeon*); a benthic mayfly nymph (*Caenis*)—note gill covers which protect gills from silt. 5. A predatory diving beetle, *Dytiscus,* adult and (right) larva. 6. Two predaceous Hemipterans, a water scorpion, *Ranatra* (Nepidae), and (right) a backswimmer, *Notonecta.* 7. A damsel fly nymph, *Lestes* (Odonata-Zygoptera); note three caudal gills. 8. Two dragonfly nymphs (Odonata–Anisoptera), *Helocordulia,* a long-legged sprawling type (benthos), and (right) *Aeschna,* a slender climbing type (periphyton). (Redrawn from Robert W. Pennak, "Fresh-water Invertebrates of the United States," 1953, The Ronald Press Company.)

both primary and secondary consumers may be found resting or moving on the bottom or beneath silt or plant debris—for example, sprawling Odonata nymphs (which have flattened, rather than cylindrical, bodies), crayfish, isopods, and certain mayfly nymphs. Descending more deeply into the bottom mud are burrowing Odonata and Ephemeroptera (which either maintain burrows or have extended parts of the body reaching to the surface of the mud for breathing), clams, true worms (Annelida), snails, and especially chironomids (midges) and other Diptera larvae which live in minute burrows.

The nekton of the littoral zone is often rich in species and numbers. Adult and larval diving beetles and various adult Hemiptera are conspicuous; some of these, especially the Dytiscids and Notonectids, are carnivorous, whereas the Hydrophylids, Haliplid beetles, and Corixid "bugs" are partly, at least, herbivorous or scavengers. Various diptera larvae and pupae remain suspended in water, often near the surface. Many of this group of animals obtain air from the surface, often carrying a bubble on the underside of the body or under the wings for use under water.

Amphibious vertebrates, frogs, salamanders, turtles, and water snakes are almost exclusively members of the littoral zone community. Tadpoles of frogs and toads are important primary consumers, feeding on algae and other plant material, whereas adults move up a trophic level or two. Cold-blooded vertebrates increase in importance as one goes south. For example, the population density and, hence, the ecological importance of turtles, frogs, and water snakes in the ponds of Louisiana and Florida are astonishing to those who are familiar only with northern ponds.

Pond fish generally move freely between the littoral and the limnetic zone, but most species spend a large part of their time in the litoral zone; many species establish territories and breed there (see Chapter 6, Section 15). Nearly every pond has one or more species of the "sunfish" or "bream" family (Centrarchidae). In the southern United States, top minnows, especially *Gambusia*, are abundant in the vegetation zones. Some species of bass, pike (*Esox*), or gar represent the end of the food chain as far as the pond ecosystem is concerned (see Chapter 3, Section 2).

The zooplankton of the littoral zone is rather characteristic and differs from that of the limnetic zone in preponderance of heavier, less buoyant crustacea which often cling to plants or rest on the bottom when not actively moving their appendages. Important groups of littoral zooplankton (Fig. 89, A) are: large, weak-swimming species of Cladocera ("water fleas"), such as some species of *Daphnia* and *Simocephalus*, some species of copepods of the family Cyclopoidea and all of the Harpacticoidea, many families of ostracods, and some rotifers.

Finally, the littoral neuston (Fig. 89, B) consists of three surface

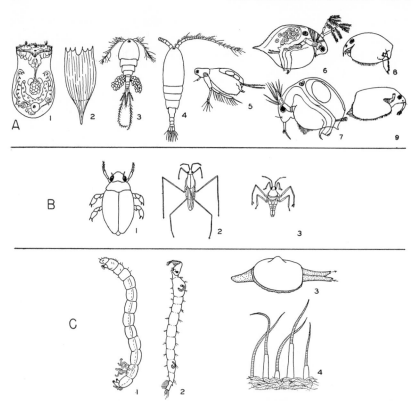

Figure 89. A. Representative zooplankton. Rotifers: 1, *Asplanchna;* 2, *Notholca* (lorica only). Copepods: 3, a cyclopoid copepod, *Macrocyclops;* 4, a calanoid copepod, *Senecella*. Cladocera (representative of each of five families): 5, *Diaphanosoma* (Sididae); 6, *Daphnia* (Daphnidae); 7, *Bosmina* (Bosminidae); 8, *Pleuroxus* (Chydoridae); 9, *Acantholeberis* (Macrothricidae).

B. Zooneuston. 1, a whirligig beetle, *Dineutes* (Gyrinidae); 2, a water strider, *Gerris* (Gerridae); 3, a broad-shouldered water strider, *Rhagovelia* (Veliidae).

C. Some characteristic profundal zone types. 1, a chironomid larva, or blood worm, *Tendipes* (note prolegs and abdominal gills); 2, a "phantom larva," *Chaoborus* (note two air sacs which apparently aid the animal in performing vertical migrations); 3, a "pea-shell" clam, *Musculium* (Sphaeriidae), with "foot" and two branchial siphons extended; 4, *Tubifex*, a red annelid which builds tubes on the bottom and vigorously waves its posterior end around in the water. (Redrawn from Robert W. Pennak, "Fresh-water Invertebrates of the United States," 1953, The Ronald Press Company.)

insects that are familiar to everyone who has even casually observed a pond: (1) whirligig beetles of the family Gyrinidae, the black "lucky bugs" of fishermen—these beetles are unique in that the eye is divided into two parts, one half for "seeing" above the water and the other half for underwater vision; (2) large water striders, family Gerridae; and (3) the smaller, "broad-shouldered" water striders, family Veliidae. Not so conspicuous are numerous protozoa and other microorganisms which are associated with the surface film (both above and below it).

Another remarkable microscopic community occurs among the sand grains at the water's edge (often called the psammolittoral habitat). Examination of this seemingly barren area reveals a remarkable number of algae, protozoa, tardigrades, nematodes, and harpacticoid copepods (see Pennak, 1939).

Nature of communities in the limnetic zone

Phytoplankton producers of the open-water zone consist of algae of the three groups previously listed and the algae-like green flagellates, chiefly the dinoflagellates, Euglenidae and Volvocidae. Most of the limnetic forms are microscopic and hence do not attract the attention of the casual observer, even though they often color the water green. Yet phytoplankton may exceed rooted plants in food production per unit area. Typical open-water phytoplankton types are shown in Figure 87. Many of these forms have processes or other adaptation to aid in floating. Turbulence, or upward-current movements of water caused by temperature differences, aids in keeping phytoplankton near the surface where photosynthesis is most effective. A characteristic feature of limnetic phytoplankton is the marked seasonal variation in population density (Fig. 90). Very high densities which appear quickly and persist for a short time are called "blooms" or phytoplankton "pulses" (see Chapter 6, Section 9, and Chapter 4, Section 3, example 7). In the northern United States ponds and lakes often exhibit a large early spring bloom and another, usually smaller,

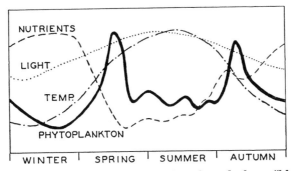

Figure 90. The probable mechanism for phytoplankton "blooms." See text for explanation.

pulse in the autumn. The spring pulse, which typically involves the diatoms, is apparently the result of the following combination of circumstances. During the winter low water temperatures and reduced light result in a low rate of photosynthesis. Nitrogen, phosphorus, and other nutrients, however, are continually being regenerated by the action of bacteria, etc., and increase in concentration. With the advent of favorable temperature and light conditions the phytoplankton organisms, which have a high biotic potential, increase rapidly since nutrients are not limiting for the moment (Fig. 90). Soon, however, nutrients are exhausted and bloom disappears. When nutrients again begin to accumulate, nitrogen-fixing blue-green algae, such as *Anabaena*, often are responsible for autumn blooms, these organisms being able to continue to increase rapidly despite a reduction of dissolved nitrogen, that is, until phosphorus, low temperature, or some other factor becomes limiting and halts the "bloom."

The limnetic zooplankton is made up of few species but the numbers of individuals may be large. Copepods, cladocerans, and rotifers are generally of first importance, and the species are largely different from those found in the littoral zone. The long-antennaed or calanoid copepods (*Diaptomus*, a common genus) are especially characteristic, although the middle-length antennaed forms (*Cyclops*) may be more abundant in smaller bodies of water. Limnetic cladocera consist of highly transparent floating forms, such as *Diaphanosoma, Sida,* and *Bosmina.* Two characteristic genera of plankton rotifers are shown in Figure 89, A. All the zooplanktonic crustacea are "strainers," filtering bacteria and phytoplankton by means of combs of setae on their thoracic appendages. These organisms thus "graze" the plants in somewhat the same manner as cattle graze vegetation on land. As might be expected, the zooplankton may exhibit "blooms" at the same time as the phytoplankton, since they largely depend on the latter. There is some question whether some of the zooplankton organisms can use organic materials not yet completely reduced by bacteria. Pond and lake water usually contains appreciable quantities of suspended organic particles and experiments have shown that some cladocera are able to utilize this material. In general, however, phytoplankton is thought to be the chief food of zooplankton. In other words, the latter are not able to "shorten" the food chain to a significant degree in nature.

Vertical diel migration is a very characteristic feature of lake limnetic zooplankton, as has been described in Part I (see Chapter 8, Section 7; Figure 81).

Copepods and cladocera demonstrate an interesting contrast in life history and method of reproduction. Both have achieved equal success, as it were, in a niche where rapid reproduction is necessary for survival. Cladocera reproduce parthenogenetically, eggs developing in a "brood chamber," which is a space between the body and the carapace shell which envelops the body of the female. Development is direct, with no larval stage. Males appear only at rare intervals, usually at the onset of unfavorable conditions. Fertilized eggs develop into ephippial, or "winter," eggs, which have a resistant shell and are capable of surviving in a dry pond. Copepods, on the other hand, do not reproduce parthenogenetically, but the female is able to store enough sperm at one copulation to last for many batches of eggs. Thus, copepods are able to compete in the matter of rapid increase with other plankton which exhibit parthenogenesis or asexual reproduction. Copepods have a larval stage, called a nauplius, which is entirely free-living. Thus, copepods and cladocerans, the "co-dominants" of the limnetic primary-consumer groups, illustrate the old adage that there is "more than one way to skin a cat," i.e., there is more than one way to accomplish the same ultimate objective.

The limnetic nekton in fresh water consists almost entirely of fish. In ponds the fish of the limnetic zone are the same as those of the littoral zone, but in larger bodies of water a few species may be restricted to the limnetic zone. Most fresh-water fish as adults feed on fairly sizable animals, that is, not on microscopic plankton. A few species, the gizzard shad, for example, have "strainers" and are plankton feeders. In the large storage lakes of the TVA system gizzard shads form an important link between producers and game fish; their presence in these lakes enables game fish, such as bass and pike, to exist on a shorter food chain and to be independent of the littoral zone. This is fortunate because raising and lowering water levels in connection with flood control often makes the littoral zone unavailable to fish. The only drawback with gizzard shad is that they become too large for game fish to eat. It would be highly desirable if a plankton-feeding fish which remains small enough to be eaten by game fish could be adapted to small fish ponds. *Signalosa*, a small shad native to the lower Mississippi valley, is a possibility for this niche.

Nature of communities in the profundal zone

Since there is no light, the inhabitants of the profundal zone depend on the limnetic and littoral zone for basic food materials. In return, the profundal zone provides "rejuvenated" nutrients, which are carried by currents to other zones (see Chapter 2, Section 3). The variety of life in the profundal zone, as might be expected, is not great, but what is there may be important. The important community constituents are bacteria and fungi, which are especially abundant in the water–mud interphase where organic matter accumulates, and three groups of animal consumers (Fig. 89, C): (1) blood worms, or hemoglobin-containing chironomid larvae and annelids; (2) small clams of the family Sphaeriidae; and (3) "phantom larvae," or *Chaoborus* (*Corethra*). The first two groups are benthic forms; the last are plankton forms which regularly move up into the limnetic zone at night and down to the bottom during the day (see Figure 91). *Chaoborus* larvae are remarkable in having four air sacs, two at each end of the body, which apparently acts as floats and also provide a reserve supply of oxygen. These larvae are only "part-time" members of the plankton, the adult being a land-dwelling midge (Diptera). Most plankton organisms in fresh water remain throughout their entire life history in this life form (i.e., holoplankton), in sharp contrast to organisms of marine plankton, many of whom are only part-time members (i.e., meroplankton). All animals of the profundal zone are adapted to withstand periods of low oxygen concentration, whereas many bacteria are able to carry on without oxygen (anaerobic). Oxygen and light, then, are the important limiting factors in this zone.

5. Lakes

As was indicated in Section 1 of this chapter, no sharp distinction can be made between lakes and ponds. There are important ecological differences, however, other than over-all size. In lakes the limnetic and profundal zones are relatively large, compared with the littoral zone. The reverse is true of the bodies of water which are generally designated as ponds. Thus, the limnetic zone is the chief "producing" region (region where light energy is fixed into food) for the lake as a whole. The phytoplankton and the nature of the bottom and its biota are of primary interest in the study of lakes. On the other hand, the littoral zone is the chief "producing" region for ponds, and the communities in this zone are of first interest. Circulation of water in ponds is generally such that limited stratification of temperature or oxygen occurs; lakes, unless very shallow, tend to become stratified at certain seasons. Let us examine this feature in some detail.

Stratification in lakes

An important characteristic of lakes is their tendency to become thermally stratified during summer and winter and to undergo a definite seasonal periodicity in depth distribution of heat and oxygen. The typical seasonal cycle, illustrated in Figure 91, may be described as follows. During the summer the top waters become warmer than the bottom waters; as a result, only the warm top layer circulates, and it does not mix with the more viscous colder water. As temperatures rise in summer the temperature differential between top and bottom waters increases, creating a zone in between called the *thermocline*. The upper, warm circulating water is the *epilimnion* ("surface lake"), and the colder, non-circulating water is the *hypolimnion* ("*under* lake"). In Figure 91 note the strong drop in temperature at the thermocline in the hot months of summer. If the thermocline is below the range of effective light penetration (i.e., compensation level), as is often the case, the oxygen supply becomes depleted in the hypolimnion since both the green plant and the surface source is cut off. Note in Figure 91 how the oxygen supply in the hypolimnion of Linsley Pond disappears in the summer. This is often referred to as the period of summer stagnation in the hypolimnion.

With the onset of cooler weather, the temperature of epilimnion drops until it is the same as that of the hypolimnion. Then the water of the entire lake begins circulating and oxygen is again returned to the depths. This is the beginning of the "fall overturn." As the surface water cools below 4° C, it expands, becomes lighter, remains on the surface and freezes, if the regional climate is a cold one. Then, winter stratification occurs, since ice and the colder epilimnion hinder circulation. In winter the oxygen supply is usually not greatly reduced because bacterial decomposition and respiration of organisms are not so great at low temperatures. Also, water holds more oxygen at low temperatures than at high ones. Winter stagnation, therefore, is not generally so severe (see Figure 91, chart at left). An exception to this generalization may occur when snow covers the ice and prevents photosynthesis, thus

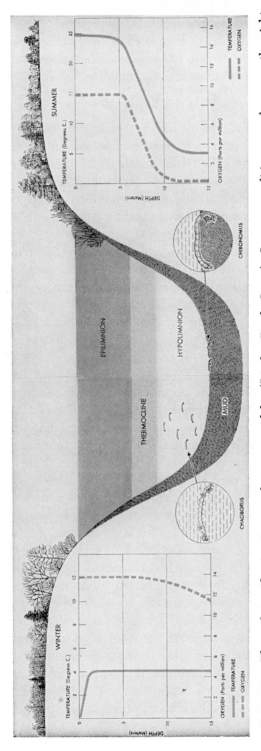

Figure 91. Thermal stratification in a north temperate lake (Linsley Pond, Conn.). Summer conditions are shown on the right, winter conditions on the left. Note that in summer a warm oxygen-rich circulating layer of water, the epilimnion, is separated from the cold oxygen-poor hypolimnion waters by a broad zone, called the thermocline, which is characterized by a rapid change in temperature and oxygen with increasing depth. Two typical hypolimnion organisms are shown (see also Figure 89). (After Deevey, 1951.)

resulting in oxygen depletion for the entire lake and "winter kill" of the fish.

In the spring, as ice melts and water becomes warmer, it becomes heavier and sinks to the bottom. Thus, when the surface temperature rises to 4° C, the lake takes another "deep breath," as it were—the *spring overturn*.

This classic picture, as outlined above, is typical for many lakes of north temperate zone in America and Eurasia, but is by no means universal. Details of thermal stratification were first worked out in Swiss lakes between 1850 and 1900 by Simony and Forel, the latter often called the "father of limnology." In 1904 Birge, who later joined with Juday in the famous team of Birge and Juday, first demonstrated thermal stratification in Wisconsin lakes. In general, the deeper the lake, the slower the stratification and the thicker the hypolimnion. As already indicated, shallow lakes and ponds may become weakly stratified or not be stratified at all. Deep lakes generally show some tendency for thermal stratification, even in the tropics. Therefore, although the details vary from lake to lake, thermal stratification of one sort or another appears to be a basic lake characteristic.

The extent of depletion of oxygen in the hypolimnion depends on the amount of decaying matter and on the depth of the thermocline. Productively "rich" lakes generally are subject to greater oxygen depletion during the summer than "poor" lakes, because the "rain" of organic matter from the limnetic and littoral zones into the profundal zone is greater in the former. Thus, fishes which are stenothermal, low-temperature tolerant can survive only in "poor" lakes where cold bottom waters do not become depleted of oxygen. As already indicated, lower organisms of the profundal zone are adapted to withstand oxygen deficiency for appreciable periods.

If waters of a lake are very transparent and will permit growth of phytoplankton below the thermocline (in the upper part of the hypolimnion), oxygen may be present here even in greater abundance than on the surface because, as indicated above, cold water holds more oxygen. We see, therefore, that the euphotic zone does not necessarily coincide with the epilimnion. The former is based on light penetration (is the "producer" zone), the latter on temperature. Often, however, they coincide roughly during the summer stagnation period.

Geographical distribution of lakes

Natural lakes are most numerous in regions which have been subject to geological change in comparatively recent times, say within the past 20,000 years. Thus lakes abound in glaciated regions of northern Europe, Canada, and northern United States. Such lakes were formed as the last glaciers retreated about 10,000 to 12,000 years ago. These are the lakes which have been most studied by European and American limnologists. Natural lakes are also numerous in regions of recent uplift from the sea, as in Florida, and in regions subject to recent volcanic activity, as in the western Cascades. Volcanic lakes, formed either in extinct craters or in valleys dammed by volcanic action, are among the most beautiful in the world. On the other hand, natural lakes are rare in the geologically ancient and well dissected Appalachian and Piedmont regions of eastern United States and in large sections of the unglaciated great plains. Thus, we see that geological history of a region determines whether lakes will be naturally present and will also greatly influence the type of lake by determining the basic minerals which are available for incorporation into the lake ecosystem. Climate, of course, is important, but sizable lakes may occur even in deserts. Artificial lakes, generally designated as impoundments, are becoming increasingly common, so that, even if a region is not endowed with natural lakes, the student may usually find examples near at hand.

Classification of lakes

Investigation of lakes over the world has shown that they possess a great variety of combinations of properties, making it difficult to select a basis for a natural classification. However, a good introduction to the fascinating subject of world lake ecology can be obtained by considering three categories: (1) the oligotrophic–eutrophic series of ordinary clear-water lakes based on productivity, (2) special lake types, and (3) impoundments.

1. *Oligotrophic–Eutrophic Series.*   Lakes in all regions may be classified according to primary productivity (see Chapter 3, Section 5), as outlined by the pioneer German limnologist, Thienemann. The productivity or "fertility" of a lake depends on nutrients received from regional drainage, and on the stage in succession and on the depth. A simplified classification is as follows, with direction of succession indicated by arrows:

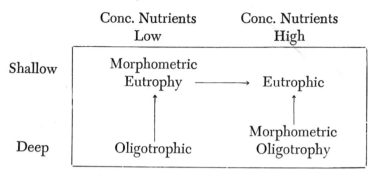

Typical oligotrophic ("few foods") lakes are deep, with the hypolimnion larger than the epilimnion, and have low primary productivity. Littoral plants are scarce and plankton density is low, although the number of species may be large; plankton blooms are rare since nutrients rarely accumulate sufficiently to produce a population eruption of phytoplankton. Because of low productivity of the waters above, the hypolimnion is not subject to severe oxygen depletion; hence stenothermal, cold-water bottom fishes such as lake trout and cisco are characteristic of and often restricted to the hypolimnion of oligotrophic lakes. There are also a few plankton forms characteristic of such lakes (*Mysis*, for example). In short, oligotrophic lakes are still "geologically young" and have changed but little since the time of formation. Given time, however, such lakes develop into *eutrophic* ("good foods") lakes which are shallower and have a greater primary productivity. Littoral vegetation is more abundant, plankton populations are denser, and "blooms" are characteristic. Because of the heavy organic content, summer stagnation may be severe enough to exclude cold-water fishes. Lake Mendota (see Table 3) and Linsley Pond (see Figure 91) are examples of eutrophic lakes which have been much studied; the Great Lakes and the Finger Lakes of New York are typical oligotrophic lakes.

2. *Special Lake Types.*   Five special lake types may be mentioned here.

(a) *Dystrophic lakes: brown water, humic, and bog lakes.* Generally have high concentrations of humic acid in water; bog lakes have peat-filled margins (where pH is usually low) and develop into peat bogs.

(b) *Deep, ancient lakes with endemic fauna.* Lake Baikal in Russia is the most famous of ancient lakes. It is the deepest lake in the world and was formed by earth movement during the

Mesozoic era (age of reptiles). Ninety-eight per cent of 384 species of arthropods are endemic (found nowhere else), including 291 species of amphipods. Eighty-one per cent of 36 species of fish are endemic. This lake is often called the "Australia of freshwater," because of its endemic fauna (see Brooks, 1950).

(c) *Desert salt lakes:* Occur in sedimentary drainages in arid climates where evaporation exceeds precipitation (thus resulting in salt concentration). Example: Great Salt Lake, Utah. Contain community composed of a few species (but sometimes abundant) which are able to tolerate high salinity. Brine shrimp (*Artemia*) are characteristic.

(d) *Desert alkali lakes:* Occur in igneous drainages in arid climates; high pH and concentration of carbonates. Example: Pyramid Lake, Nevada.

(e) *Volcanic lakes:* Acid or alkaline lakes associated with active volcanic regions (and receiving waters from the magma); extreme chemical conditions, restricted biota. Examples: some Japanese and Philippine lakes.

3. *Impoundments.* Artificial lakes, of course, vary according to the region and to the nature of the drainage. Generally, they are characterized by fluctuating water levels and high turbidity. Some of the practical problems concerning fish production in impoundments are discussed in Chapter 12, Section 6.

6. Ponds

As indicated in the previous section, ponds are small bodies of water in which the littoral zone is relatively large and the limnetic and profundal regions are small or absent. Stratification is of minor importance. Ponds may be found in most regions of adequate rainfall. They are continually being formed, for example, as a stream shifts position, leaving the former bed isolated as a body of standing water or "oxbow." Such ponds can be designated as flood-plain ponds since they occur on stream flood plains and are subject to flooding during high water. Because of the accumulation of organic materials on flood plains, small flood-plain ponds may be quite productive. In the Piedmont region of the southeast, where glacial lakes and ponds are lacking, we have found that flood-plain ponds are very favorable sites for class study since they contain a rich and varied life and illustrate various principles of the pond ecosystem. Natural ponds are also formed in limestone regions when depressions or "sinks" develop, due to solution of the underlying strata.

Temporary ponds, that is, ponds which are dry for part of the year, are especially interesting and support a unique community. Organisms in such ponds must be able to survive in a dormant stage during dry periods or be able to move in and out of ponds, as can amphibians and adult aquatic insects. Some temporary pond animals are shown in Figure 92. The fairy shrimps (Eubranchiopoda) are especially remarkable crustaceans which are well adapted to temporary ponds. The eggs survive in the dry soil for many months, whereas development and reproduction occur in a short time in late winter and spring while water is present. Fairy shrimp even occur in temporary pools in the granite on top of Stone Mountain, Georgia, where they are completely isolated vertically as well as horizontally from any other bodies of water! As is true of other marginal habitats, the temporary pond is a favorable place for those organisms adapted to it, because interspecific competition is much reduced (see Chapter 7, Section 2). Even though a temporary pond contains water for only a few weeks, a definite seasonal succession of organisms may occur, thus enabling a surprisingly large variety of organisms to utilize a very limited amount of physical habitat (see Figure 92).

Artificial ponds, of course, are the result of the damming of a

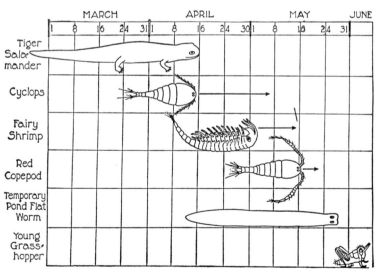

Figure 92. Succession of animals in a temporary pond in Illinois. The length of the animal's body plus the length of the arrow indicate the dates between which the adults of each of the five species were found. The drying up of the pond and appearance of land organisms is indicated by the young grasshopper. (From Welch, modified after Shelford, 1919.)

stream or basin by man, or by animals such as the beaver. Prior to about 1920, most man-made ponds in the United States were "mill ponds," formed by damming sizable streams for the purpose of providing power for small mills. At the present time a very large number of "farm ponds" are being constructed which differ from "mill ponds" in that stream water is largely detoured around the pond, in order to prevent loss of nutrients and erosion, or the pond is constructed in a basin without a permanent stream. Such ponds have relatively little water flowing through them, and are often artificially fertilized and managed so as to discourage rooted vegetation. Thus, producers are all phytoplankton and, in a sense, food-chain relations resemble those of lakes. However, such ponds are rarely deep enough for stratification. The contrast between a managed "farm pond" and a pond with a vegetated littoral zone is shown in the two pictures of the frontispiece. A "farm pond" can be much more efficient than an unmanaged pond or mill pond from the standpoint of production of a large biomass of fish, but it is less interesting to the naturalist because the variety of organisms is reduced in favor of large numbers of the desired species (see pages 50-51; 435-36).

Beaver ponds are a characteristic feature of wilderness areas of the north and of mountains of the west. A beaver pond generally has a short ecological life history, as such ponds are abandoned when the supply of food trees in the vicinity becomes reduced. Thus, under primeval conditions, the beaver was a very important factor in opening up the forests and in maintaining both terrestrial and aquatic seral stages. Along large rivers and on coastal plains beaver often do not construct ponds but live in holes in the bank of streams and thus become essentially stream animals.

7. Lotic (running-water) communities

General comparison of lotic and lentic habitats

One does not have to be an expert, nor does one need to sample all of the varied manifestations of life, to appreciate differences between standing- and running-water habitats. Comparison of a stream (Fig. 93) and a pond or lake makes an excellent ecological study, one that will bring out important principles. An ecology class, for example, can very profitably spend a couple of hours in a field investigation of an example of each type of habitat. Results will probably be most satisfactory if the class is divided into "teams," each assigned to sample the physico-chemical and biological aspects of a significant portion or zone. Thus, everyone contributes to the study and no one is left standing on the bank! If this field sampling is followed by a little laboratory work, many of the significant features of both environments will become apparent via the comparison and contrast method. When the results are tabulated, it will be found that the biotic community in streams is quite different from that in ponds, even if the identification of lower plants and invertebrates is carried only to genus (or only to family). Discovery of differences in organisms leads naturally into a consideration of the chief differences in the physical and chemical limiting factors. This, in turn, should suggest basic differences in food-chain arrangements and ways in which productivity in the two types of ecosystems might be studied. All of this, it is hoped, should whet the appetite for a return to the pond and stream for further observations, or even promote explorations into the literature!

In general, differences between streams and ponds revolve around a triad of conditions: (1) current is much more of a major controlling and limiting factor in streams; (2) land–water inter-

Figure 93. A small, rapidly flowing stream, the habitat for swift-water organisms. (U. S. Soil Conservation Service Photo.)

change is relatively more extensive in streams, resulting in a more "open" ecosystem and a "hetertrophic" type of community metabolism (see Fig. 72); and (3) oxygen tension is generally more uniform in streams, and there is little or no thermal or chemical stratification. Let us briefly discuss each of these in order.

1. *Current.*   Although possession of a definite and continuous current is of course a prime characteristic of lotic habitats, streams and lakes are not sharply divided in this regard. Thus, velocity of the current varies greatly in different parts of the same stream (both longitudinally and transversely to the axis of flow) and from one time to another. In large streams or rivers the current may be so reduced that virtually standing-water conditions result. Contrariwise, wave action along rocky or sandy shores of lakes (especially in the absence of rooted plants which might buffer the wave action) may virtually duplicate stream conditions. Consequently, what would generally be considered pond organisms are often found in quiet pools of streams, and stream animals may be found in the wave-tossed portion of lakes. Nevertheless, current is the most important primary factor which (1) makes for a big difference between stream and pond life, and (2) governs differences in various parts of a given stream. Hence it is certainly a factor worth primary consideration and measurement.

The velocity of current is determined by the steepness of the surface gradient, the roughness of the stream bed, and the depth and width of the stream bed. Several types of current meters have been devised, but it is difficult to measure velocity under stones and in crevices where organisms live. At any given point there is a "micro-stratification" of current. Where fish are concerned or where the general nature of the stream community over an appreciable stretch is being considered, the surface gradient alone gives a good index to average current conditions. The gradient in feet per mile (or smaller units), for example, can easily be determined from topographic maps or can be measured with simple surveying instruments in the field. In Ohio, for example, Trautman (1942) found that distribution of bass and other fish was well correlated with gradient of flow. Small-mouth bass, for example, were found largely in stream sections having a gradient of 7 to 20 feet per mile; they were almost never collected where the gradient was below 3 or above 25 feet per mile.

2. *Land–Water Interchange.*   Since the depth of water and the cross-section area of streams is much less than that of lakes,

the land–water surface junction is relatively great in proportion to the size of the stream habitat. This means that streams are more intimately associated with the surrounding land (Fig. 93) than are most standing bodies of water. In fact, most streams depend on land areas and on connected ponds, backwaters, and lakes for a large portion of their basic energy supply. Streams, to be sure, have producers of their own, such as fixed filamentous green algae, encrusted diatoms, and aquatic mosses, but these are usually inadequate to support the large array of consumers found in streams. Many of the primary consumers in streams are detritus feeders which depend, in part at least, on organic materials which are swept or fall in from terrestrial vegetation (compare Fig. 72). Sometimes plankton and detritus coming into the stream from quieter waters are important. Thus, although lakes form a fairly closed ecosystem or are "little worlds unto themselves," streams form an open ecosystem interdigitated with terrestrial and lentic systems. For this reason measurement of primary productivity (see Chapter 3, Section 5) has been difficult. Because of the lack of depth, temperature of water in streams fluctuates to a greater extent than it does in lentic habitats. Since there is thorough mixing, the temperature and the concentration of dissolved substances are usually the same from top to bottom.

3. *Oxygen.*   Although stream organisms face more extreme conditions in regard to current and temperature than do pond organisms, oxygen is not as likely to be as variable under natural conditions in streams. Because of the small depth, large surface exposed, and constant motion, streams generally contain an abundant supply of oxygen, even when there are no green plants. For this reason stream animals generally have a narrow tolerance and are especially susceptible to reduced oxygen. Therefore, stream communities are especially susceptible to any type of organic pollution which reduces the oxygen supply. When organic material, whether sewage or wastes from a paper mill, is dumped in large quantities into streams, oxygen in the water is used up in the process of bacterial decay. Stream pollution of this type, as well as of the "toxic waste" type, is one of the most important problems facing mankind in heavily populated and industrialized regions. Some of the practical aspects of this problem, including methods of measuring the effects of pollution, are discussed in Chapter 12, Section 7.

Nature of lotic communities

As was outlined in Section 2 of this chapter, streams generally exhibit two major habitats, rapids and pools. Consequently, broadly speaking we may first think in terms of two stream community types, rapids communities (Fig. 93) and pool communities. Some of the characteristic organisms of these two community types are shown in Figure 94. Within these broad categories the type of bottom, whether sand, pebbles, clay, bedrock, or rubble rock, is very important in determining the nature of the communities and the population density of community dominants. As streams work down to base-level conditions, the distinction between rapids and pools becomes less and less until a channel habitat is developed in large rivers. The biota of a river channel resembles that of the rapids, except that population distribution is highly "clumped," owing to the frequent absence of firm substrates.

Current is the major limiting factor in rapids, but the hard bottom, especially if composed of stones, may offer favorable surfaces for organisms (both plant and animal) to attach or cling. The soft, continually shifting bottom of pool areas generally limits smaller benthic organisms to burrowing forms, but the deeper, more slowly moving water is more favorable for nekton, neuston, and plankton. The composition of rapids communities is likely to be 100 per cent different from that of the quiet water zones of ponds and lakes. Consequently, we generally think of organisms in rapids communities as being "typical" stream organisms. Pool communities, on the other hand, may be expected to contain some organisms which also occur in ponds. For example, the gyrinid beetles "gyrate" as well on the surface of a quiet pool as on the surface of the littoral zones of ponds, while bluegills, typical pond fish, also reside in deeper pools of streams.

Other conditions being equal, sand or soft silt is generally the least favorable type of bottom and supports the smallest number of species and individuals of benthic plants and animals. Clay bottom is generally more favorable than sand; flat or rubble rocks generally produce the largest variety and highest density of bottom organisms. Generally, benthic invertebrates have a higher density in rapids communities, whereas stream nekton and burrowing forms, such as clams, burrowing Odonata and Ephemeroptera, are more abundant in pools. Stream fish commonly find

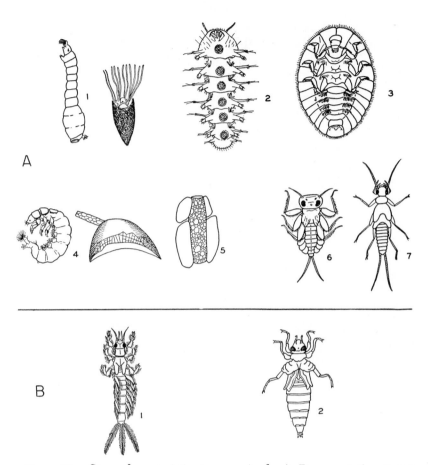

Figure 94. Some characteristic stream animals. A. Representative genera of the rapids community, illustrating various adaptations for living in swift current. This group is often aptly called the "torrential fauna." 1. A black-fly larva, *Simulium* (Simuliidae), and its pupa (right) in a cocoon attached to a rock; note sucker at posterior end of the larva and the "head net" used for straining food from the water. 2. A blepharocerid larva, *Bibiocephala* (note the row of ventral suckers). 3. A "water penny," *Psephenus,* the larva of the riffle beetle (Psephenidae). 4. A net-spinning caddis, *Hydropsyche,* with its net (open end faces upstream) and case. 5. The case of a caddis, *Goera,* with "ballast" rocks attached to the side. 6. A mayfly nymph, *Iron,* and 7, a stonefly nymph, *Isogenus,* both with flattened, streamlined bodies adapted to clinging to the undersides of stones. (*Note:* most stonefly nymphs have two "tails" and most mayfly nymphs have three "tails," as shown in B-1. *Iron* is atypical in this respect.)

B. Two burrowing types living in stream banks or bottoms of pools. 1. A burrowing mayfly nymph, *Hexagenia.* 2. A burrowing dragonfly nymph, *Progomphus.* (Redrawn from Robert W. Pennak, "Fresh-water Invertebrates of the United States," 1953, The Ronald Press Company.)

refuges in pools and feed in or at the base of rapids, thus linking pool and rapids communities.

It might be assumed that plankton would be absent from streams, since such organisms are at the mercy of the current. Although it is true that plankton is much less important in stream economy, compared with its dominant position in lake ecosystems, streams do have plankton. In small streams plankton, if present, originates in lakes, ponds, or backwaters connected with streams and is soon destroyed as it passes through rapids. Only in slow-moving parts of streams and in large rivers is plankton able to multiply and thus become an integral part of the community. Despite the transitory nature of much of the stream plankton, it may supply a not unimportant source of food in some rivers. In the Illinois River plankton is continually replenished in large quantities from a series of productive flood-plain lakes which are joined to the river. In the Mississippi River and its large tributaries, at least one species of fish, the primitive and unique *Polyodon*, feeds largely on zooplankton.

Organisms in rapids communities, and to a lesser extent those inhabiting pool communities, show adaptations for maintaining position in swift water. Some of the most important of these are:

1. *Permanent attachment to a firm substrate,* such as a stone, log, leaf mass, etc. In this category would be included the chief producer plants of streams which are: (1) attached green algae, such as *Cladophora,* with its long trailing filaments; (2) encrusting diatoms which cover various surfaces; and (3) aquatic mosses of genus *Fontinalis* and others which cover stones even in the swiftest current. Also, a few animals become fixed, such as freshwater sponges and caddis fly larvae, which cement their cases to stones.

2. *Hooks and suckers.*   A great many rapids animals have either hooks or suckers which enable them to grip even seemingly smooth surfaces. Note how many of the animals in Figure 94 are so equipped. The two diptera larvae, *Simulium* and *Blepharocera,* and the caddis, *Hydropsyche* (see Figure 94), are especially remarkable in this connection and are often the only animals able to withstand the pounding of swift rapids and waterfalls. *Simulium* not only has a sucker at the posterior end of the body but also attaches itself by means of a silken thread. If dislodged, the legless larvae are kept from being swept very far down stream by their "safety rope" and work their way back up the thread to a

favorable attachment place. In addition to hooks, *Hydropsyche*, the net-spinning caddis, cements a net around itself which acts not only as a shelter but also as a trap for animal and plant material suspended in the water.

3. *Sticky undersurfaces.*   Many animals are able to adhere to surfaces by their sticky undersurfaces. Snails and flatworms present good examples.

4. *Streamlined bodies.*   Nearly all stream animals, from insect larvae to fish, exhibit definite streamlining which means that the body is more or less egg-shaped, broadly rounded in front and tapering posteriorly, to offer minimum resistance to water flowing over it.

5. *Flattened bodies.*   In addition to streamlining, many rapids animals exhibit extremely flattened bodies which enable them to find refuge under stones and in crevices, etc. Thus, the body of stonefly and mayfly nymphs living in swift water is much flatter than the body of nymphs of related species living in ponds.

6. *Positive rheotaxis* (*rheo*, current; *taxis*, arrangement). Stream animals almost invariably orient themselves upstream and, if capable of swimming movements, continually move against the current. This is an inherent behavior pattern. In contrast, many lake animals, when placed in a current of water, merely drift with the current and make no attempt to orient themselves or move against it. An inherent behavior pattern for positive rheotaxis is probably just as important an adaptation as the morphological features cited above.

7. *Positive thigmotaxis* (*thigmo*, touch, contact).   Many stream animals have an inherent behavior pattern to cling close to a surface or to keep the body in close contact with the surface. Thus, when a group of stream stonefly nymphs are placed in a dish, they seek to make contact with the underside of sticks, debris, or whatever is available, even clinging to each other if no other surface is available.

Thienemann (1926), the German limnologist, in his delightful essay on "the brook," has pointed out that adaptation for stream life among animals might have arisen in two ways. First, specialized structures and physiological responses may have arisen in widely different orders and families not naturally adapted to running water through natural selection. Phylogenetic development from simple skin folds to complicated suckers in the diptera would be an example. Second, animals may already have possessed favorable form or function and could therefore occupy swift water without further change. Thienemann called this preadaptation the "taking-advantage principle" (*Ausnutzungsprinzip*). Snails as a group have a sticky "foot," regardless of where they live. Thus snails, flatworms, etc. merely need to "take advantage" of their basic attribute in order to become a part of stream communities.

8. Longitudinal succession in streams

In lakes and ponds the prominent zonation is horizontal, whereas in streams it is longitudinal. Thus, in lakes, successive zones from the middle to the shore represent, as it were, successively older seral stages from a "young" oligotrophic condition to land communities. Likewise in streams we find increasingly older stages of development from source to mouth. Changes are more pronounced in the upper part of streams because the gradient, volume of flow, and chemical composition change rapidly. The change in composition of communities is likely to be more pronounced in the first mile than in the last fifty miles. A very instructive study of longitudinal succession can be made by an ecology class. Stations may be selected at intervals along the upper reaches of a small stream and teams assigned to make collections with comparable techniques. Results may then be tabulated in the form of a "succession table," as illustrated in Chapter 8, Section 4.

The longitudinal distribution of fish in a stream may be selected as a specific example. Shelford (1911a) and Thompson and Hunt (1930) made such studies in Illinois streams, where the gradient of flow was not greatly different from source to mouth. Headwaters species generally exhibited wide tolerances and were found throughout the length of the stream, whereas other species occupied successive sections of the stream. Thompson and Hunt found that the number of individuals decreased downstream, but the size of the fish increased, so that biomass density remained about the same. Table 18 shows the distribution of fish in a stream in the Virginia mountains. A distinct longitudinal succession occurs along a steep gradient of temperature, current velocity (highest at upper end of stream), and pH. Low temperatures and swift current limit the fish along the upper high altitude length of Little Stony Creek to relatively few species (trout, darters, swift-water minnows). Longitudinal succession should not be thought of in terms of a uniform, continuous change; specific conditions and

Table 18. *Longitudinal distribution of fishes in Little Stony Creek*[*]

Stations	1	2	3	4	5	6	7	8	9	10	11	12	13	14
pH	5.6	5.6	5.8	5.8	5.9	6.2	6.4	6.6	7.0	7.0	7.1	7.2	7.2	7.4
Temperature (°C)	15	15	16	16	17	18	18	18	18	19	19	20	20	21
Salvelinus f. fontinalis	X	X	X	X	X	X	X	X	X	X				
Rhinichthys atratulus obtusus					X	X	X		X			X	X	
Catonotus f. flabellaris							X			X			X	X
Salmo gairdnerii irideus								X	X	X	X	X	X	X
Cottus b. bairdii												X	X	X
Campostoma anomalum													X	X
Notropis albeolus														X
Rhinichthys cataractae														X
Catostomus c. commersonnii														X

[*] From Burton and Odum (1945). Stations are approximately one mile apart.

populations may reappear at intervals, as is indicated by the discontinuous distribution of some species.

9. Springs

Springs are the aquatic ecologist's natural constant temperature laboratory. Because of the relative constancy of the chemical composition, velocity of water, and temperature in comparison with lakes, rivers, marine environments, and terrestrial communities, springs hold a position of importance as study areas that is out of proportion to their size and number. An account of the community metabolism of two different types of springs has been given in previous chapters (see especially pages 62-65; 249).

Many springs, like the large Florida limestone springs, seem to be in a steady state, with rapid growth of organisms but a constant standing crop (see Fig. 15, page 63). In the spring itself the organisms do not modify their environment causing succession because, as the water is altered by photosynthesis and respiration, it passes downstream and is replaced by new water of the same properties from underground. These conditions make it possible to study whole communities under constant, known conditions. The cost of a similar set-up in the laboratory would be prohibitive.

Some of the types of springs about which knowledge is available are: (1) hot springs, usually with a high salinity, of volcanic areas, such as Iceland, New Zealand, western United States, and North Africa; (2) the large hard-water springs in limestone districts of Florida, Denmark, and North Germany, having the average temperature of the region in which they occur; and (3) small soft-water springs emerging through shales, sandstones, and crys- talline rocks; because of their small size these springs are more affected by the environment.

Studies on the hot springs have established the upper ecological temperature tolerances for survival and propagation for types of organisms as follows:

	Degrees F.
Bacteria	190
Blue-green algae	176
Protozoa	129
Insects	122
Fishes	122

Spring communities are characterized by relatively small num- bers of species. In hot springs this is due to relatively few organ- isms being adapted physiologically to the high temperatures and high salinities. In springs having the same temperature as the regional environment, the more stable conditions seem to provide fewer ecological niches. Springs are further simplified by the absence of plankton.

In a constant temperature environment as provided by large springs, it is possible to separate the effects of light and tempera- ture. Thus, in Iceland hot springs, Tuxen (1944) found that the temperature remained constant and favorable for the growth of algae during the long winter, but there was little light for photo- synthesis. Consequently, the algal population density decreased in winter and the faunal population was reduced to a low level for lack of food and oxygen. A similar though less pronounced rhythm related to seasonal variations in light has been demonstrated for constant temperature Florida springs (H. T. Odum, 1957).

The community composition of a spring run changes with changing conditions as one goes downstream, as is the case in any stream (see the preceding section). However, conditions in a large spring run remain relatively more constant at any given point, producing a kind of succession in steady states. In a North Africa hot spring, for example, only blue-green algae were found in the boil. Proceeding down the run ostracods, crabs (which could tolerate high salinity), frogs, and finally the normal regional stream biota were found at successive points. Such a stream is a natural ecological gradient from high temperature and high salin- ity to conditions of lower temperature and lower salinity.

The constant temperature properties of springs permit organisms to exist in regions where they do not otherwise occur. Thus, arctic insects occur in German springs because of the lower summer temperatures there, and organisms of warmer climates occur in the Icelandic hot springs. There seems little question that springs have provided refuges for aquatic organisms during geological periods when climatic changes have occurred.

10 · Marine ecology

1. The marine environment

For centuries man regarded the sea as a restless surface which first hindered, then aided, his efforts to explore the world. He also learned that the sea was a source of food which could be harvested, by dint of great effort, to supplement the products of land and fresh water. Biologists early became intrigued with the amazing variety of life to be found along the shores and among the coral reefs. Yet the great bulk of the sea remained largely a mysterious realm which might harbor all manner of sea serpents, for all anyone knew. It was only in 1872 that HMS Challenger, one of the first ships to be specifically equipped for the study of the sea, put forth on her now famous voyages. Since that time the study of the sea has proceeded with increasing tempo, aided by many oceanographic vessels as well as by marine laboratories on shore. Progress has been especially rapid since about 1930, with the development of new equipment such as echo-sounders, underwater cameras, and nets for high speed sampling at great depths. From physical oceanography and the older marine biology, a vigorous new science of marine ecology* has emerged. Increased knowledge is verifying what scientists had suspected, namely, that the ocean not only is the cradle of life but is still today the greatest reservoir of life itself and of the vital elements needed by life everywhere. The sea is thus a major force in shaping conditions of life on land and in fresh water as well.

* *Oceanography* deals with study of the sea in all of its aspects, physical, chemical, geological, and biological. *Marine ecology* deals with the ecological aspects of oceanography.

The features of the sea which are of major ecological interest may be listed as follows:

1. The sea is big; it covers 70 per cent of the earth's surface.

2. The sea is deep, and life extends to all its depths. Although the density of living things is by no means uniform, apparently there are no abiotic zones in the ocean. Thus, the marine habitat is much "thicker," as well as greater in area, than the land and fresh-water portion of the biosphere combined. There can be little

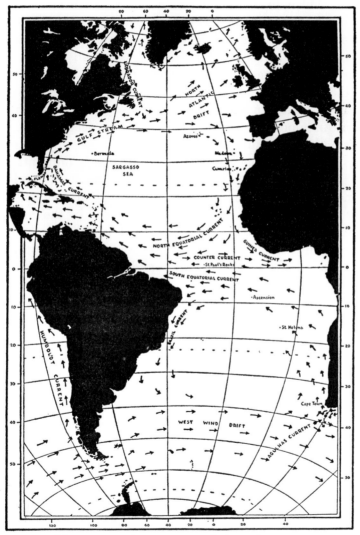

Figure 95.   The main surface currents of the Atlantic Ocean. (Colman, "The Sea and Its Mysteries," 1950, G. Bell & Sons, Ltd.)

doubt that the total marine biomass ("living weight") is far greater than the combined biomass of land and fresh water.

3. The sea is continuous, not separated as are land and freshwater habitats. All the oceans are connected. Temperature, salinity, and depth are the chief barriers to free movement of marine organisms.

4. The sea is in continuous circulation; air temperature differences between poles and equator set up strong winds such as the trade winds (blowing steadily in the same direction the year around) which, together with rotation of the earth, create definite currents. In Figure 95 the major currents of the Atlantic Ocean are shown. The mechanics of these currents are complicated and need not concern us here (see Sverdrup, Johnson, and Fleming, 1942; Coker, 1947; or other references in oceanography). Suffice it to say that the major currents act as giant pinwheels which run clockwise in the northern and counterclockwise in the southern hemisphere. An important process called *upwelling* occurs where winds consistently move surface water away from precipitous coastal slopes, bringing to the surface cold water rich in nutrients which have been accumulating in the depths. The most productive marine areas are often located in regions of upwelling (which occur largely on western coasts), as evidenced by the large tuna and sardine fisheries off Portugal and California and the high population of fish-eating sea birds off the coast of Peru, which have deposited countless tons of nitrate- and phosphate-rich guano in that region. Were it not for these currents, the upwellings, and the deep currents resulting from temperature and salinity differences in the water itself, bodies and materials would pass permanently into the depths, carrying nutrients beyond the reach of "producers" in the photic surface regions. As it is, nutrients do get "lost" in the deep sediments for long periods (see Chapter 2, Section 3, Figures 7 and 8). Currents also greatly influence the climates of land areas. The Gulf Stream, for example, moderates the climate of Northwest Europe, and the Humboldt Current brings cool conditions almost to the equator along the western coast of South America.

5. The sea is dominated by waves of many kinds and by tides produced by the pull of moon and sun. Tides are especially important in the shoreward zones where marine life is often especially varied and dense. Tides are chiefly responsible for the marked periodicities in these communities (see Chapter 8, Section 7).

Since tides have a periodicity of about 12½ hours, high tides occur in most localities twice daily, being about 50 minutes later on successive days. Every two weeks when sun and moon are "working together" the amplitude of tides is increased (the so-called *spring* tides when high tides are very high and low tides very low), whereas midway in the fortnightly periods the range between low and high tide is smallest (the so-called *neap tides* when sun and moon tend to cancel one another). The tidal range varies from less than 1 foot in the open sea to 50 feet in certain enclosed bays. There are many factors which modify tides so that tidal patterns vary in different places over the world.

6. The sea is salty. The average salinity or salt content is 35 parts of salts by weight per 1000 parts of water, or 3.5 per cent. This is usually written: 35 °/oo (recall that fresh water usually has a salinity of less than 0.5 °/oo). About 27 °/oo is sodium chloride and most of the rest consists of magnesium, calcium, and potassium salts. Since the salts dissociate into ions, the best way to picture the chemistry of the sea is as follows (in parts per thousand):

Positive Ions		*Negative Ions*	
Sodium	10.7	Chloride	19.3
Magnesium	1.3	Sulfate	2.7
Calcium	0.4	Bicarbonate	0.1
Potassium	0.4	Carbonate	0.007
		Bromide	0.07

Since the proportion of the radicals remains virtually constant, total salinity may be computed by determining the chloride content (which is easier than determining total salinity). Thus, 19 °/oo chlorinity approximates 35 °/oo salinity.

Since temperature and salinity represent two of the important limiting factors in the sea, it is instructive to plot them together in the form of *hydroclimographs*, as shown in Figure 96. Each polygon represents a specific locality; each point on a polygon is the monthly average temperature plotted against salinity, 1 being January and 12 December. Compare these graphs with the temperature–moisture climographs of terrestrial habitats (Figs. 29 and 30). In Figure 96 note that salinity varies within very narrow limits in the open ocean but is seasonally quite variable in the estuarine (brackish) waters of bays and river mouths. Organisms of the open ocean are usually stenohaline (i.e., have narrow limits of tolerance to changes in salinity; see Chapter 4,

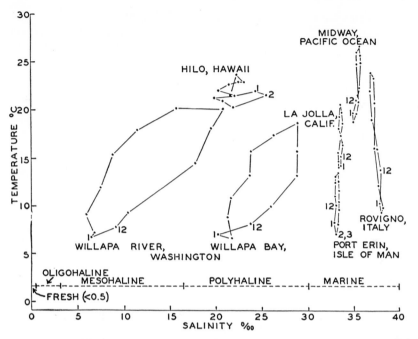

Figure 96. Temperature–salinity hydroclimographs for estuarine (brackish) and marine localities. Note that seasonal variation in both temperature and salinity is pronounced in estuarine habitats, whereas salinity is virtually constant in true marine habitats. (Redrawn from Hedgpeth, 1951.)

Section 2), whereas organisms of inshore brackish waters are generally euryhaline.

Most marine organisms have an internal salt content similar to that of the water of their environment (i.e., are isotonic with sea water), and hence osmoregulation poses no problem. Marine bony fish, however, have a lower concentration of salts in blood and tissues (i.e., are hypotonic). Such fish have a "problem" in regard to osmoregulation which is the reverse of that confronting fresh-water fish (see Chapter 9, Section 1). Dehydration is prevented by ingestion of water and active excretion of salt through the gills. The osmoregulation in fresh-water and marine bony fishes has already been illustrated in Figure 85.

7. The concentration of dissolved nutrients is low and constitutes an important limiting factor in determining the size of marine populations. Whereas the concentration of sodium chloride and other salts mentioned in paragraph 6 is measured in parts per thousand, nitrates, phosphates, and other nutrients are so diluted

that they are measured in parts per billion.* Also, the concentration of these vital biogenic salts varies greatly from place to place and from season to season. Despite the fact that nutrients are continually being washed into the sea, their importance as limiting factors is no less in marine than in terrestrial or fresh-water environments (see Chapter 2, Section 3, and Chapter 4, Section 3). The low concentration of nutrients does not necessarily indicate total scarcity, since these materials are in such "demand" by organisms that they may be taken out of circulation as rapidly as they are released. As previously indicated, currents prevent permanent loss of many nutrients, although carbon and silicon may be lost by deposition of shells on the bottom of the ocean. Only in a few places of vigorous upwelling are nutrients so abundant at times that phytoplankton cannot exhaust them (i.e., nutrients are not limiting). One such area in the antarctic supports the world's greatest concentration of whales (or did until recent slaughter by man), which feed on the superabundant plankton. An excellent account of the nutrient cycles in the sea has been prepared by Harvey (1955).

2. The marine biota

The marine biota is varied; consequently it would be difficult to list "dominant" groups, as was done for fresh water (see Chapter 9, Section 3). Coelenterates, sponges, echinoderms, annelids, and various minor phyla which are absent or poorly represented in fresh water are very important in the ecology of the sea. The bacteria, algae, crustacea, and fish play a dominant role in both aquatic environments, with diatoms, green flagellates, and copepods equally prominent in both. The variety of algae (the brown and red algae being chiefly marine), crustacea, mollusks, and fish is greater in the sea. On the other hand, seed plants (spermatophytes) are of little importance in the sea, except for eel grass (*Zostera*) and a few other species in certain coastal waters. Insects are absent, except in brackish water, the crustacea being the "insects of the sea," ecologically speaking. The great richness of the marine biota is well illustrated when the plankton of the sea (Figures 99-101) is compared with the less varied plankton of fresh water.

* In practice, nutrients are measured in microgram-atoms per liter (see Figure 111), or in milligram-atoms per cubic meter.

3. Zonation in the sea

The same ecological classification as outlined for fresh water (see Chapter 9, Section 2) may be applied to the sea, except that it is customary to use a different set of terms for habitats, as shown in Figure 80. Also, an additional "way of life" term is commonly used with reference to the sea, namely, *pelagic.* Pelagic life includes the plankton plus the nekton and the neuston (the latter generally unimportant), or all of the life in the open water.

Generally, a continental shelf extends for a distance offshore, then the bottom drops off steeply (the continental slope) until the abyssal is reached. The shallow water zone on the continental shelf is the *neritic* ("near shore") zone. It is logically subdivided into supratidal, intertidal (between high and low tides; also called littoral zone), and subtidal. The region of the open ocean beyond the continental shelf is designated as the *oceanic* region; that portion within the range of effective (for photosynthesis) light penetration, and hence the "producing" region, is the *euphotic* zone, which is equivalent to the limnetic zone of fresh water. The vast regions of the ocean beyond effective light penetration are the *bathyal* zone of the continental slope region and the *abyssal* zone which begins at about 2,000 meters. Within the latter there may be tremendous "deeps" below 6,000 meters (these very deep areas are sometimes known as *hadal* zone). Bruun (1957a) has called the abyssal the "world's largest ecological unit." It is, of course, an incomplete ecosystem despite its extent because the primary energy source lies far above in the euphotic zone. It should not be inferred from Figure 97 that the continental slope or the floor of the ocean is smooth; there are numerous submarine canyons, trenches, and rugged "mountain" ranges. Recent work has demonstrated that great underwater avalanches periodically modify those canyons.

Within these primary zones, which are based largely on physical factors, well marked secondary zonation, both horizontal and vertical, is generally evident from the distribution of communities. Communities in each of the primary zones, except the euphotic, have two rather distinct vertical components: the benthic or bottom dwellers (benthos) and the pelagic. As in the large lakes, the producer plants of the sea come in small packages, i.e., the microscopic phytoplankton, although large seaweeds (multicellular algae) are important in limited areas. Primary consumers

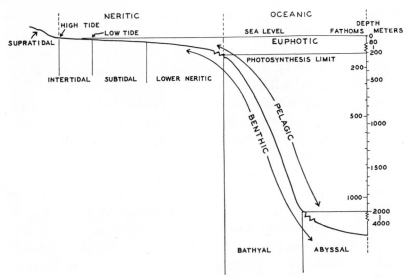

Figure 97. Zonation in the sea. (Redrawn from Hedgpeth, 1951.)

consequently are largely zooplankton. Larger animals are either plankton feeders (or feed on detritus derived from plankton) or are carnivorous. There are few large, strictly herbivorous animals corresponding to the deer, cattle, and horses of the land.

The sea, in contrast with both land and fresh water, contains a varied and important group of sessile (fixed) animals, many of which have a plant-like appearance (as indicated by such common names as "sea anemone," "sea pansy," etc.) Zonation of such animals on the sea bottom is often as striking as zonation of trees on a mountain (as illustrated in subsequent sections), and, to carry the analogy further, they provide shelter for many smaller organisms, as do plants on land. Commensalism and mutualism are widespread and important interactions between many marine species (see Chapter 7, Section 4). Fixed marine animals, and benthos in general, usually have a pelagic stage as part of their life history. Therefore, from the community standpoint, benthic life is a part of zonal communities rather than a major community rank in itself (see Chapter 8, Section 1). However, because of their stability, the benthic organisms provide a good basis for the classification of zones.

4. Quantitative study of plankton

Not only does plankton occupy the key role in the ocean ecosystem but it lends itself to quantitative sampling. Much work in marine ecology has centered around the study of plankton. In 1830 J. Vaughan Thompson and in 1845 Johannes Müller used what is now called a plankton net (the name "plankton" was not proposed until 1887). Müller was studying the life history of the starfish and towed a fine-meshed net through the sea in an effort to capture larvae of the starfish. He was impressed with the great wealth of floating life which had been more or less overlooked. Müller transmitted his enthusiasm to Ernst Haeckel who, along with other contemporary biologists, became greatly excited over this new world of life to be obtained by towing "Müller nets" through the water. Thus, Müller and Haeckel inadvertently became pioneer ecologists, and it was Haeckel who later, in 1869, coined the word ecology itself!

A plankton net is generally made of bolting silk, the strands of which are held firmly by binding twists. Such nets vary from 18 to 200 meshes per inch. In most quantitative studies nowadays a closing net is used so that a given depth can be sampled without contamination while the net is being lowered and raised. Even the finest silk net catches only a portion of the plankton biomass (*net plankton*); bacteria and many of the small phytoplankton organisms pass through the smallest meshes (*nannoplankton—nanno*, dwarf). As was indicated in Chapter 6, Section 2, the total plankton population biomass can be determined as dry weight after a sample of water is evaporated down, and the producer part of the plankton can be determined by extracting pigments or by counting or volumetric methods. Zooplankton may be selectively sampled by using nets with appropriate sized meshes.

Among the more specialized equipment may be mentioned the ingenious device called the "Hardy continuous plankton recorder," which may be towed behind a ship for long distances. Plankton is embedded in a strip of gauze as the water passes through it. The gauze continually rolls up into a tank of preservative as the passing water turns a propeller at the rear of the instrument, thus providing a permanent transect sample. Knowledge of distribution and abundance of plankton over large areas is important in predicting location and yield of commercial fishes which are directly dependent on the plankton. Possibilities in this direction have scarcely been touched. Unfortunately, from the standpoint of sampling at least, the distribution of plankton in the open ocean has not been as uniform as was once thought. Often, in fact, the distribution is very patchy with concentrations of phytoplankton occurring in different places from concentrations of zooplankton. It is not known whether this peculiar distribution is the result of zooplankton eating up the phytoplankton as fast as produced or if there are secretions of antibiotics which result in "mutual exclusion" (Harvey, 1955).

The important work of Gordon Riley and his co-workers should be mentioned (summarized in a monograph by Riley, Strommel, and Bumpus, 1949). They found that the amount and seasonal distribution of both phytoplankton and zooplankton in any region could be predicted by means of a formula based on certain important limiting factors of the environment and physiological coefficients determined from laboratory experimentation. In very

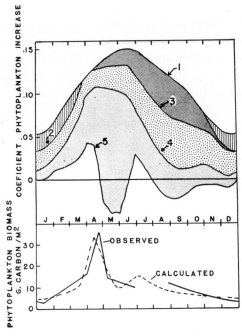

Figure 98. Theoretical operation of six limiting factors on phytoplankton (upper figure), and observed and calculated density during one annual cycle in the waters at Georges Bank off the coast of New England (lower figure). The limiting factors are: (1) light and temperature; (2) turbulence (which carries cells below photic zone); (3) phosphate depletion; (4) phytoplankton respiration; and (5) zooplankton grazing. Only during spring and late summer are conditions favorable for rapid growth of the population. (After Riley, 1952a.)

simplified and non-mathematical form the formula they devised for estimating phytoplankton production is as follows:

$$\left[\begin{array}{l}\text{Rate of change}\\ \text{of phytoplankton}\\ \text{density per unit}\\ \text{time}\end{array}\right] \text{ equals } \left[\begin{array}{l}\text{rate of}\\ \text{photosyn-}\\ \text{thesis}\end{array}\right] \text{ minus } \left[\begin{array}{l}\text{rate of}\\ \text{respi-}\\ \text{ration}\end{array}\right] \text{ minus}$$

$$\left[\begin{array}{l}\text{rate of}\\ \text{"grazing"}\\ \text{i.e., loss to}\\ \text{herbivores}\end{array}\right] \text{ minus } \left[\begin{array}{l}\text{rate}\\ \text{of}\\ \text{sinking}\end{array}\right] \text{ plus } \left[\begin{array}{l}\text{rate of up-}\\ \text{ward movement}\\ \text{due to turbu-}\\ \text{lent eddies}\end{array}\right]$$

Respiration is largely determined by temperature, and photosynthesis was found to be largely limited by temperature, light, and phosphate concentration. Knowing the density of herbivores, the "grazing pressure" was determined from data obtained in laboratory cultures. Although the computation is complex, the loss, if any, as a result of the sinking of plant cells below the euphotic zone can be determined from physical oceanographic data. The theoretical operation of the six major limiting factors on phytoplankton of a specific locality together with observed and calculated density are shown in Figure 98. In general the observed was within 25 per cent of the calculated, remarkably close considering the complexity of the situation.

This work on phytoplankton is a good demonstration that the principle of limiting factors (see Chapter 4) can be translated into quantitative terms, and that natural populations, as well as those under simplified conditions in the laboratory, can be predicted within a reasonable range of error.

5. Communities of the neritic zone

Composition of communities of the neritic zone

Producers. Phytoplanktonic *diatoms* and *dinoflagellates* are the twin dominants of the producer trophic level almost everywhere in the ocean. Characteristic marine types are shown in Figure 99. In the neritic zone large multicellular attached algae or "sea weeds" are also locally important, mostly on rocky or other hard bottoms in shallow water. They are attached by hold-fast organs, not roots, and often form extensive "forests" or "kelp beds" just below the low-tide mark. In addition to the *green algae* (Chlorophyta), also prominent in fresh water, these attached species belong to the more or less exclusively marine Phaeophyta, or *brown algae*, and the Rhodophyta, or *red algae*. These three groups show a depth distribution more or less in the order named (with red algae deepest). The brown and red colors are due to pigment which masks the green chlorophyll and, as described in Chapter 4 (page 107) these pigments aid in absorption of greenish-yellow light which penetrates to the greatest depth. Some of the fixed algae are of economic importance as sources of agar and other products. On northern rocky coasts "seaweed" harvest is a regular industry.

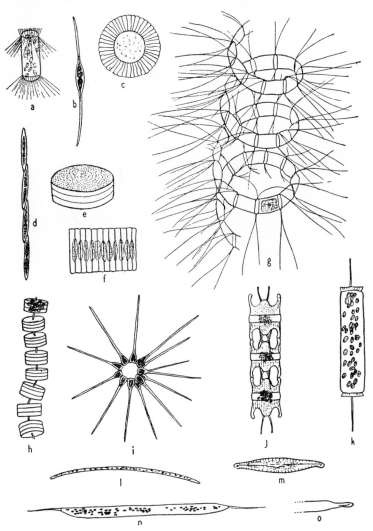

Figure 99A. Phytoplankton producers of the sea: **diatoms.** Genera pictured are: *a, Corethron; b, Nitzschia closterium; c, Planktoniella; d, Nitzschia seriata; e, Coscinodiscus; f, Fragilaria; g, Chaetoceros; h, Thalassiosira; i, Asterionella; j, Biddulphia; k, Ditylum; l, Thalassiothrix; m, Navicula; n, o, Rhizosolenia semispina*, summer and winter forms. Note that some of the genera of fresh-water diatoms shown in Figure 87 also occur in the sea.

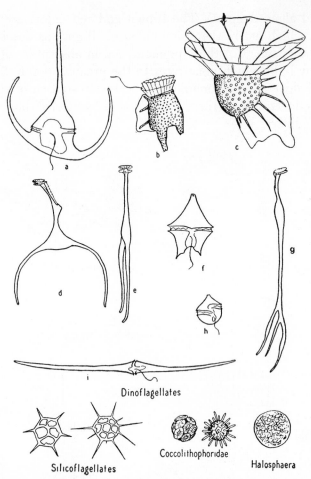

Dinoflagellates

Silicoflagellates

Coccolithophoridae

Halosphaera

Figure 99B.   Dinoflagellates and other miscellaneous phytoplankton. Genera pictured are: *a, Ceratium; b, Dinophysis; c, Ornithocercus; d, e, Triposolenia,* front and side views; *f, Peridinium; g, Amphisolenia; h, Goniaulax; i, Ceratium.* (Sverdrup, Johnson, and Fleming, "The Oceans, Their Physics, Chemistry, and General Biology," 1946, published by Prentice-Hall, Inc.)

Neritic phytoplankton, at least in temperate regions, undergoes a seasonal density cycle similar to but even more distinct than that in eutrophic lakes (see Chapter 9, Section 4). Generally, there are two major "blooms" of larger phytoplankton, one in the spring and another in the late summer or fall (as in Fig. 98). The mechanism of this seasonal periodicity is believed to be the same as described for lakes (see Figure 90). Although an increase in primary production occurs during blooms, the total production during the summer period between blooms may actually be greater.

Consumers: Zooplankton.   Characteristic types of the varied animal plankton are shown in Figures 100 and 101. Organisms which remain for their entire life cycle in the plankton are called *holoplankton*, or permanent plankton. In addition to copepods (see Marshall and Orr, 1955, for a thoroughgoing study of the important genus, *Calanus*) and protozoa, which are also important in fresh water, marine permanent plankton contains "wing-footed" mollusks (Pteropoda), tiny jellyfish, and various minute worms not represented in fresh water. A considerable portion of plankton is *meroplankton*, or temporary plankton, in sharp contrast to fresh

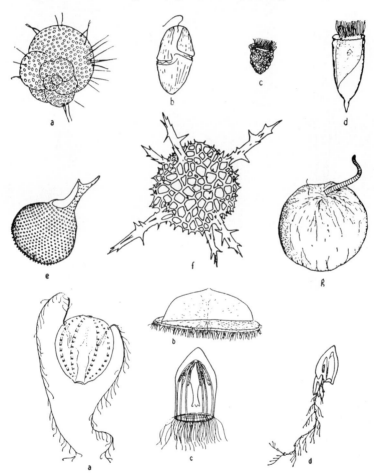

Figure 100A. Characteristic animals of the permanent plankton (holoplankton). **Protozoa** (upper): *a, Globigerina* (a foraminiferan); *b, Gymnodinium,* and *g, Noctiluca* (dinoflagellates); *c, Stenosomella* and *d, Favella* (tintinnids); *e, f, Protocystis* (radiolarians). **Coelenterates and Ctenophora** (lower): *a, Pleurobrachia* (a comb-jelly or ctenophoran); *b, Velella,* and *d, Diphyes* (siphonophores); and *c, Aglantha* (a small jellyfish). Note that the dinoflagellates in this group are consumers, whereas other members of the same group (Figure 99B) are producers (i.e., synthesize food).

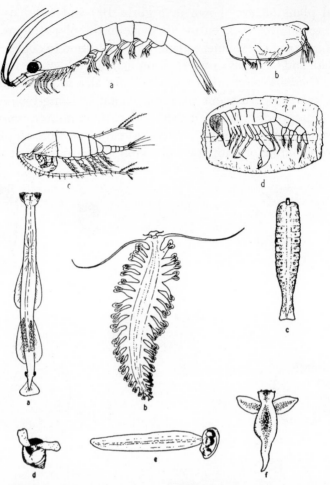

Figure 100B. Other characteristic animals of the permanent plankton (holoplankton). **Crustacea** (upper): *a, Euphausia* (a euphausiid or "krill"); *b, Conchoecia* (ostracod); *c, Calanus* (copepod); *d, Phronemia* (an amphipod in the empty shell of a pelagic tunicate). **Miscellaneous** (lower): *a,* an arrow worm (*Sagitta*); *b,* an annelid (*Tomopteris*); *c,* a nemertean (*Nectonemertes*); *d* and *f,* pteropod mollusks (*Limacina* and *Clione*); *e,* a tunicate (*Oikopleura*). (Sverdrup, Johnson, and Fleming, "The Oceans, Their Physics, Chemistry, and General Biology," 1946, published by Prentice-Hall, Inc.)

water (see Chapter 9, Section 4). Most of the benthos, and much of the nekton (fish, for example) as well, in the larval stage are tiny forms which join the plankton assemblage for varying periods before settling to the bottom or becoming free-swimming organisms. Many of these temporary plankton forms have special names, as indicated in Figure 101. As might be expected, the meroplankton varies seasonally according to the spawning habits of the parental stock, but there is sufficient overlapping to insure a quantity of meroplankton at all seasons.

Consumers: Benthos.   As was indicated in Section 3, the marine benthos is characterized by the large number of sessile or relatively inactive animals which exhibit marked zonation. Bottom organisms are generally distinct for each of the three primary

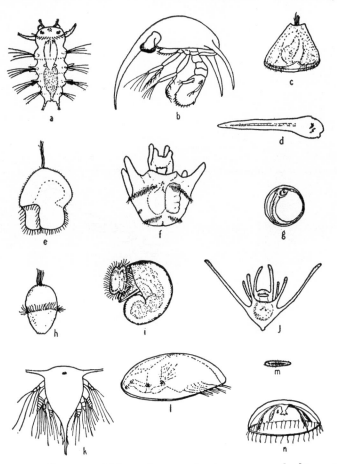

Figure 101. Larvae which make up the temporary plankton (meroplankton) of the sea. *a*, chaetate larva of the annelid *Platynereis; b*, zoea of the sand crab *Emerita; c*, cyphonautes larva of a bryozoan; *d*, tadpole larva of a sessile tunicate; *e*, pilidium larva of a nemertean worm; *f*, advanced pluteus larva of a sea urchin; *g*, fish egg with embryo; *h*, trochophore larva of a scaleworm; *i*, veliger larva of a snail; *j*, pluteus larva of a brittle starfish; *k*, nauplius larva of a barnacle; *l*, cypris larva of a barnacle; *m*, planula larva of a coelenterate; *n*, medusa stage of a sessile hydroid. (Sverdrup, Johnson, and Fleming, "The Oceans, Their Physics, Chemistry, and General Biology," 1946, published by Prenctice-Hall, Inc.)

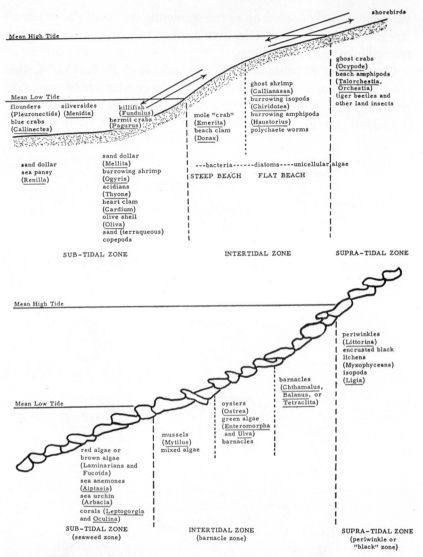

Figure 102. Transects of a sandy beach (upper) and of a rocky shore (lower) at Beaufort, N. C., showing zones and characteristic dominants. (Upper diagram based on data of Pearse, Humm, and Wharton, 1942; lower based on data of Stephenson and Stephenson, 1952.)

neritic zones (supratidal, intertidal, and subtidal) diagrammed in Figure 97. At one extreme, at or above the high-tide mark, organisms must be able to withstand desiccation and air temperature changes since they are only briefly covered by water or spray. In the subtidal region, on the other hand, organisms are continually covered. The constant ebb and flow of tides between the tide marks produces an environmental gradient in regard to exposure to air and water. Despite the continuous change, benthic animals and plants do not necessarily change gradually from one species to another, but dominants often form distinct bands within the intertidal zone.

In a given region the series of benthic subcommunities which will be found to replace one another from the shore to the edge of the neritic shelf depends largely on the type of bottom, whether sand, rock, or mud. In Figure 102 a transect of a typical sand beach is compared with that of a rocky substrate (man-made breakwaters and piers are similar to natural rocks) in the region of Beaufort, N.C. The most important dominants are indicated. Very few dominants are common to both series. Population density is often less on the sand beach because shifting sand does not provide as stable a substrate as rock; yet it is better populated than first appearances indicate. Most of the larger animals are specialized burrowers and the unicellular algae and bacteria which live among the sand grains would not be noticed. Some of the highly specialized sand burrowers are shown in Figure 103. The mole crab, *Emerita,* one of the most remarkable, is capable of "sinking" backward into the sand in a few seconds. These crabs feed by extending their feathery antennae above the sand and collecting plankton from the flowing water when the tide comes in. Other animals, such as worms, feed by ingesting sand and detritus which enters their burrows and extracting the food material after it is in their intestines.

Barnacles, mollusks, and attached algae are characteristic of the rocky shore series as shown (Fig. 102). Still another series of bottom populations occurs on mud bottoms. Various deep-burrowing clams and snails, as shown in Figures 103A and 103B

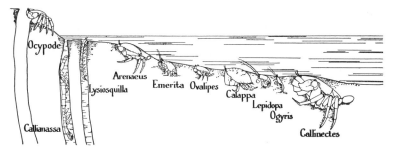

Figure 103A. Burrowing crustaceans in resting positions in the sand of the neritic region.

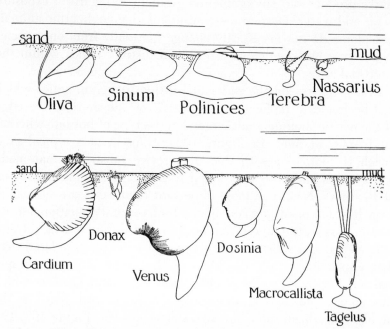

Figure 103B. Burrowing gastropods (upper) and clams (lower) which are characteristic of sand (left) and mud (right) flats of the neritic region. (After Pearse, Humm, and Wharton, 1942.)

(center and right side of the diagrams), are characteristic of this series. If the slope is such as to produce extensive mud flats, the density of clams is often great. It is interesting to note that mixed mud and sand seems to be more favorable than either coarse sand or fine mud. Increased variety and population density at sand–mud junctions is, perhaps, an example of the edge-effect principle (see Chapter 8, Section 8).

Although the diagrams in Figure 102 represent a specific locality, the same general arrangements have been reported in widely scattered localities. Thus, T. A. and Anne Stephenson (1949), who have studied zonation on rocky coasts all over the world, report that a periwinkle zone, a barnacle zone, and a seaweed zone were characteristic of nearly all the coasts they visited, even though the species of periwinkles, barnacles, and algae differed. One should not be misled by their names into thinking that these zones are separate aggregations of animals and plants; actually there are plenty of algae (small, inconspicuous species) in the periwinkle and barnacle zones and many animals in the seaweed zone. In fact, the similarity of various intertidal zones in chlorophyll content (on a M^2 basis) suggests that they may be similar in primary productivity (see Table 10, page 86).

Less is known about the communities of the lower neritic zone, which may extend for miles in regions with a wide continental shelf. Investigation of this area is not so convenient as is that of the intertidal zone, which is exposed to full view at each low tide. The type of bottom is important, as in the intertidal area. Populations are not necessarily arranged in concentric zones but may form a "patchwork." One of the earliest studies is that of C. G. J. Petersen (1914–1918), who thoroughly investigated the benthos of neritic waters of the important fishing grounds between Denmark and Norway. He found that there were eight primary "associations" in this vast area. Clams, brittle starfish, sea urchins, polychaete worms, and burrowing crustacea were the chief dominants. Some of the "associations" contained 20 or more important species of large bottom invertebrates, some only a few. In some instances there was only one major dominant; in others, dominance was shared by a number of species. This kind of variation is typical of communities everywhere.

Studies of benthic aggregations have been continued and extended by Thorson (1955), who finds that the same type of level-bottom substrata at similar depths in widely different geographical regions support parallel groupings of invertebrates. These often belong to the same genera but to different species, thus making a chain of ecologically similar aggregations that replace each other according to latitude and temperature. Bottom aggregations in deeper water are, of course, incomplete communities composed of heterotrophic organisms which depend on producers in the surface waters. Primary consumers are largely detritus feeders which may be divided into two types: (1) filter feeders, which remove particles from the water and (2) deposit feeders, which consume sedimented materials. The former usually predominate on sandy and the latter on muddy bottoms. Wilson (1952) has shown by means of elaborate experiments that pelagic larvae of benthic polychaetes do not settle at random, but respond to particular chemical conditions of the substrata to which they are adapted. When ready to metamorphose into sedentary adults, the larvae "critically examine" the bottom; if the chemical nature is "attractive" they settle, if not they may continue planktonic life for weeks. High density of predators is a seemingly incongruous feature of many ocean bottom communities. However, Thorson

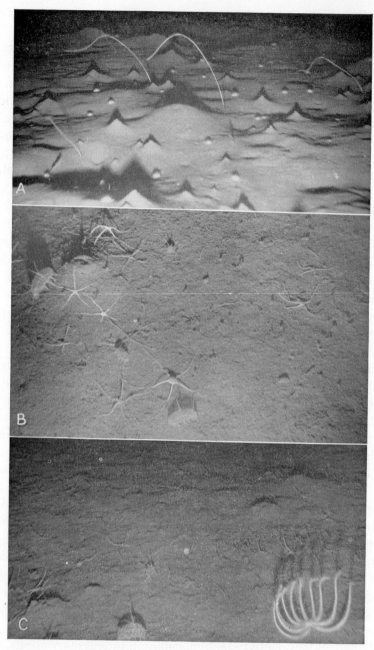

Figure 104. See opposite page for legend.

finds that many predators, such as brittle-stars, do not feed for long periods during reproduction thus allowing pelagic larvae of clams and other prey to settle and grow to a size which makes them less vulnerable to predation. Here again we have an example where standing crop data alone would be misleading as to what "goes on" in the community.

The development of underwater cameras has extended our knowledge of marine bottom communities not only on the continental shelf but in deeper waters as well. Three remarkable photographs taken at increasing depths are shown in Figure 104. Both population density and intrapopulation distribution (see Chapter 6, Section 12) of certain animals can be determined from such pictures. The fact that one of the conspicuous animals shown has actually never been collected indicates how little is yet known about life on the bottom of the sea.

Consumers: Nekton and Neuston. In addition to the vast array of fish species, some of the larger crustacea, turtles, mammals (whales, seals, etc.), and marine birds comprise the active swimmers and surface dwellers. Individuals of this group commonly, but not necessarily, range over a considerable area and become part-time members of several communities, as is characteristic of secondary and tertiary consumers in general. Nevertheless, the nekton (and even the birds) are limited by the same "invisible barriers" of temperature, salinity, and nutrients, and by the type of bottom as are organisms with less power of movement. Both horizontal zonation and vertical stratification may be ex-

---

Figure 104. Photographs (by means of a special underwater camera called the benthograph) of the ocean bottom at three different depths off southern California (San Diego Trough). A, at 295 feet. Note abundant sea urchins (probably *Lytechinus*) appearing as globular, light-colored bodies, and the long curved sea whips (probably *Acanthoptilum*). Burrowing worms have built the conical piles of sediment at the mouth of their burrows. (Emery, 1952). B, at 3,600 feet. Vertical photograph of about 36 square feet of bottom which is composed at this point of green silty mud having a high organic content. Note the numerous brittle starfish (Ophiuroidea) and several large sea cucumbers (Holothuroidea). The latter have not been identified as to species as they have never been dredged from the sea and have only been seen in bottom photographs! (Official Navy photo, courtesy U. S. Navy Electronics Laboratory, San Diego.) C, at 4,350 feet. Note in the right foreground the ten arms of a probable comatulid crinoid (a relative of the starfish which is attached to the bottom by a stalk-like part). Small worm tubes and brittle starfish litter the surface, and two sea cucumbers may be seen in the left foreground. Continual activity of burrowing animals keeps the sea bottom "bumpy." Bottom edge of the picture represents a distance of about 6 feet. (Emery, 1952.)

pected even though they are not as immediately apparent as in the case of the benthos and plankton. Also, strange to say, although the individual range of nekton may be great, the geographic range of a species may be less than that of many invertebrates.

As indicated in Figure 102, silversides, killifish, and flounders are characteristic of waters at the low-tide mark on the mid-Atlantic coast. These and other species of the same habitat move back and forth with the tides, feeding on benthos of the intertidal zone when it is covered with water. Likewise, shore birds move back and forth on the intertidal zone hunting for food when it is uncovered. It is remarkable that anything is left after these alternate attacks from land and sea! The flounders and rays are the most specialized of bottom fishes, their bodies and coloring blending with the sand and mud. Some species of the former are remarkable for their ability to change color and "match" their background.

In addition to an array of bottom fishes, other species living nearer the surface are very important in neritic communities. Members of the herring family (Clupeidae), including the herring, menhaden, sardine (pilchard), anchovy, etc., are especially important. These fish are largely plankton feeders, although some may feed on benthos and other fish at times. Plankton is strained from the water by means of a built-in "net" formed by the gill rakers. Since even the finest filter apparatus, like the finest silk net, fails to catch most of the phytoplankton, the adult fishes subsist largely on zooplankton, and are thus secondary consumers. Several studies have shown that when the fish passes through a stretch of water it does not take the same sample as does a net drawn through the same area; apparently the fish is able to selectively reject some forms and to actively seek others. Species of plankton feeders can thus avoid competition (see Gause's rule, Chapter 7, Section 2) not only if "meshes" of the filters are different but also if active selection of items is different.

Although some of the bottom fish lay their eggs on the bottom and guard them as do many fresh-water fish, most marine fish, including the more pelagic ones, lay large numbers of eggs which float (aided by oil droplets and other flotation adaptations) and receive no attention from the parent. Two other characteristics of pelagic fish are important: (1) their tendency to aggregate or "school," undoubtedly a valuable asset in the shelterless open water (see discussion of aggregation, Chapter 6, Section 13), and (2) their tendency to perform definite seasonal migrations. The latter may be due in part to the fact that the eggs and later the larvae drift helplessly in the currents until the fish become large enough to make the return trip to the breeding grounds.

The great commercial fisheries of the world are almost entirely located in neritic regions, or at least not far from the continental shelf.° Since, as already indicated, the highest primary productivity occurs in northern waters and in regions of cold water upwelling, it is not surprising that the largest commercial fisheries occur in such regions. The herring fisheries of the north Atlantic (see phenomena of "dominant age class," shown in Figure 46), which have been operating for centuries, and the sardine fisheries in the upwelling region off southern California are two examples. Although a large number of fish are of commercial importance, a relatively few species make up the bulk of the world commercial catch. On the Atlantic coast, for example, the northern food fishes are principally herring, cod, haddock, and halibut, whereas toward the south mullet, sea bass, weakfish, drums, and Spanish mackerel are sought. Taylor (1951) estimated that three fourths of the world catch belongs to five groups, which he lists as follows (in the order of abundance):

1. The herring-like fish;
2. The cod-like fish (including haddock and pollack);
3. The salmons;
4. The flounder-like fish (including soles, plaices, halibut);
5. The mackerel-like fish (including tuna, bonitos).

The cod and flounder groups are bottom types and are sought with trawls; fish of the other groups are caught in the upper waters with nets or seines of various types. As indicated in Table 9 (p. 78) and in the discussion in Part III, only a small fraction of the potential fisheries resources of the sea is harvested by man.

In addition to the predatory fish, such as sharks, marine birds are important tertiary consumers of the sea. Sea birds (also seals and sea turtles), to be sure, are a link between land and sea, since they must breed on land, but their food comes from the sea. Therefore, these air breathers are just as much a part of the food chains of the sea as are the fish and invertebrates on which they

° Fisheries for tuna and mackerel over deep water (especially off the western coast of Europe) are an exception, but here again the best areas are in regions of upwelling.

feed. The role of birds in "completing" the nitrogen and phosphorus cycles has been mentioned (see Chapter 2, Section 3; Figure 8). As with other marine organisms, birds are concentrated near shore and especially in the productive regions; it is no mere coincidence that the great colonies of gannets (see Table 11, item V) of the north Atlantic or the unbelievable concentrations of cormorants and pelicans off the coast of South America are found in regions of rich plankton and fish life. A variety of niches are occupied by birds and each of the major zonal communities which we have discussed has its characteristic birds. Shore birds frequent the supratidal and intertidal zones (Figure 102); cormorants, sea ducks, and pelicans the subtidal areas; and petrels and shearwaters the lower neritic zone farther out to sea. Birds even show a vertical distribution in feeding areas in the water. Figure 69 illustrates how two species of cormorants which seem to be closely associated and competing for the same food actually occupy different niches, because one feeds on bottom fish and invertebrates whereas the other finds its food among the herring-like fishes in the open waters above.

Decomposers: Bacteria. The distribution of bacteria in the sea is apparently similar to that which has been described for

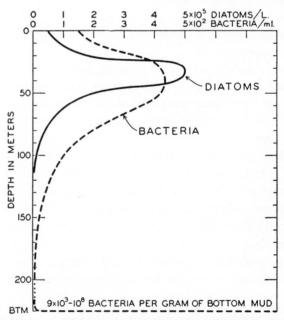

Figure 105. Graph showing vertical distribution of bacteria in the sea. (Sverdrup, Johnson, and Fleming, "The Oceans, Their Physics, Chemistry, and General Biology," 1946, published by Prentice-Hall, Inc.)

Figure 106. Red mangrove (*Rhizophora mangle*) at low tide on the west coast of Florida. Note prop roots which promote deposition of silt and provide a solid substrate for attachment of marine organisms.

lakes. Horizontally, bacteria are most abundant in zones where plant and animal life is most abundant. The vertical distribution is well shown in Figure 105. Note the large bacterial population which coincides with maximum phytoplankton abundance, and the very much greater peak on the bottom, specifically in the mud–water junction where there is maximum concentration of

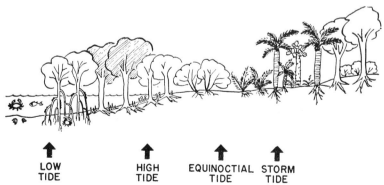

LOW   HIGH   EQUINOCTIAL   STORM
TIDE   TIDE   TIDE   TIDE

Figure 107. Zonation in a tropical mangrove swamp. The five zones between low and storm tide are: *Rhizophora, Avicennia, Laguncularia, Hibiscus,* and *Acrostichum.* (From Dansereau, "Biogeography; an ecological perspective," 1957, Ronald Press, N. Y.)

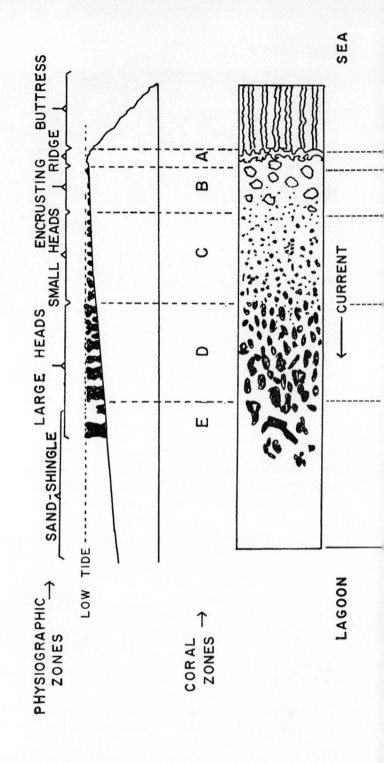

OCCURRENCE OF CORAL SPECIES:					
AVERAGE TOTAL CORAL (POLYP) BIOMASS (g/M²)		99	40	46	105
AVERAGE TOTAL CONSUMER BIOMASS (g/M²)		**139**	132	64	162
AVERAGE TOTAL PRODUCER (ALGAE) BIOMASS (g/M²)		652	717	696	635
Turbinaria globularis	X				
Heliopora caerula	x				
Millepora murrayi	x				
Millepora platyphylla	x	x		X	X
Stylophora mordax		x			
Goniastrea retiformis		x			
Montipora foveolata and *verrilli*		x			
Acropora recumbens and *corymbosa*		x			
Favia stelligera		x	x		
Acropora conferta and *humilis*		x	x		
Porites lobata		x	x	X	
Favites abdita			x		
Cyphastrea chalcidicum			x		
Porites lutea			x		
Pocillopora elegans			x		
Acropora tubicinaria			x		
Favia pallida			x	X	
Plesiastrea versipora			x	X	
Favites halicora				X	
Pocillopora verrucosa				X	
Acropora, sp.				X	X
Pocillopora danae					X

Figure 108. Cross section of a windward coral reef on Eniwetok Atoll showing zonation and distribution of biomass and coral species. Note that while the species of coral are quite different in different zones, the total amount of coral per square meter varies by less than a factor of 3 and the total producer biomass is virtually the same in the major part of the reef. The entire reef functions as a community. (After E. P. and H. T. Odum, 1957.)

organic matters ready to be "regenerated" into inorganic nutrients. In some waters the primary decomposition apparently takes
place in the water mass while in other situations most of it occurs
in sediments. The importance of bacteria is further emphasized
when it is recalled that much oil, which is so essential to modern
mechanized civilization, is formed from organic marine sediments
(see Emery and Rittenberg, 1952).

Two very interesting and distinctive neritic communities of
tropical and subtropical waters which deserve special mention are
mangrove swamps and coral reefs. Both are important "land
builders" which help form islands and extend shores. Mangroves
are among the few emergent land plants which tolerate the
salinities of the open sea. Different species form zones in the intertidal region, or even beyond. Next time you take a trip to
Florida, note that the red mangrove (*Rhizophora mangle*) forms
the outermost zone. It has extensive prop roots which reduce tidal
currents, cause extensive deposition of mud and silt and provide
surfaces for attachment of marine organisms (Fig. 106). Its seeds
sprout while still on the tree, the seedlings drop off and float in
the water until they lodge in shallow water where well developed
roots may take hold, perhaps to start a new island! The black mangrove (*Avicennia nitida*) forms a zone nearer shore; its roots stick
up above the mud like a bunch of asparagus. To observe the full
development of the mangrove community, however, one needs to
go further south where growth forms are larger and zonation more
complex (Fig. 107). Davis (1940), who has studied the ecology
of mangroves, believes that mangroves are not only important in
extending coasts and building islands, but also in protecting coasts
from excessive erosion which might otherwise be produced by
fierce tropical storms.

Coral reefs are among the most remarkable of all communities;
they are widely distributed near shore or in other shallow waters
of warm seas. As described by Darwin reefs are of three types;
barrier reefs along continents, fringing reefs around islands, and
atolls which are horseshoe-shaped ridges of reefs and islands with
a lagoon in the center (see Allee and Schmidt, 1951). Ecological
relations of corals on the Great Barrier Reef off Australia have
been extensively studied by Yonge (1940). Although corals are
animals a coral reef is by no means an animal community which is
completely dependent on surrounding waters for basic food; in
many cases, at least, the reef is a complete community with the

usual metabolic predominance of plants. Calcareous algae (*Porolithon*) may also contribute as much to the formation of the limestone substrate as do corals (or more, perhaps), especially where there are strong currents.

Some coral reefs are apparently among the most productive of all natural communities (Odum and Odum, 1955; Kohn and Helfrich, 1957; see also Table 6, page 72). Reefs on the atolls of the central Pacific, in fact, are oases in a desert since the productivity of the reef is many times that of the relatively infertile open ocean. This striking differential is maintained by the more or less continuous algae carpet exposed to year around favorable conditions of light and temperature, by efficient nutrient recirculation and by marked symbiosis between various plant and animal components of the reef. Figure 108 illustrates a transect across such a reef, showing marked zonation and taxonomic diversity but relative uniformity of trophic composition. The intimate association between plant and animal components in a coral colony is shown in Figure 109. Note that algae occur on and in the calcareous skeleton as well as inside the bodies of the animals, with the result that the colony may contain three times as much plant as animal tissue. At night the polyps extend their tentacles and capture such plankton as may pass over the reef from ocean waters; during the day the continuous sheet of algae manufactures food at a rapid rate, using nutrients released by consumers and decomposers. The reef as a whole functions as a community. Food produced and dis-

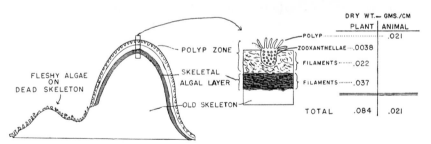

Figure 109. Cross section of a coral colony or "head" showing distribution of plant and animal components. Ecological evidence indicates that the small round algal cells, the zooxanthellae (which are apparently dinoflagellates), as well as the green filaments in the skeleton (which often occur in distinct bands below the polyp zone) are symbiotic or mutualistic with the coral animal polyps. The coral colony contains a larger amount of plant than animal tissue. Whether covered by coral or not the reef presents an almost continuous blanket of algae to the incoming sun radiation. In the living coral the polyp zone and skeleton is translucent allowing light to penetrate to deep bands of algae. (After H. T. and E. P. Odum, 1955.)

lodged in the shallow, swift water sections may be consumed by fish and other organisms in the quieter waters so that at least no more material is lost from the reef than is gained from adjacent ocean communities. One reason there are so many fish on a reef (in addition to high primary productivity) is that so many of them are omnivorous or herbivorous and resort to "grazing" on the alage and coral (which, as shown in Fig. 109, contain large amounts of plant material). All in all there is no better way to become impressed with the functional operation of a community than to put on a face mask and explore a coral reef.

6. Communities of the oceanic region

The euphotic zone

The lighted parts of the oceanic region are not as rich in species and generally support less dense populations, compared with coastal regions. However, since water is usually more transparent in the open ocean, the producing region may be deeper; consequently in comparing coastal and oceanic regions, the total quantity of phytoplankton underlying a unit area of surface should be used as a unit of measurement rather than density per cubic unit. In any event the euphotic area is so much larger than the neritic area that it must be given major consideration when the oceans as a whole are considered.

Communities in this region, of course, consist entirely of organisms with a pelagic way of life. Some oceanic species are also common in the neritic zone, but many (see Figure 110) seem to be restricted to the oceanic zone. A large portion of the zooplankton consists of permanent forms (holoplankton), since the benthos, which largely contributes to the meroplankton, is absent. It is a striking characteristic of both zooplankton and fish that they are either extremely transparent or blue in color, both conditions making them all but invisible. Colman (1950) describes the experience of seeing "a yellowish-green object as big as a pea moving through the water." When he finally captured the "pea," it proved to be a large, colorless shrimp (similar to B in Figure 110), five inches long; the "pea" was the animal's stomach full of food, the only thing visible in the water!

Phosphates appear to be no less important a limiting factor in the open ocean than near shore. However, limiting effects of low phosphate concentrations become less important as temperature increases (Riley et al., 1949). (See compensation principle, Chapter 4, Section 1.) In Figure 111 the density of plankton and the concentration of phosphates in a Pacific transect are shown. A rather close relationship exists between surface phosphate and plankton abundance. The rich local areas located in the regions of great nutrient upwelling were mentioned at the beginning of this chapter.

The chief commercial fishes of the open sea are the mackerels, herrings, bonito, and tunny. Oceanic birds are a characteristic group the easy observation of which often breaks the monotony of

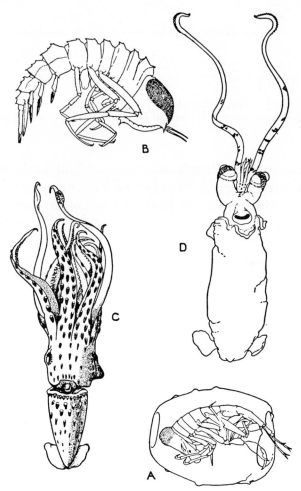

Figure 110.   Pelagic crustaceans and squids from the euphotic zone in the North Atlantic. A, *Phronima; B, Cystisoma; C, Calliteuthis,* and *D, Bathothauma* (squids). (From Colman, "The Sea and Its Mysteries," 1950, G. Bell & Sons, Ltd., after Moyne and Blackie.)

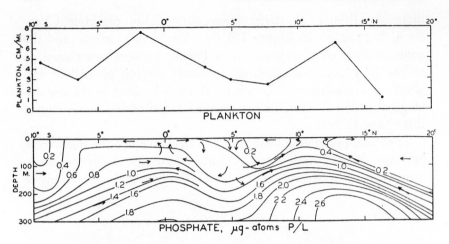

Figure 111. Density of plankton in a transect across the Pacific Equatorial Countercurrent, compared with concentration of phosphate in the same section. Note that plankton is most abundant where surface waters have high phosphate concentration. (Sverdrup, Johnson, and Fleming, "The Oceans, Their Physics, Chemistry, and General Biology," 1946, published by Prentice-Hall, Inc.)

long ocean voyages. Petrels, albatrosses, frigate birds, and some species of terns, tropic birds, and boobies are, except for the breeding season, independent of land. One might assume that these birds would not know the meaning of "zonation," but this is far from true. As Murphy (1936) aptly expressed it: "The majority of oceanic birds are bound as peons to their own specific types of surface water." Likewise, the abundance of oceanic birds depends, indirectly, on the abundance of plankton. The same can be said for whales, which are, perhaps, the most remarkable of all marine animals, since they are as a group (order Cetacea) the chief air-breathing vertebrates which are completely independent of land. Whales belong to two types, the whalebone whales, which feed on plankton by means of great strainers, and the toothed whales, which feed on nekton (Fig. 112, lower). A hypothetical pyramid showing energy relations between whales and principal organisms in their food chain is shown in Figure 113.

In summary, this very brief discussion has emphasized that although conditions of existence in the open ocean require certain specialization in order to survive in that environment, the various niches have been filled by organisms. Distribution is controlled by the "invisible" but none the less real barriers of temperature, salinity, currents, etc. Density, on the other hand, as in all habi-

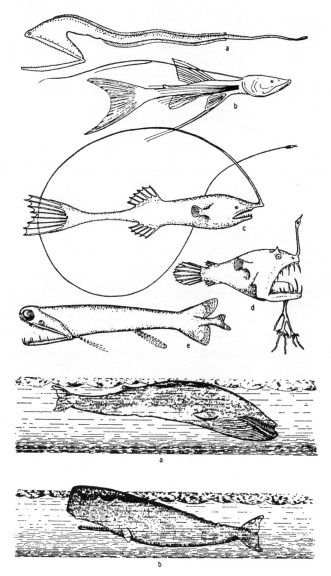

Figure 112. Vertebrates of the sea. Upper: A few deep sea fishes which sport enormous mouths or bizzare appendages. Species and depths (in meters) of habitat are as follows: *a, Macropharynx longicaudatus,* 3500; *b, Bathypterois longicauda,* 550; *c, Gigantactis macronema,* 2500; *d, Linophryne macrodon,* 1500; *e, Malacostus indicus,* 2500. Lower: Two types of whales: *a,* a whalebone whale, the blue whale; *b,* a toothed whale, the sperm whale. (Sverdrup, Johnson, and Fleming, "The Oceans, Their Physics, Chemistry, and General Biology," 1946, published by Prentice-Hall, Inc.)

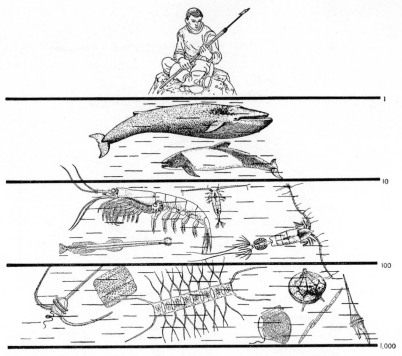

Figure 113. A hypothetical pyramid showing energy relations between whales and principal organisms in their food chain. The ratio of phytoplankton net production to production of zooplankton and whales is indicated by numbers to the right of the diagram. (Pequegnat, W. E., in *Scientific American*, Vol. 198. Jan., 1958.)

tats the world over, is ultimately determined by primary productivity (see Chapter 3, Section 5), which brings us back to the fundamental principles of the ecosystem and limiting factors (Chapters 2 and 4).

Bathyal and abyssal regions

Since there are no producers in the deep-water regions, communities depend on organic matter from euphotic zones. As the bodies of plants and animals sink or are carried slowly into the depths, they are acted upon by scavengers and bacteria; consequently, most of the organic material is reduced to inorganic form by the time it reaches great depth. Density of life in the depths, therefore, (1) depends on the productivity of the lighted zone "above" (obviously currents vary the source for any given deep region), and (2) is generally inversely proportional to the depth. Yet there seems to be some life, however sparse, at all levels, indicating that some organic matter "gets through." Circulation of the oceans is such that some oxygen is also available.

Large areas of the bottom of the ocean are covered with finely divided sediments, commonly called "oozes." Siliceous shells, especially diatoms, are conspicuous in northern waters, while calcareous shells, especially of the protozoan *Globigerina,* predominate in other regions. In very deep areas few shells reach the bottom, which is more or less bare "red clay." The deep-sea benthos features curious species of crustacea, echinoderms, and mollusks. Correlated with the soft "footing," many of the bottom invertebrates have long appendages, abundant spines, stalks, or other means of support (Fig. 104).

The pelagic life, especially the nekton, of the bathyal and abyssal zones remain, perhaps, the least known of all oceanic life, for the obvious reason that it is difficult to devise nets fast enough to catch active forms at great depths. This is the region of "sea serpents," if there are any. In fact, the giant squid, which is definitely fact and not fancy, could easily be mistaken for a sea serpent should it appear on the surface, since its tentacles are 30 to 40 feet long.

Deep-sea fish, a few of which are shown in the upper part of Figure 112, are a curious lot. Even though there is not enough light for photosynthesis in the bathyal zone, some light does penetrate deeply, especially in clear tropical seas. Thus, we find that some deep-sea fish exhibit greatly enlarged eyes; others have very small ones, of little apparent use. Few, however, lose their eyes completely. Many animals of the depths produce their own light by means of luminescent organs (Clarke and Backus, 1956), and some fish use a "light" (attached to a movable spine) as bait to attract their prey. Another interesting characteristic of deep sea fish is the enormous mouth and the ability to swallow prey larger than themselves. Meals are few and far between in the deeps, and fish are adapted to make the best of their opportunities!

The "echo-sounder," which has proved so useful in sounding the bottom, is now sensitive enough to record the location of concentrations of animals ("false bottoms," "phantom bottoms," or "deep-scattering layers"). According to Revelle (1951), echo-sounder records "often show as many as five or six separate sound-reflecting layers, at depths of 20 to 400 fathoms. All of these exhibit vertical motion correlated with changes in light intensity. When it is raining the layers rise nearer the surface; when the sun comes out, the layers go deeper. At sunset, the echo-sounder records a vertical migration up to the sea surface of some organisms making up the layers. But some remain behind and do not rise, so that some layers observed in the daytime are still present at night at about the same depth but in lower concentration." Thus we see that stratification and periodicity are just as characteristic of this part of the ocean as they are of lakes (see Chapter 8, Sections 6 and 7). Also, it is evident that, to produce a sound-reflecting layer, the density of life in the very dimly lit depths must be greater than has been suspected.

7. Estuarine waters

An estuary (*aestus*, tide) is a river mouth where tidal action brings about a mixing of salt and fresh water. Shallow bays, tidal marshes and bodies of water behind barrier beaches are included under the heading of "estuarine waters." As shown in Figure 96, estuarine or brackish water may be classified as oligo-, meso-, or polyhaline, according to the average salinity. This only tells part of the story, since salinity at any given location varies during the day, month, and year. Strong currents are also characteristic of this environment. Variability is a key characteristic, and organisms living in this habitat must have wide tolerances.

Although salinity and other conditions are intermediate between fresh-water and the sea, almost all of the strictly aquatic organisms are of marine origin, contributions from fresh-water being minor. However, semi-aquatic components (marsh grass, mammals, etc.), which may be very important, are derived from terrestrial and fresh-water biota. Estuaries often prove to be more productive than either the adjacent ocean or fresh-water, apparently due to the "nutrient trap" produced by the mixing of waters of different salinity (Fig. 114) and the favorable action of oscillating tidal currents in transporting nutrients, food and waste

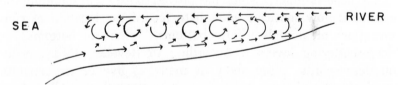

Figure 114. Schematic diagram of circulation in an estuary showing how mixing of lighter fresh water with heavier sea water tends to produce a "nutrient trap," which retains and recirculates nutrients within the estuary.

materials. The type and extent of estuaries depends on the physiography of the coast, the substrate and the amplitude of the tides. Figure 115 shows a diagramatic cross section of a type of estuarine ecosystem which is often extensive along muddy, coastal plain coasts. Three distinct production units are involved in primary fixation of energy. A small part of the marsh grass is consumed on the stalk by insects and other terrestrial herbivores, but most of it is consumed by the marine organisms in the form of detritus as has been described on page 52. The algae which live on and in the mud and which are exposed with each tide make a by no means small contribution to total primary production of the system (L. R. Pomeroy, 1959). At times the mud banks are golden brown with diatoms and, far from being "barren" as the casual observer might think, are sites of intense photosynthesis. As with other aquatic environments, the phytoplankton, the third contributor to primary production, may vary considerably with the seasons. "Red tides," which are large blooms of certain dinoflagellates, sometimes develop in estuaries (Ragotzkie and Pomeroy, 1957). These blooms also reach monstrous proportions in coastal waters of the world (for example, along the Gulf of Mexico in Florida), and they can cause extensive destruction of fish. While the mechanism responsible for red tides is not yet understood, it seems likely that an accumulation of favorable nutrients and probably also organic growth substances (which are known to be required by dinoflagellates) are involved.

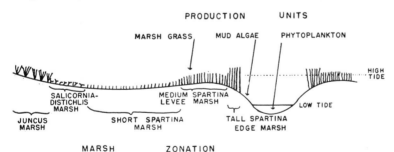

Figure 115. Zonation in a salt marsh in a Georgia estuary showing the three distinct types of producers which contribute to the metabolism of the system. A large portion of the marsh is covered by a single species of plant, *Spartina alterniflora*, which, however, exhibits distinct life forms or ecotypes according to physiographic conditions. The *Spartina* zones are just as different in inherent productivity and associated animal populations as are zones composed of different species. Functionally, the entire marsh is a unit since most of the marsh grass is not consumed until it has been broken down into detritus by tidal and bacterial action and transported to all parts of the marsh.

When a bay or part of a river mouth is temporarily cut off from the sea by a sand bar, the salinity may actually increase beyond that of the open ocean due to evaporation. The few species of the estuaries which are able to tolerate such high salinities may become very abundant. It is interesting to note that the community which develops in such cases is not at all related to the brine shrimp-brine fly community of inland salt lakes.

Estuaries may be productive of fish and other sea food (oysters, shrimp). Also, estuaries serve as nursery grounds for neritic species. Peneid shrimp, mullet, menhaden and other species may spend the early part of their life in estuaries feeding on the abundant plankton and detritus, then move to off-shore waters where they may be eventually harvested by man. Thus, the estuary, especially if shallow, extensive in area and "muddy," may make a major contribution to the productivity of coastal waters. In some areas it has proved advantageous to practice "fish farming" by controlling water flow and using fertilizers. Some aspects of oyster biology are outlined on pages 96 and 443-444.

The potential high productivity of estuaries has often not been appreciated by man, who has frequently classed them as "worthless" areas suitable only for the dumping of waste materials or useful only if drained or filled and planted with some terrestrial crop. When the high costs of such changes are considered, it may well be that utilization in the natural state is preferable, especially since seafood is a dietary item that vegetables can not replace.

11 · Terrestrial ecology

1. The terrestrial environment

We now come to the land, generally conceded to be the most variable, in terms of both time and geography, of the three major environments. The number of niches is large and the possible interactions between populations occupying these niches is correspondingly great. Consequently, the principles of population and community ecology assume great importance in the study of terrestrial environments. These principles have been fully discussed in Chapters 5 through 8, and many terrestrial examples given. The productivity of terrestrial ecosystems has been considered in Chapter 3 (see especially Tables 5 to 8 and Figure 18). Likewise, the general physical characteristics of the land environment have been outlined in Chapter 4, Section 5. Therefore, this chapter will be concerned mainly with the composition of and the geographical variation in terrestrial communities.

The following points should be kept in mind in comparing land with water as a habitat:

1. Moisture itself becomes a major limiting factor on land. Terrestrial organisms are constantly confronted with the problem of dehydration (see Chapter 4, Section 5, subdivision 3).

2. Without the moderating blanket of water, temperature variations and extremes are pronounced in the air medium (see Chapter 4, Section 5, subdivision 1).

3. On the other hand, the rapid circulation of air throughout the globe results in a ready mixing and a remarkably constant content of oxygen and carbon dioxide (see Chapter 4, Section 5, subdivision 5).

4. Although soil offers solid support, air does not. Strong skeletons have been evolved in both land plants and animals, and also special means of locomotion have been evolved in the latter.

5. Land, unlike the ocean, is not continuous; there are important geographical barriers to free movement.

6. The nature of the substrate, although important in water (as indicated in previous chapters), is especially vital in terrestrial environments. Soil, not air, is the source of highly variable nutrients (nitrates, phosphates, etc.); it is a highly developed ecosystem in its own right (see Chapter 4, Section 5, subdivision 8).

In summary, we may think of climate (temperature, moisture, light, etc.) and substrate (physiography, soil, etc.) as the two groups of factors which together with population interactions determine the nature of terrestrial communities and ecosystems.

2. The terrestrial biota; biogeographic regions; ecological equivalents

Evolution on land has featured the development of the higher taxonomic categories of both the plant and the animal kingdoms. Thus, the most complex and specialized of all organisms, namely, the seed plants, the insects, and the warm-blooded vertebrates, are dominant on land today. The last named, of course, include a growing human population which, year by year, exerts a greater control in the operation of terrestrial ecosystems. This does not mean that many lesser forms are absent or unimportant; bacteria, for example, have vital roles in terrestrial ecosystems.

Although man and his closest associates (domestic plants and animals, rats, fleas, and pathogenic bacteria!) show a wide distribution over the earth, each continental area tends to have its own special flora and fauna. Islands often differ greatly from the mainland. Alfred Russell Wallace, who with Darwin co-authored one of the first statements of natural selection, early realized this and set up one of the first systems of biogeographical regions. As shown in Figure 116, floristic kingdoms as envisioned by the plant geographer are very similar to faunal regions as mapped by the animal geographer. The main difference is the recognition by the former of the Cape region of South Africa as a distinct major region. Although small in area the Union of South Africa has an exceptionally rich flora of over 1,500 genera, 500 (30 per cent) of which are endemic, that is, found nowhere else. Many of the unique species have been widely cultivated in European gardens. When both plants and animals are considered, the Australian region, of course, is the most isolated; South America ranks next. Both these areas have a large number of endemic species. Madagascar, which has long been separated from Africa, is sometimes considered a separate region.

Organisms which occupy the same ecological niche in similar

communities of different biogeographical regions are known as *ecological equivalents.* Ecological equivalents may not even be closely related from a taxonomic standpoint. Cacti (family Cactaceae), for example, which are so prominent in new world deserts (especially Neotropical region) are completely absent

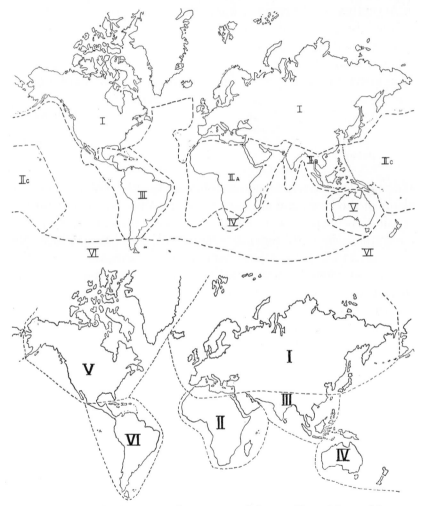

Figure 116. The biogeographic regions of the world as delimited by students of the flowering plants (upper map) and by animal geographers (lower map). The floristic regions or "kingdoms" as mapped by Good (1953) are as follows (upper map): I. Boreal; II. Paleotropical with subdivisions A—African, B—Indo-Malaysian, and C—Polynesian; III. Neotropical; IV. South African; V. Australian; VI. Antarctic. The zoogeographic regions (after deBeaufort, 1951) are as follows (lower map): I. Palearctic; II. Ethiopian (African); III. Oriental; IV. Australian; V. Neoarctic; VI. Neotropical. Regions I and V are often united as the Holarctic region, because considerable interchange of fauna has occurred between them.

from the old world, but in African deserts species of the Euphorbiaceae look exactly like cacti, having developed a similar spiny and succulent (water storing) life form. Equally striking examples are common in the animal kingdom. Jack rabbits are characteristic of grassland areas of western North America and fill an important niche among the primary consumers. In the grasslands of Argentina there are no jack rabbits, but the "jack rabbit niche" is filled by the Patagonian cavy, a relative of the guinea pig (rodent) which has long hind legs and big ears and acts much like a jack rabbit. Another illustration is provided by the following comparison of the large grazing herbivores of four continents:

North America	Eurasia	South Africa	Australia
Bison	Saga antelope	Numerous	The large
Pronghorn	Wild horse	species	kangaroos
antelope	(Kulan)	Antelope,	
	Wild asses	Zebras, etc.	

We may say that the kangaroos of Australia are ecological equivalents of the bison and antelope of North America; or perhaps we should say "were," since man's cattle and sheep now largely replace them in both regions. The native grasses on which the herbivores feed present a very similar appearance throughout the world even though species and often genera may be sharply restricted to a given floristic region. The point to emphasize is that the discontinuity of land environment results in similar communities being stocked with different species. Compare Figure 116 with the map of the communities, Figure 120. For a broad treatment of biogeography from the ecological viewpoint see the book by Dansereau (1957).

3. General structure of terrestrial communities

Composition of terrestrial communities

So varied are terrestrial organisms that ecologists have not agreed upon a simplified classification of life forms and life habits similar to the benthos-plankton-nekton series (see Chapter 9, Section 2) generally used with reference to aquatic organisms. Such a classification for terrestrial communities would be useful, but must await further study. The general classification of major food niches, i.e., producer–consumer–decomposer series, is quite applicable to land, however.

Producers. The outstanding feature of terrestrial communities is the presence and usually the dominance of large rooted green plants which not only are the chief food makers but provide shelter for other organisms and play an important role in holding and modifying the earth's surface. Although there are soil algae of importance, there is nothing on land to compare with the phytoplankton of water environments. The vegetation, which is the term generally used for all the plants of an area, is such a characteristic feature that we generally classify and name land communities on the basis of it rather than on the basis of physical environment as is often convenient in aquatic situations (see Chapter 8, Section 3).

A large number of life forms are represented which adapt land plants to almost every conceivable situation. Terms such as "tree," "shrub," "grass," and "forb," are, of course, widely used and provide the broad basis for the recognition of major terrestrial communities, which are to be described later in this chapter. From the more detailed floristic standpoint, one of the most widely used classifications of life form is that originally proposed by Raunkaier (1934). Raunkaier's life forms are based on the posi-

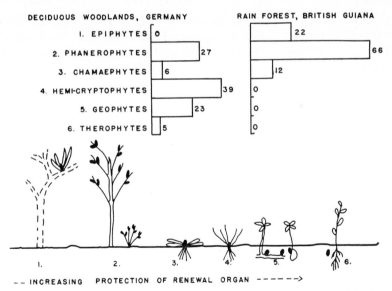

Figure 117. Raunkaier's life forms of terrestrial plants. The six life forms are diagramed in the lower sketch with the renewal buds (or seeds in No. 6) shown as oval black bodies. The upper bar graphs compare a temperate and a tropical forest in regard to the per cent of species in the flora which belong to the six life forms. Note that life forms of the rain forest (where there are no unfavorable cold or dry periods) all have exposed buds, while flora of the northern forest contains a large percentage of life forms with protected renewal organs. (Upper graph redrawn from Richards, 1952; lower diagram redrawn from Braun-Blanquet, 1932.)

tion of the renewal bud or organ, and the corresponding protection provided during unfavorable cold or dry periods. The six primary categories, shown in Figure 117, are as follows:

Epiphytes, air plants; no roots in the soil.

Phanerophytes, aerial plants; renewal buds exposed on upright shoots. Five sub-groups include: trees, shrubs, stem succulents, herbaceous stems and lianas (vines).

Chamaephytes, surface plants; renewal bud at the surface of the ground.

Hemi-cryptophytes, tussock plants; bud in or just below soil surface.

Cryptophytes or *Geophytes,* earth plants; bud below surface on a bulb or rhyzome.

Therophytes, annuals; complete life cycle from seed in one vegetative period; survive unfavorable seasons as seeds.

In general, the series represents one of increasing adaptation to adverse conditions of temperature and moisture. As shown in Figure 117, the majority of species in the tropical rain forest are phanerophytes and epiphytes, whereas more northern forests contain a higher proportion of "protected" life forms. The flora of extreme deserts and alpine areas would likely be composed mostly of annuals. However, in the study of local situations one should guard against assuming that the proportion of species in the different categories is an indicator of climate since edaphic factors and the stage in succession greatly influence life form composition (Cain, 1950). Raunkaier's life form "spectrum" is most useful as an ecological descriptive device when the categories are weighted on a quantitative or community basis, that is, numbers of individuals as well as numbers of species considered (see Cain, 1945; Stern and Buell, 1951). In many deserts, for example, the majority of species may be annuals but a few species of shrubs often make up the most important part of the vegetation from the standpoint both of the standing crop and of the annual production of dry matter. In other words, the life form spectrum of the vegetation (community) and the life form spectrum of the flora are not necessarily the same.

Consumers. Correlated with the large number of niches provided by the vegetation, land communities have an extremely varied array of consumers. Primary consumers include not only small organisms such as insects but very large herbivores, such as the hoofed mammals. The latter are a unique feature of land with but few parallels in aquatic communities (large plant-eating turtles, for example). Thus, the "grazers" of land are a far cry in size and structure from "grazers" of water, i.e., the zooplankton. The variety and abundance of insects and other arthropods, of course, is another important feature of terrestrial communities. Although perhaps more intensively studied by ecologists than any other groups of animals, insect ecology yet remains so little understood that mankind still relies largely on trial and error methods in his attempts to control or manage insect populations. Finally, we should mention the birds which are found in practically every land community and provide especially favorable material for ecological study.

Decomposers. Organisms which carry on the "mineralization of organic matter" are, as in the other major environments, chiefly the bacteria and the fungi. Decomposer organisms are found throughout terrestrial communities but are especially abundant in the soil, the upper layers being the site of major operations. Waksman (1932, 1952) has classified soil bacteria and fungi as follows:

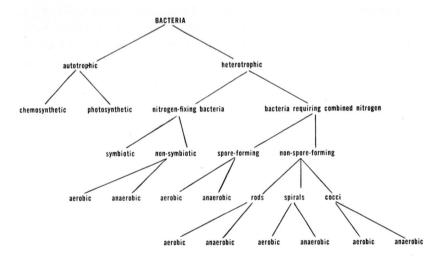

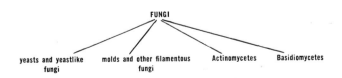

Table 19. *Quantitative distribution of bacteria and fungi (microbiota) in soil**

Type of soil	Depth	Cocci	Azotobacter cells	Bacilli	Yeast cells	Pieces of fungus mycelium
Forest soil	Surface	1,379	156	1,212	1	47
	10 cm.	991	82	466	31	34
	20 cm.	281	188	169	–	7
Brown loam soil	Surface	870	188	376	84	5
	10 cm.	569	184	106	1	3
Sandy soil	Surface	519	155	192	79	3
	10 cm.	407	112	153	23	19
	20 cm.	269	51	139	8	3

Number of bacteria in millions per gram; Number in millions per gram

* Data from Waksman (1932).

The autotrophic bacteria, which are producers, have already been discussed in Chapter 2 (pages 18-19). The heterotrophic bacteria are the true decomposers and by far the most numerous. Table 19 will serve to illustrate the abundance of bacteria and fungi in soil. In general, the larger the surface area of the soil (the smaller the particle size) the larger the microbial population. Note in Table 19 that microorganisms are less numerous in sandy soils which contain less organic material. They also decrease in number with depth, but bacteria probably go deeper than any other organisms.

As we have stressed earlier, numbers are a poor indication of what small organisms are doing or how fast they are doing it. The vital role of the nitrogen-fixing bacteria and the mycorrhizal fungi have already been outlined in Chapter 2 and 7 respectively, and need not be dealt with here. Winogradsky (1949) found that the soil of fallow fields, where the organic matter consisted largely of plant remains, contained numerous bacteria, but these were mostly non-spore-formers which have a relatively low rate of metabolism. When soluble organic matter was added to the soil, spore-formers with high rates of metabolism became dominant. As soon as this organic matter was decomposed the spore-formers went back to spores and the slower species again took over.*

Temperature and water are especially important in regulating the activity of decomposers; since these factors are more variable on land than in aquatic habitats, it is easy to see why decomposi-

* Winogradsky used the term "autochthonous" for microbial populations of soils or sediments of low oxidizing capacity and "zyngenous" for populations of soils of high oxidizing capacity.

tion in soil often proceeds in a sporadic fashion. Most bacteria and fungi require a microenvironment with a higher water content than that required by the roots of higher plants, for example. Consequently, in regions with prolonged dry periods (or prolonged cold periods), annual production in the ecosystem may exceed the annual decomposition. For example, in the chaparral vegetation of southern California where there is a long dry period, Kittredge (1939) found that a stand protected from fire for 50 years had 15 tons of dry, undecayed litter per acre, whereas a stand without fire for only 14 years had only 5.3 tons of litter per acre. The annual production of litter (as determined by placing large trays under the shrubs to catch falling leaves, twigs, etc.) was found to be about the same for both stands. In dry vegetation types, periodic fires apparently may compensate for the lag in decomposition. The slower rate of decomposition under anaerobic as compared with aerobic conditions has already been illustrated (Figure 5, page 23). Clay minerals (montmorillonite) are another factor which apparently may inhibit the decomposition of organic matter in soil (Lynch and Cotnoir, 1956).

During the past few years there has been an increase in interest in soil respiration measurements on intact soils in nature as a means of assaying the total activity of decomposers. Lundegårdh (1954) gives a comprehensive treatment of such studies. Roots and numerous small animals contribute to soil respiration, of course, in addition to the bacteria and fungi, but in most cases a large percentage of the oxygen consumed or carbon-dioxide released is the result of the activity of the latter. Measurements made in the field with comparatively simple apparatus can be especially interesting from a comparative standpoint, as shown in Table 20.

Table 20. *Comparative amounts of carbon-dioxide evolved from the soils of contrasting ecosystems occurring in the same locality**

Ecosystem	CO_2 evolved grams/M^2/hr.
Orchard grass on silt loam	8.80
Oak forest on silt loam	7.75
Pine plantation on silt loam	3.70
Birch-hemlock forest on podzolized sandy loam	3.12
Similar sandy loam partially sterilized by excrement from a heron rookery	1.35

* Data from Wallis and Wilde, 1957.

Succession and climax

Because land communities modify their environment, they undergo orderly succession and tend to reach a climax or stable state. This has been fully discussed in Chapter 8, Sections 4 and 5.

Stratification

Stratification is usually evident in land communities as in aquatic ones. Broadly speaking, the litter and soil make up one series of strata and the air and vegetation above ground make up another (see Figure 78). In a sense this division is comparable to the benthic and pelagic division of marine communities.

Organisms of the soil may be divided into three groups according to size (see Fenton, 1947):

1. *The microbiota,* which includes the soil algae (mostly green and blue-green types), the autotrophic and heterotrophic bacteria, the fungi, and the protozoa.

Table 21. *Quantitative distribution of small invertebrates in soil**

Animals extracted by Berlese funnel	Number in thousands per acre	Per M^2
Mites	89,603	22.1
Collembolans	28,053	6.9
Thysanopterans	1,437	
Insect larvae	888	
Ants	662	
Proturans	601	
Iapygids	546	
Chelonecthids	518	
Symphylans	414	1.7
Insects, various	409	
Diplopods	387	
Spiders	372	
Pauropods	177	
Chilopods	138	
Earthworms	91	
Others	68	
Total	124,367	30.7

Percentages of above animals occurring at various depths

In litter	65 per cent
In soil—0–2 inches	30 per cent
2–5 inches	5 per cent

* Data from Pearse (1946). Numbers represent averages of extracted population of soil (including litter) to depth of 5 inches in four forest communities (oak and pine on sand and clay) in North Carolina.

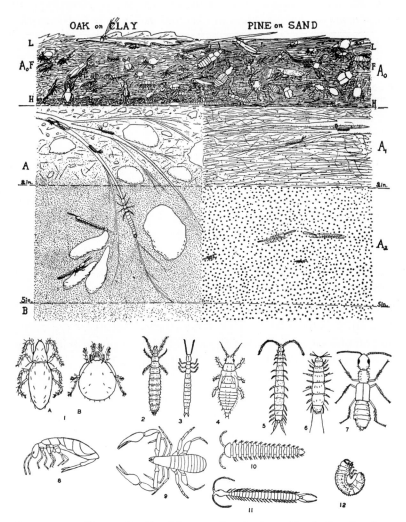

Figure 118. Upper: Profile of litter and soil of two North Carolina forests showing some of the characteristic animals. Note concentration of animals ir the A₀ horizon, and burrows in the clay subsoil. Lower; Representative arthropods of the mesobiota of litter and soil commonly obtained by the Berlese funnel sample method (see Table 21): 1, two oribatid mites (A–*Eulohmannia*, B–*Pelops*); 2, a proturan (*Microentomon*); 3, an iapygid (*Iapyx*); 4, a thrips (a thysanopteran); 5, a symphylan (*Scolopendrella*); 6, a pauropod (*Pauropus*); 7, a rove beetle (Staphylinidae); 8, a springtail or collembolan (*Entomobrya*); 9, a pseudoscorpion (or chelonecthid); 10, a millipede (or diplopod); 11, a centipede (or chilopod); 12, a scarabaeid beetle larva or grub. (Upper diagram, after Pearse, 1946. Lower diagram: 1 redrawn from Baker and Wharton, 1952; 2, 3, 4, 12 redrawn from Chu, 1949.)

Table 22. *Numbers and biomass (as live weight) of three important components of the mesobiota in two contrasting soils in Denmark** [*]

Habitat	Enchytraeids		Nematodes		Microarthropods	
	Nos/M² × 1000	Biomass gms/M²	Nos/M² × 1000	Biomass gms/M²	Nos/M² × 1000	Biomass gms/M²
Pasture soils (mull-type)	11–45	1–3	10,000	13.5	48	2
Heath with raw humus soil (mor-type)	50	7	1,500	2	300	4–5

[*] Data from Overgaard-Nielsen, 1955.

2. *The mesobiota,* which includes the nematodes, the small oligochaete worms (*Enchytraeids*), the smaller insect larvae, and the microarthropods; of the latter the soil mites (Acarina) and springtails (Collembola) are often the most abundant of forms which remain permanently in the soil. Figure 118 shows a profile of litter and soil of two North Carolina forests, with some of the characteristic organisms in situ, and also depicted separately. These animals have been extensively studied because they may be conveniently extracted from the soil by means of a device known as a Berlese funnel or the similar Tullgren funnel. In these devices, organisms are forced down through a core of soil (removed from the field without disturbing normal texture, animal burrows, etc.) by heat and light until they fall into a vial of preservative. Some results obtained with this kind of extraction are shown in Table 21. Like the plankton net, the Berlese funnel is selective in that it does not sample all components equally well. Nematodes, which are usually abundant, are but little removed by the light and heat treatment. However, if the funnel is filled with warm water and the soil enclosed in a mesh or gauze, the nematodes move out of the soil and drop by gravity to the bottom on the funnel. This type of device is called a Baermann funnel. A modification in which heat and water are applied from below works well for enchytraeids. Numbers and biomass of three important groups of the mesobiota in two contrasting soils of Denmark are shown in Table 22. These data were obtained by using the extraction method most efficient for each component.

From Table 22 we see that the microarthropods (see also Table 21) and the enchytraeids are to be numbered in the thousands per square meter but the nematodes are counted in the millions per square meter. The biomass, however, of the three groups is not too different, ranging from 1 to 13 grams per square meter. In his studies of soil nematodes Overgaard-Nielsen (1949, 1949a), found density to range from about 1 to about 20 million/M^2. A large per cent of nematodes apparently feed on bacteria, another large per cent (up to 40 per cent) on roots of plants and on soil algae, while not more than 2 per cent feed on other animals. Nematodes are most numerous on mineral (mull-type) soil where their biomass may be equal to that of earthworms; in this event, however, their oxygen consumption would be 10 times that of the more conspicuous earthworms (Overgaard-Nielsen, 1949a). Yet nematodes apparently account for about only one per cent of the respiration of soil (Bunt, 1954), which, as already indicated, is primarily microbial. In agricultural soils, certain species of nematodes may become serious parasites of roots of plants and are difficult to erradicate from infested soil. In contrast to the nematodes, the microarthropods and the enchytraeids generally reach their greatest biomass in organic soils (see Table 22).

3. *The Macrobiota*, which includes the roots of plant, the larger insects, earthworms (Lumbricidae) and other organisms which can easily be sorted by hand. The burrowing vertebrates such as moles, ground squirrels and pocket gophers might also be included in this group. Very frequently the roots of plants would comprise the largest biomass component in the soil, but, of course, their metabolism per gram would be relatively low. J. E. Weaver and his colleagues have for many years made intensive studies of the root systems of prairie grasses. They have found that the dry weight of roots ranged from 2 to 5 tons per acre or approximately 450 to 1200 grams per square meter (see Weaver, 1954). Recent studies utilizing radioactive phosphorus as a tracer have indicated that a portion of the root system of grasses may be inactive at any given time (see Burton in Comar, 1957). Secretions and excretions from roots provide food as well as inhibitory and stimulatory substances for the microbiota, while dead roots, of course, provide a major substrate for decomposers. Among the larger animals of the soil many insects are but temporary inhabitants during hibernation or pupation. Earthworms resemble nematodes in being most abundant in mineral soils, especially calcareous clay soils where they may reach a density of 300/M^2.

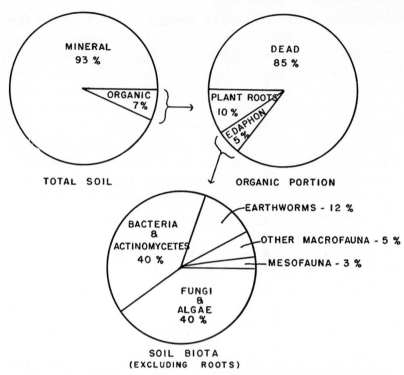

Figure 119. The living and the non-living components of a meadow soil in terms of the dry weight of the "standing crop." The edaphon includes all of the soil biota exclusive of the roots of higher plants. Although living organisms make up but a small part of the weight of soil, their activity and "turnover" rates may be quite high and, therefore, their importance relatively much greater than is indicated by the size of their standing crops. (Redrawn from Tischler, 1955.)

All of the macrobiota, are very important in mixing the soil and maintaining a "living sponge" consistency.

The mechanical breakdown of plant litter into forms readily decomposed by microbes is one of the main "jobs" performed by soil animals. Studies in the Netherlands have shown that the diplopod, *Glomeris,* and numerous other soil animals assimilate only 5 to 10 per cent of dead leaf material which they ingest (that is, weight of feces = 90 to 95 per cent of ingested food) (Drift, 1958). It was further found that feces were decomposed more rapidly by microorganisms than mechanically pulverized leaves not previously ingested by animals.

The series of pie diagrams in Figure 119 give a good overall picture of the "standing crop" situation in soil including both living and nonliving components. Thus, we see that the living components of the soil comprise but a small percentage of the total weight of soil, but because of their high rates of activity these seemingly tiny components are dominant factors in the functioning of the entire terrestrial ecosystem. Much work yet remains to be done before a detailed metabolic picture can be presented. The following summary papers and books on soil ecology may be consulted for additional information: Jacot, 1940; Kühnelt, 1950; Waksman, 1952; Birch and Clark, 1953; Tischler, 1955; Kevan, 1955; Thornton, 1956; Norman, 1957; also works of Overgaard-Nielsen and Lundegårdh, previously cited. As this cross section of references indicates, work on soil biology has been especially intensive in Europe.

Life in the terrestrial community above the ground consists of three broad groups: (1) the rooted plants (2) the *epiphytes* (or periphytes), the term here used to include both plants and animals which cling to or are attached to the major plants; and (3) the *permeants,* which include the highly motile animals such as birds, reptiles, mammals and active flying insects. The latter organisms move freely (or "permeate") from one strata to another and from one community to another. However, motile animals are by no means indiscriminate in habitat selection (see Chapter 8, Section 6).

4. Structure of vegetation; phytosociology

Because the standing crop of producers, i.e., the vegetation, is such a conspicuous and stable feature of terrestrial environments, the composition of vegetation as such has received a great deal of attention. The quantitative study of the structure of vegetation is called *phytosociology,* the principal aim of which is to describe vegetation, explain or predict its pattern, and classify it in a meaningful way. There have been a number of different approaches to this phase of descriptive ecology. One approach is based on the principle of succession and stems from the work of Warming, Cowles, Clements and others. Emphasis is placed on quantitative relationships of the few species which are judged to be dominant on the theory that these largely control the community and thereby the occurrence of the large number of rarer species (see Chapter 8, pages 250-2). Another approach which was mentioned in Chapter 8 (pages 254-5) involves the study of vegetation along a gradient and the concept of the "continuum." As also pointed out in Chapter 8, a functional approach based on productivity of strata and other components promises to be helpful in elucidating structure (see also Filzer, 1951; Monsi and Oshima, 1955). By far the most intensive approach to phytosociology is that of the European school of ecologists with which the name of Braun-Blanquet is associated (see the 1932 English translation by Fuller and Conard, or the revised German edition of Braun-Blanquet's *Pflanzensoziologie* published in 1951). While a full consideration of the immense amount of work of this school must be reserved for advanced texts in plant ecology, we may briefly consider the underlying concepts. Becking (1957) has prepared an excellent review of the work of what he calls the "Zurich-Montpellier school," and the following paragraph is based on this summary.

The Braun-Blanquet approach is basically floristic. A complete knowledge of the flora is required since numerical relationships of all the species of higher plants, down to the smallest mosses and lichens, are considered. The aim is an objective analysis in terms of the actual floristic composition existing at the time of study; only after this composition is described are communities delimited and successional relations considered. In essence, the approach is based on two beliefs: (1) that there are distinct species combinations which repeat themselves in nature and (2) that because of the complex interaction of plants and habitat, the floristic composition of the vegetation as a unit is more meaningful than a list of component species. Study procedures follow two steps. First comes the field analysis, which involves the selection of sample plots or quadrats and the enumeration of all plants in them. The species-area curve (see Oosting, 1956; Vestal, 1949; Goodall, 1952) is widely used to determine proper size and number of sample plots, and the sampling is usually done by strata (moss layer, herb layer, shrub layer, tree layer, etc.). Density, cover (vertical projection of aerial parts), frequency (per cent plots occupied), sociability (degree of clumping) and other indices are tabulated for each species. The second step involves the synthesis of the data to determine the degree of association of plant populations. Frequency curves, as illustrated in Figure 83 (page 282), are often used to determine the homogeneity or heterogeneity of a particular stand of vegetation. In formulating abstract community units or "associations," considerable emphasis is placed on indicators according to the concept *constancy*, that is, the per cent of plots containing the species, and, especially, according to the concept of *fidelity*, which is defined as the degree of restriction of a species to a particular situation. A species with high fidelity is one with a strong preference for, or a limitation to, a particular community; to a certain extent, at least, objective statistical methods can be applied to this concept (Goodall, 1953). As we have already indicated in Chapter 4 (page 143), ecological indicators of this sort are usually not the abundant and dominant species. In general, then, the Zurich-Montpellier approach places the emphasis on the numerous rare species of the community rather than on the few common species.

5. The study of whole terrestrial ecosystems

The discussions in the preceding sections has served to emphasize that many terrestrial ecosystems such as forests have a particularly complex structure involving numerous species, marked stratification and variable physical environment. Therefore, in the quantitative study of such systems quite different methods are required for different ecological groups, which means that sampling problems need to receive much attention (for an introduction to such problems see Oosting, 1956, for plants and Dice, 1952a, for animals). Thus, bacteriological techniques are needed for the soil microbiota, Berlese funnels or other extraction methods for the mesobiota, and still other procedures for the macrobiota. The vegetation itself presents special problems as we have seen. The "epiphytes" may often be directly studied, or sampled with sweep nets. The "permeants" require still other techniques, such as direct observation, trapping in the case of mammals, and the mapping of territories in the case of birds.

In local situations there is much to be gained from singling out a restricted component and subjecting it to a variety of sampling and experimental procedures in order to find the best methods and establish confidence limits for the data. At the same time it is important that whole systems be studied simultaneously since certain functional interrelations can not be readily determined by piecemeal study. For this kind of study, at the present time at least, it is best to find a situation where major components of the ecosystem are present, but where species composition and sampling procedures are either already known or can be readily determined. Old fields, salt marshes, grasslands, deserts and tundras are examples of ecosystems where one person, or a small team of

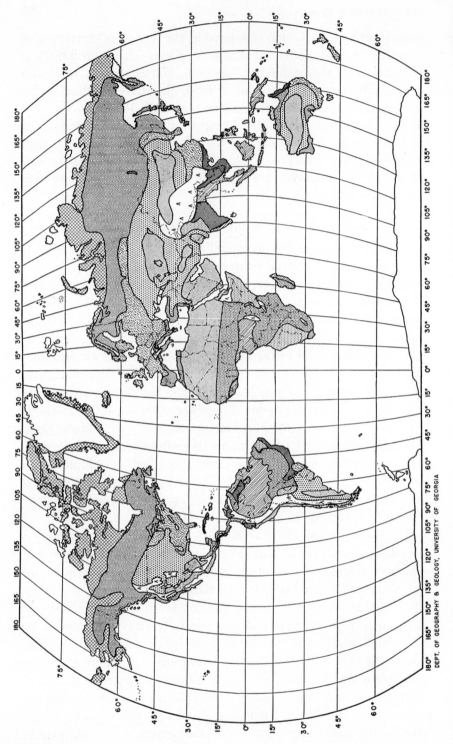

DEPT. OF GEOGRAPHY & GEOLOGY, UNIVERSITY OF GEORGIA

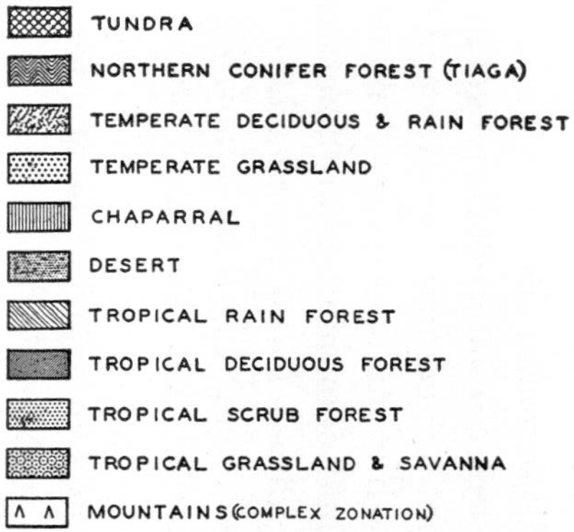

TUNDRA

NORTHERN CONIFER FOREST (TAIGA)

TEMPERATE DECIDUOUS & RAIN FOREST

TEMPERATE GRASSLAND

CHAPARRAL

DESERT

TROPICAL RAIN FOREST

TROPICAL DECIDUOUS FOREST

TROPICAL SCRUB FOREST

TROPICAL GRASSLAND & SAVANNA

MOUNTAINS (COMPLEX ZONATION)

Figure 120. Schematic map of the major biomes of the world. Note that only the tundra and the northern conifer forest have some continuity throughout the world. Other biomes of the same type (temperate grassland or tropical rain forest, for example) are isolated in different biogeographical regions (compare Figure 97) and, therefore, may be expected to have ecologically equivalent but often taxonomically unrelated species. The pattern of the major biomes is similar to but not identical with that of the primary soil groups as mapped in Figure 34. (Map prepared using Finch and Trewartha's (1949) map of original vegetation as a basis.)

persons can become familiar with all the major items and still have
time to study how the components operate together!

6. Distribution of major terrestrial communities, the biomes

Regional climates interact with regional biota and substrate to
produce large, easily recognizable community units, called *biomes*
(Fig. 120). The biome is the largest land community unit which
it is convenient to recognize. In a given biome the *life form* of the
climatic climax vegetation (see Chapter 8, Section 5) is uniform.
Thus, the climax vegetation of the grassland biome is grass, although the species of dominant grasses may vary in different parts
of the biome. Since the life form of the vegetation, on the one
hand, reflects the major features of climate and, on the other, determines the structural nature of the habitat for animals, it provides a sound basis for a natural ecological classification (see
Clements and Shelford, 1939, and Carpenter, 1939).

The biome includes not only the climatic climax vegetation,
which is the key to recognition, but the edaphic climaxes and the
developmental stages as well, which in many cases are dominated
by other life forms. Thus, grassland communities are temporary
developmental stages in the deciduous forest biome where the
broad-leaved deciduous tree is the climax life form. Many organisms require both the developmental and the climax stages in
succession or the ecotones between them (see Chapter 8, Section
8); therefore, all of the communities in a given climatic region,
whether climax or not, are natural parts of the biome (see Figures
75 and 77).

The biome is identical with major "plant formation" as the term
is used by plant ecologists, except that it is a total community unit
and not a unit of vegetation alone. Animals as well as plants are
considered. In general, the biome may be said to occupy a major
"biotic zone" when this expression is used to mean a community
zone and not a floral or faunal unit. Biome is the same thing as
"major life zone" as used by European ecologists, but not the
same thing as "life zone" as used in North America. In North
America, "life zone" generally refers to a series of temperature
zones proposed by C. Hart Merriam in 1894 and widely used by
students of the birds and mammals. The original temperature
criteria have been abandoned and Merriam's life zones are currently based on the distribution of organisms. These zones have,
therefore, become more and more community zones, and in many

cases are the same as biome divisions or subdivisions, except for
terminology. For a comparison of biomes and Merriam's life zones,
see E. P. Odum (1945).

The biomes of the world are shown in Figure 120 in a semidia-
grammatic manner. Biomes and some subdivision are shown in

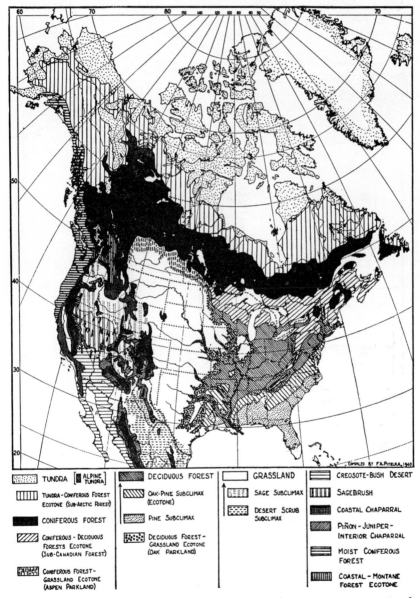

Figure 121. The biomes of North America, with extensive ecotones and
certain sub-regions (zones) indicated. (After Pitelka, 1941.)

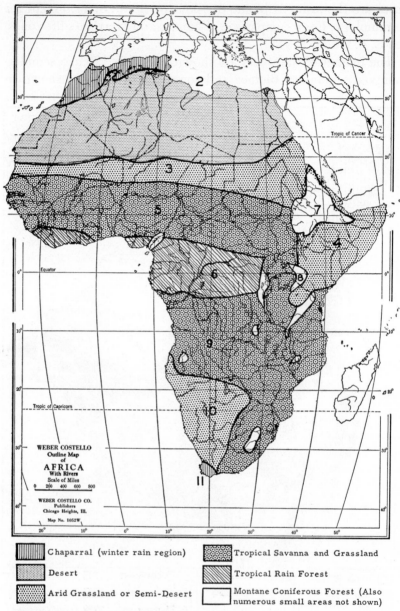

Africa.

Chaparral (winter rain region)   Tropical Savanna and Grassland

Desert   Tropical Rain Forest

Arid Grassland or Semi-Desert   Montane Coniferous Forest (Also numerous small areas not shown)

Figure 122.   The biotic regions of Africa. The six major biomes are indicated by the legend. Note that only a relatively small part of the continent is "jungle" (i.e., tropical rain forest). The very extensive tropical savanna and grassland is the fabulous "big game" country. Some of the larger faunal areas are numbered as follows: 1, Barbary; 2, Sahara; 3, Sudanese Arid; 4, Somali Arid; 5, Northern Savanna; 6, Congo Lowland; 7, Abyssinian Highland; 8, Kenya Highland; 9, Southern Savanna; 10, Southwest Arid; 11, Cape Town "winter rain" region. All of the faunal areas are part of the Ethiopian or African biogeographic region (see Figure 116), except the Barbary, which is Palearctic. (Map based on sketch-map of Moreau, 1952.)

more detail for North America and Africa in Figures 121 and 122. Although biomes are largely complete communities, they are not necessarily sharply separated from one another. Something of the nature of ecotones between biomes is indicated in Figure 121. Let us now consider briefly the principal biomes of the world.

The tundra

There are two tundra biomes covering large areas, one in the Palearctic and one in the Nearctic region. Many species occur in both since there has been a land connection between them. Low temperatures and a short growing season (about 60 days) are the chief limiting factors. The ground remains frozen except for the upper few inches during the open season. The tundra is essentially an arctic grassland; the vegetation consists of lichens (reindeer "moss"), grasses, sedges, and dwarf woody plants. "Low tundra" is characterized by a thick, spongy mat of living and undecayed vegetation (reduction by bacteria is very slow because of low temperatures), often saturated with water and dotted with ponds when not frozen. "High tundra," especially where there is considerable relief, may be bare except for a scanty growth of lichens and grasses. Two views of the low coastal plain tundra are shown in Figure 123. Although the growing season was shorter in the swales (upper photo) than in raised polygonal ground (because snow was deeper and remained on longer) the net primary productivity was found to be much greater in the former (R. E Shanks, personal communication).

Despite the rigors of the environment (see Figure 39, page 142), many warm-blooded animals remain active throughout the year. These include the caribou (and its ecological equivalent, the reindeer of Eurasia), musk ox, arctic hare, arctic fox, lemming, ptarmigan, and others. Migratory birds and insects, especially (or so it seems to the visitor) the biting diptera (mosquitoes, black flies), are conspicuous during the short summer.

The tundra food chains have been discussed (see Chapter 3. Section 2). In Chapter 6, Section 9, it was pointed out that violent oscillations in population density of some animals are characteristic of tundra communities. When the lemmings reach a peak of abundance the effect of their grazing on the vegetation is marked; in the region of Figure 123, for example, plots from which lemmings were excluded contained 36 per cent more grass in August than those heavily utilized during the spring and summer. During lemming "highs" predatory birds such as owls and jaegers are

Figure 123. Two views of the tundra on the Arctic coastal plain near Point Barrow, Alaska. The upper photo shows a broad swale at the head of a stream system about two miles inland from the coast. The arctic grass *Dupontia fischeri* and the sedge *Carex aquatalis* are the dominant plants which are rooted in a peaty layer of a half-bog soil. The area is typical of what may be reasonably regarded as "climax" on the low tundra sites near the coast. Shown in the picture are sample quadrats set up to measure net

abundant and breed, whereas few birds and little or no breeding are observed when the lemmings are scarce (Pitelka, Tomich, and Treichel, 1955).

Northern coniferous forest biomes

Stretching as broad belts all the way across both North America and Eurasia (Fig. 120) are the vast northern evergreen forest regions. Extensions occur in the mountains even in the tropics. The identifying life form is the needle-leaved evergreen tree, especially the spruces, firs, and pines (Fig. 124). A dense shade thus exists the year around, often resulting in poor development of shrub and herb layers. However, the continuous blanket of chlorophyll present the year around results in a fairly high annual production rate despite low temperature during half of the year (Ovington, 1957). The coniferous forests are among the great lumber producing regions of the world. Coniferous needles decay very slowly, and the soil develops a highly characteristic podzol profile (see Figure 32). The soil may contain a fair population of small organisms but comparatively few larger ones. Many of the larger herbivorous vertebrates, such as the moose, snowshoe hare, and grouse, depend, in part at least, on broad-leaved developmental communities for their food. The seeds of the conifers provide important food for many animals such as squirrels, siskins and crossbills.

Like the tundra, seasonal periodicity is pronounced and populations tend to oscillate. The snowshoe hare–lynx cycles are classic examples (see Figure 54). Coniferous forests are also subject to outbreaks of bark beetles and defoliating insects (sawflies, budworms, etc.), especially where stands have but one or two dominant species (Fig. 56). For an account of the conifer forest biome of North America, see Shelford and Olson (1935).

---

production during the 6-weeks growing season. In the background is an exclosure to keep out lemmings which are abundant in this area during the peak of their 3 to 4 year population cycle. The lower photo shows a site about 10 miles inland with raised polygonal ground in the foreground and a swale and shallow lake in the background. The cottongrass *Eriophorum vaginatum* is the conspicuous plant with the cottony tufts of fruit. Ice wedges underlying the troughs seen in the foreground contribute to the buildup of the raised polygons. Such patterned ground is characteristic of the greater part of the Arctic coastal plain, where relief is not great. (Photographs by R. E. Shanks, E. E. Clebsch and John Koranda, August, 1956.)

Figure 124. Two samples from extensive coniferous forest biomes. Upper: This Englemann spruce–white fir forest in northern Idaho is a good example of the extensive spruce–fir communities which are climax in northern coniferous forest biome. Lower: On the warmer, moist coast of northern California the coniferous life form culminates in the magnificent redwood (*Sequoia sempervirens*) forests, rivaled only by the "big trees" (*Sequoia gigantica*) of the moist western slopes of the Sierras. The moist coniferous forests of the west coast are generally considered a distinct biome (see Figure 121). (U. S. Forest Service Photo.)

Moist coniferous forest biome

Forests of a distinctive type occur along the west coast of North America from central California to Alaska (see Figure 121), where temperatures are higher, seasonal range is relatively small and the humidity is very high. Although dominated by the conifer life form, these forests are quite different foristically and ecologically from the northern coniferous forest. Rainfall ranges from 30 to 150 inches; fog compensates for the lower rainfall in southern areas so that the humidity is everywhere high and the precipitation/evaporation ratio is extremely favorable. Oberlander (1956), for example, found that fog may account for 2 to 3 times more water than the annual precipitation and that some tall trees in position to intercept coastal fog as it moves inland may get as much as 50 inches of "rainfall" dripping down from the limbs! Because water is usually not a severe limiting factor, the forests of the west coast region are often called "temperate rain forests."

Western hemlock (*Tsuga heterophylla*), western arborvitae (*Thuja plicata*), grand fir (*Abies grandis*), and douglas fir (*Pseudotsuga*), the latter on drier sites or subclimax on wet sites, are the big four among the dominant trees in the Puget Sound area where the forest reaches its greatest development. Southward, the magnificent redwoods (Figure 124) are found, and northward the sitka spruce (*Picea sitchensis*) is prominant. Unlike the drier and more northern coniferous forests, the understory vegetation is well developed wherever any light filters through, while mosses and other moisture-loving lesser plants are abundant. The "standing crop" of producers in this biome is indeed impressive, and, as can be imagined, the production of lumber per unit area is potentially very great if the harvest-regeneration and nutrient cycles can be maintained. As with all ecosystems where such a large percentage of nutrients may be tied up in the biomass, there is great danger that overexploitation may reduce future productivity.

Temperate deciduous forest biomes

Deciduous forest communities (Fig. 125) occupy areas with abundant, evenly distributed rainfall (30 to 60 inches) and moderate temperatures which exhibit a distinct seasonal pattern. Temperate deciduous forest originally covered eastern North America, all of Europe, and part of Japan, Australia, and the tip of South America. Since leaves are off the trees and shrubs for part of the year, the contrast between winter and summer is great.

Figure 125. Climatic climax and edaphic climax in the deciduous forest biome of eastern North America. Upper left: Climatic climax oak-hickory forest with well developed understory in Maryland. (U. S. Soil Conservation Service Photo.) Upper right: Virgin stand of Delta hardwoods (red gum, *Liquidambar styraciflua*) in Mississippi, a product of local soil and water conditions. (U. S. Forest Service Photo.) Lower left: A virgin longleaf pine forest on the southeastern coastal plain, a "fire" edaphic climax (see Figure 36). (U. S. Forest Service Photo.) Lower right: A pine forest of about the same age (100-125 years), which has been protected from fire; deciduous trees are rapidly replacing the pines.

Herb and shrub layers tend to be well developed, as is also the soil biota. There are a large number of plants which produce pulpy fruits and nuts, such as acorns and beechnuts. Animals of the original forest of North America included the Virginia deer, bear, gray and fox squirrels, gray fox, bobcat, and wild turkey. The red-eyed vireo, wood thrush, tufted titmouse, ovenbird, and several woodpeckers are characteristic small birds of the climax stages.

Although the deciduous forest regions are not as extensive as coniferous forest regions, they represent one of the most important biotic regions of the world because "white man's civilization" has achieved its greatest development in these areas. This biome is, therefore, greatly modified by man and much of it is replaced by cultivated and forest edge communities.

The deciduous forest biome of North America has a large number of important subdivisions which have different climax forest types. Some of these are:

> The beech–maple forest of the north central region;
> The maple–basswood forest of Wisconsin and Minnesota;
> The oak–hickory forest of western and southern regions;
> The oak–chestnut forest of the Appalachian mountains (with chestnut now wiped out by fungus diseases—see Chapter 7, Section 3, Fig. 70);
> The mixed mesophytic forest of the Appalachian plateau;
> The pine forest (see Chapter 8, Section 5, and Chapter 3, Section 9) of the southeastern coastal plain.

Each of these has distinctive features, but many organisms, especially the larger animals, range through two or more of the subdivisions (i.e., are "binding species"). As has been pointed out (see pages 135, 138, 269), the southeastern coastal plain is peculiar in that only a very small portion of the area is or ever was actually occupied by the climatic climax vegetation, because of the immaturity of the soils and the action of fires. Although large areas are covered by edaphic climax (or disclimax) pines, most of the southeastern coastal plain is clearly a distinctive subdivision of the deciduous forest biome rather than a separate major biome. There are extensive ecotones between the deciduous forest and the northern coniferous region (the hemlock–white pine–northern hardwood region), and between the deciduous forest and the grassland (see Figure 121).

An excellent summary of the vegetation of deciduous forest communities has been compiled in book form by E. Lucy Braun (1950).

Broad-leaved evergreen subtropical forest biomes

Where the moisture remains high but temperature differences between winter and summer become less pronounced, the temperate deciduous forest gives way to the broad-leaved evergreen forest climax. This community may be seen in the "hammocks" of

Florida, and is weakly developed along the Gulf and South Atlantic coasts. A "hammock" is an area of mature soils which has
had some protection, at least from continuous fires, thus allowing
a climatic climax community to develop. Much of Florida, in
common with the southeastern coastal plain in general, does not
support the climatic climax but is covered with developmental
stages and edaphic climaxes (pines, swamp forests, and marshes,
especially) for reasons mentioned in the preceding paragraphs.
Thus, Davis (1943) estimated that only 140 thousand acres out
of nearly 10 million acres of southern Florida is occupied by "hammock" forests.

Plant dominants of the evergreen broad-leaved forest range
from the more northerly live oaks (*Quercus virginiana*), mag-
nolias, bays, and hollies to more tropical species such as strangler-
fig (*Fiscus aurea*), wild tamarind (*Lysiloma*), and the gumbo
limbo (*Bursera*). Palms such as the sabal or cabbage palm (*Sabal
palmetto*) are also often prominent. Vines and epiphytes are characteristic. The latter group includes many ferns, the bromeliads
(pineapple family), and orchids which support characteristic
fauna of small animals. As is generally true of tropical and sub-
tropical communities, dominance in the trophic groups is "shared"
by more different species than is the case in northern communities
(see Chapter 8, Section 2). For a picture of a forest which is intermediate between the hammock forest and the temperate deciduous forest see Figure 37, page 140.

A fine example of the climax broad-leaved forest which is being
preserved is Royal Palm Hammock on Paradise Key in the Everglades National Park. It is interesting to note that although there
are many plants of tropical origin in this forest, not a single species
of land bird or mammal is tropical in origin (there are tropical
water birds in the area), apparently because Florida has never
been connected with extensive tropical communities to the south.
This illustrates again the importance of geography in determining
composition of communities.

Temperate grassland biomes

Grasslands (Fig. 126) cover very large areas and are extremely
important from man's viewpoint. Grasslands provide natural pastures for grazing animals, and the principal agricultural food
plants have been evolved by artificial selection from grasses.
Many early civilizations developed in grassland regions, hence

man should be familiar with the ecology of grasslands. However, no biome type has probably been abused to a greater degree by man. Even today, the great mass of people fail to understand the limiting factors involved and thousands of acres continue to be converted into useless desert (see discussion of range management, Chapter 12, Section 9).

Grasslands occur where rainfall is too low to support the forest life form but is higher than that which results in desert life forms. Generally, this means between 10 and 30 inches, depending on temperature and seasonal distribution. Temperate grasslands generally occur in the interior of continents (see Figure 120). Grassland soils are highly characteristic and contain large amounts of humus, as has been previously indicated (see Chapter 4, Section 5, subdivision 8, Figure 32).

In North America the grassland biome is divided into east-west zones, i.e., tall grass, mixed grass, short grass and bunch grass prairies, determined by the rainfall gradient, which is also a gradient of decreasing primary productivity (see Table 7, page 73). Some of the important perennial species classified according to the height of the above-ground parts are as follows:

Tall grasses (5 to 8 feet), big bluestem (*Andropogon gerardi*), switchgrass (*Panicum virgatum*), Indiangrass (*Sorghastrum nutans*), and in bottomlands the sloughgrass (*Spartina pectinata*).

Mid grasses (2 to 4 feet), little bluestem (*A. scoparius*), needlegrass (*Stipa spartea*), dropseed (*Sporobolus heterolepis*), western wheatgrass (*Agropyron smithii*), June grass (*Koeleria cristata*), Indian rice grass (*Oryzopsis*) and many others.

Short grasses (0.5 to 1.5 feet), buffalo grass (*Buchloe dactyloides*), Blue grama (*Bouteloua gracilis*), other gramas (*Bouteloua*, sp.), and the introduced bluegrass (*Poa*).

Roots of all the species penetrate deeply (up to 6 feet) and the weight of roots of healthy plants will be several times that of the tops. Weaver and Zink (1946) found that three years were required (starting from seedling) for little bluestem and grama grass to develop maximum standing crop of roots; after that, there was no further increase, the annual growth equaling the annual loss. The growth form of the roots is important. Some of the above species, for example, big bluestem, buffalo grass and wheatgrass have underground rhyzomes and are thus sod-formers. Other species, such as little bluestem, June grass, and needlegrass are bunchgrasses and grow in clumps. Two life forms are contrasted

Figure 126. Upper: View of grassland in North Dakota, with edaphic climax forest along the river in the background. Shown in the picture is the camp of a University of Illinois ecology field class which visited areas in the major biomes of central North America during the summer of 1939. Lower: Short-grass grassland, Wainwright National Park, Alberta, Canada, with herd of American bison, originally one of the important animals of the grassland biome. The animal in the center background is wallowing. Old "buffalo wallows" often may be detected in the grassland many years after the bison have been extirpated.

in Figure 127, which shows little bluestem, a bunch type mid grass, and sideoats grama, which is a bunch type short grass. The geographical origin of species is of special ecological importance in grasslands. Species of northern genera, such as *Stipa, Agropyron* and *Poa,* renew growth early in the spring, reach maximum development in late spring or early summer (when seeds are produced), become semi-dormant in hot weather but resume growth in autumn and remain green despite frosts. Warm-season species of southern genera, on the other hand, such as *Andropogon, Buchloe,* and *Bouteloua* renew growth late in the spring, but grow continuously during the summer, reaching maximum standing crop in late summer or autumn with no further growth during the latter period. From the standpoint of annual productivity of the whole ecosystem, a mixture of cool and warm season grasses might be favorable especially since rainfall is likely to be most abundant in spring or fall in some years and in midsummer in other years.

Forbs (composites, legumes, etc.) generally comprise but a small part of the producer biomass in climax grasslands, but are consistently present. Certain species are of special interest as in-

Figure 127. Two important climax grasses of the grassland biome in North America. Left: Little bluestem (*Andropogon scoparius*), the most important native grass in the moist, tall-grass prairie regions (see Figure 121) in the eastern part of the grassland biome. Right: Sideoats grama (*Bouteloua curtipendula*), a widely distributed "grama" grass in the mixed and short grass areas east of the Rockies. (U. S. Soil Conservation Service Photo.)

dicators (i.e., they have a high "fidelity," see Hanson, 1950). Increased grazing and/or drought tends to increase the percentage of forbs which are also prominent in early seral stages. Secondary succession in the grassland biome, and the rhythmic changes in vegetation during wet and dry cycles have been described in earlier chapters (see page 102 and page 264). The automobile traveler in mid-continent United States should bear in mind that the conspicuous annual forbs of the roadsides, such as the Russian thistle tumbleweed (*Salsola*) and sunflowers (*Helianthus*) owe their luxuriance to man's continual disturbance of the soil.

A large proportion of mammals of the grassland are either running or burrowing types. Aggregation into colonies or herds is characteristic; this life habit provides some measure of protection in the open type of habitat. The important large grazing animals native to grasslands in various biogeographic regions were listed on page 370. Burrowing rodents, such as ground squirrels, prairie dogs, and gophers, are important. Where man has reduced the population of rodent predators such as coyotes, kit foxes and badgers, a "rodent epidemic" often results; likewise rodents increase when the grassland is overgrazed by cattle or other hoofed animals. Characteristic birds of North American grasslands include the prairie chickens, meadowlarks, longspurs, horned larks, and rodent-eating hawks; ecological equivalent species occur in other parts of the world.

In all of the grasslands the large grazing mammals, whether native or domesticated, are major dominants which are as important as basic climate and soil conditions in determining the nature of the community since some species of grasses and other plants are more sensitive to grazing pressure than others. In the man-made grasslands of England, some of which have been overgrazed for centuries, Bradshaw (1957) has demonstrated that some grass species develop ecotypes with inherent low productivity even when transplanted to ungrazed experimental gardens. Under heavy grazing pressure it becomes of survival value for the plant to grow slowly (even when moisture and other conditions would favor rapid growth) and thus avoid being killed completely by the grazing animal! Similar low-yielding ecotypes were found in alpine regions where extreme conditions had the same effect as intense grazing. In these cases inherent productivity of species and probably of whole ecosystem as well becomes just as much an adaptive characteristic as any structural feature. Likewise the effects of prairie fires and of primitive man must be considered in interpreting the present-day conditions (see Sauer, 1950; Malin, 1953). For general discussions of the grassland biome in North America see Chapter 8 in Clements and Shelford (1939), Carpenter (1940), Weaver (1954), Weaver and Albertson (1956), and Malin (1956). The UNESCO Arid Zone Research reports (Vol. VI–VIII, 1955–57) contain a great deal of descriptive material and extensive bibliographies on plant and animal (including human) ecology of grasslands of various parts of the world.

Tropical savanna biomes

Tropical savannas (grasslands with scattered trees or clumps of trees) are found in warm regions with 40 to 60 inches of rainfall but with a prolonged dry season when fires are an important part of the environment. The largest area of this type is in Africa, but sizable tropical savannas or grasslands also occur in South America and Australia. Since both trees and grass must be resistant to drought and fire, the number of species in the vegetation is not large, in sharp contrast to adjacent equatorial forests. Grasses belonging to such genera as *Panicum, Pennisetum, Andropogon,* and *Imperata* provide the dominant cover while the scattered trees

Figure 128. A view of the tropical savanna of Africa. Grass, scattered trees, which have picturesque shapes, dry season fires, and numerous species of large mammalian herbivores are unique features of this biome-type. (Photograph by Donald I. Ker, Ker & Downey Safaris Ltd., Nairobi, East Africa.)

are of entirely different species from those of the rain forest. In Africa, the picturesque Acacias, Baobab trees (*Adansonia*), arborescent Euphorbias and palms dot the landscape. Often single species of both grass and trees may be dominant over large areas.

In number and variety, the population of hoofed mammals of the African savanna is unexcelled anywhere else in the world. Antelope (numerous species), wildebeest, zebra and giraffe graze or browse and are sought by lions and other predators in areas where the "big game" has not been replaced by man and his cattle. Insects are most abundant during the wet season when most birds nest, whereas reptiles may be more active during the dry season. Thus, seasons are regulated by rainfall rather than by temperature as in the temperate grasslands.

A view of the African savanna country including the three conspicuous components, namely, grass, scattered trees and mammalian herbivores, is provided by Figure 128. Ecological problems of tropical grasslands are discussed in the UNESCO reports mentioned on page 401, and some of the interesting features of this biome are pictured by Aubert de la Rue, et al. (1957).

Desert biomes

Deserts (Fig. 130) generally occur in regions with less than 10 inches of rainfall, or sometimes in regions with greater rainfall very unevenly distributed. Scarcity of rainfall may be due to: (1) high sub-tropical pressure, as in the Sahara and Australian deserts, (2) geographical position in rain shadows (see Figure 26, page 111), as in the western North American deserts or (3) high altitude, as in Tibetan, Bolivian or Gobi deserts. Most deserts receive some rain during the year and have at least a sparse cover of vegetation, unless edaphic conditions of the substrate happen to be especially unfavorable. Apparently the only absolute deserts where little or no rain falls are those of the central Sahara and north Chili.

Walter (1954) has measured net production of a series of deserts and semi-arid communities which lie along a rainfall gradient in Africa. As shown in Figure 129, the annual production of dry matter was a linear function of rainfall, at least up to 600 cms. (24 inches), illustrating the sharpness with which moisture acts as an overall ("master") limiting factor. Note that annual net primary productivity of true deserts is less than 2,000 kg/hectare (or less than about 0.5 gms/M^2/day).

When deserts are irrigated and water no longer is a limiting factor, the type of soil becomes of prime consideration. Where texture and nutrient content of the soil are favorable, irrigated deserts can be extremely productive because of the large amount of sunlight. However, the cost per pound of food produced may be high due to the high cost of development and maintenance of irrigation systems. Very large volumes of water must flow through the system; otherwise salts may accumulate in the soil (as a result of rapid evaporation rate) and become limiting. Old World deserts are full of ruins of old irrigation systems. In many cases no one knows just what has caused this condition. At least these ruins should warn us that the irrigated desert will not continue to bloom indefinitely without due attention to the basic laws of the ecosystem.

There are three life forms of plants which are adapted to deserts: (1) the annuals which avoid drought by growing only when

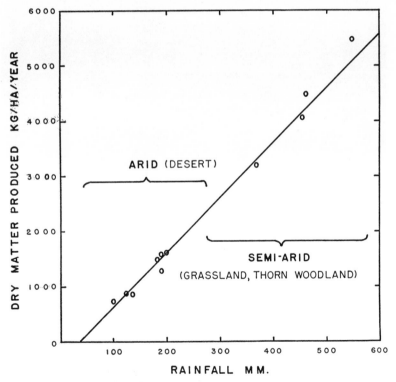

Figure 129. The annual production of dry matter (in kilograms/hectare/year) in a series of arid and semi-arid zones of vegetation which lie along a rainfall gradient in West Africa. (After Walter, 1954.)

Figure 130. Two types of desert in western North America, a "cool" desert in Idaho (above) dominated by sagebrush (*Artemisia*) and a "hot" desert in Arizona (below) dominated by creosote bush (*Larrea*). Note the characteristic growth form of the desert shrub (numerous branches ramifying from ground level) and the rather regular spacing. With equivalent rainfall, the shrubs of the cool desert would tend to be closer together and the herbaceous cover somewhat better developed because of more favorable precipitation/evaporation relationship. (Upper photograph by U. S. Forest Service, lower by R. R. Humphrey.)

there is adequate moisture (see pages 94-95, 372), (2) the succulents, such as the cacti, which store water and (3) the desert shrubs which have numerous branches ramifying from a short basal trunk bearing small, thick leaves that may be shed during the prolonged dry periods. The desert shrub presents very much the same appearance throughout the world even though species may belong to diverse taxa (another striking example of ecological equivalence). As has already been explained (see page 113), adaptation to arid conditions involves the ability to avoid wilting and remain dormant for long periods rather than a marked increase in transpiration efficiency.

From an ecological standpoint it is convenient to distinguish two types of deserts on the basis of temperature, namely, hot deserts and cool deserts. All desert vegetation has a highly characteristic "spaced" distribution in which individual plants are scattered thinly with large bare areas in between (see Figure 130). In some cases, at least, it has been shown that root antibiotics play a part in keeping plants spaced apart (see Bonner, 1950). In any event, spacing reduces competition for a scarce resource; otherwise intense competition for water might result in the death or stunting of all of the plants.*

In North America, the creosote bush (*Larrea*) is a widespread dominant of the southwestern hot desert, and sagebrush (*Artemisia*) is the chief plant over large areas of the more northern cool deserts of the Great Basin (Figure 130). Bur sage (*Franseria*) is also widespread in southern areas whereas at higher altitudes where moisture is a little greater, the giant cactus (Sahuaro) and palo verde are conspicuous components (Figure 131). Eastward, a considerable amount of grass is mixed with desert shrubs to form a desert grassland type; unfortunately the grass has suffered greatly from overgrazing. In the cool deserts, especially on the alkaline soils of the internal drainage regions, saltbushes of the family Chenopodiaceae, such as shadscale (*Atriplex*), hop sage (*Grayia*), winter fat (*Eurotia*) and greasewood (*Sarcobatus*) occupy extensive zones. In fact "chenopods" are widely distributed in arid regions in other parts of the world

* One wonders if mankind might not learn a lesson from the desert, where the relationship between population size and resources is sharply drawn. Certainly, a human culture which allows its density to exceed resources to the extent of intellectual and/or physical stunting of all individuals demonstrates poor adaptation. "Birth control" in the desert is a perfectly natural thing which allows maximum development of individuals.

as well. The sagebrush and shadscale communities have already been described in Chapter 8. The succulent life form, including the cacti and the arborescent Yuccas and Agaves, reaches its greatest development in the Mexican deserts (and in neotropical region), with some species of this type extending into the shrub deserts of Arizona and California, but this life form is unimportant in the cool deserts. In all deserts annual forbs and grasses may make quite a show during brief wet periods. The extensive "bare ground" in deserts is not necessarily free of plants. Mosses, algae and lichens may be present, and in sands and other finely divided soils they may form a stabilizing crust; also the bluegreen algae (often associated with lichens) are of importance as nitrogen-fixers (Shields, et al., 1957).

Desert animals as well as plants are adapted in various ways to lack of water. Reptiles and some insects are "pre-adapted" because of impervious integuments and dry excretions (uric acid and gaunin). Desert insects are "wax-proofed" with substances which remain impermeable at high temperatures (Edney, 1957). While evaporation from respiratory surfaces can not be eliminated, it is reduced to the minimum in insects by the internally invaginated spiracle system. It should be pointed out that the production of metabolic water (from breakdown of carbohydrates), often the only water available, is not in itself an adaptation; it is the conservation of this water that is adaptative, and, as is the case with tenebrionid beetles (a characteristic desert group), the ability to increase production of metabolic water at low humidities (Edney, 1957). Mammals, on the other hand, are not very well adapted as a group (because they excrete urea, which involves the loss of much water), yet certain species have developed remarkable secondary adaptations. These include rodents of the family Heteromyidae, especially the kangaroo rat (*Dipodomys*) and the pocket mouse (*Perognathus*). These animals can live indefinitely on dry seeds and do not require drinking water. They remain in burrows during the day, and conserve water by excreting very concentrated urine and by not using water for temperature regulation. The Schmidt-Nielsens (1949) found that relative humidity in the burrow was 30 to 50 per cent, compared with 0 to 15 per cent in the desert above ground during the daytime. The relative humidity in the desert at night when the animals are above ground was about the same as that in the burrows during the day. Thus, a diel rhythm enables these animals to live in a more favorable environment. Other desert rodents, wood rats (*Neotoma*), for example, are unable to live solely on dry food, but survive in parts of the desert by eating succulent cacti or other plants which store water. In his review of the metabolism of desert mammals Schmidt-Neilsen (1952) points out that these mammals are of two types, those such as the kangeroo rat or Old World Jerboa (*Jaculus*) which do not use water for temperature regulation, and those such as the camel which do. The latter must drink although they can go for long periods on water stored in the body. Birds seem to belong to the later category (Bartholomew, and Dawson, 1953) and probably need at least an occasional drink from dew or other sources; hence birds are most abundant where water or succulent foods are available. Man, of course, is physiologically very poorly adapted to deserts.

The vegetation of the North American deserts has been well described by Shantz (1942), Billings (1951) and many others. In going through the vast amount of literature summarized in the UNESCO reports, one is impressed with the fact that almost all of the information on the deserts of the world is purely descriptive in nature; there is almost nothing known about the actual "workings" of desert ecosystems, that is, the rates of production and consumption, the turnover rates of various populations of plants and animals, the action of limiting factors, environmental hormones, etc. Since microbial decomposers will be sharply limited by dryness, one wonders if this is compensated for by a seemingly large population of rodent herbivores, but we do not even know how much of the annual production is consumed by these forms (or even what the annual production is). As we have stressed throughout this text, one can never understand an ecosystem simply by describing it, no matter how detailed the description and classification of the standing crop may be. Deserts should provide especially favorable sites for functional studies because of the limited number of taxa, the limited stratification and the sharpness of the physical factors. Since man has singularly failed to "understand" the desert, and often runs into troubles when he attempts to irrigate or otherwise modify the desert, studies of this type would be of immense practical importance, especially since

Figure 131. A rather luxuriant "hot" desert near Tuscon, Arizona which includes cholla and barrel cacti (foreground), and giant saguaro cacti and palo verde trees (background), as well as the desert shrubs. This desert is at a higher altitude, and hence has better moisture relations than the creosote bush desert shown in the lower photograph of Figure 130. (U. S. Soil Conservation Service Photo.)

arid and semi-arid (grassland) areas make up such a large portion of the earth's surface.

Chaparral biomes

In mild temperate regions with abundant winter rainfall but dry summers, the climax vegetation consists of trees or shrubs with hard, thick evergreen leaves. Under this heading we are including both the chaparral proper or "coastal chaparral" in which the shrub life-form is predominant (Fig. 132, lower photograph) and the "broad-sclerophyll woodland," which contains scattered trees. A "picture" of the climate of the winter rain region is shown in Figure 28 (page 118). Chaparral communities are extensive in California and Mexico, along the shores of the Mediterranean Sea and along the southern coast of Australia. A large number of plant species may serve as dominants, depending on the region and local conditions. Fire is an important factor which tends to perpetuate shrub dominance at the expense of trees. Thus, the chaparral may be partly, at least, a "fire disclimax," as is the long-leaf pine forest of the southeastern states.

In California, about five to six million acres of slopes and canyons are covered with chaparral. Chamiso (*Adenostoma*) and manzanita (*Arctostaphylos*) are common shrubs which often form dense thickets, and a number of evergreen oaks are characteristic, also, as either shrubs or trees. The rainy or growing season generally extends from November to May. Mule deer and many birds inhabit the chaparral during this period, then move north or to higher altitudes during the hot dry summer. Resident vertebrates are generally small and dull-colored to match the dwarf forest; the small brush rabbits (*Sylvilagus bachmani*), wood rats, chipmunks, lizards, wren-tits, and brown towhees are characteristic. The population density of breeding birds and insects is high as the growing season comes to a close, then decreases as the vegetation dries out in late summer. This is the season when fires may sweep the slopes with incredible swiftness. Following a fire, the chaparral shrubs sprout vigorously with the first rains and may gain maximum size in 15 to 20 years. The role of fire in California chaparral has been reviewed by Sweeney (1956), who reports that fire stimulates the germination of some seeds and is essential to the persistence of certain herbaceous species in the flora. The general structure of the vegetation has been well described by Cooper (1922), while a brief discussion of both plants and animals of the chaparral biome in California is given by Cogswell (1947). (See also Figure 44, page 169.)

Because some of the chaparral slopes are relatively frost-free they are used for orchard culture. The greatest value to man, however, lies in watershed protection. Not only do the steep, loosely consolidated slopes erode easily, but disastrous floods are

Figure 132.   Biome types intermediate between grassland and northern conifer forest. Upper: Piñon-puniper woodland in Arizona; the "pigmy conifers" from a very open, park-like stand. Lower: Chaparral in California. The species appearing in the picture is *Eriodictyon tomentosum*. (U. S. Forest Service Photo.)

propelled into the thickly populated lowlands if the chaparral community does not remain in a healthy condition. Hellmers, Bonner and Kelleher (1955) found that nitrogen, as well as moisture, was a limiting factor; these authors suggested that density of chaparral vegetation on slopes above cities might be increased by nitrogen fertilization.

The chaparral of the winter rain areas of the Mediterranean region is locally called "macchie" while similar vegetation in Australia is called "mellee scrub." In the latter, trees and shrubs of the genus *Eucalyptus* are dominant. It is not surprising that Australian "Eucalypts" do well in California chaparral region where they have been widely introduced and largely replace the native woody vegetation in urban areas.

Piñon-juniper biome

The piñon-juniper woodland, or the "pigmy conifers" (Fig. 132, upper photograph), appear to occupy a sufficiently large area in the interior of the Great Basin and Colorado River regions of Colorado, Utah, Arizona, New Mexico, Nevada, and west-central California and to have a sufficiently distinctive biota to be considered a biome. Or this community type could be considered a subdivision of the northern coniferous forest biome. Moisture is the critical factor, the 10 to 20 inches of unevenly distributed rainfall accounting for the park-like growth of small piñon pines (*Pinus edulis* and *P. monophylla*) and cedars (several species of the genus *Juniperus*) as shown in Figure 132. This community occupies a wide belt between desert or grassland and the heavier coniferous forests of higher altitudes. The piñon "nuts" and cedar berries are important food for animals. The piñon jay, the gray titmouse, and the bush tit are characteristic permanent resident birds, the first two being largely restricted to this biome. For additional information on the pigmy conifers, see Woodbury (1947) and Hardy (1945).

Tropical rain forest biomes

The variety of life perhaps reaches its culmination in the tropical rain forests which occupy low-lying areas near the equator. Rainfall exceeds 80 or 90 inches a year and is distributed over the year, usually with one or more relatively "dry" seasons (5 or less inches per month). If the dry season is too severe (less than 2 inches of rainfall per month) and prolonged, the rain forest gives

A

B

Figure 133. A, An aspect of the African tropical rain forest with festoons of lianas (on the left) and a very bushy undergrowth due to the well-lit gap produced by a watercourse. Mayombe Range (Middle Congo, French Equatorial Africa). (Photograph by E. Aubert de la Rüe.) B, A clearing in

way to the deciduous forest even though the annual rainfall is 80 inches. Rain forests occur in the Amazon and Orinoco basins in South America (the largest continuous mass) on the Central American isthmus, in the Congo, Niger, and Zambezi basins of central and western Africa, in Madagascar, and in the Indo–Malay–Borneo–New Guinea regions. The variation in temperature between winter and summer is less than that between night and day. Seasonal periodicities in breeding and other activities of plants and animals are largely related to variations in rainfall, or regulated by inherent rhythms. For example, some trees of the family Winteracae apparently show continuous growth while other species in the same family show discontinuous growth with formation of rings (Studhalter, 1955). Rain forest birds may also require periods of "rest" since reproduction often exhibits periodicity unrelated to season (Miller, 1955). The suddenness and force of rain showers are unknown in other biomes.

As shown in Figure 133 the rain forest has a characteristic appearance wherever it occurs, even though the floristic composition changes markedly from one geographical point to another. Trees are evergreen, tall (but not the tallest or the largest in the world; trees of a moist temperate coniferous forest are bigger, for example), shallow rooted and often have swollen bases or "flying buttresses." There is a profusion of climbing plants, especially woody lianas, and epiphytes which often hide the outline of the trees. The "strangler figs" and other arborescent epiphytes are especially noteworthy. The striking difference in distribution of life forms in the rain forest as compared with temperate forests is illustrated in Figure 117. The number of species of plants is very large; often there will be more species of trees in a few acres than in the entire flora of Europe. The tropical rain forest is the ultimate in "jungle" growth, although low light intensity results in poor development of herbaceous vegetation on the ground which may actually be bare in spots.

As was discussed in Chapter 3 (page 77), it seems likely that the productivity of the intact rain forest is high so long as there is a rapid cycling of scarce nutrients, etc. When the complex biolog-

---

the tropical rain-forest of Petit Inini in French Guiana. It shows the structure of the forest; the very straight smooth light-colored trunks and the lianas which they support. In the foreground, a plantation of manioc, the roots of which form the staple diet of the native people in the Guianas and Brazil. (Photograph by E. Aubert de la Rüe.)

ical structure of the forest is destroyed, the productivity may drop sharply (as shown by poor crop production on rain forest land) More study of "functional" aspects is needed. It should be em- phasized that although the variety of life is greater than in tem- perate forests, this does not mean that the total biomass or, es- pecially, the productivity is necessarily greater.

Stratification of communities is extremely well developed; a much larger proportion of animals live in the upper layers of the vegetation than is the case in temperate forests where most of life is near the ground level. For example, 31 of 59 species of mam- mals in British Guiana are arboreal and 5 are amphibious, leaving only 23 which are mainly ground dwellers (Haviland, 1927). In addition to the arboreal mammals, chameleons, iguanas, geckos, arboreal snakes, frogs and birds are abundant. Ants and the orthoptera, as well as butterflies and moths, are ecologically im- portant. Symbiosis between animals and ephiphytes is wide- spread. As in the case of the flora, the fauna of the rain forest is incredibly rich in species. For example, in a six square mile area on Barro Colorado, a well studied bit of rain forest in the Panama Canal Zone, there are 20,000 species of insects compared to only a few hundred in all of France. Numerous archaic types of both ani- mals and plants survive in the numerous niches of the unchanging environment. Many scientists feel that the rate of evolutionary change and speciation is especially high in the rain forest which, therefore, has been a source of many species that have invaded more northern communities.

Fruit and termites are staple foods for animals in the tropical forest. One reason why birds are often abundant is that so many of them, such as fruit-eating parakeets, toucans, hornbills, cot- ingas, trogons and birds-of-paradise, are herbivorous. Because the "attics" of the jungle are crowded, many bird nests and insect cocoons are of a hanging type, enabling them to escape from army ants and other predators. Although there are some spec- tacularly bright birds and insects which occupy the more open situations, the vast array of rain-forest animals are inconspicuous and many of them are nocturnal.

When the rain forest is removed it either does not come back, or it comes back very slowly. A secondary forest often develops which includes soft wood trees, such as *Musanga* (Africa), *Cecropia* (America) and *Macoranga* (Malaysia). The secondary forest looks lush but is quite different from the virgin forest, both ecologically and floristically. As we have already indicated, failure to regenerate may be related to nutrient losses; much study is needed. There is urgent need to preserve tracts of rain forest to serve as laboratories for the study of ecology and evolution.

Because of the denseness of the vegetation, it is difficult to photograph the rain forest, except from a water course or clearing (as in Fig. 133). Sanderson (1945) aptly expresses it this way: "The principal difficulty encountered in studying a jungle is that you can never see it. This may sound absurd. An average jungle is about 100 feet tall, and is shaped like a much-flattened

Figure 134.   A dissection of a tropical rain forest in British Honduras. Semi-diagrammatic representation of a plot (140 feet by 15 feet) of tropical rain forest in the wet sere, known locally as "mixed tall cohune." The scale is dramatically demonstrated by the man, 6 feet tall, in halo under banak tree to right.

Trees and tall shrubs: 1, unidentified; 2, wild coffee (*Rinorea guatemalensis*); 3, white copal (*Protium sessiliflorum*); 4, cacho venado (*Eugenia capuli*); 5, waika plum (*Rheedia edulis*); 6, mammee ciruela (*Lucuma* sp.); 7, ironwood (*Dialium guianense*); 8, negrito (*Simaruba glauca*); 9, red copal (*Protium copal*); 10, mountain trumpet (*Cecropia mexicana*); 11, timber sweet (*Nectandra* sp.); 12, unidentified; 13, maya (*Miconia* sp.); 14, banak (*Virola brachycarpa*); 15, matapalo (*Ficus* sp.); 16, kerosene wood (indet.); 17, cohune (*Orbignya cohune*); 18, monkeytail (*Chamaedora* sp., and *Synecanthus* sp.); 19, hone (*Bactris* sp.); 20, capuka (*Geonoma glauca*); 21, tree-fern (indet.). (Sanderson, "Living Treasure," 1945, published by Viking Press.)

and inverted saucer, so that its edges slope down all around to meet the earth. When you enter it you become lost. You can't see the wood for the trees, and you often can't see the trees for the creepers, lianas, and epiphytic green plants that grow all over them. If you fly over a jungle in an airplane, you see even less, for nothing but a gently undulating, bumpy green mat is unfolded beneath you. If you climb a tree, you still do not gain any real conception of the jungle generally, for ants, leaves, humming-birds, and a riot of tangled vegetation obscure the view and bother you. In order, therefore, to find out just how any particular jungle or forest is constituted, it is necessary to dissect it." The results of one of Sanderson's "dissections" is shown in Figure 134. Note that 21 different species of trees were found in an area of less than one-twentieth of an acre; very few of these species are represented by more than two individuals in the sample. In contrast, a temperate forest sample of the same size would likely contain only a few species and not so many "layers." The diagram, of course, does not show the numerous creepers and epiphytes.

Above about 2000 feet elevation the rain forest changes to a cloud forest. The species of plants and animals change and the richness of flora and fauna diminishes. Trees become smaller with more twisted and branched trunks. Lianas and epiphytes, however, remain prominent. Hanging mosses, ferns, lichens and orchids dripping with moisture give the forest its characteristic appearance. Above 6000 to 10,000 feet vegetation is not unlike that of temperate coniferous forest.

For additional information on the rain forest, see Richards (1952) and Bunning (1956). For a beautifully illustrated descriptive ecology of both plants and animals of the rain forest and other tropical biomes, see the book of Aubert de la Rue, Bourliere and Harroy (1957).

Tropical scrub and deciduous forest biomes

Where moisture conditions are intermediate between desert and savanna on one hand and rain forest on the other, tropical scrub or thorn forests and tropical deciduous forests may be found. As shown in Figure 120, these cover very large areas. The key climatic factor is the imperfect distribution of a fairly good total rainfall. Thorn forests, which are often referred to as "the bush" in Africa or Australia and the "Caatinga" in Brazil, contain small hard-wood trees often grotesquely twisted and thorny; leaves are small and are lost during dry seasons. Where the precipitation is greater or more regular a well developed deciduous forest is found, such as the widespread monsoon forests of tropical Asia. Wet and dry seasons of approximately equal length alternate so that the seasonal appearance of "winter" and "summer" is as striking as in a temperate deciduous forest.

Zonation in mountains

The distribution of biotic communities in mountainous regions is complicated, as would be expected in view of the diversity of physical conditions. Major communities generally appear as irregular bands, often with very narrow ecotones (or none, in the sense of a transition community with characteristics of its own; see Chapter 8, Section 8). Small scale maps such as those shown in Figures 121 and 122 are inadequate to bring out this feature. On a given mountain four or five major biomes with many zonal subdivisions may be present (Fig. 135). Consequently there is closer contact between biomes and more interchange of biota between different biomes than occurs in non-mountainous regions.

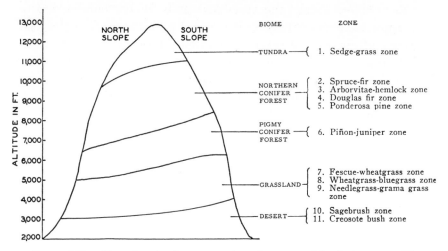

Figure 135. Zonation in the mountains of western North America. The diagram does not refer to a specific mountain but shows general conditions which might be expected in the central Rockies (so-called "intermountain" region) of Utah. North, south, east, or west of this region zonation may be expected to vary somewhat. Thus, the creosote bush and the piñon-juniper zone are absent northward and eastward. Eastward an oak-mountain mahogany zone or westward various zones in the chaparral biome occur between the grassland and the northern conifer forest. (Diagram modified from Woodbury, 1945; zone data from Daubenmire, 1946.)

On the other hand, similar communities are more isolated in the mountains since mountain ranges are rarely continuous. In general, many species which are characteristic of a biome in its broad, non-mountainous phase are also characteristic of the belt-like extensions in the mountains. As a result of isolation and topographic differences many other species are unique to the mountain communities. (See Bliss, 1956, for a comparison of alpine and arctic tundra.)

Importance of the historical approach

It should be emphasized that the biome classification as outlined and illustrated in the previous pages is based on the *potential* conditions which result from natural forces that are now operating in different parts of the world. Such a classification provides a point of reference for evaluating man's influence on the environment. Only if we know something of the natural potentialities and limiting factors can we determine best usage. Again we come back to the simple mathematical concept of constants and variables (Chapter 6). Therefore, it is important to preserve samples of natural communities in each biome (the constant) for comparison with modified areas (the variables) as is further emphasized in Chapter 12, Section 1. Also, it is equally important that the past history of an area be carefully studied. Malin (1953) points out that "casual or random excursions into historical material to find data that appear to fit a preconceived frame of reference, or to serve a particular purpose," are to be avoided. Historical research in ecology must be conducted with an open mind and without a preconceived goal if we are to fully understand the biotic communities as we find them today.

III · Applied ecology

Introduction

Ecology has many applications which contribute to the well-being of human society. We have made a special point to cite practical applications as illustrations for many of the basic principles outlined in Part I. As stated in the Preface, the applied worker learns most of the needed details in the actual practice of his profession or from consulting books and papers dealing with the particular specialty. A detailed discussion of applications, therefore, is beyond the scope of this volume. Nevertheless, it is instructive to list a few of the applied fields, emphasizing the principles involved. This listing will also give the beginning student some idea of the professional opportunities open to the trained ecologist.

Modern human society is depending more and more on the technical skills of its trained persons. However, there is great danger in over-specialization, since the work of one specialist may counteract that of another; too many cooks may ruin the pie, as it were. This can be avoided if we make certain that special applications are based on sound principles, and that applied workers first become thoroughly grounded in the principles of ecology.

In addition to the positive contribution, ecology can also provide a valuable protective function in assembling data and principles which will prevent man from destroying his own environment (and thus himself) in his enthusiasm for the use of new-found powers. Since the first edition of this book was written, the atomic age has made a dramatic appearance, creating a whole new set of ecological possibilities, and thereby a whole new chapter in this revised edition!

12 • Applications: natural resources

1. Conservation of natural resources in general

Conservation in the broadest sense is probably the most important application of ecology. Unfortunately, the term "conservation" suggests "hoarding," as if the idea were simply to ration static supplies so that there would be some left for the future. The aim of good conservation is to insure a continuous yield of useful plants, animals, and materials, by establishing a balanced cycle of harvest and renewal. Thus, a "no fishing" sign on a pond may not be as good conservation as a management plan which allows for removal of several hundred pounds of fish per acre year after year. The principle of the ecosystem, therefore, is the basic and most important principle underlying conservation (see Chapter 2, Section 1).

It is customary to divide natural resources into two categories: renewable and non-renewable. Although it is true that coal, iron, and oil deposits are not renewable in the same sense as forests or fish, nevertheless nitrogen, iron, and energy sources are renewable just as much as living resources. Man need never lack vital materials so long as the biogeochemical cycles operate in such a way that materials as well as organisms are "reassembled" as fast they are "dispersed" (see Chapter 2, Section 3).

Although "hoarding" may not be the long-time aim of good conservation, there are instances in which complete restriction of use constitutes good conservation. The setting aside of natural areas for study and esthetic enjoyment is an example. With the increase in human population, it becomes more important that adequate

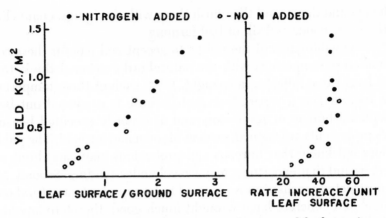

Figure 136. Relationship between net production and leaf area in agricultural crops. Where nutrients and water are non-limiting, the yield tends to be proportional to the leaf surface exposed per square meter ground surface. (After Watson in Milthrope, 1956.)

production rate is as high as that in the more fertile natural communities. As indicated in Chapter 3, there seems to be little hope of increasing photosynthetic efficiency of large scale field crops, but much could be done to prolong the period of maximum production, as nature often does in naturally adapted ecosystems. It has been generally found that the yield of field crops is more dependent on the total photosynthetic surface than on the rate of carbon assimilation itself (Milthrope, 1956). As shown in Figure 136, the yield of crop plants increases with an increase of leaf surface per unit of ground surface up to a ratio of about 3 (that is, leaf surface 3 times the area of ground covered by the crop); at the higher yields (when nutrients are non-limiting), the rate of dry matter increase per unit leaf surface tends to be constant. Thus, crops which leaf out quickly might increase the period of maximum production, as might also a system of mixed species each adapted to a different part of the season (as in a natural grassland which contains both "cool season" and "warm season" species). Other possibilities are suggested by the ecological approach.

Azzi (1956) has pointed out that by stressing the limiting factor approach, "agricultural ecology" can fill a gap between the work of the soil scientist and the agronomist. He summarizes a large volume of research which seeks to determine the specific factors and their interaction which are limiting at different stages in the life cycle of the plant. Often it is found that the critical factor at one stage is quite different from the critical factor at another stage.

The chemical control of insects, although primarily an entomo-
logical and chemical problem, also enters the realm of ecology
since organisms other than the intended victim may be affected.
The ecologist must sometimes put a damper on the enthusiasm
of the chemist and the chemical engineer who can synthesize new
poisons and develop effective methods of application faster than
the total effects in nature can be determined. This is especially
true when poisons are to be used in complex ecosystems such as
orchards, forests, and marshes. It is one thing to apply an insecticide to a crop field where the situation is well known and under
control; it is quite a different thing to spray a forest without any
knowledge of the effect the poison might have on natural control
mechanisms. In a number of well established cases the use of insecticides has "backfired," because of the destruction also of useful
organisms such as honeybees (which pollinate many fruit trees
and crops) and beneficial insect parasites. In some cases the pest
increased in abundance the year after application because of the
reduction in natural density-dependent control exerted by parasites. In other cases, a reduction in numbers of a pest has resulted
in the increase in numbers of another pest which is more resistant
to the insecticide. In many cases, mites, which were held in check
by the normal insect population (either through competition or
predation or both), have increased in destructiveness when the
insect population was reduced by sprays. As a result of research
during the past 10 years, the ecology of DDT is now fairly well
known (for a convenient summary, see Hoffmann and Linduska,
1949). Next to insects, fish and amphibians are most vulnerable:
birds and mammals are more tolerant to direct poisoning. We
know that, in general, DDT applied to forests or orchards at the
rate of 1 pound per acre and added to water at the rate of 0.1
pound per acre may effectively control certain foliage pests and
mosquito larvae without killing useful birds and fish. However,
increasing the application five or ten fold may seriously reduce the
population of useful animals. During the time these facts were
being obtained, numerous new and more powerful insecticides
have been developed, many of which are now being used without
adequate knowledge of their total effects. One of these is Dieldrin
which is several times more toxic to birds and mammals than
DDT, yet is being used over very large areas at the rate of two
pounds or more per acre. Dieldrin remains active in the soil for a

long time and thus may effect population attributes even if the individuals are not killed outright. DDT and Dieldrin belong to the class of insecticides called "chlorinated hydrocarbons," all of which are chemically stable and remain poisonous for a long time. Another group are known as "organic phosphates," of which malathion and parathion are examples. These break down and lose potency quickly, but some types are extremely poisonous, at least for a brief period. Here is a field of study which needs the increased attention of the applied ecologist. For additional information see Stickel and Springer (1957), Springer (1956), Rudd and Genelly (1956).

In addition to the killing of beneficial organisms, excessive use of insecticides is creating other problems such as toxic residues in soil and human foods, off flavors in foods, and the development of resistance by pests themselves. Clifford (1957) reports that 60 per cent of market milk samples contained residues of chlorinated pesticides; these were mostly tracer amounts but some samples contained as much as 1.5 ppm, enough to kill DDT susceptible flies. As it becomes apparent that chemical control of pests can not be the only answer, a renewed interest in biological control is developing. It is clear that biological control can not be effective in intensive agriculture where crop has a high unit value, but there are excellent possibilities for biological control or combination of biological and chemical control in orchards, forage crops and others where unit value is lower. There have been many examples where the introduction of a parasite has been effective, especially in the case of introduced pests. Two classic examples are the control of the cottony-cushion scale (*Icerya*) by the lady beetle (*Rodolia*) and the control of prickly pear cactus (*Opuntia*) in Australia by the introduced moth *Cactoblastis cactorum*. Recently, control of a weed (*Hypericum perforatum*) in western U.S. rangeland has been effected by a combination of two beetles, one which attacks the foliage and one which attacks the roots (Holloway, 1957; Huffaker, 1957). Huffaker points out that insects which consume only a part of their hosts are superior to predators in effecting long term control, and this jibes well with the population theory outlined in Chapter 7. For a general review of biological control of insects see Clausen (1956). Finally, it should be emphasized that biological control also includes the avoidance of unnecessary introduction of new pests, crop rotation, soil conservation and other measures which maintain a varied and healthy ecosystem in which population eruptions of pests are less likely to occur. In the long run this is probably the most important "biological control" of all (Recall our discussion of homeostasis in the ecosystem in Chapter 2).

The soil conservation movement in the United States, following as it has (and none too soon) an era of widespread destructive exploitation by one-crop systems, is based on the sound principle of the ecosystem and of the cyclic use and renewal of the soil. The soil conservation program is also an outstanding example of co-operation between local people and the Federal government. In each of the soil conservation districts the program is run by the local people with technical help but not dictation from the central government.

Forestry is definitely recognized as a field of applied ecology, as indicated by the fact that Forestry schools include ecology in the basic curriculum. Ecological succession (see Chapter 8, Section 4) and the concepts of climatic climax and edaphic climax (see Chapter 8, Section 5; Figure 77) are basic to practical forestry. In some regions the valuable commercial trees are climax, and the problem is to speed the return of climax following harvest. In other regions the valuable species are not climax, and the problem is to arrest succession and maintain the desired forest community. Cutting procedures, artificial planting, fire (see Chapter 4, Section 5, Paragraph 9) and chemicals are all tools which have been tried, but many of the problems remain unsolved. The hazards of severe insect damage in pure stands, apparently resulting from the absence of effective density-dependent insect mortality, have been discussed (page 196; see also Graham, 1951). Attempts are now being made to increase the primary productivity of forest lands by fertilization; this offers possibilities for future research. Nutrient cycles in forest soils is an especially needy field of research.

The ratio of harvest to growth is very different in different parts of the U.S.A. In the west, harvest (about 25 billion board feet per year) is double annual growth, but this is not necessarily bad since most of the timber is from old forests where net production is naturally very low (annual growth balanced by mortality and decay). As old forests are gradually replaced by younger ones, the aim is to manage the latter on a continuous yield basis. In the south and east, where most of the cut is from young forests, growth more nearly balances the harvest.

Figure 137. Land-use classification. See text for explanation. (U. S. Soil Conservation Service Photo.)

3. Land use

When the human population of an area is small, poor land use may affect only the people who are guilty of bad judgment. As the population increases, however, everyone suffers when land is improperly used, not only because of decreased food production but because everyone eventually pays for rehabilitation. For example, if grasslands in regions of low rainfall are plowed up and planted to wheat (poor land use), a "dust bowl" or temporary desert will sooner or later be the result. Rehabilitation is expensive, and all of us as taxpayers will have to pay. If the grass cover is maintained and moderately grazed (good land use), no dust bowl will be likely to develop. Land use is thus everybody's business, and land-use science is one of the most important applications of ecology.

To simplify land use to the point where everyone can understand the principles and apply them, land managers have established a classification, as shown pictorially in Figure 137. The classification is based on natural ecological features such as soil, slope, and natural biotic community. Each land type has definite uses which can be sustained without loss of productivity. Thus, types I and II can be continuously cultivated with only simple precautions such as crop rotations and strip cropping, whereas types III and IV require increasing restriction for maintenance. Land is classed as type I if it is highly suited to cultivation by virtue of favorable physical, chemical, and biological characteristics. It must be level or gently sloping, not subject to erosion, neither stony nor with a permanently high water table, and capable of supplying sufficient moisture and plant nutrients for moderate to high yields. Class III and class IV land, on the other hand, is subject to erosion or loss of fertility when cultivated unless intensive precautions are taken (complex terraces, long rotations, and minimum use for "row crops"). Types V through VII are not suitable for cultivation and should be used for permanent pasture or forest; type VIII is productive only in its natural state as a habitat for game and fur-bearers, etc. Fortunately, misused lands often can be rehabilitated by converting to proper use, provided deterioration has not gone too far (see Figure 4). Regeneration may be speeded up by special mechanical and biological procedures. However, it is much more sensible to avoid misuse in the first place.

For good reading in the field of land use, see Sears' "Deserts on the March" (1935) and Graham's "Natural Principles of Land Use" (1944).

4. Wildlife management

While the expression "wildlife" would seem to be a broad one, covering any or all non-cultivated and non-domesticated life, it actually is largely used with reference to game and fur-bearing vertebrates, and to the plants and lesser animals which interact directly with the game species. Even fish, which are often "wild," are excluded from the wildlife category and treated under other headings. As we shall note later, there is some reason for this separation, since ecological principles of major importance in conservation of game and fish are somewhat different.

Wildlife management is a field of applied ecology which ranks high in the public interest. In recent years it has become a well established profession in America, attracting many young men with a love for the out-of-doors. Numbers of "wildlife technicians" are trained by the land-grant colleges, some of which have established special research and teaching units in cooperation with the State and Federal governments.

Wildlife management is concerned not only with game production on type VIII land which is not suitable for anything else, but also with game "crops" which may also be produced on more productive land being used primarily for agriculture or forestry.

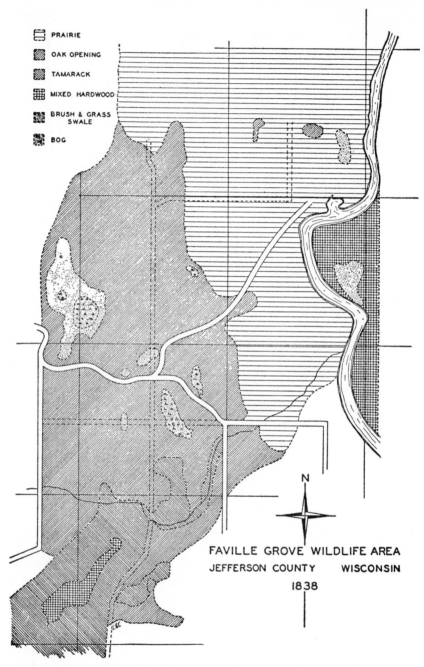

Figure 138. A prairie–forest ecotone in Wisconsin; the Faville Grove land-scape as it appeared to the first white settlers, in 1838. Compare Figure 139. (After Hawkins, 1940.) See also Table 23.

Table 23. *Breeding status of game and shore birds at or near Fayville Grove, Wisconsin, in 1838, when the first white settlers arrived, compared with a century later* (See Figures 138-139) [*]

Species	Breeding status 1838	1938	Remarks
Quail	Uncommon	Uncommon	Occasional periods of abundance in between; 1 bird per 40 acres in 1938
Pheasant	None	Common	First birds seen locally about 1930; 1 bird per 10 acres in 1937
Ruffed grouse	Common	None	A single "wanderer" seen in winter of 1936–37
Hungarian partridge	None	Common	First bird seen locally about 1922; 1 bird per 8 acres in 1937
Prairie chicken	Abundant	Rare	Steady decline since 1900; 26 birds counted in 1937
Canada goose	Irregular Uncommon	None	Last nested locally about 1870
Mallard	Common	Regular Uncommon	1 or 2 pairs have attempted to nest at Faville Grove each of last 3 years
Blue-winged teal	Common	Regular Uncommon	3 nests found in 1937 (about average for recent years)
Wood duck	Common	None	Most common breeding duck in 1880
Wilson's snipe	Common	Irregular Rare	One nest found in 1936
Woodcock	Regular Uncommon	Prob. irreg.	Young birds seen on area in July; may have been migrants
Upland plover	Common	Common	25 birds per section in 1938; 19 nests found in 1937 at Faville Grove. 25 nests found in 1938

[*] Data from Hawkins (1940).

The principle of ecological succession (see Chapter 8, Section 4) is basic since each game species is best adapted to a particular seral stage. Likewise all the principles of population ecology are applicable to game species (see Chapters 6 and 7). The "edge effect" idea is also important (see Chapter 8, Section 8), not only because many game species are "edge" species, but because in intensively farmed regions the "edges" are the only available habitat for wildlife. The fact that man tends to create a "forest edge" habitat is well illustrated in Figures 138 and 139. When the original prairie and forest were broken up into numerous very small patches and the marshes drained, a few species of the original game and shore birds were able to adapt to the change (Table 23). Species not adapted to the "edge" condition decreased or dis-

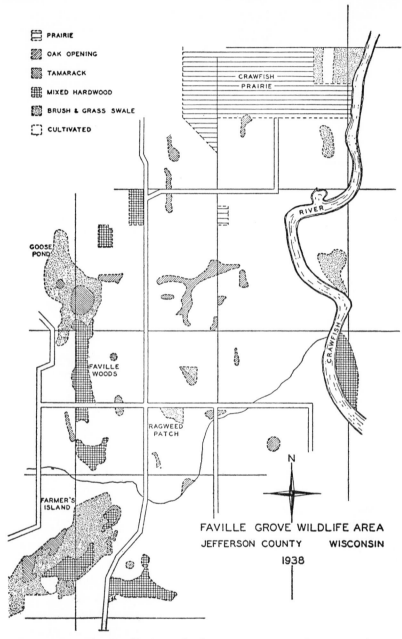

PRAIRIE

OAK OPENING

TAMARACK

MIXED HARDWOOD

BRUSH & GRASS SWALE

CULTIVATED

CRAWFISH
PRAIRIE

RIVER

GOOSE
POND

CRAWFISH

FAVILLE
WOODS

RAGWEED
PATCH

N

FARMER'S
ISLAND

FAVILLE GROVE WILDLIFE AREA

JEFFERSON COUNTY   WISCONSIN

1938

Figure 139.   The Faville Grove landscape as it appeared in 1938, after 100 years of agricultural development. Forest and original prairie are reduced to small patches, with much "edge." (After Hawkins, 1940.) See also Table 23.

appeared, to be replaced by other species which were able to survive in the new habitat. Thus, prairie chickens and ruffed grouse were replaced by introduced pheasants and Hungarian partridges, species which had become adapted to intensively farmed areas of Europe.

This brings us to the point that efforts to foster and increase game population have been generally directed along three major lines: (1) preservation of breeding stock by means of game laws restricting the harvest, etc.; (2) artificial stocking; and (3) habitat improvement. When game begins to get scarce, people generally think and act in the order listed above, which is sometimes unfortunate, since the third item is often more important than the first two. If suitable habitat is lacking (as indicated above), protection or stocking is useless.

Although the need for preserving a number of organisms as a source for offspring is obvious, regulation of harvest is often difficult in practice. Often the game manager does not have good data on population density on which to base hunting regulations. Improvement of census methods (see Chapter 6, Section 2) is constantly needed. Another difficulty is that fixed bag limits result in more or less density-independent mortality, whereas density-dependent mortality is more effective in insuring a stable population, as has been indicated (Chapter 6, Section 11). For example, in the absence of natural predators or parasites, deer populations subjected to constant but moderate hunting pressure tend to exceed the carrying capacity of the habitat and may seriously injure the forest vegetation (see Chapter 7, Section 3). Thus, if hunting pressure could be light when the population is low but increase percentagewise when the population increases, destructive "irruptions" perhaps could be prevented. In some European game preserves a density-dependent system of this sort is used; hunting is stopped when a prescribed number of individuals are taken, the number varying with the total size of the population (Leopold, 1936).

If game animals of a given species are present in a locality, artificial stocking of the species is generally futile, as most state game departments have discovered by sad experience. For example, thousands of Mexican quail were introduced at considerable expense in all parts of the southeast (where ample stocks of the same species were already present), with the total result exactly zero (Stoddard, 1932). That this must be the case is evident

Figure 140. An "artificial" forest edge, produced by planting lespedezas (legumes) of two heights, designed to provide habitat and food for quail and other wildlife on farms in the southeastern United States. A strip of sericea lespedeza 10 feet wide is planted next to the cultivated field, then four rows of bicolor lespedeza shrubs. (U. S. Soil Conservation Service Photo.)

from principles of population growth form and carrying capacity (see Chapter 6, Section 8, and also Section 10). Stocking, therefore, is generally useful only in a new environment or in one from which the species in question has previously been exterminated, or perhaps where hunting pressure is very great.

Next to stocking, probably the least understood phase of game management involves predator-prey relationships. Often artificial control of predators is not only ineffective but harmful to the game population or its habitat (as in the case of deer, see page 239). At other times, some control of predators may be advisable. Much more fundamental work is needed; certainly predator control should not be undertaken unless careful study of the entire population dynamics has been made.

Assuming a reasonable protection of the breeding stock and no unusual predator or parasite problem, the size of game populations will depend on the amount of habitat and the primary productivity of that habitat. Thus, habitat improvement is the most effective method of increasing game, although possibilities vary with the region. Success in this venture requires much study and experimentation and often does not bring the quick results the sportsman desires. In the long run, however, it is the only sound way to game abundance. Figure 140 illustrates only one of many methods of habitat improvement; in this case an effective forest edge is created by planting legumes of two heights. Not only do these plants enrich the soil and provide cover, but their seeds provide food for quail, etc. Such methods will prove effective where cover and food are limiting factors but not where there is plenty of natural cover and food; in the latter case efforts are best directed toward improvement or enlargement of the natural environment in other ways. The use of controlled burning in this connection has been mentioned (see Chapter 4, page 139). In some cases increase in game has been produced by artificial feeding (as is practiced in oriental fish culture, page 78), but the desirability of this has been questioned. Standard American texts in wildlife management are Leopold (1933) and Trippensee (1948).

We may well close this brief review with a comment on the introduction of exotics, that is, of species not native to the region. Since species introduced into a new environment often either fail entirely or succeed so well that they become pests (rabbits in Australia, for example), all introductions are to be considered with extreme care. In general, if there is a suitable species native to the region, it is better to concentrate on management of this species rather than to attempt to introduce a substitute. If, on the other hand, the environment has been so changed by man that native forms are unable to survive, introduction of a species adapted to the new environment may be in order. Thus, when grain fields replaced grasslands in the middle west, there was little hope of maintaining a large population of prairie chickens. Introduction of pheasants, which are adapted to grain field habitat, has served a useful purpose in this area. The use of climographs in this connection has been discussed, as has also the importance of selecting an adapted ecotype (pages 119-122). For further discussion of wildlife introductions see King (1942) and Levi (1952).

5. Pond management

The principles of pond management have been well covered in Chapter 3 and Chapter 9, Section 6). Management consists of increasing primary productivity, usually by applying fertilizers, and establishing a fish population of specific composition best suited

Table 24.   *Results of experiments with various stocking combinations in fertilized Alabama ponds**

Stocking Largemouth bass with other species Number/Acre	Average annual catch Pounds/Acre	Years in each experiment	Fish recovered on draining Pounds/Acre
100 bass	42.2	4	32.9
1500 green sunfish + 100 bass	74.9	2	91.1
1500 shellcrackers + 150 bass	188.6	3	161.1
750 shellcrackers + 750 bluegills + 150 bass	214.5	3	197.2
1500 bluegills + 150 bass	239.4	3	371.3
1500 bluegills + 25 white crappie + 150 bass	282.2	3	301.7

* Data from Swingle (1952).

to the type of harvest desired. The species used will depend on the locality and whether food or sport is of primary concern. Herbivorous species, of course, yield the most food. In the European plan of fish farming, a system of "fallowing" is effective in maintaining high productivity (Neess, 1946). At intervals ponds are drained and crops planted; fertility is greatly increased on reflooding. For sport fishing a predator–prey combination of two or more species has proved most satisfactory. There has been much trial-and-error experimentation to determine the best combinations and stocking ratios. Table 24 shows results of Swingle's (1952) extensive experiments which indicate that a bass–bluegill population established by a 1 to 10 stocking ratio is best for the southeastern United States. Other combinations work better in other regions. There is much yet to be learned about "why" various combinations behave the way they do. Despite careful planning, prey species often get ahead of the predator species, resulting in crowding, stunting, and poor sport fishing. For this reason small ponds are best, because they can be easily drained and the cycle started again if they get out of "balance." The best fishing occurs during the "rising" phase of the population growth curve (see Figure 48, page 184). In general, it is not likely that a pond can be over-fished by hook and line, because of the high natality and rapid growth rate of fish; "under-fishing," with consequent crowding and stunting of growth, is more likely.

At the present time, the least known aspect of pond management involves what happens in the food chain between the application of a fertilizer and the population interaction of the fish. The results of overfertilization were discussed on page 96. In general a fertilizer which is released slowly is better than one which merely creates a bloom that may have little effect (or perhaps a detrimental effect) on the slow growing fish population. Almost nothing is known about what kinds of algae are most efficiently transformed into fish flesh (see Mortimer and Hickling, 1954, for a review of pond fertilizer problems).

6. Impoundments

Large impoundments are an increasingly important feature of the landscape (see Chapter 9, Section 5). One of the difficulties with impoundments is that they usually are expected to serve several purposes, and it would be too much to expect that all purposes could be served with maximum efficiency as a result of any one type of management. Thus, if power or large scale irrigation is of primary concern, large, main-stream reservoirs may be best. If flood control is desired, then there must be periodic "drawdowns," so that the lake can absorb flood waters; this may reduce the power output and will affect recreational uses. For preventing erosion, small headwaters impoundments may be best. The fallacies of thinking *only* in terms of large, expensive main-stream impoundments have been mentioned (Chapter 4). In this connection, the following comparison of a big dam versus a series of small dams located on the tributaries is instructive (Table 25). These proposals were prepared independently by two different agencies for the same region. It is clear that, of the plans detailed here, the multiple impoundment plan costs much less, destroys less productive farm land, impounds an equal volume of water, and would be

Table 25. *Comparison of a large main-stream reservoir plan with an alternate plan for smaller headwaters reservoirs proposed for the same watershed**

	Main-stream reservoir plan	Multiple head-waters reservoir plan
Number of reservoirs	1	34
Drainage area, sq. miles	195	190
Flood storage, acre feet	52,000	59,100
Surface water area for recreation, acres	1,950	2,100
Flood pool, acres	3,650	5,100
Bottoms inundated, acres	1,850	1,600
Bottoms protected, acres	3,371	8,080
Total cost	$6,000,000	$1,983,000

* Data from Peterson (1952).

more effective in soil conservation and flood control. It would, however, not create as much electric power.

Fish management is much more difficult in impoundments than in ponds because (1) it is not practical to use inorganic fertilizers (area too large and too much fertilizer would be carried out of the lake), and (2) it is difficult to control the composition of the fish population, since various species have access through the streams entering the impoundment. Generally, fishing is excellent in impoundments for the first few years, because accumulated organic matter in the watershed results in temporary high productivity. Also, the fish population is in the active growth stage. Later, however, fishing may become disappointing because of a decrease in productivity and the tendency for natural succession (see Chapter 8, Section 4) to lead from game fish to less desirable "rough" fish. Commercial harvest of "rough" fish is a possibility. Perhaps the most promising method of maintaining productivity can be combined with flood-control procedures as follows. During the "drawdown" periods the exposed areas can be planted in crops which "extract" minerals from the soils that were unavailable to the aquatic algae. When the shore zone is reflooded, the decay of the crops quickly releases nutrients. This plan, of course, is based on the same principle as the pond "fallowing" system mentioned in the preceding section. For a summary of fish management in impoundments, see Wood (1951). For additional information of the "big dam vs. little dam" controversy see Leopold and Maddock, 1954.

7. Stream pollution

The reasons why streams are especially sensitive to pollution have been indicated (see Chapter 9, Section 7). Broadly speaking, there are three types of pollution: (1) industrial or chemical pollution, involving discharge into streams of toxic substances or of organic industrial by-products which reduce oxygen supply; (2) domestic pollution, involving sewage and other organic materials which reduce oxygen and create septic conditions; and (3) soil pollution resulting from excessive erosion of the watershed. There is often little excuse for the first type of pollution since the chemicals released often may be used profitably if reclaimed. Progressive industrial companies hire aquatic ecologists and engineers to help them prevent pollution, since these companies know that prevention of pollution is profitable in the long run to themselves

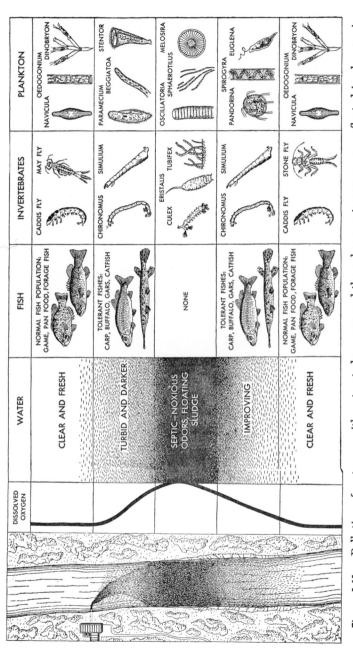

Figure 141. Pollution of a stream with untreated sewage and the subsequent recovery as reflected in changes in the biotic community. As the oxygen dissolved in the water decreases (curve to the left), fishes disappear and only organisms able to obtain oxygen from the surface (as in Culex mosquito larvae) or those which are tolerant of low oxygen concentration are found in zone of maximum organic decomposition. When bacteria have reduced all of the discharged material the stream returns to normal. (After Eliassen, Scientific American, Vol. 186, No. 3, March, 1952.)

as well as to the public at large. Domestic pollution can exert a desirable fertilizing effect if the "load" is reduced by effective treatment before discharge into the stream. Excessive silt in streams resulting from poor land use has undesirable effects and, therefore, is a form of pollution. Langlois (1945), for example, has indicated that in Lake Erie beds of aquatic vegetation, which were important fish-spawning grounds, have been literally smothered by river silt.

Pollution may be detected and measured (1) by chemical tests of the water, (2) by the presence of specific "indicator" organisms, such as coliform bacteria, which are present in sewage, or (3) by the effect on the aquatic community as a whole. Chemical tests may be broadly classified under two heads: (1) tests for specific pollutant substances, and (2) tests to determine the amount of oxygen present in a sample or the amount of oxygen that can be consumed by the oxidizable material present. The most frequently used test in the latter category is the 5-day "Biochemical Oxygen Demand," or "B.O.D.," test, in which a water sample is incubated in the dark at 20° C for five days and the amount of oxygen consumed is determined from the amounts present at the beginning and at the end of the incubation period. (See "Standard Methods for the Examination of Water and Sewage," American Public Health Association, New York, 1946.) Chemical tests are sometimes not satisfactory for detecting industrial pollution because the discharge of pollutants is often periodic; water in the stream might be quite normal between periods of discharge. The effect on organisms, however, is more prolonged, hence they may be better "measures." Figure 141 illustrates some of the changes in the composition of stream communities which occur as the result of sewage discharge.

Patrick (1949) has developed and used extensively a method which is based on the effect on community structure rather than the presence or absence of particular species. This method is dependent on the interaction of the principle of limits of tolerance (see Chapter 4, Section 2) and the principle of competition (see Chapter 7, Section 2). When oxygen, for example, is reduced as a result of pollution, the number of species and individuals in groups which are not tolerant is greatly reduced. On the other hand, the number of species, as well as the number of individuals, of tolerant groups may increase in the absence of competition from the eliminated species, especially if potential productivity remains unchanged or is increased (as by organic discharge). If

pollution exerts severe limiting effects, then all organisms are reduced. Since it is generally easier to determine the approximate
number of common species present than to measure the population density, Patrick bases her method entirely on the number of
species present. As shown in Figure 142, a healthy stream community contains a moderate number of species of all ecological
groups present in the region (the 100 per cent level in the diagram
represents the average number of species in a series of normal,
unpolluted stations). Where pollution is severe, many groups are
absent, and even tolerant species are reduced. In moderately
polluted stations the number of species of tolerant groups is increased more or less in proportion to the reduction in the number
of species in non-tolerant groups. This provides a sensitive method
which might detect pollution where chemical tests or indicator
species might fail to show anything.

8. Marine fisheries

As indicated in Figure 18 (page 75), the primary productivity of
coastal waters compares favorably with that of land and fresh
water; yet, as shown in Table 9 (page 78), man's harvest from the
ocean is very low. Thus, only about half a pound of fish per acre is
harvested from the oceans as a whole and only about 15 pounds in
the most favorable neritic areas, compared with hundreds of
pounds of beef or carp harvested per acre from good pastures or
ponds. Unless man consumes algae directly, it is probable that the
harvest from the sea cannot equal that of land on a per acre basis
for two reasons: (1) seafood items such as fish, oysters, and shrimp
are secondary or tertiary consumers and therefore "higher on the
ecological pyramid" than cattle or carp (see Chapter 4, Section 3),
and (2) the food energy fixed by algae is consumed by a wide
variety of animals, many of which are not harvestable or edible.
Nevertheless, it is probable that the oceans contain large harvestable food reserves which are not now being used by man.

Taylor (1951) has made an excellent analysis of marine fisheries resources. He points out that the sea fertilizes itself and requires no labor in cultivation and thus has advantages over land
even if the yield per acre is less. Since most marine commercial
fish have a high potential natality rate (millions of eggs per
female in many cases), the size of the breeding stock is less important than environmental condition during development of eggs
and larvae in determining population size (Merriman, 1949). The

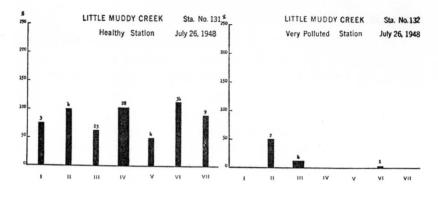

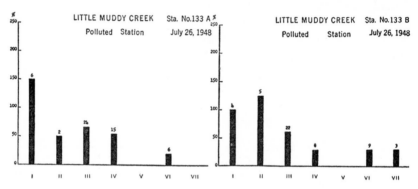

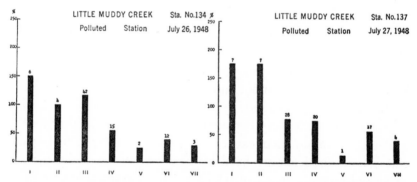

Figure 142. A method of measurement of stream conditions based on community composition as illustrated by a comparison of normal ("healthy"), polluted, and very polluted stations on the same Pennsylvania stream. One hundred per cent on the scale represents the average number of species in a series of healthy stations, each bar comprising a specific ecological group, as follows: I, blue-green algae and certain green algae; II, oligochaetes, leeches, and pulmonate snails; III, protozoa; IV, diatoms, red algae, and most green algae; V, most rotifers, clams, prosobranch snails, and triclad worms; VI, insect larvae and crustaceans; VII, fish. Under conditions of pollution the number of species in tolerant groups I to IV remains the same or increases, whereas species in groups V to VII decrease. Under extreme pollution all groups decrease with only a total of half a dozen species or less being present. (After Patrick, 1949.)

Page 442

phenomenon of the dominant age class has been illustrated (Fig. 46). Conservation effort should be directed toward harvesting fish at optimum size for greatest yield on a continuous year after year basis. While overfishing is not likely to exterminate a commercial species, it can and does reduce the biomass harvested to the point of poor return. The total biomass of a brood is small the first year and increases each year as long as the increase in growth of individuals is greater than the loss from natural mortality (see Table 11, example V-1); sooner or later an age is reached when natural mortality reduces the total weight of the age class (even though individual fish may still be increasing in size). Theoretically, it would be best to harvest all fish at the age of maximum brood weight. Actually, such great selectivity is impractical, but it can be approached by regulation of net size and fishing rate or pressure (see Russell, 1942).

Although larger sized fish are generally more valuable, especially to the sports fisherman, it sometimes proves commercially more feasible to harvest fish in small sizes. Thus, the herring off the coast of Maine are harvested as "sardines" (under 9 inches in length), whereas in the North Sea larger individuals of the same species comprise the principal harvest.

Conservation of oysters, clams, shrimp, lobster, etc. (these, of course, are not "fish," but are commercially considered under the heading of marine fisheries) involves somewhat different problems. The habitat of this group is often limited in area, and the organisms often have narrow limits of tolerance to certain environmental factors, especially at critical life history stages. Each species has its own problems; we need to cite only one case as an illustration.

Oysters appear to be stenophagic. The delicate food-gathering apparatus can take only certain sized phytoplankton or organic detritus. Pollution, fertilization, or any other factor which might change the type of phytoplankton in the estuarine waters may eliminate the oyster (see page 96). Oysters have high biotic potentials, as do marine fish, and might be expected to recover quickly (assuming the environment remains suitable) when the population is reduced by man; however, this has not proved to be the case. Oyster beds depleted by over-exploitation have not rejuvenated even when no longer "fished." This is due, partly at least, to the reduction in attachment surfaces and number of larvae as well as vulnerability of young oysters to predators. This seems to be a clear illustration of Allee's principle (see Chapter 6, Section 14), that is, the species does not thrive unless the adult population density remains at a certain level, a high level in this case. Below a minimum density, the population will be slow to recover or may fail entirely unless man can help out in some way. Rehabilitation has been successfully accomplished by a system of oyster "farming" which involves providing artificial sites for larval attachment. After the larvae (called "spat") have "set" they may be moved to favorable feeding waters for "fattening" even though no natural "setting" could occur in such waters! As with all "farming," diseases, parasites, and competitors must receive some share of attention and control. For reviews of oyster biology see Korringa (1952), Loosanoff (1954), Galtsoff (1956).

As natural oysters have declined in the seafood market, the harvest of shrimp has increased (Taylor, 1951). The life history and ecology of the shrimp is different from that of the oyster, and is not too well known. It is obvious that intensive study is needed to make certain that this promising new sea "crop" does not follow the same history of decline as shown by the oyster.

9. Range management

As was indicated in the discussion of the grassland biomes (Chapter 11, Section 4), man seems to have an uncanny knack for abusing grassland resources. A succession of deteriorated civilizations in the grassland regions of the old world stand as mute evidence of this fact. Fortunately for the new world, the science of range management is coming of age while the destructive trends may yet be reversed. For the future of our great west and the country as a whole, there is no more important phase of applied ecology than range management.

Figure 143 illustrates the basic problem of range management in a nutshell. The key word is "overgrazing." When a man builds an artificial pasture by dint of hard labor and cold cash, he would no more think of destroying it by misuse than he would think of burning down his house. Yet is seems difficult for man to learn that natural pastures and man-made pastures operate according to the same principles. It is as Leopold so aptly expressed it (see Section 1), namely, that man has difficulty understanding organic cause and effect in things which he himself has not built.

To determine the range's carrying capacity for grazing animals two considerations are paramount: (1) the primary productivity and (2) the per cent of the net productivity which can be removed annually and still leave the grass plant with enough reserve to enable it to maintain future productivity. Because of generally low rainfall net productivity of ranges in low, between 150 and 500 grams dry matter/M^2/year for the great plains region of the United States. Productivity is apparently a more or less linear

Figure 143.   Effect of overgrazing on a Texas grassland; mesquite, cactus, and other "desert" plants gradually replace the grass.

function of rainfall either from year to year or from place to place, but more data are needed (Major, 1951). If continued productivity is to be insured, only about half of the annual production should be consumed by cattle (Costello, 1944). Knowing the rainfall one could calculate how many pounds of meat might be produced, and adjust the number of animals accordingly. However, it does not work out quite so simply because seasonal distribution of rainfall, the quality of the forage (especially protein-carbohydrate ratio), the palatability, season of growth, etc., all complicate the picture. For this reason, range managers have found that community or ecosystem indicators (see Chapter 4) provide the most practical means of determining whether or not a range is being utilized properly (Humphrey, 1949).

When the natural grassland is overgrazed, unpalatable "weeds" (annuals) and desert shrubs invade (sagebrush, mesquite, etc.). Even before this happens there are subtle changes in community structure, such as a decrease in density or loss of vigor of sensitive species, which can be recognized; it is this kind of criterion which the range manager uses to judge range condition. The lower the rainfall, the less the primary productivity in the first place and the quicker the range becomes depleted. If overgrazing continues, essentially a man-made desert results ("disclimax," see Chapter 8, Section 5). Once established, the desert vegetation may be hard to eradicate. Rodents and grasshoppers increase with overgrazing. Unnecessary control of predators may aggravate the rodent problem. Attempts to rehabilitate the range by rodent or insect control alone is a good example of what Leopold would call "isolated project management," which ignores the primary cause. Only by correcting the original excessive grazing pressure and considering the grassland community as a whole can permanent results be obtained.

The effect of trampling by grazing animals in compacting the soil can also be important. When too many animals are confined for too long the soil may become "sodbound" and productivity reduced, even after the animals are removed. Essentially, the consumer-regenerating portion of the ecosystem is hampered by poor aeration of the soil, and this in turn inhibits the production mechanism. Plowing or ripping with subsoil chisels has proved useful in small pastures, but such a procedure would be too expensive for large tracts of rangeland. As we have emphasized many times the whole ecosystem, not merely the producers, must be considered.

Signs of various degrees of overgrazing may be seen everywhere in our western states. One needs only to watch the fences to note the contrast between grazed and ungrazed sides. Fortunately, the damage in many places is of such a nature that it can be corrected in a fairly short time. Fire, bulldozers, and chemicals can be used to remove the desert shrubs or weeds; if grazing pressure is temporarily removed, or at least reduced, the native grasses usually return if soil has not been damaged by wind erosion, etc. Arranging for rotation of pastures is very important since this allows the grassland periods of rest. Scattering the watering places also helps prevent local pressure. There are many other techniques, if we will but use them. For further discussion of various aspects, reference may be made to the textbooks of Sampson (1952), or of Stoddart and Smith (1955), the review by Costello (1957).

Because natural grasslands have evolved over long periods of time during which they have been subjected to varying use by animals and man, the historical aspect of the range is of great importance (see page 418). Thus, the study of range conditions should be approached with an open mind. Unfavorable conditions may not always be the result of recent grazing history. As stated by Malin (1953) "Overgrazing must bear justly the responsibility of a number of evils, but it has become a convenient scapegoat for a multitude of situations where the proper answer should be 'Nobody knows.'"

13 · Applications: public health and welfare

Ecology has important applications in the field of public health. For example, the prevention of animal-borne diseases of man is often an ecological as well as a medical problem. Malaria, yellow fever, typhus (two types), plague, rabies, Rocky Mountain spotted fever, and encephalitis are just a few in the formidable list of such diseases. Many in this group are especially important in the warmer regions of the earth. Prevention of water-borne diseases and general sanitation are other areas which have ecological aspects (see Chapter 12, Section 7). The United States Public Health Service and the state health departments now offer excellent professional opportunities for the ecologist as well as for those trained in bacteriology and medicine.

Animals involved as intermediate hosts in the transfer of diseases to man include the biting diptera (mosquitoes, etc.), lice, arachnids (ticks, etc.), and mammals (especially rodents). Consequently, it is the ecology of these animals that primarily concerns the public health biologist. As has been indicated in the general discussion of the community concept (see Chapter 8, Section 1), control of a specific disease carrier is often accomplished more efficiently and cheaply by control of the organism's environment or community than by direct attack on the organism itself. Such control, however, involves other effects which must also be considered. Therefore, as with any other specialist, the public health biologist cannot ignore the total ecosystem if he is to (1) effectively separate cause from effect (compare rodent–deteriorated grassland relation mentioned in the previous section), and

(2) avoid undesirable secondary effects (see previous discussion of insect control in Chapter 12, Section 2).

Urbanization and intense land use ameliorate some public health problems but create others. Strange to say, for example, the population of certain insects and rats may increase with the increase in the size of cities; this results from the deterioration of housing and the development of slums in the older sections of the city. Matheson (1953) reports that in England the houses infested with bedbugs increased from about 0.1 per cent in towns with 25,000 houses to 1.0 per cent in towns with more than 100,000 houses.

In the prevention of animal-borne diseases the life history and parasite–host relations (see Chapter 7, Section 3) of animals involved must first be studied. Next in importance are various aspects of the population ecology of the carriers or the pests. Nearly all the principles discussed in Chapter 6 have their application here. We may take one example from the extensive studies of Davis, Emlen, and others on the Norway rat population of Baltimore to illustrate the value of a population ecology study (for a convenient summary of this work, see Davis, 1951, 1953). Significant findings may be listed in outline form as follows:

1. Rats increase in sigmoid fashion (see Chapter 6, Section 8), the upper asymptote being determined by food and harborage (available habitat).

2. Two types of population change were observed: increase up to carrying capacity and fluctuations due to changes in carrying capacity. Where conditions did not change, the rat population remained at the same level for as long as seven years (no evidence of marked population oscillations).

3. Natality rate of Norway rats is surprisingly uniform the world over, averaging 10 young weaned per female per year. Maximum natality (see Chapter 6, Section 4) was determined to be about 37 young per female per year. Mortality averaged 95 per cent of the population per year.

4. Density was largely the result of the balance between natality and mortality controlled by the immediate environment; dispersal from one block to another was of little importance in determining the number of rats present.

5. Shelter and food were density-proportional limiting factors (see Chapter 6, Section 11), that is, a reduction of 10 per cent in

either item resulted in 10 per cent reduction of the population regardless of its size.

6. Intraspecific competition, predators, and death by traps or poisons, however, were density-dependent, that is, percentage reduction in population increased with increasing population size.

7. Predation was rarely sufficient for practical control, even when intensified by man. Cats prefer garbage and are much overrated in rat control. Pathogens are well adjusted. Ordinary city trapping crews get only one half of the rats; after trapping, the population quickly returns to the former level and no permanent benefit is obtained.

8. Sanitation, which removes food and cover, is feasible on a scale not possible with poisons, trapping, predation, etc.; it is the best method of permanently reducing the rat population. When sanitation is applied, rats do not leave, but die or fail to reproduce.

9. The following estimates of the *rat population of Baltimore* made before and after a program of sanitation in the slum areas indicate that this method is effective:

1944 (before sanitation program)	400,000 rats
1947 (during program)	165,000 ”
1949 (after completion)	65,000 ”

It is noteworthy that the control of most diseases of lower animals which are transmissible to man (there are 87 of these "zoonoses" according to the World Health Organization technical reports) requires the same thorough understanding of the ecology of the vector as outlined in the above example. For example, where malaria control has been achieved it has always been through measures directed at the mosquito and not at the parasite in the human body (Bates, 1957). Monographs on mosquitos (Bates, 1949) and mosquito-borne diseases (Boyd, 1949; Strode, 1951) contain a large body of excellent autecological data which makes possible the determination of the weak link in the life cycle and best limiting factor which man can apply. A novel use of a highly specific artificial limiting factor in the control of an insect is reported by Baumhover et al. (1955). Screw-worm flies were exterminated from an island by the release of x-ray sterilized males into the population. A gigantic attempt is now being made to eliminate this fly from Florida in the same way. If such a method will work for a large area, it will certainly be preferable to the mass application of insecticides to the countryside, which, as we have already indicated, often does more harm than good.

Probably the greatest problem in public health in the near future is not the control of specific diseases but the control of pollution of the general environment (water, air, soil), which can bring with it ill-health of all kinds. Irritating and toxic air-borne substances or "smog" is already a health factor in all large cities, and is especially serious in certain regions, such as southern California. Smog in the latter area has even been shown to inhibit photosynthesis and plant growth, some varieties of plants being especially sensitive (Koritz and Went, 1953). Radioactive pollutants, of course, are becoming a major problem, as will be discussed in the next chapter. At the same time, radioactive "tracers" can be extremely useful in the detection of pollution of all types. Ely (1957), for example, reports that the radioactive isotope scandium-46 mixed with sewage effluent and discharged into the sea off southern California made possible a rapid determination of dispersal patterns and the detection of very minute amounts of effluent on the beaches. As a result, the design of the disposal system was corrected long before beach pollution became a hazard to people.

14 · Radiation ecology*

Radiation ecology is concerned with radioactive substances, radiation and the environment. There are two rather distinct phases of radioecology which require different approaches. On the one hand we are concerned with the effects of radiation on individuals, populations, communities and ecosystems. The other important phase of radiation ecology concerns the fate of radioactive substances released into the environment and the manner by which the ecological communities and populations control the distribution of radioactivity. The rapid development of atomic energy for military and peaceful purposes and the spread of potentially dangerous materials into the environments have made radiation ecology of major concern.

Materials like radioactive strontium and radioactive iodine are falling from the skies after atomic blasts. Elsewhere such materials are going into soils and natural waters as atomic wastes. Many organisms take up these substances and concentrate them in their tissues. In high concentrations such substances and their radiations have biological effects including induction of mutation, cancers and death. In the extremely dilute amounts now found in many environments effects are little known and presumed to be negligible, but there is much controversy. In this chapter are presented some of the aspects of a new subject in its infancy.

This chapter is a revised version of a previous article (E. P. Odum, 1956) prepared while the author held a National Science Foundation Senior ...p which enabled him to take part in research programs at several ...mic Energy Installations.

1. Review of nuclear concepts and terminology of ecological importance

In order to facilitate subsequent discussion and presentation of data, some of the more important concepts and terms used in radiation ecology are listed and very briefly discussed below. There are numerous books and review articles to which the student may refer for details and additional material. For the ecologist, the three-volume compilation edited by Hollaender (1954), the well-written book of Comar (1955) and the latest edition of the "Radiological Health Handbook"* are particularly useful. Instrumentation, especially as applicable to ecological problems, is still in a pioneer phase and can be discussed only in the most general terms. So rapidly is technology advancing that anything written along these lines which is more than three years old is likely to be out of date; thus, one should seek information directly from the specialist.

Types of ionizing radiations

In previous parts of the book we have considered radiations such as light, which are widely used by organisms for their benefit. Such radiations carry relatively small amounts of energy and do little damage when they are absorbed by organisms. Other radiations which are able to remove electrons from atoms and attach them to other atoms, thereby producing positive and negative *ion pairs,* are known as *ionizing radiations.* It is believed that ionization is the chief cause of injury to protoplasm and that the damage is proportional to the number of ion pairs produced in the absorbing material. Of the three ionizing radiations of primary ecological concern two are corpuscular (alpha and beta) and one is electromagnetic (gamma radiation and the related x-radiation). Important features of these types of radiation are diagrammed in Figure 144. The relative penetration of air and organism is shown, and the amount of ionization is indicated by the relative length and thickness of the black bars for both external and internal radiation sources. Ionizing radiations are sent out from radioactive materials on earth and are also received from outer space.

Corpuscular radiation consists of streams of atomic or sub-

* May be obtained from U. S. Dept. of Commerce, Office of Technical Services, Washington, D.C.

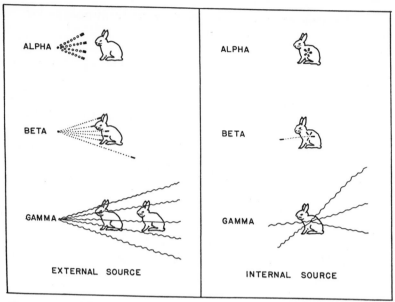

Figure 144.   Schematic comparison of the three types of ionizing radiations of greatest ecological interest, showing relative penetration and specific ionization effect. The diagram is not intended to be quantitative.

atomic particles which transfer their energy to whatever they strike. Since they have definite mass, the particles travel only a short distance through air or matter, but on being stopped they produce a large amount of ionization locally. *Ionizing electromagnetic radiations,* on the other hand, are like light, only of much shorter wavelength (see Fig. 23, Chapter 4). They travel great distances and readily penetrate matter, releasing their energy over long paths (the ionization is dispersed). *Alpha particles* are parts of helium atoms and are huge in the atomic scale of things. They travel but a few centimeters in air and may be stopped by a sheet of paper or the dead layer of the skin of man. *Beta particles* are high speed electrons. They are much smaller and may travel a number of feet in air or up to a couple of centimeters in tissue. As shown in Figure 144, *gamma rays* penetrate biological materials easily; a given "ray" may go right through an organism without having any effect or it may produce ionization over a long path. Their effect depends on the number and energy of the rays and the distance of the organism from the source (since intensity decreases exponentially with distance). Thus we see that the alpha, beta, gamma series is one of increasing penetration but decreasing concentration of ionization and local damage. Therefore, biologists often class radioactive substances which emit alpha or beta particles as "internal emitters," because their effect is likely to be greatest when absorbed, ingested or otherwise internally deposited, or, in the case of small or thin "unshielded" organisms (such as microorganisms or leaves of plants), deposited on the surface. Conversely, radioactive substances which are primarily gamma emitters are classed as "external emitters" since they are penetrating and can produce their effect without being taken inside. However, as we shall see later, gamma radiation from within or beta from without cannot be ignored, especially when whole populations are being considered.

There are other types of radiation which are of at least indirect interest to the ecologist. *Neutrons* are large uncharged particles which in themselves do not cause ionization, but, like a bull in a china shop, they wreak local havoc and cause ionization by bumping atoms out of position. For a given amount of absorbed energy, "fast" neutrons may do ten times, and "slow" neutrons five times, the local damage of gamma rays. Neutrons are restricted to the vicinity of reactors or atomic explosions, and will not be a factor in general environment. They are of primary importance in the production of radioactive substances which can and do become widely distributed in nature. *X-rays* are electromagnetic radiations very similar to gamma rays, but are not sent out from radioactive substances dispersed in the environment. Since they have the same effect as gamma rays and are easily obtained from an x-ray machine, we may conveniently use them in experimental studies on individuals, populations or even small ecosystems. *Cosmic rays* are radiations from outer space which are mixtures of corpuscular and electromagnetic components. The intensity of cosmic rays in the biosphere is low. Cosmic rays and ionizing radiation from natural radioactive substances in soil and water produce the "background radiation" to which the present biota is adapted. In fact, the biota may depend on this background radiation for maintaining genetic fluidity. Background varies three to four fold in various parts of the biosphere. In this chapter we are concerned primarily with the artificial radioactivity which is added to the background.

Units of measurements

In order to measure radiation phenomena one must sometimes measure the amount of radiation energy which is being sent out and which is capable of causing ionizations and damage. The radiation dose to organisms is measured in terms of the energy absorbed. At other times it is important to measure the amount of radioactive substance which is sending out the radiations. Each wave or particle of radiation is sent out when an atom of radioactive substance disintegrates. By counting the number of disintegrations taking place, one may determine the amount of source radioactivity. Thus there are two different kinds of measurements, each with a different name.

The basic unit of the quantity of a radioactive substance is the curie (c), which is defined as the amount of material in which 3.7×10^{10} atoms disintegrate each second. The actual weight of material making up a curie is very different for a long-lived, slowly decaying isotope as compared with a rapidly decaying one. Approximately one gram of radium, for example, is a curie while very much less (about 10^{-7} grams) of newly formed radiosodium would emit 3.7×10^{10} disintegrations a second! Since a curie represents a rather large amount of radioactivity from the biological standpoint, smaller units are widely used: *millicurie* (mc) = one thousandth curie or 10^{-3} c; *microcurie* (μc) or 10^{-6} c; *millimicrocurie* (mμc) or 10^{-9} c; and *micromicrocurie* ($\mu\mu$c) or 10^{-12} c. The possible range of activity is so tremendous that one must be careful about the position of that decimal point! The curie indicates how many alpha or beta particles or gamma rays are streaming from a radioactive source, but this information does not tell us what effect the radiation might have on organisms in the line of fire.

The other important aspect of radiation, radiation dose, has been measured with several scales. The most convenient unit for all types of radiation is the *rad*, which is defined as the absorbed dose of 100 ergs of energy per gram of tissue. Since many of the radioactive substances with which the ecologist is most concerned emit combinations of electromagnetic and corpuscular radiations, a unit is needed that is good for all kinds of radiations. The *roentgen* (r) is an older unit, which strictly speaking is to be used only for gamma and x-rays. Actually, so long as we are dealing with the effects on living organisms, the rad and the roentgen are nearly the same. A unit 1/1000 smaller, namely the milliroentgen (mr) or the millirad (mrad), is convenient for the kind of radiation levels often encountered in the environment.

As has already been indicated, a given amount of radioactive material, one millicurie, for example, which emits corpuscular radiations may deliver a greater dose to a gram of biomass than the same amount of a gamma emitter *if* the radiation actually reaches the site in question. It is important to emphasize that the roentgen or rad is a unit of total dose. The *dose rate* is the amount received per unit time. Thus, if an organism is receiving 10 mr/hour, the total dose in a 24-hour period would be 240 mr or 0.240 r. As we shall see, the time over which a given dose is received is a very important consideration.

Radioisotopes (radionuclides) of ecological importance

There are various kinds of atoms of each elemental substance, each with a slightly different make-up, some radioactive, some not radioactive. These varieties of elements are called isotopes. Thus there are several isotopes of the element oxygen, several isotopes of the element carbon, etc. The isotopes that are radioactive are the unstable ones which disintegrate into other isotopes releasing radiations at the same time. Each isotope is identified by a number, its atomic weight; each radioactive isotope also has a characteristic rate of disintegration that is indicated by its half-life. Some radioisotopes of ecological importance are listed in Table 26. Thus one will note in Group B of Table 26 that calcium-45 is the radioactive isotope of calcium which has atomic weight 45 and loses half its radioactivity every 160 days. Half-life is constant for a given isotope (i.e., the rate of decay is not affected by environmental factors) and varies from a few seconds to many years, depending on the isotope. In general, extremely "short-lived" isotopes are of little interest ecologically. A variable which affects the penetrating power of radiation is its energy. Most radionuclides of ecological interest have energies between 0.1 and 5 Mev (million electron volts). Relative energy of each isotope in Table 26 is indicated (see standard references for exact values).

Table 26. *Radioisotopes of ecological importance*

Group A.   Naturally occurring isotopes which contributes to background radiation.

Isotope	Half-life	Radiations emitted	
Uranium-235 (U^{235})	7×10^8 yrs.	Alpha[3]	Gamma[0]
Uranium-238 (U^{238})	4.5×10^9 yrs.	Alpha[3]	
Radium-226 (Ra^{226})	1620 yrs.	Alpha[3]	Gamma[0]
Thorium-232 (Th^{232})	1.4×10^{10} yrs.	Alpha[3]	
Potassium-40 (K^{40})	1.3×10^9 yrs.	Beta[2]	Gamma[2]
Carbon-14 (See group B.)			

[0] Very low energy, less than 0.2 Mev; [1] Relatively low energy, 0.2-1 Mev; [2] High energy, 1-3 Mev; [3] Very high energy, over 3 Mev.

Table 26. *(Continued)*

Group B.   Isotopes of elements which are essential constituents of organisms, and, therefore, important as tracers in community metabolism studies as well as because of the radiation they produce.

Isotope	Half-life	Radiations emitted	
Calcium-45 (Ca^{45})	160 days	Beta[1]	
Carbon-14 (C^{14})	5568 yrs.	Beta[0]	
Copper-64 (Cu^{64})	12.8 hrs.	Beta[1]	Gamma[2]
Iodine-131 (I^{131})	8 days	Beta[1]	Gamma[1]
Iron-59 (Fe^{59})	45 days	Beta[1]	Gamma[2]
Hydrogen-3 (Tritium) (H^3)	12.4 yrs.	Beta[0]	
Manganese-54 (Mn^{54})	300 days	Beta[2]	Gamma[2]
Phosphorus-32 (P^{32})	14.5 days	Beta[2]	
Potassium-42 (K^{42})	12.4 hrs.	Beta[3]	Gamma [2]
Sodium-22 (Na^{22})	2.6 yrs.	Beta[1]	Gamma[2]
Sodium-24 (Na^{24})	15.1 hrs.	Beta[2]	Gamma[2]
Sulfur-35 (S^{35})	87.1 days	Beta[0]	
Zinc-65 (Zn^{65})	250 days	Beta[1]	Gamma[2]

Also barium-140 (Ba^{140}), bromine-82 (Br^{82}), cobalt-60 (Co^{60}), molybdenum-99 (Mo^{99}) and other trace elements.

Group C.   Isotopes important in fission products entering the environment through fallout or waste disposal.

Isotope	Half-life	Radiations emitted	
The strontium group			
Strontium-90 (Sr^{90}) and	28 yrs.	Beta[1]	
daughter yttrium-90 (Y^{90})	2.5 days	Beta[2]	
Strontium-89 (Sr^{89})	53 days	Beta[2]	
The cesium group			
Cesium-137 (Cs^{137}) and	33 yrs.	Beta[2]	Gamma
daughter barium-137 (Ba^{137})	2.6 min.	Beta	Gamma[1]
Cesium-134 (Cs^{134})	2.3 yrs.	Beta[1]	Gamma[2]
The cerium group			
Cerium-144 (Ce^{144}) and	285 days	Beta[1]	Gamma[0]
daughter praseodymium-144 (Pr^{144})	17 min.	Beta[2]	Gamma[2]
Cerium-141 (Ce^{141})	33 days	Beta[1]	Gamma[1]
The ruthenium group			
Ruthenium-106 (Ru^{106}) and	1 yr.	Beta[0]	
daughter rhodium-106 (Rh^{106})	30 sec.	Beta[3]	Gamma[2]
Ruthenium-103 (Ru^{103})	40 days	Beta[1]	Gamma[1]
Zirconium-95 (Zr^{95}) and daughter niobium-95 (Nb^{95})	65 days	Beta[1]	Gamma[1]
	35 days	Beta[0]	Gamma[1]
Barium-140 (Ba^{140}) and daughter lanthanum-140 (La^{140})	12.8 days	Beta[1]	Gamma[1]
	40 hrs.	Beta[2]	Gamma[2]
Neodymium-147 (Nd^{147}) and daughter promethium-147 (Pm^{147})	11.3 days	Beta[1]	Gamma[1]
	2.6 yrs.	Beta[1]	Gamma
Yttrium-91 (Yt^{91})	61 days	Beta[2]	Gamma[1]
Plutonium-239 (Pu^{239})	2.4×10^4 yrs.	Alpha[3]	Gamma[1]
Iodine-131 (see group B)			
Uranium (see group A)			

Table 26. (*Continued*)

Group D. Isotopes which are useful as animal "tags" because of the energetic gamma rays detectable at a distance.

Isotope	Half-life		Radiations emitted	
Cobalt-60 (Co^{60})	5.27	yrs.	Beta[1]	Gamma[2]
Scandium-46 (Sc^{46})	85	days	Beta[1]	Gamma[2]
Tantalum-182 (Ta^{182})	115	days	Beta[1]	Gamma[2]

The greater the energy the greater the potential danger to biological material within the range of the particular type of radiation. On the other hand, energetic isotopes are easier to detect in very small amounts and hence make better "tracers."

From the ecological point of view, radionuclides fall into several rather well-defined groups as shown in Table 26. Naturally occurring radionuclides form one group, (A), while isotopes of metabolically important elements form another group, (B), especially important as tracers. A third important group of isotopes, (C), are those produced by the fission of uranium, etc.; they involve mostly elements which are not metabolically essential (I^{131} is an exception). However, this group is the dangerous group because fission isotopes are produced in large amounts in both nuclear explosions and controlled nuclear operations, which produce power or other useful forms of energy. While most of these isotopes are not essential constituents of protoplasm, many behave chemically in a way similar to vital elements and thus become concentrated in living systems. For example, strontium isotopes, because they behave like calcium, readily enter food chains and become concentrated in the bone in a radiosensitive tissue, the bone marrow. Note that a number of isotopes in group C have a "daughter isotope" (an isotope formed during the decay of another isotope), which may be more energetic than the "parent."

2. Comparative radiosensitivity

Almost nothing is known about the possible effects of low-level, long continued radiation on ecological systems, but we can at least approach the subject by taking a look at the considerable body of data on radiosensitivity. Even before the current upsurge of interest in the biological effects of ionizing radiations, enough work had been done with x-rays to indicate that organisms differed widely in their ability to tolerate massive doses. It should be emphasized that doses used in most studies are much higher than we expect to

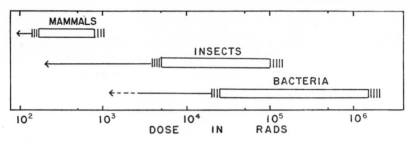

Figure 145. Comparative radiosensitivity of three groups of organisms to single acute doses of x- or gamma radiation. See text for explanation.

contend with in the general environment (assuming we do not have an all-out nuclear war).

Comparative sensitivity of three diverse groups of organisms to single doses of x- or gamma radiation is shown in Figure 145. The left ends of the bars indicate levels at which severe effects on reproduction (temporary or permanent sterilization, for example) may be expected in the more sensitive species of the group, and the right ends of the bars indicate levels at which a large portion (50 per cent or more) of the more resistant species would be killed outright. Thus, while a dose of ten thousand rads may affect the division rate of a sensitive microorganism, a dose of one million rads or more might be required to completely kill all bacteria, including spores and other resistant stages. Similarly, 5,000 rads will sterilize some species of insects, but 100,000 rads may be required to kill all individuals of the more resistant species. Following the same general criteria, mammals rate as the most sensitive of all organisms. As far as the meager data indicate, most seed plants and invertebrate animals would fall somewhere between mammals and bacteria, while lower vertebrates are but slightly more resistant than mammals.

Table 27. *Age variation in radiosensitivity in Drosophila*

Stage in life cycle	LD_{50} dose (r) of x-rays according to	
	Packard (1935, 1945)	Jenkins (1957)
Egg before cleavage	290	—
Egg during cleavage (1.5 hours)	163	—
Embryo, 3 hours old	861	170-200
Embryo, 4 hours old	—	500
Embryo, 5.5 hours old	1,044	—
Embryo, 7.5 hours old	—	810
Young larva	1,300	—
Pupa	—	2,800
Adult	100,000	85,000

We must be quick to point out that this picture is misleading from the ecological point of view, because even the resistant groups have stages in their life cycle or critical periods in their population growth which are affected by much lower doses. This lower order of sensitivity is indicated in Figure 145 by the arrows which extend to the left of the bars, and more specifically by the data in Tables 27 and 28. In *Drosophila*, which is one of the more resistant insects, a dose in the neighborhood of 10^5 r is required to kill half of the adult flies (i.e., "lethal dose for 50 per cent" or "LD_{50}"), while as little as 163 r may kill half the individuals at the most sensitive stage in development. A dose rate as low as 8 r/day has been shown to have a measurable effect on the growth and development of grasshopper neuroblasts. Likewise, barley, which, in common with most seed plants, can "take" a lot of radiation as a mature plant, is measurably affected during the early stages of development (Table 28) by doses no higher than that which would be critical for mammals. Most studies have shown that sensitivity decreases with age, and that cleavage stages (when all cells are rapidly dividing) are often especially vulnerable. In fact, any component, whether a part of an organism, a whole organism or a whole population, which is undergoing rapid mitosis is likely to be affected by comparatively low levels of radiation regardless of taxonomic relationships.

One reason why populations of small organisms are resistant to x- and gamma radiation is that their biomass is so small per unit volume of environment that there is comparatively little living matter to absorb the energy. However, other factors than size are also involved. Isolated mammal cells are more sensitive than microorganisms of comparable size (Puck and Marcus, 1956).

Small organisms also have high reproductive potentials and may quickly recover from damage to the population. If 90 per cent of

Table 28. *Age variation in radiosensitivity in barley**

Stage in life cycle when irradiated	Per cent affected in later development by single doses of 50-250 r x-rays		
	Histologically	Germination	Lethals and semi-lethals
1-2 cell embryo	28	20	17
3-8 cell embryo	41	19	9
Pro-embryo	65	9	4
Late pro-embryo	65	1	0
Differentiating embryo	12	9	2

* Data from Mericle and Mericle (1957).

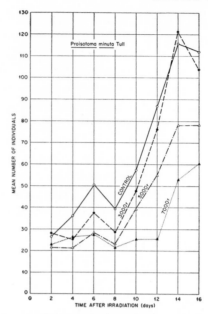

Figure 146.   The effect of acute gamma radiation on the growth of Collembola population units. (After Auerbach, Crossley and Engelman, 1957.)

bacteria were killed, for example, the remaining 10 per cent could quickly repopulate the area. On the other hand, if 90 per cent of the cells of a large complex organism were damaged, it is evident that recovery would not occur. Consequently, the effect of electromagnetic radiation on small organisms is often one of a temporary stopping or slowing down of growth. This kind of effect is well shown in Figure 146, which depicts the results of irradiating population units of springtails (*Collembola*), which are small soil arthropods. With an increasing dose population growth is delayed for a longer period but it eventually begins again at essentially the same rate as the controls.

The survivorship curve (see Chapter 6, page 168) is another useful device for evaluating radiation effects on population units. Figure 147 shows the results of a study in which large numbers of individuals of flour beetles were irradiated in repeated tests. The shape of the survivorship curves gives a good picture of the effect on the population in which the time element is considered. With single doses of 3000 r, survival of irradiated insects after 200 or 300 days was actually greater than that of the controls; the same results were obtained by chronic doses of 100 r daily. Apparently, these levels slow down development a bit so that the early period of life is prolonged. In nature, of course, this might not be an advantage since the slowed down individuals might not be able to compete as well in other ways. As the dose increases, greater and greater depression of the survivorship curve occurs.

To summarize, in most experimental work so far, irradiation of large organisms with electromagnetic ionizing rays has been essentially a matter of the effect on individuals (which, being large, can not avoid being "hit" in critical places), while irradiation of small organisms has often been a matter of populations of hundreds or thousands of individuals, many of which may escape damage entirely. As already emphasized, alpha and beta particles produce intense local effects in small areas, which means that small organisms like insects or bacteria might, under certain environmental circumstances, be more vulnerable than large organisms to corpuscular radiation. For example, a mammal egg, shielded as it would be by the body of the mother, would not be affected by a quantity of beta emitting isotopes deposited in the soil. A grasshopper egg or soil organism, on the other hand, would receive the full intensity of the radiation. Little work has yet been done on the ecological levels to evaluate these possibilities.

Even more interesting, perhaps, than differences between diverse organisms are the striking differences in radiosensitivity

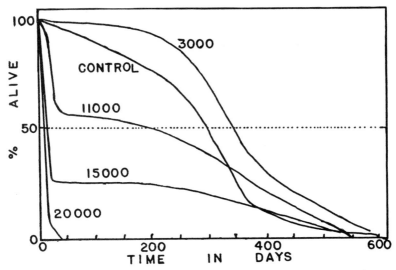

Figure 147. Survivorship curves for populations of *Tribolium* subjected to single acute doses of gamma radiation of 3, 11, 15 and 20 thousand roentgens as compared with control populations not subjected to ionizing radiation. (After Cork, 1957.)

Table 29.   *Species variation in radiosensitivity of higher plants to
chronic exposure to gamma radiation**

Species of plant	Dose rate—r/day for 7-18 weeks, producing	
	Mild effects (slight decrease in size and vigor)	Severe effects (acute stunting; semi-lethal)
Lilium longiflorum	20	30
Tradescantia paludosa	20	40
T. ohiensis	35	65
Vicia faba	60	90
Coleus blumei	100	240
Chrysanthemum (hybrid)	140	250
Chenopodium album	250	450
Solanum tuberosum	300	600
Petunia hybrida	300	700
Allium cepa	400	800
Linum usitatissimum	600	1100
Digitaria (crabgrass)	1000	1800
Brassica oleracea (broccoli)	1400	2500
Gladiolus (hybrid)	4100	6000

* Data from Sparrow and Christensen (1953).

of related organisms. Selected data on plants and insects are
shown in Tables 29 and 30. The data of Sparrow and Christensen (1953) are especially interesting, because a very large number
of species of seed plants were tested under comparable circumstances. A few of their data are shown in the table to indicate the
range. Some species proved to be 200 times more sensitive to
chronic exposure to gamma radiation, and species belonging to the
same genus sometimes differ in regard to sensitivity. The authors
suggested that species with large chromosomes were more vulnerable than species with small chromosomes. In insects, a fivefold
difference in the "sterilizing dose" has been demonstrated (Table
30). Individuals and especially "strains" or "subspecies" of the
same species have also been shown to exhibit marked differences
in the tolerance to x-rays. In plants and microorganisms, "x-ray
sensitive" strains have been described, for example, in wheat
(Smith, 1942), where a considerable difference in susceptibility
may involve only one or a few genes. Variations in sensitivity in
different strains of laboratory mice are well known. Black mice,
for example, are less sensitive than white mice, whereas hybrids
between the two strains have been reported to be more resistant
than either parent (Rugh and Wolff, 1958).

Differential sensitivity is of considerable ecological interest. Should a system receive a higher level of radiation than that under which it evolved, nature will not take it "lying down," so to speak; adaptations and adjustments will occur along with the elimination of sensitive strains or species. So long as the eliminated component is replaced by a similar component which "does the same job" in the community, not much overall effect on the system may result (assuming the eliminated component is not man!). If, on the other hand, the components in question are different or belong to different trophic levels, a considerable total effect might result, which would disturb the adjustment of the system. Certain possibilities in this direction are suggested by the experiments of C. J. Rohde and S. I. Auerbach (see Auerbach, 1958) at Oak Ridge, who irradiated populations of predator and prey mites. As shown in Figure 148 the predator population was more sensitive and declined in numbers, while the prey population increased as a result of relaxing predator pressure when the dose was between 8 and 25×10^3 r. Some very interesting work has been started by Robert B. Platt in which whole intact plant communities which grow on granite outcrops are brought into the laboratory and irradiated under different conditions of light, temperature and moisture. Preliminary results (Platt, 1957) indicate that certain species can be eliminated from the community at doses which appear to have little affect on other species. In this case, as with the mites, high doses were used and it is not known if the same relative effect might be achieved with very low but long continued doses. For such work the laboratory setup is not suitable, because communities or populations cannot be kept isolated for long periods of time and remain in the same condition as they were in nature.

There may be no actual threshold for radiation damage. Geneticists have generally agreed that there is no threshold for genetic

Table 30. *Species variation in radiosensitivity in insects**

Species of insect	Single dose (r) x- or gamma radiation necessary for 100% sterilization
Screw-worm fly (Callitroga)	5,000
Habrabracon wasp	7,500
Drosophila	16,000
Powder post (Lyctus) beetle	32,000

* Data from Jenkins (1957).

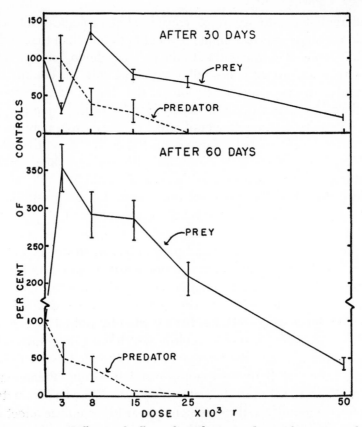

Figure 148. Differential effect of single acute doses of gamma radiation on predator and prey populations of mites. The predator species proved to be more sensitive; as its numbers declined the density of the prey species increased as compared with the unirradiated controls. (After Auerbach, 1958.)

effects. Thus, the problem of the future becomes clear; effects must be put on a quantitative scale and the range that is "tolerable" or "bad" determined in the light of necessity. At present, we resort to the stopgap measure of establishing "minimum permissible levels" for both dose and amount of different isotopes in the environment. This is a good procedure so long as it is recognized that these permissible levels do not actually represent any known thresholds. Actually, during the past few years the "permissible levels" for man have been revised downward. There is a widespread feeling that since man seems to be as radiosensitive as any other organism, all we need do is "monitor" the radiation levels and keep them low in that microenvironment where man actually lives. Loutit (1956) sums up this viewpoint as follows: "It is our belief that, if we take sufficient care radiobiologically to look after mankind, with few exceptions the rest of nature will take care of itself. Sensitivity to ionizing radiations is well correlated with the degree of evolutionary complexity. Thus, man and his domestic mammals will be expected to be among the first to suffer from over-exposure to radiation." A number of reasons why this may be an oversimplification have been brought out in the previous discussion. In the next section we will find dramatic reasons why we cannot ignore what goes on in the vast part of the biosphere in which man does not actually live—streams, the sea, the soil. These reasons concern biogeochemical cycles and food chains.

3. The fate of radioactive isotopes in the environment

When radioisotopes are released into the environment, they quite often become dispersed and diluted, but they may also undergo unexpected movements and concentrations. Thus, an isotope might be diluted to a relatively harmless level on release into the environment, yet become concentrated by organisms or a series of organisms to a point where it would be critical. In other words we could give "nature" an apparently innocuous amount of radioactivity and have her give it back to us in a lethal package!

Some of the best data on the concentrative tendencies in certain food chains have been obtained by radioecologists at the AEC Hanford Plant, located on the Columbia River in Washington. Here, very small (practically tracer) amounts of highly soluble radioactive isotopes are released into the water at a rather constant rate, providing an excellent opportunity for detailed study under more or less equilibrium conditions. In this case, radioisotopes released into the river are not primarily fission products but represent normal constituents of water, which have become radioactive by induction (neutron capture, etc.) as water passes through the reactors. Also, radioactive materials get into the local environment via waste gases released into the air (I^{131} especially), and via waste fluids containing fission products. Hanford thus provides a preview of the three ways by which environments become contaminated. Some examples of the concentration of isotopes (originating in each of the three ways) in natural food chains are

Table 31. *Concentration of radioisotopes in food chains as shown by the ratio of isotopes in organisms to that in the environment*

1. P^{32}—Columbia River: [*]

	Water	Vege- tation	Insects, Crustaceans	Vertebrates	Eggs
Swallows, adults	1	—	0.5	75,000	—
Swallows, young	1	—	3.5	500,000	—
Geese and ducks	1	0.1	0.1	7,500	200,000

2. Long-lived mixed fission products in holding pond: [*]

	Water	Vegetation	Birds
Coots	1	3	250 in muscle (mostly Cs^{137}). 500 in bone (mostly Sr^{90}).

3. I^{131} aerial contamination at Hanford: [*]

	Vegetation	Jack Rabbit Thyroids	Coyote Thyroids
Terrestrial food chain	1	500	100

4. P^{32} and other isotopes in Columbia River: [†]

	Water	Phyto- plankton	Aquatic insects	Bass
Aquatic food chain	1	1000	500	10

[*] Data from Hanson and Kornberg, 1956.
[†] Data from Foster and Rostenbach, 1954.

shown in Table 31. The ratio of a radionuclide in the organism to that in the environment is often called the *concentration factor*. As may be seen from the table, this factor may be very large. As was explained in Chapter 2, a radioactive tracer behaves chemically essentially the same as the non-radioactive element. Therefore, the observed concentration by the organism is not the result of the radioactivity, but merely demonstrates in a measurable manner the difference between the density of the element in the environment and in the organism. For example, the concentration of phosphorus in the Columbia River is very low, only about 0.00003 mg/gms water (ie., 0.003 ppm) whereas the concentration in bird egg yolks is about 6 mg/gms. Thus, a gram of egg yolk contains two million times more phosphorus than a gram of water in the river. We would not expect to find a concentration factor for radioactive phosphorus quite this high since, while it was moving through the food chain to the eggs, some decay would occur, thus reducing the amount. Occasionally a concentration factor as high as 1,500,000 was recorded, but the average was lower, as shown in Table 31.

While radioactivity does not affect the uptake of the isotope by living systems, it may, of course, affect the tissues once it is absorbed. In the case of the eggs mentioned above, the amount in the egg was still not enough (despite high concentration) to reduce the hatchability (Hanson and Kornberg, 1956). However, if the concentration of P^{32} in the river water were allowed to reach the maximum permissible level for drinking water (instead of being held well below this level), the birds and eggs would certainly suffer radiation damage as well as become unfit for human food (Foster and Davis, 1956). The point is that allowance must be made for "ecological concentration." Isotopes which are naturally concentrated in certain tissues (such as iodine in the thyroid or strontium in the bone) and/or those with long effective half-lives are obviously the ones to watch out for. Also, the concentration factor is likely to be greater in nutrient-poor environments than in nutrient rich ones. For example, if the concentration of phosphorus in the Columbia River were high instead of low, less P^{32} would get into the bones and eggs. In general, concentration factors may be expected to be greater in fresh water than in the ocean, and greater in water than on land, but there are many complicating factors which could produce exceptions. The data in Table 32 are interesting in this regard since they show that sheep in poor pastures get more radiostrontium in their bones than sheep in fertile pastures.

In Figure 149 the Columbia River data are expressed in terms of the ratio between radioactive and stable phosphorus, providing a good picture of the time required for phosphorus to pass along the food chain. Algae and plankton absorb P^{32} quickly, but by the time it reaches the fish, radioactive decay has reduced the amount. The crayfish, which is mostly a scavenger, is the last to get hold of the material and hence has the lowest amount of P^{32} per unit of stable phosphorus.

Man's opportunity to learn more about environmental processes through the use of radioactive tracers balances the possible troubles he may have with environmental contamination. Radioactive tracers have already been well exploited by the physiologist, but the ecologist is just beginning to develop techniques for studies in "community metabolism" as it becomes clear that with proper precautions radioactive tracers can be used as safely in the field as in the laboratory (see Figure 151). We need not go into detail here since numerous examples of the usefulness of isotopes in

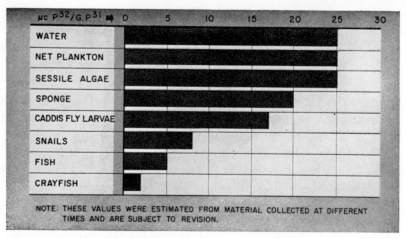

Figure 149. Specific activity of radioactive phosphorus (amount P[32] per gram of P[31]) in the water and organisms of the Columbia River at a point where P[32] enters the river at a relatively constant rate. Exchange between algae or plankton and the water is so rapid in terms of the 14 day half-life of P[32] that specific activity is virtually the same in the former as in the latter. However, specific activity in organisms which obtain their phosphorus through the food chain (fish, for example) is considerably less as a result of radioactive decay and a lower turnover rate. (After Foster, 1958.)

ecology have already been given in the earlier chapters of this book, for example, the determination of turnover time for phosphorus in lakes, the measurement of productivity with carbon-14, or the tracing of sewage by the use of scandium-46, to mention a few.

Before beginning a field experiment, it may be desirable to set up an experimental "ecosystem" as a model in order to determine what might be learned with a larger operation. Figure 150 shows what happened when a single "dose" of P[32] (about 170 microcuries/60 gallons of water) was added to an aquarium "ecosystem" which consisted of natural river water low in phosphate, bottom mud, plankton, mud algae, attached algae on glass sidewalls, fish and small invertebrates. The radioactivity was first removed by the plankton, which reached a peak in less than a day. Uptake by bottom and sidewall algae was slower, while maximum levels in animals which fed on the algae were not reached for 11 to 18 days. Finally, activity became more and more concentrated in the sediments by way of animal feces and decomposing algae. After a month all but 2 to 5 per cent of the P[32] had been removed from the water. However, when water having an initial high content of non-radioactive phosphate was used, very little of the P[32] was removed by organisms or sediment; 80 to 90 per cent was still remaining in the water after a month. Such an experiment indicates the role that different materials might have in "decontamination" and suggests that substances with the largest active surface area will be important. The importance of the non-radioactive phosphorus, already present in the environment, in determining the rate of uptake of radioactive phosphorus by an organism is also shown.

Figure 151 illustrates one method which we have used in our own work at the AEC Savannah River Plant to study movements of isotopes in grassland communities. An exposure chamber is placed over a unit of vegetation (a square meter, for example) and a solution of an isotope is sprayed directly on the plants (with an atomizer). When the proper chemical form is used, many isotopes are readily absorbed into the plant through the leaves. "Foliar absorption," in fact, is now widely used as a means of fertilizing orchards and other cultivated plants; isotopes have been an immense help in working out the details of such procedures (Wittwer, 1957). After the "hot quadrat" (a new term in ecology!) has been prepared the plants and animals can be sampled at intervals to determine the fate of the isotope and the

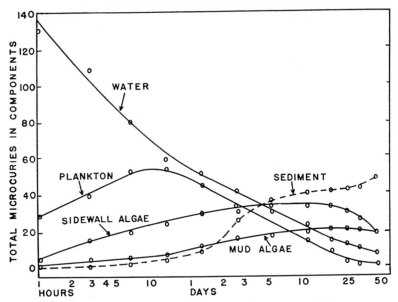

Figure 150. Movement of radioactive phosphorus into different components of an aquarium ecosystem following a single addition of P^{32} to the water. (After Whittaker, 1953a.)

Figure 151. The use of radioactive isotopes in community metabolism studies on the University of Georgia experimental areas in the AEC Savannah River Operations area. Handling isotopes in the field involves the same precautions as in the laboratory. In the upper photograph, concentrated solution is being removed from a shielded container for dilution to amount desired for foliar application on a plot of old-field vegetation. Note rubber gloves, protec-

rate at which it is transported in the food chain. Another method which we have used to isolate specific food chains involves injecting the isotope directly into the stems of individuals belonging to a single species of plant in a quadrat, leaving all other species untagged (Figure 151, lower photo). Any animals which become radioactive would thus belong to the food chain which began with the tagged species of plant. When P^{32} was used, we found that it was translocated rapidly to all parts of the plant including roots, flowers and developing seeds. Within two or three days the activity appeared in a considerable portion of the arthropod population of the vicinity including predators such as spiders. Radioiodine, on the other hand, did not spread through the plant as readily and was transferred to a smaller portion of the animal biomass. Pendleton and Grundmann (1954) have used similar methods in their studies of insect-plant relationships.

In addition to tagging whole communities, certain isotopes have proved useful in the study of the movements of individual animals. The radioactivity in the animals can be detected with a portable counter so that one can locate and identify individuals released previously. The method has been widely used with insects such as mosquitoes and houseflies; Jenkins (1957) summarized the already large literature on the "radio-tagging" of insects, while Pendleton (1956) discussed the possibilities for animals in general. The hard gamma emitters are especially useful with animals which are hidden from view, such as bark beetles, grubs in soil, reptiles, or small mammals. However, isotopes are largely population tags and are not usually suitable in situations where one wishes to recognize individuals. In many cases radioactive tags have no special advantage over other types of tags. For example, toe clipping, ear punching, or ordinary metal tags would be more useful than radioactive tags for most small mammal population research. Because isotope work does involve technical difficulties as well as potential hazard, the ecologist should not use isotopes unless

---

tive clothing and disposable absorbent paper covering the bed of the truck. In the middle photo, the isotope is being sprayed uniformly on the vegetation under the exposure chamber, which has a plastic top and rubber sleeves. Each step is carefully "monitored" (note operator on right) to make certain no contamination extends beyond the controlled area. The lower photo shows the tagging of individual plants by means of a special syringe, which injects the isotope into the stem. Note the plastic shield, which greatly reduces the beta radiation which might be received by the hands of the operator.

the information thereby gained could not be obtained with simpler techniques.

The recently published symposium on atomic radiation in oceanography and fisheries contains fine material on this phase of radiation ecology not previously available in one place (Revelle, 1957).

4. The fallout problem

The radioactive dust that falls to earth after atomic explosions is called fallout. The kind of fallout depends on the type of bomb. First, it may be well to distinguish between the two types of nuclear weapons, the fission bomb in which heavy elements such as uranium and plutonium are split, with the release of energy and radioactive "fission products," and the fusion bomb or the thermonuclear weapon in which light elements (deuterium) fuse to form a heavier element, with the release of energy and neutrons. Since an extremely high temperature (millions of degrees) is required for the latter, a fission reaction is used to "trigger" the fusion reaction. In general, the thermonuclear weapon produces less fission products and more neutrons than does a fission weapon per unit of energy released. According to Glasstone (1957), about 10 per cent of the energy of a nuclear weapon is in residual nuclear radiation, some of which becomes widely dispersed in the biosphere. The amount of fallout produced depends not only on the type and size of the weapon, but also on the amount of environmental material which gets mixed up in the explosion. The neutrons emitted during blasts induce radioactivity in surrounding material.

Fortunately, the atmosphere itself is difficult to activate. Carbon-14 is the chief result, but, because of its weak beta activity and extensive dilution, little or no hazard results. However, an increase of C^{14} in the biosphere is not without ecological interest. Rafter and Fergusson (1957) report that C^{14} in the atmosphere has apparently been increasing exponentially since the beginning of extensive weapons tests. In 1957, the amount was 6.7 per cent greater than that present in 1954. These authors cut down a 7-year-old pine tree (in New Zealand) and analyzed separately the annual rings of wood and the one-year and two-year needles (which remain attached in the species studied). Increase in C^{14} in the wood and foliage paralleled the increase in the atmosphere. The 1957 pine needles were enriched by 4.8 per cent as compared with the 1956 needles. They also found an increase in the ocean at New Zealand, indicating that the artificially produced isotope was finding its way from the air into marine ecosystems.

Generally, activation of surface materials by neutrons is also not very great. However, in the Pacific where atomic devices have been fired over coral islands or lagoons, isotopes which are not fission products have turned up in the ocean as well as in plankton and fish. According to the most recent comprehensive survey of the waters in the Marshall Island vicinity, non-fission isotopes of cobalt, iron and zinc were more prominent than had been expected (Seymour et al., 1957). Interestingly enough, non-fission products, which apparently are activated metals of the weapon (iron, especially), have been found in abundance in marine animals but not in land plants or animals of adjacent islands (Lowman et al., 1957).

For the most part, fission of uranium produces most of the environmental contaminants (Table 26). Fallout from weapons differs from atomic waste materials in that the radioactive isotopes are fused with iron, silica, dust and whatever happens to be in the vicinity to form relatively insoluble particles. These particles, which under the microscope often resemble tiny marbles of different colors vary in size from several hundred microns to almost colloidal dimensions.

As the mushroom cloud rises following a nuclear test, some of the material may fall back around "ground zero," but most of the particles move off with the cloud; a considerable portion of these particles are then deposited along a surprisingly narrow path extending for many miles. The fallout path may have a "midline" of maximum activity only 1 to 5 miles wide. So accurately can the path be predicted (from the study of upper wind conditions), that continental tests are set off only when the path will extend across many miles of desert where human beings and their domestic animals do not reside permanently. However, the very smallest particles do not "fall out" in this narrow path but become widely dispersed and travel around the world several times before reaching the ground; in addition, the more powerful "megaton" weapons eject material into the stratosphere where it may remain for years. At the present time there is a worldwide fallout rate, estimated by Libby to be about 1.5 microcuries/square mile/year, which results

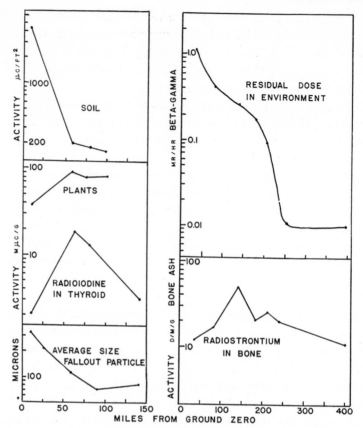

Figure 152. Total radioactivity in soil and on plants, average size of fallout particles, and the amount of radioiodine and radiostrontium in jack rabbits as a function of distance along the midline of fallout patterns following nuclear weapons tests. (Redrawn from Nishita and Larson, 1957.)

from materials accumulated in the upper atmosphere and the stratosphere. In 1956 the average soil contamination was about 5 mc/Km² (Bryant et al., 1957).

The smaller particles are more soluble and travel greater distances. Atomic devices detonated high in the air produce much less but more soluble fallout debris than those detonated on or near the surface of the earth. Even larger particles, however, eventually weather and become soluble. For example, alpha isotopes were found in pack rats some years after the detonation of the first atomic bomb in New Mexico (Leitch, 1951). It is important to note that there may be a delay in the entrance of fallout materials into biological systems.

While the radiation dose, as measured in "r" or "mr" per hour, decreases rapidly along the midline of the fallout path, with increasing distance from ground zero, plants and animals living 100 or more miles away may actually absorb more of certain isotopes than do individuals of the same species living, as it were, in the very shadow of the bomb. This rather surprising finding, repeatedly documented by radioecologists working at the Nevada Test Site (see report by Nishita and Larson, 1957), is apparently to be explained by the fact that the smaller particles which fall at a distance stick to the leaves of plants and dissolve more readily (especially under the action of animal digestive juice) and, therefore, enter the food chain more quickly. A picture of this sort is shown in Figure 152. Note that the radiation level as measured in the soil (or above the soil surface) and the size of the fallout particle decreased with distance; in contrast, contamination on the leaves of plants did not decrease but even increased, while the peak load of radioiodine in jack rabbit thyroids occurred at 60 miles and that of radiostrontium in the bone at about 130 miles. It is important to note that Sr^{90} has two gaseous precursors ($Kr^{90} \rightarrow Rb^{90} \rightarrow Sr^{90}$) and is, therefore, formed at a relatively late time (several minutes) after a bomb detonation with the result that it becomes included in the small particles (those less than 40 microns).

So far, no evidence has been found that the increase in radioiodine and radiostrontium in desert plants and animals, resulting from a single fallout pattern, approaches the body burden level necessary for extensive biological damage. Areas which have been crossed by several fallout patterns are now being studied closely. Figure 153 shows a portion of a midline fallout study station set up to determine in detail the quantity and fate of radioactive debris which came down as the "cloud" passed over the desert.

Now let us turn our attention from the more local to the worldwide aspect of fallout. Three fission products, namely, Sr^{90}, I^{131} and Cs^{137}, have been detected in human tissues (Anderson et al., 1957), demonstrating that fallout isotopes can and do enter the food chain of man as readily as they do that of the jack rabbit. Cesium resembles strontium in having gaseous precursors and is thus associated with it in "long distance fallout." Cesium behaves like potassium and is readily absorbed by organisms, but it remains in the body only a short time compared to strontium (rapid turnover).

Since radioiodine is produced by weapons or reactors in large

Figure 153. Fallout study station in the Nevada saltbush desert. In the
upper photo, an air sampler may be seen to the left; detectors for measurement of radiation at two levels and weather instruments are shown to the
right. The dominant desert shrubs in the area belong to the genera *Grayia,
Eurotia* and *Ephedra.* In the lower picture, trays containing plastic pellets
have been set out to collect fallout particles which come down to earth. The
pellets catch and hold particles which later may be washed free from the
inert plastic, thus providing a quantitative sample as well as "pure fallout"
for experimental studies. Fallout particles are difficult to separate from the
soil itself. Note also the portable survey meter for determining the general
radiation level in the vicinity. (Photos by courtesy of the Atomic Energy
Project of the University of California at Los Angeles.)

quantities, it is not hard to understand how it becomes widely dispersed, adheres to plants and then is quickly concentrated in the
thyroids of vertebrates. Despite its short half-life, it reaches the
end of the food chain, as shown in Figure 154. After each series
of nuclear tests, the I^{131} level increased in cattle thyroids and, to a
lesser extent, in human thyroids.

As far as man is concerned, the internal concentration of the three isotopes (as of 1956) is below what is considered harmful. The Sr^{90} level in the bones of children after two years of extensive nuclear tests was about 0.001 microcurie per person (Libby, 1956) or about 1 micromicrocurie per gms. calcium (since there are about 1000 gms Ca/person). One microcurie per person (or 1000 $\mu\mu c$/ gm Ca) is the lowest level anyone now believes might result in an increase in blood or bone cancer rate. As shown in Table 32, sheep in hill pastures of England are already up to 160 $\mu\mu c$/gm Ca; this fact suggests what might happen should man feed entirely on vegetables. As may be seen from Figure 154, the peak level of radioiodine in the thyroids of humans during the 1955 test series was about 0.005 millimicrocuries per gram wet tissue (Comar et al., 1957); the maximum permissible level in man for continuous exposure is now listed as 15 millimicrocuries per gram. Note in Figure 152 that jack rabbits living at the 60 miles point along the fallout path had about 20 millimicrocuries per gram; kangaroo rats were found to have as much as 200 in the same study. Therefore, we see that if man were forced to obtain all his food from a restricted contaminated area, he might easily be obtaining at least temporary levels which he would not want to risk.

Thus, we see that while there seems to be little to worry about radiation in *average* worldwide levels, local situations could change the picture drastically. Young children under four years of age accumulate Sr^{90} more rapidly than adults and are pre-

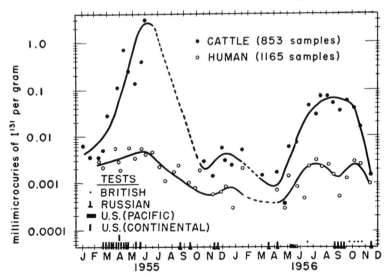

Figure 154. Summary of iodine-131 levels in human and cattle thyroids as correlated with nuclear weapons tests during 1955–1956. (After Comar et al., 1957.)

Table 32. *Comparison of the amount of Sr^{90} (resulting from fallout) in 1956 at different trophic levels in two contrasting ecosystems, in the British Isles*[*]

	Hill pasture Acid peat soil, pH 4.3			Valley pasture Brown loam soil, pH 6.8		
	Amount Sr^{90} $\mu\mu$c/gm dry material	$\mu\mu$c/gm calcium	Concen-tration factor[†]	Amount Sr^{90} $\mu\mu$c/gm dry material	$\mu\mu$c/gm calcium	Concen-tration factor[†]
SOIL (average top 4 inches)	0.112	800	1	0.038	2.6	1
GRASS	2.5	2100	21	0.250	41	6.6
SHEEP BONE	80	160	714	4.4	8.7	115

[*] Data from Bryant et al., 1957.
[†] Ratio of the amount per gram in environment (soil) to amount per gram biological material.

sumedly more radiosensitive. Caster (1957) suggests that the minimum permissible level compatible with reasonable safety and public health could be exceeded in 10 to 15 years.

The general ecological picture with regard to strontium from fallout is well summarized by the data in Table 32. Because the concentration of calcium is very low in the soil of the hill pasture, and also because the mat-like vegetation catches the fallout before it reaches the ground, a much greater amount of strontium is transferred to the animals. The amount of Sr^{90} per gram of calcium is actually less in bone than in grass because strontium is discriminated against by bone tissue in favor of calcium. In general, a predator is likely to obtain a lower "body burden" of radio-isotopes than a herbivore because of both the operation of discriminatory processes and the time lag which permits radio-active decay (see Figure 149 and Table 31).

5. Waste disposal

Although fallout problems are presently in the public eye, waste disposal from peaceful uses of atomic energy is potentially a far greater problem, assuming again that we do not have an all-out atomic war. Not enough attention is now being given to the ecological aspects of waste disposal, which could be the limiting factors to full exploitation of atomic energy. According to the 1957 AEC waste disposal report (cited on page 497), tanks with a capacity of 103 million gallons have been constructed at the three large atomic energy sites at a cost of 60 million dollars, and these tanks are already over half full of high level wastes.

The low-level wastes are too voluminous to contain and must be released into the environment; they thus enter the sphere of the ecologist! The 1957 AEC report indicates that about 9 billion gallons of liquid wastes having 2 million curies of radioactivity are already being discharged per year, chiefly into large rivers, the sea and the soil. So great is the diluting power of water and air and the fixation power of most soils that the present quantity of low level wastes, impressive as it may be in terms of gallons or curies, is but a drop in the bucket of nature. However, when atomic power becomes a major source of industrial energy in the latter half of this century the environmental situation becomes more critical. Competitive industry will want to reduce the cost of waste disposal, and the environmental problems will no longer be re-

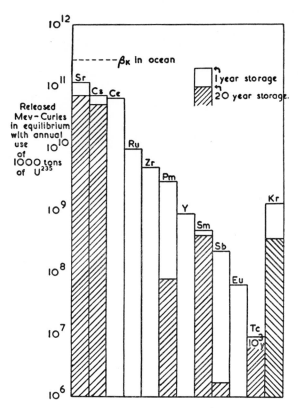

Figure 155. Equilibrium activities of individual fission products which would be built up by an annual use of 1000 tons of fissionable materials after one year and after 20 years storage before disposal, in comparison with the total K^{40} activity (natural radioactivity) of all the oceans. (From Glueckauf, 1956.)

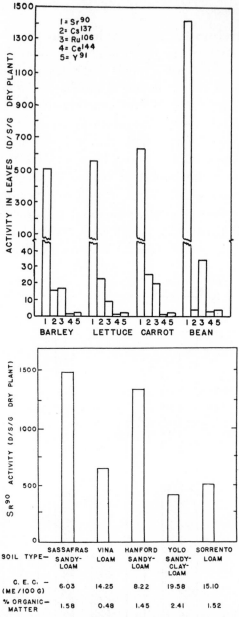

Figure 156. Upper graph: Uptake of Sr[90] (1), Cs[137] (2), Ru[106] (3), Ce[144] (4), and Y[91] (5) by different crop plants grown on Hanford sandy loam soil contaminated at the level of 100 disintegrations per second of isotope per gram dry soil. In this soil strontium is removed by plants to a much greater extent than are other significant fission products. Lower graph: Uptake of Sr[90] by bean plants grown on different types of soil contaminated as above. In general, the greater the cation exchange capacity (C.E.C.) and per cent organic matter the less the uptake. In other words, less of the radioactive contaminant is removed per gram of dry plant matter produced in fertile soils than in poor soils. (Graphs prepared by E. M. Romney from data of Romney, Neel, Nishita, Olafson and Larson, 1957.)

stricted to a few very carefully controlled and guarded "exclosures" (i.e., fenced domains from which people are excluded for one reason or another), but will be spread around so that bad situations could easily develop at any point in any kind of environment.

Figure 155 presents a "line up" of the waste isotopes in the approximate order of their importance in terms of the amount of radiation they produce. As already discussed, this tells only part of the story, because some isotopes become ecologically concentrated to a much greater extent than others. In any event the isotopes are the same ones important in fallout, and, by all odds, the number one problem is strontium-90. In fact, if both Sr^{90} and Cs^{137} could be removed and the rest stored for one year, the activity would drop by 1000 and the toxicity to man would decrease by 25,000 (Glueckauf, 1955).

Not included in the list in Figure 155 are alpha-emitting isotopes of uranium and plutonium which are present in waste materials. These have such long half-lives and are so potentially dangerous that their removal (at least to a large extent) is mandatory before disposal can take place.

Since liquid wastes are relatively soluble compared with fallout, the isotopes quickly enter biological cycles when released into the

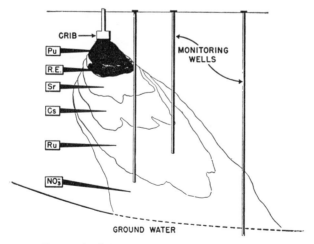

Figure 157. Disposal of high level liquid wastes in the ground at the Hanford Atomic Products Operations Plant showing the relative movement through the desert soils by significant isotopes. (Brown, Parker and Smith, 1956.)

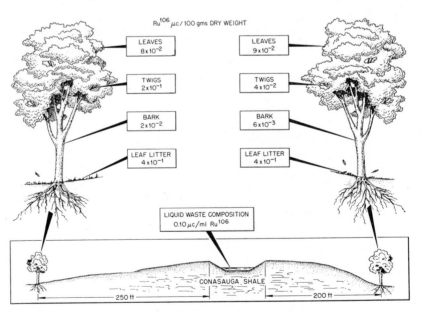

$Ru^{106} \mu c / 100$ gms DRY WEIGHT

LEAVES	LEAVES
8×10^{-2}	9×10^{-2}

TWIGS	TWIGS
2×10^{-1}	4×10^{-2}

BARK	BARK
2×10^{-2}	6×10^{-3}

LEAF LITTER	LEAF LITTER
4×10^{-1}	4×10^{-1}

LIQUID WASTE COMPOSITION
$0.10 \mu c/ml$ Ru^{106}

CONASAUGA SHALE
250 ft   200 ft

TYPICAL RUTHENIUM^{106} CONCENTRATIONS IN TREE COMPONENTS
IN VICINITY OF RADIOACTIVE WASTE PITS

Figure 158. Upper photo: Aerial view of three waste pits for the disposal of intermediate level radioactive wastes at Oak Ridge, Tennessee. In the lower left hand corner may also be seen the upper end of the White Oak lake basin, a disposal site for low level wastes. Originally, water was im-

environment. It is especially important to know how the uptake by plants occurs and to know the environmental factors which may affect the rate of uptake since this would be the usual way that isotopes get into the food chain. As may be seen in Figure 156, the type of soil as well as the kind of plant greatly affects the rate of uptake under experimental conditions.

Since it is becoming evident that soil pits are among the most economical and convenient sites for disposal of low and inter- mediate wastes (Struxness et al., 1956), especially in the case of the hundreds of laboratories and smaller installations which we can envision in the future, the movement of waste materials through the soil (and hence their availability to roots or the water table) is of prime importance. Figure 157 shows the results of early tests at the Hanford plant, which indicated that ruthenium moved further than any other radioactive isotope. It was the only one to approach the deep water table of the semi-arid region. At Oak Ridge, where the soil is underlain by beds of shale and lime- stone, ruthenium, having moved some distance horizontally from waste pits, as shown in Figure 158, appeared in the leaves of trees. This was an unexpected result and indicated the need for intensive field study. In this case, ruthenium is more important than stron- tium as far as the biota of the region are concerned.

The possibilities of large scale waste disposal in the ocean is being actively debated, and many small scale tests have been made. Ocean disposal is especially attractive to small, densely populated countries, which do not have large areas of idle land. While the dilution factor may be large, one again runs into the tendency of many organisms to concentrate isotopes, particularly in shallow coastal seas where there is a large standing crop of littoral organisms. For example, Seligman and Dunster (1956) report that only a few curies per day may be safely released into the Irish Sea because of the concentrative tendency of commer- cially harvested seaweed and other marine organisms.

---

pounded in this basin forming White Oak Lake, which was the site of some of the first radioecological research (Krumholz 1954). The fertile bottom of the drained lake is now serving as an important laboratory for the study of the fate of isotopes in terrestrial ecosystems. Lower figure: Cross section of a waste pit pictured in the above photograph showing lateral movement of ruthenium-106 through the shale and into trees 200 to 250 feet on either side of the pit. (Photos courtesy Oak Ridge National Laboratory, Radioecology Studies.)

6. Future radioecological research

In this brief review we have tried to show that the problems of radioactivity in the environment are not yet critical, but will undoubtedly become more critical in the future. We have tried to indicate some of the exciting possibilities for study made possible by isotopes. Now is the time to study before serious contamination occurs. The rates of cycling, the dispersions and concentrations, the radiation dose to populations, community metabolism and all the other aspects discussed need vastly more study. Each significant isotope needs to be experimented with in tracer amounts both in the laboratory and in the field, *but especially in such ecosystems where the major components and processes have already been studied.* The ecologist should remember that many aspects of the study of the biological effects of radiation are best done in the laboratory; however, ultimate effects on man and nature can not be understood until the "fate" of isotopes in ecological systems is well known, which means that carefully planned field research is equally important. In the not too distant future, the radioecologist may well be one of those who must help decide when to contain and when to disperse the waste materials of the atomic age. If the ecologist does not know what to expect in the biological environment, who will?

15 · Applications: human society

In recent years the ecological approach to the study of human society has developed into the distinct field of human ecology in which sociologists, anthropologists, geographers as well as ecologists have found a meeting ground. The books of Hawley (1950) and Quinn (1950) summarize the development of the field from the sociological side which began with Galpin's (1915) work in rural sociology, and with the studies in the "ecology of cities" made by Robert E. Park, R. D. McKenzie, E. W. Burgess, and their students in the 1920's (see Park, Burgess, and McKenzie, 1925). Adams (1935), Brews (1935), Allee (1951), Darling (1951), Bates (1952), Sears (1957), and other workers in animal and general ecology have been especially interested in the application of ecological principles to human society. The recent international symposium (Thomas (ed.) 1956) will serve to bring out other approaches and viewpoints.

If we conceive of population ecology in the broad sense as discussed in Chapters 5 to 8, then human ecology is essentially the population ecology of a very special species—man! It is broader than demography (the field of human population analysis), since it deals with the relations of the population to external factors and larger units as well as with internal dynamics. It is likewise broader than human geography, which emphasizes the impact of physical factors on civilization. Populations of men, like other populations, are a part of larger units, i.e., biotic communities and ecosystems. Although man greatly modifies many of these units of which he becomes a part, he does not "create" them and is dependent on them, as is any other organism. Therefore, the study of general ecology can contribute to the social sciences through the conecting link of human ecology by emphasizing the natural processes which insure that the rate of flow of materials, food, etc. needed by mankind will be cyclic and adequate (see Chapter 2). However, we must go beyond the principles of general ecology because human society has several very important characteristics which make the human population unit quantitatively, if not qualitatively, different from all other populations. In the first place, man's flexibility in behavior and his ability to control his surroundings are greater than those of other organisms. In the second place, man develops culture, which, except to a very rudimentary extent, is not a factor in any other species. As James B. Conant (1952) has emphasized, it is essential that we recognize "a sharp cleavage between animal behavior and human conduct." In so doing, however, it is equally important not to lose sight of man's essential natural environment, which along with his cultural environment determines his ecology. Sears (1957) has emphasized that it is the relationship between the ratio: resources/population density, and culture, which is the all important consideration. Let us now consider the interaction of the "natural" and the "cultural" aspects of human ecology.

One of the main features, as indicated above, which distinguishes human populations from other populations is the degree of dominance of which man as a group is capable (see Chapter 8. Section 2, for discussion of ecological dominance). Although dominance is an obvious concept and easy to talk about in general terms, it is difficult to measure quantitatively. Man often assumes that he is 100 per cent dominant over his surroundings when actually this may be far from the case. He may air-condition his home and office and thus think he is independent of the climate, but unless he also air-conditions all his food plants and animals, he is still going to be very much affected by hot and cold weather, droughts, etc. Likewise, a farmer may think he has his corn field under full control, yet phosphorus may be escaping down the hill to the ocean at such a rapid rate that, from the standpoint of his future welfare, he is not controlling the situation at all but only disrupting it! At this point it is pertinent to refer to the philosophical discussion of the "biosphere" vs. the "noosphere" (page 26) and to the quotations from Hutchinson (pages 27, 31) and Leopold (pages 422-423) regarding man's place in ecosystems and the part he plays in biogeochemical cycles.

In an essay Kohler (1952) has suggested that evolution is proceeding to a higher level of complexity, which he calls the "societal organism." For example, he says that "it does appear quite certain that further human progress will not result merely from the biological improvement of individual man. It will be the integration process, the formation of the new organic entity that will determine the future development of man." This "entity" is a higher level than the ecosystem as the concept is used in this book, and is similar to Vernadsky's "noosphere." As previously pointed out (page 26), man has not yet reached this level, and there is great danger in assuming that he will do so as a matter of course and without conscious effort. Careful study and cooperation with natural cycles rather than wholesale "tamperings" beyond our ability to comprehend would seem to be the sensible road to take if we are to avoid detours (perhaps permanent!) in the achievement of true dominance and the complete orderliness of man and his environment. Because of the nature of the thermodynamic laws (see Chapter 3, Section 1) Kohler thinks that "orderliness" is necessary to counteract the natural tendency for complex units to disperse (i.e., to go to pieces). Complete domination of nature is probably not possible and would be precarious since man is a very "dependent" organism who lives "high" on the food chain. It would be much safer (and much more pleasant) if man accepts the idea of sharing the world with many other organisms instead of looking at every square inch as a possible source of food or site to make over into something artificial.

It would seem from the foregoing discussion that quantitative estimation of dominance might be of value. Comparison of various man-dominated communities and ecosystems with natural units preserved as "natural areas" should be fruitful, as previously suggested in Chapter 12. Another important approach involves obtaining information on the rate of energy flow and the rate of basic material transfer in biogeochemical cycles; in other words, adding numerical terms to the arrows in such diagrams as shown in Figures 7, 8 (pages 32-34) and Figure 11 (page 47).

Now let us examine the role of culture in human ecology. Howard W. Odum (1953) has defined culture as "the way people live in identified areas, times and settings"; it is "the sum total of cumulative processes and products of societal achievement." He also points out that folk-culture is a basic and relatively constant portion of the culture complex, as compared, for example, with technological or urban culture which may change rapidly in a relatively short time. Groups of people often retain the same cultural traits when they move from one environment to another. Thus, some central Europeans consider the carp a good food fish and brought it with them to America, whereas other cultural groups in America scorn this fish entirely, despite the fact that it has become readily available in streams and lakes of this country as a result of introduction by the former group. As another example of the slowness of change in basic folk-culture, we might cite Wirth's (1928) "The Ghetto," a study of a group of people who kept their old way of living when they came to the new world as a result both of their own traditions and of the pressure of neighboring cultural groups.

Sears (1957) has described a number of cultural patterns which are well adapted to the environment, and a number which are not. Among the former are farming systems in some of the small prosperous European countries. Among the latter are many examples of the failure of technology to keep in adjustment with the natural environment; for example, building factories and homes on the flood plains of rivers and then having them washed away by floods which are bound to come sooner or later. A great many of the "disasters" resulting from floods, dust bowls, etc., which one reads about in the papers (and pays for in money for rehabilitation) are not caused by nature but by man's stupidity in his treatment of nature.

Although cultural patterns are definitely related to the natural environment, distinctly different human societies and ecosystems may develop in the same environment as a result of different basic cultures. As an extreme example, we need only to compare the civilization developed by the American Indian in the temperate deciduous forest biome with what the white man has done with the same natural environment. Since cultural patterns are so important and may persist for long periods of time, the historical and anthropological aspects are very important. Although the white man has established an entirely different kind of society in America, compared with that of the Indian, this new society is nonetheless greatly influenced by the impact of the former culture on the natural environment. For example, the magnificent open stands of pine in the southeast which the white man used to build his ships and homes were the result, in part at least, of the cultural pattern of burning which was practiced for centuries by the Indians (see page 394). The importance of the history of both man and the bison in relation to the grassland has been mentioned (Chapter 11, Section 4; Chapter 12, Section 9).

Many individuals among the higher animals show concern for the welfare of mates, young, and even associates, but it seems safe to say that only in man is the individual capable of showing concern for the welfare of the population as a whole. Thus, public health and welfare are unique features of human society, although, it must be admitted, this cultural pattern is relatively new and far from effective, as far as the world as a whole is concerned. Certainly there must be much improvement in this line before the "societal organism" can be considered a reality.

A very important approach to the integration of man and nature is to be found in the concept of regionalism as especially developed by Howard W. Odum and his students (see Odum and Moore, 1938; Odum, 1951). Regionalism, as an approach to the study of society, is based on the recognition of distinct differences in both cultural (past and present) and natural attributes of different areas which, nevertheless, are interdependent. Therefore, it is profitable to separate out regions on the basis of both natural and cultural indices and subject them to study in order to obtain a perspective for integration into a larger unit such as the United States. "The primary objectives of regionalism are found in the end product of integration of regions more than in the mere study and development of regions themselves" (H. W. Odum, 1951). Biomes (Figures 120–122), climatic zones, and zonal soil groups (Fig. 34) provide logical natural bases for regional classification, while agriculture, industry, education, income, etc. provide cultural indices. One difficulty has been that sociological statistics on which cultural indices are based usually refer to political units (states, counties) which may not coincide at all with natural units.

Nearly all of the various principles and concepts in population ecology discussed in Chapters 5 to 8 have application in the study of human ecology. In fact, a number of important techniques and concepts were first worked out with reference to human populations, and then found to apply broadly to all populations. The problems of internal population structure have received considerable attention in the literature of human ecology. A specific example of the effect of environment on age distribution has been given (Fig. 46). As was indicated at the beginning of this chapter, the growth and development of cities have been a focal point. Cities show characteristic gradients from high- to low-income

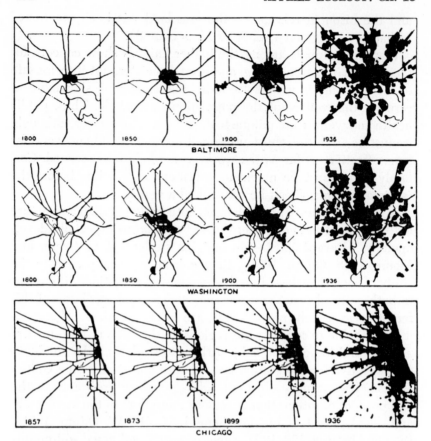

Figure 159. The growth of three cities in the United States between 1800 and 1936. (From Interregional Highways Message from the President of the United States, 78th Congress, 2nd Session, House Document No. 379, Washington, D.C., 1944.)

groups, stratification, succession, and many other standard ecological processes. Schmid (1950), in a review on "the ecology of the American city," states that "the ecological structure of the large American city conforms to a consistent and regular pattern in which the socio-economic status of the population is a dominant feature." Ecological principles have important applications in city planning, since topography, drainage, and other natural features, as well as existing cultural features, must be coordinated in planning for city expansion if costly alterations are to be avoided later (see Quinn, 1950, Chapter 9).

One aspect of the growth of cities is shown in Figure 159. With the improvement of transportation during the last few decades, these cities have "exploded" with numerous suburbs, many of which are becoming more or less complete units in themselves. Certain biological problems associated with the growth of cities have been mentioned (Chapter 13). There are even more difficult social problems. Man, by both conscious effort and trial and error, is apparently seeking a balance between the advantages of aggregation (Chapter 6, Section 14) on the one hand, and isolation or "territoriality" (Chapter 6, Section 15) on the other. The break-up of cities suggests that aggregation can reach a point beyond which the advantage to the population as a whole declines. This, perhaps, is another example of Allee's principle which is concerned with the relative effects of "undercrowding" and "overcrowding" (see Figure 64). In any event, rapidly changing population distribution patterns have important effects on land use, wildlife management, and other fields of applied ecology.

Perhaps the most "violent" topic in human ecology revolves around the future size of the human population and its consequences in terms of the future welfare of man. Probably the human population has undergone a number of growth phases coincident with changes in "carrying capacity" resulting from the opening up of new territory or the development of greater efficiency in food production. In recent times the population of the world and also that of the United States seem to be following the sigmoid growth form (see Chapter 6, Section 8). We have warned against predictions based on extrapolation of sigmoid curves. There are two principal reasons why we cannot be certain that the density of man will level off: (1) we do not know whether the carrying capacity of the world for man will be or can be increased, and (2) we cannot be sure that human populations will not exceed the carrying capacity, as did the Kaibab deer when adequate checks were removed (see page 239). The concept of density-dependent control has important applications in this regard since, as previously pointed out (Chapter 6, Section 11), a population levels off best and does not exceed the upper asymptote when strong density-dependent factors are operating. When such factors are weak the population tends to exceed the carrying capacity, with starvation, disease, etc. bringing about an inevitable decline. It would certainly be desirable for man to avoid this type of population oscillation (which, of course, actually occurred in the middle ages in Europe, China, etc. and would have occurred in Ireland had not people been able to emmigrate to America during the potato famine). Intraspecific competition, and sometimes parasites and predators, can produce effective density-dependent control. With man, of course, we do not wish to depend on the latter! Therefore, if populations do level off and remain below carrying capacity, we shall probably have to depend on intra-population forces. In industrial civilizations we see that density-dependent action does indeed take place, since the birth rate declines as crowding occurs, due to voluntary birth control, etc. However, in China and India—perhaps a more "simple ecosystem"?—such action seems less effective; density continually rises to or above the carrying capacity of the environment, food chains become shorter (see Chapter 3, Section 2), and such progressive philosophies as democracy mean little to the hungry people!

In discussing man's "population problem," people often go back to Thomas R. Malthus, whose famous "Essay on the Principle of Population" went through six editions between 1798 and 1826. Malthus brought out the fact, which has been amply demonstrated to apply to organisms generally, that populations have an *inherent* ability for exponential growth (see Chapter 6, Section 7). This does not mean that populations continue to grow in such a manner, or even that such growth is actually realized. Nor does it mean that populations *necessarily* exceed their food supply. Malthus was not aware that there was a difference between density-dependent and density-proportional or density-independent factors, or that the former *can* operate to effectively prevent overpopulation. Therefore, it is not fair to brand Malthus a "false prophet"; he should be credited with clarifying one important principle of population growth.

Differences of opinion on the future trend of the human population do not follow academic lines. There are thoughtful and learned men in both the biological and social sciences who feel that the danger of overpopulation is very great, and there are equally learned men in both fields who take the opposite view. Thus, biologist William Vogt, in his best-seller "Road to Survival" (1948), presents evidence to indicate that we should not count on a very great increase in primary productivity. Social scientists Burch and Pendell, in their book "Population Roads to Peace and War" (1945), also "view with alarm." On the other side, many agricultural scientists and economists feel that the world capacity for man has scarcely been approached and can be greatly increased in the future (see Bennett, 1949). Other writers, such as

Luck (1957), are "optipessimists." Basic ecological theory, as outlined in Chapter 3, warns us not to assume that high yields of food obtained on small areas can also be obtained on large areas. Since we can't "eat" atomic energy, this new source of industrial energy won't help us except indirectly, as we may be able to use it to prolong the photosynthetic system or increase efficiency of utilization and transport.

During the past five years, however, an almost unanimity of opinion has decided that some degree of birth control is going to be necessary. As well expressed by Leonard (1957) "production of vast chlorella farms, along with increased agricultural yields, might buy time in which the world could stabilize its population" but sooner or later "some measure of population control is necessary."

The relationship between population density and food production is well shown in Figure 160. The countries which are most crowded (i.e., have the smallest acreage per capita) also have the highest food production, except for India and Asia generally, which are in bad shape because they are both overcrowded and inefficient in food production. Japan has a much more efficient agriculture than the U.S., but the point is that individual people in the U.S. are very much better fed and have a generally higher

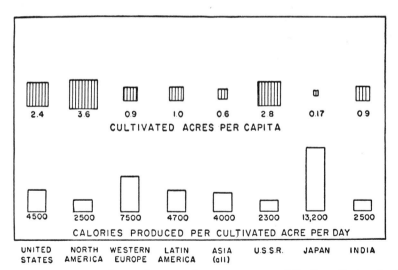

Figure 160. Population density of man per acre of food-producing land in comparison with food production per acre in different parts of the world (After Brown, Bonner and Wier, 1957.)

standard of living. It is evident that it is food per person which is important; *both* density and productivity must be considered, not just the latter.

Only one thing seems clear. It would be very pleasant and much easier to solve social problems if the population density remained large enough to avoid the disadvantages of "undercrowding" but never became so great that the average person could not have the opportunity of catching that big bass (a "symbol" of space for recreation) instead of having to use all available water areas to raise carp for food; or so great that everybody could not enjoy that steak (symbol of high quality foods) instead of having to subsist on cereals! (See Chapter 3, Sections 2 and 3.)

The fact that the disagreement over future trends and carrying capacities does not follow academic lines would seem to indicate that the difference of opinion is not due to narrowness of viewpoint or to overemphasis of any one set of data. Controversy here simply indicates that we do not have the information needed for sound prediction. In other words, we just don't know—and probably would not know what to do about it if we did! Although it is a blow to our ego as men, we are forced to admit that we know less about our own population than we know about that of some other organisms—which is little enough! Consequently, a lot of diligent study of man and nature (as a unit, not separately) is in order before we can even begin to entertain the idea that we are masters of our destiny.

Bibliography

NOTE: A few books and summary papers which contain useful bibliographies are included in this list, in addition to the references which are actually cited in the text.

Adams, Charles C. 1935. The relation of general ecology to human ecology. Ecol., 16:316–335.

Albertson, F. W.; Tomanek, G. W.; and Riegel, Andrew. 1957. Ecology of drought cycles and grazing intensity on grasslands of Central Great Plains. Ecol. Monogr., 27:27–44.

Allee, W. C. 1931. Animal Aggregations: A Study in General Sociology. University of Chicago Press, Chicago.

———. 1951. Cooperation among Animals with Human Implications. Schuman, New York (revised edition of Social Life of Animals, W. W. Norton & Co., New York, 1938).

Allee, W. C.; Emerson, A. E.; Park, Orlando; Park, Thomas; and Schmidt, Karl P. 1949. Principles of Animal Ecology. W. B. Saunders, Philadelphia.

Allee, W. C., and Schmidt, K. P. 1951. Ecological Animal Geography (2nd ed.). John Wiley & Sons, New York.

Allen, Shirley W. 1955. Conserving Natural Resources; Principles and Practice in a Democracy. McGraw-Hill Book Co., Inc., New York.

Anderson, W. C.; Schuch, R. S.; Fisher, W. R.; and Langham, Wright. 1957. Radioactivity of people and foods. Science, 125:1273–1278.

Andrewartha, H. G., and Birch, L. C. 1953. The Lotka-Volterra theory of interspecific competition. Australian J. Zool., 1:174–177.

———. 1954. The Distribution and Abundance of Animals. University of Chicago Press.

Atomic Energy Commission, Division Reactor Development. 1957. Status report on handling and disposal of radioactive wastes in the AEC program. U. S. AEC Report Washington, 742:1–41.

Aubert de la Rue, Edgar; Bourliere, Francois; and Harroy, Jean-Paul. 1957. The Tropics. Alfred A. Knopf, New York.

Auerbach, Stanley I. 1958. The soil ecosystem and radioactive waste disposal to the ground. Ecol., 39:522–529.

Auerbach, S. I.; Crossley, D. A.; and Engelman, M. D. 1957. Effects of gamma radiation on collembola population growth. Science, 126:614.

Azzi, Girolamo. 1956. Agricultural Ecology. Constable, London.

Baker, Edward W., and Wharton, G. W. 1952. An Introduction to Acarology. The Macmillan Co., New York.

Barick, F. B. 1950. The edge effect of the lesser vegetation of certain Adirondack forest types with particular reference to deer and grouse. Roosevelt Wildl. Bull., 9:1–146.

Bartholomew, George A., and Dawson, W. R. 1953. Respiratory water loss in some birds of southwestern United States. Physiol. Zool., 26:162–166.

Bartsch, A. F., and Allum, M. O. 1957. Biological factors in the treatment of raw sewage in artificial ponds. Limnol. and Oceanogr., 2:77–84.

Bates, Marston. 1945. Observations on climate and seasonal distribution of mosquitoes in eastern Colombia. J. Anim. Ecol., 14:17–25.

———. 1949. The Natural History of Mosquitoes. The Macmillan Co., New York.

———. 1952. Where Winter Never Comes. A Study of Man and Nature in the Tropics. Charles Scribner's Sons, New York.

———. 1957. Application of ecology to public health. Ecol., 38:60–63.

Baumhover, A. H.; Graham, A. J.; Hopkins, D. E.; Dudley, F. H.; New, W. D.; and Bushland, R. C. 1955. Screw-worm control through release of sterilized flies. J. Econ. Entomol., 48:462–466.

Becking, Rudy W. 1957. The Zurich-Montpellier School of Phytosociology. Bot. Rev., 23:411–488.

Beecher, William J. 1942. Nesting Birds and the Vegetation Substrate. Chicago Ornithological Society, Chicago.

Bennett, M. K. 1949. Population and food supply: the current scare. Scient. Monthly, 68:17–26.

Bertalanffy, Ludwig von. 1957. Quantitative laws in metabolism and growth. Quart. Rev. Biol., 32:217–231.

Billings, W. D. 1951. Vegetational zonation in the Great Basin of western North America. Internatl. Union Biol. Sc., France, Ser. B, 9:101–122.

———. 1952. The environment complex in relation to plant growth and distribution. Quart. Rev. Biol., 27:251–265.

———. 1957. Physiological ecology. Ann. Rev. Plant Physiol., 8:375–392.

Birch, L. C., and Clark, D. P. 1953. Forest soil as an ecological community with special reference to the fauna. Quart. Rev. Biol., 28:13–36.

Birch, L. C. 1948. The intrinsic rate of natural increase of an insect population. J. Anim. Ecol., 17:15–26.

———. 1957. The meaning of competition. Am. Nat., 41:5–18.

Birge, E. A. 1904. The thermocline and its biological significance. Tr. Amer. Micro. Soc., 25:5–33.

Blackman, F. F. 1905. Optima and limiting factors. Ann. Botany, 19:281–298.

Bliss, L. C. 1956. A comparison of plant development in microenvironments of arctic and alpine tundras. Ecol. Mongr., 26:303–337.

Bodenheimer, F. S. 1937. Population problems of social insects. Biol. Rev., 12:393–430.

———. 1938. Problems of Animal Ecology. Oxford University Press, London.

Bond, R. M. 1933. A contribution to the study of the natural food-cycle in aquatic environments. Bull. Bingham Oceanographic Coll., 4:1–89.

Bonner, James. 1950. The role of toxic substances in the interaction of higher plants. Bot. Rev., 16:51–64.

Bormann, F. H. 1956. Ecological implications of changes in photosynthetic response of Pinus taeda seedlings during ontogeny. Ecol., 37:70–75.

Boyd, M. (Editor.) 1949. Malariology. Two Volumes. W. B. Saunders, Philadelphia.

Boysen-Jensen, P. 1949. The production of matter in agricultural plants and its limitation. Det. Danske Videnskal Selskab. Biol. and Med., 21:1–28.

Bradshaw, A. D. 1957. Genecology of productivity of grasses (abstract). J. Anim. Ecol., 26:242.

Braun, E. Lucy. 1950. Deciduous Forests of Eastern North America. Blakiston Co., Philadelphia.

Braun-Blanquet, J. 1932. Plant Sociology: the study of plant communities (Translated and edited by G. D. Fuller and H. C. Conard). McGraw-Hill Book Co., Inc., New York.

———. 1951. Pflanzensoziologie. Springer-Verlag, Wien.

Brews, J. W. 1935. Human Ecology. Oxford University Press, London.

Briggs, L. J., and Shantz, H. L. 1914. Relative water requirement of plants. J. Agri. Res., 3:1–63.

Brody, Samuel. 1945. Bioenergetics and Growth. Reinhold, New York.

Brooks, John L. 1950. Speciation in ancient lakes. Quart. Rev. Biol., 25:30–60; 131–176.

Brown, A. H. 1953. The effects of light on respiration using isotopically enriched oxygen. Am. J. Bot., 40:719–729.

Brown, Frank A. 1958. Studies of the timing mechanisms of daily, tidal, and lunar periodicities in organisms. In: Perspectives in Marine Biology, pp. 269–282. University of California Press, Berkeley.

Brown, Harrison; Bonner, James; and Weir, John. 1957. The Next 100 Years. Viking Press, Inc., New York.

Brown, R. E.; Parker, H. M.; and Smith, J. M. 1956. Disposal of liquid wastes to the ground. Proc. Int. Conf. Peaceful Uses Atomic Energy, 9:669–675.

Bruun, Anton F. 1957. The Galathea Deep Sea Expedition. (Translated from the Danish by Reginald Spink.) The Macmillan Co., New York.

———. 1957a. Animals of the abyss. Sc. Am., 197:50–57.

Bryant, F. J.; Chamberlain, A. C.; Morgan, A.; Spicer, C. S. 1957. Radio-strontium in soil, grass, milk and bone in U.K.; 1956 results. J. Nuclear Energy, 6:22–40.

Buchanan, D. C.; Nakao, A.; and Edwards, G. 1953. Carbon isotope effects in biological systems. Science, 117:541–545.

Buell, M. F. 1956. Spruce-fir and maple-basswood competition in Itasca Park, Minn. Ecol., 37:606.

Bullock, T. H. 1955. Compensation for temperature in the metabolism and activity of poikotherms. Biol. Rev., 30:311–342.

Bump, Gardner; Darrow, R. W.; Edminster, F. C.; and Crissey, W. F. 1947. The Ruffed Grouse: Life History, Propagation, Management. New York Conservation Department, Albany.

Bunning, Erwin. 1956. Der tropische Regenwald. Springer-Verlag, Berlin-Göttingen-Heidelberg.

Bunt, J. S. 1954. The soil-inhabiting nematodes of Macquarie island. Australian J. Zool., 2:264–274.

Burch, Guy I., and Pendell, Elmer. 1945. Human Breeding and Survival: Population Roads to Peace or War. Penguin, New York.

Burkholder, Paul R. 1952. Cooperation and conflict among primitive organisms. Amer. Sc., 40:601–631.

Burkholder, Paul R., and Bornside, George H. 1957. Decomposition of marsh grass by aerobic marine bacteria. Bull. Torrey Bot. Club, 84:366–383.

Burr, G. O.; Hartt, H. E.; Brodie, H. W.; Tanimoto, T.; Kortschak, H. P.; Takahashi, D.; Ashton, F. M.; and Coleman, R. E. 1957. The sugar cane plant. Ann. Rev. Plant. Physiol., 8:275–308.

Burton, G. W., and Odum, E. P. 1945. The distribution of stream fish in the vicinity of Mountain Lake, Virginia. Ecol., 26:182–193.

Buzzati-Traverso, Adriano A. (Editor.) 1958. Perspectives in Marine Biology. University of California Press, Berkeley.

Cain, Stanley A. 1944. Foundations of Plant Geography. Harper & Bros.. New York.

——. 1945. A biological spectrum of the flora of the Great Smoky Mountains National Park. Butler Univ. Bot. Studies, 7:1–14.

——. 1950. Life-forms and phytoclimate. Bot. Rev., 16:1–32.

Cain, Stanley A., and Evans, Francis C. 1952. The distribution patterns of three plant species in an old-field community in southeastern Michigan. Contr. Lab. Vert. Biol., Univ. Mich., 52:1–11.

Callison, Charles H. 1957. America's Natural Resources. Ronald Press, New York.

Cannon, Helen L. 1952. The effect of uranium-vanadium deposits on the vegetation of the Colorado Plateau. Am. J. Sc., 250:735–770.

——. 1953. Geobotanical reconnaissance near Grants, New Mexico. Geol. Surv. Circ. 264:1–8.

——. 1954. Botanical methods of prospecting for uranium. Mining Engineering, Feb.: 217–220.

Cannon, Walter B. 1939. The Wisdom of the Body. W. W. Norton & Co., New York.

Carpenter, J. R. 1939. The biome. Am. Midl. Nat., 21:75–91.

——. 1940. The grassland biome. Ecol. Monogr., 10:617–684.

——. 1940a. Insect outbreaks in Europe. J. Anim. Ecol., 9:108–147.

Carthy, J. D. 1956. Animal Navigation. Charles Scribner's Sons, New York.

Caster, W. O. 1957. Strontium-90 hazard: relationship between maximum permissible concentration and population means. Science, 125:1291.

Chapman, R. N. 1928. The quantitative analysis of environmental factors. Ecol., 9:111–122.

——. 1931. Animal Ecology, with Special Reference to Insects. McGraw-Hill Book Co., Inc., New York.

Christensen, A. M., and McDermott. 1958. Life history and biology of the oyster crab, *Pinnotheres ostreum* Say. Biol. Bull., 144:146–179.

Christian, John J. 1950. The adreno-pituitary system and population cycles in mammals. J. Mamm., 31:247–259.

——. 1956. Adrenal and reproductive responses to population size in mice from freely growing populations. Ecol., 37:248–273.

Chu, H. F. 1949. How To Know the Immature Insects. Wm. C. Brown, Dubuque, Iowa.

Clarke, F. W. 1924. The Data of Geochemistry. U. S. Geol. Surv. Bull. No. 228.

Clarke, George L. 1933. Diurnal migration of plankton and its correlation with changes in submarine irradiation. Biol. Bull., 65:402–436. (See also Biol. Bull. 67:432–455.)

——. 1946. Dynamics of production in a marine area. Ecol. Monogr., 16:321–335.

——. 1948. The nutritional value of marine zooplankton with a consideration of its use as emergency food. Ecol., 29:54–71.

——. 1954. Elements of Ecology. John Wiley & Sons, Inc., New York.

Clarke, George L., and Backus, R. H. 1956. Measurement of light penetration in relation to vertical migration and records of luminescence of deep-sea animals. Deep-Sea Res., 4:1–14.

Clausen, C. P. 1956. Biological control of insect pests in continental United States. U.S.D.A. Tech. Bulletin 1139.

Clements, Frederic E. 1916. Plant succession: analysis of the development of vegetation. Publ. Carnegie Inst., Wash., 242:1–512. (See also reprinted edition, 1928, entitled "Plant Succession and Indicators," Wilson, New York.)

Clements, Frederic E., and Shelford, V. E. 1939. Bio-ecology. John Wiley & Sons, Inc., New York.

Clifford, Paul A. 1957. Pesticide residues in fluid market milk. Publ. Health Repts. 72:729–734.

Coffin, C. C.; Hayes, F. R.; Jodrey, L. H.; Whiteway, S. G. 1949. Exchanges of materials in a lake as studied by the addition of radioactive phosphorus. Can. J. Research Section C, 27:207–222.

Cogswell, Howard L. 1947. Chaparral Country. Aud. Mag., 49:75–81.

Coker, Robert E. 1947. This Great and Wide Sea. University of North Carolina Press, Chapel Hill.

———. 1954. Streams, Lakes, Ponds. University of North Carolina Press, Chapel Hill.

Cole, LaMont C. 1946. A theory for analyzing contagiously distributed populations. Ecol., 27:329–341.

———. 1951. Population cycles and random oscillations. J. Wildl. Mgt., 15:233–251.

———. 1957. Sketches of general and comparative demography. Cold Spring Harbor Sym. Quant. Biol., 22:1–15.

Colman, John S. 1950. The Sea and Its Mysteries. W. W. Norton & Co., New York.

Comar, C. L. 1955. Radioisotopes in Biology and Agriculture. Principles and Practice. McGraw-Hill Book Co., Inc., New York.

———. (Editor.) 1957. Atomic Energy and Agriculture. Amer. Assoc. Adv. Sc., Publ. No. 49:1–450.

Comar, C. L.; Trum, B. F.; Kuhn, U. S. G., III; Wasserman, R. H.; Nold, M. M.; and Schooley, J. C. 1957. Thyroid radioactivity after nuclear weapons tests. Science, 126:16–18.

Conant, James B. 1952. Modern Science and Modern Man. Columbia University Press, New York.

Cooke, Wm. B. 1958. Ecology of the fungi. Bot. Rev., 24:341–429.

Cooke, W. C. 1924. The distribution of the pale western cut-worm. *Porosogrotis orthogonia* Morr: a study in physical ecology. Ecol., 5:60–69.

Cooper, William S. 1922. The broad-sclerophyll vegetation of California; an ecological study of the chaparral and its related communities. Carnegie Inst. Wash. No. 319:1–124.

Cork, J. M. 1957. Gamma-radiation and longevity of the flour beetle. Radiation Res., 7:551–557.

Costello, D. F. 1944. Important species of the major forage types in Colorado and Wyoming. Ecol. Monogr., 14:107–134.

———. 1957. Application of ecology to range management. Ecol., 38:49–53.

Cowles, H. C. 1899. The ecological relations of the vegetation of the sand dunes of Lake Michigan. Bot. Gaz., 27:95–117; 167–202; 281–308; 361–391.

Cragg, J. B., and Pirie, N. W. (Editors.) 1955. The Numbers of Man and Animals. The Macmillan Co., New York.

Craig, Harmon. 1954. Carbon 13 in plants and the relation between carbon 13 and carbon 14 variations in nature. J. Geol., 62:115–149.

Craighead, J. J., and Craighead, F. C., Jr. 1956. Hawk, Owls and Wildlife. The Stackpole Co., Harrisburg, Penna.

Crocker, Robert L. 1952. Soil genesis and the pedogenic factors. Quart. Rev. Biol., 27:139–168.

Crombie, A. C. 1947. Interspecific competition. J. Anim. Ecol., 16:44–73.

Curtis, J. T. 1955. A prairie continuum in Wisconsin. Ecol., 36:558–566.

Curtis, J. T., and McIntosh, R. P. 1951. An upland forest continuum in the prairie-forest border region of Wisconsin. Ecol., 32:476–496.

Cutting, C. L. 1952. Economic aspects of utilization of fish. Biochem. Soc. Symposium No. 6. Biochemical Society. Cambridge, England.

Daisley, K. W. 1957. Vitamin B_{12} in marine ecology. Nature, 180:142–143.

Dansereau, Pierre. 1949. Introducao À Biogeografia. Rev. Brasil. de Geografia, 11:1–92.

———. 1951. Description and recording of vegetation on a structural basis. Ecol., 32:172–229.

———. 1957. Biogeography: an Ecological Perspective. Ronald Press, New York.

Darling, F. Fraser. 1938. Bird Flocks and the Breeding Cycle. Cambridge University Press, Cambridge, England.

———. 1951. The ecological approach to the social sciences. Amer. Sc., 39: 244–254.

Daubenmire, R. F. 1946. The life zone problem in the northern intermountain region. Northwest Science, 20:28–38.

———. 1947. Plants and Environment. John Wiley & Sons, Inc., New York.

———. 1956. Climate as a determinant of vegetation distribution in eastern Washington and northern Idaho. Ecol. Monogr., 26:131–154.

Davidson, James. 1938. On the growth of the sheep population in Tasmania. Tr. Roy. Soc. S. Australia, 62:342–346.

Davidson, James, and Andrewartha, H. G. 1948. Annual trends in a natural population of *Thrips imaginis* (Thysanoptera). J. Anim. Ecol., 17:193–199; 200–222.

Davis, David E. 1951. The characteristics of global rat populations. Am. J. Pub. Health, 41:158–163.

———. 1953. The characteristics of rat populations. Quart. Rev. Biol., 28:373–401.

Davis, John H., Jr. 1940. The ecology and geologic role of mangroves in Florida. Publ. Carnegie Inst., Wash., 517:303–412.

———. 1943. The natural features of southern Florida, especially the vegetation of the Everglades. Fla. Geol. Surv. Bull. No. 25.

Dearborn, Walter F., and Rothney, J. W. M. 1941. Predicting the Child's Development. Harvard University Press, Cambridge.

deBeaufort, L. F. 1951. Zoogeography of the Land and Inland Waters. Sidgwick and Jackson, London.

Deevey, Edward S., Jr. 1947. Life tables for natural populations of animals Quart. Rev. Biol., 22:283–314.

———. 1950. The probability of death. Sc. Am., 182:58–60.

———. 1951. Life in the depths of a pond. Sc. Am., 185:68–72.

———. 1952. Radiocarbon dating. Sc. Am., 186:24–28.

Dendy, J. S. 1945. Predicting depth distribution in three TVA storage type reservoirs. Tr. Am. Fish. Soc., 75:65–71.

Dice, Lee R. 1952. Measure of spacing between individuals within a population. Contr. Lab. Vert. Biol., Univ. Mich., 55:1–23.

———. 1952a. Natural Communities. University of Michigan Press, Ann Arbor.

Dobzhansky, Th.; Cooper, D. M.; Phaff, H. J.; Knapp, E. P.; and Carson, H. L. 1957. Studies on ecology in Yosemite region of California. IV. Differential attraction of species of *Drosophila* to different species of yeast. Ecol., 37:544–550.

Dowdy, W. W. 1947. An ecological study of the arthropoda of an oak-hickory forest with reference to stratification. Ecol., 28:418–439.

van der Drift, J. 1958. The role of the soil fauna in the decomposition of forest litter (abstract). XVth International Congress of Zoology, Sect. IV, Paper 3.

Droop, M. R. 1957. Vitamin B_{12} in marine ecology. Nature, 180:1041–1042.

Dublin, L. I., and Lotka, A. J. 1925. On the true rate of natural increase as exemplified by the population of the United States, 1920. J. Am. Statist. Assoc., 20:305–339.

Duxbury, A. C., and Yentsch, Charles. 1956. Plankton pigment monographs. J. Mar. Res., 15:92–101.

Dyksterhuis, E. J. 1946. The vegetation of the Fort Worth prairie. Ecol. Monogr., 16:1–29.

Dyson-Hudson, V. R. D. 1956. The daily activity rhythm of *Drosophila subobscura* and *D. obscura*. Ecol., 37:562–567.

Edmondson, W. T. 1955. Factors affecting productivity in fertilized sea water. Papers in Marine Biology and Oceanography. Suppl. to: Deep Sea Res., 3:451–464.

———. 1956. The relation of photosynthesis by phytoplankton to light in lakes. Ecol., 37:161–174.

Edmondson, W. T., and Anderson, G. C. 1956. Artificial eutrophication of Lake Washington, Limnol. and Oceanogr., 1:47–53.

Edney, E. B. 1957. The water relations of terrestrial arthropods. Cambridge Manage. in Exp. Biol. No. 5. Cambridge University Press.

Einarsen, A. S. 1945. Some factors affecting ring-necked pheasant population density. Murrelet., 26:39–44.

Eliassen, Rolf. 1952. Stream pollution. Sc. Am., 186:17–21.

Ellenberg, Heinz. 1950. Landwistschaftliche pflanzensoziolgie. Band 1. Unkrautgemeinschaftenals Zeiger fur Klima und Boden. Stuttgart: Eugen Ulmer.

Elton, Charles. 1927. Animal Ecology. The Macmillan Co., New York. (2nd Ed. 1935; 3rd Ed. 1947.)

———. 1933. The Ecology of Animals. Methuen, London.

———. 1942. Voles, Mice and Lemmings: Problems in Population Dynamics. Oxford University Press, London.

———. 1949. Population interspersion: an essay on animal community patterns. J. Ecol., 37:1–23.

Elton, Charles, and Miller, R. S. 1954. The ecological survey of animal communities: with a practical system of classifying habitats by structural characters. J. Ecol., 42:460–496.

Ely, Ralph L. 1957. Radioactive tracer study of sewage field in Santa Monica Bay. I.R.E. Trans. Nuclear Sc., NS-4:49–50.

Emerson, R. 1929. Relation between maximum rate of photosynthesis and chlorophyll concentration. J. Gen. Physiol., 12:609–622.

Emery, K. O. 1952. Submarine photography with the benthograph. Scient. Monthly, 75:3–11.

Emery, K. O., and Rittenberg, S. C. 1952. Early diagenesis of California basin sediments in relation to origin of oil. Bull. Am. Assoc. Petr. Geologists, 36:735–806.

Emlen, John T. 1952. Social behavior in nesting cliff swallows. Condor, 54: 177–199.

Erdean, R.; Kerry, R.; and Stephenson, W. 1956. The ecology and distribution of intertidal organisms on rocky shores of the Queensland mainland. Australian J. Mar. and Freshwater Res., 7:88–146.

Errington, Paul L. 1945. Some contributions of a 15-year local study of the northern bobwhite to a knowledge of population phenomena. Ecol. Monogr., 15:1–34.

———. 1946. Predation and vertebrate populations. Quart. Rev. Biol., 21:144–177; 221–245.

Evans, Francis C., and Cain, Stanley A. 1952. Preliminary studies on the vegetation of an old field community in southeastern Michigan. Contr. Lab. Vert. Biol., Univ. Mich., 51:1–17.

Evenari, M. 1949. Germitation inhibitors. Bot. Rev., 15:153–194.

Farner, Donald S. 1955. The annual stimulus for migration: experimental and physiologic aspects. In: Recent Studies in Avian Biology (edited by Wolfson). University of Illinois Press, Urbana.

Fautin, Reed W. 1946. Biotic communities of the northern desert shrub biome in western Utah. Ecol. Monogr., 16:251–310.

Fenton, G. R. 1947. The soil fauna; with special reference to the ecosystem of forest soil. J. Anim. Ecol., 16:76–93.

Filzer, Paul. 1956. Pflanzengcmeinschaft und Umwelt, Ergebnisse und Probleme der Botanischen Standortforschung. Stuttgart, Enke.

Finch, Vernon C., and Trewartha, Glenn T. 1949. Physical Elements of Geography. McGraw-Hill Book Co., Inc., New York.

Fisher, James, and Vevers, H. G. 1944. The breeding distribution, history and population of the north Atlantic gannet (*Sula bassana*): Changes in the world numbers of the gannet in a century. J. Anim. Ecol., 13:49–62.

Fleischer, W. E. 1935. The relation between chlorophyll content and rate of photosynthesis. J. Gen. Physiol., 18:573–597.

Fleming, R. H., and Laevastu, T. 1956. The influence of hydrographic conditions on the behavior of fish. FAO Fisheries Bull., 9:181–196.

Florkin, Marcel (Morgulis, Sergius, Editor). 1949. Biochemical Evolution. Academic Press, New York.

Fogg, G. E. 1955. Nitrogen Fixation. New Biology, No. 18, pp. 52–71. Penguin Books, London.

Forbes, S. A. 1887. The lake as a microcosm. Bull. Sc. A. Peoria. Reprinted in Ill. Nat. Hist. Surv. Bull., 15:537–550, 1925.

Foster, R. F. 1958. Radioactive tracing of the movement of an essential element through an aquatic community with specific reference to radiophosphorus. Publ. della Stazione Zool. di Napoli. (In press.)

Foster, R. F., and Davis, J. J. 1956. The accumulation of radioactive substances in aquatic forms. Proc. Int. Conf. Peaceful Uses Atomic Energy, 13:364–367.

Foster, R. F., and Rostenbach, R. E. 1954. Distribution of radioisotopes in the Columbia River. J. Am. Water Wks. Assoc., 46:663–640.

Frank, Peter W. 1952. A laboratory study of intraspecies and interspecies competition in *Daphnia pulicaria* and *Simocephalus vetulus*. Physiol. Zool., 25:178–204.

———. 1957. Coactions in laboratory populations of two species of *Daphnia*. Ecol., 38:510–518.

Freeman, T. W. 1957. Pre-famine Ireland. Manchester University Press.

Friederichs, K. 1930. Die Grundfragen und Gesetzmässigkeiten der landund forstwirtschaftlichen Zoologie. Paul Parey, Berlin. 2 Vols.

Frisch, K. Von. 1950. Bees, their vision, chemical senses, and language. Cornell Univ. Press, Ithaca.

Fulton, J. F. (Editor.) 1950. Howell's Textbook of Physiology (16th ed.). W. B. Saunders, Philadelphia.

Gaarder, T., and Gran, H. H. 1927. Investigations of the production of plankton in the Oslo Fjord. Rapp. et Proc.-Verb., Cons. Int. Explor. Mer., 42:1–48.

Galpin, C. J. 1915. The Social Anatomy of an Agricultural Community, Res. Bull., No. 34. Agr. Exp. Sta., University of Wisconsin, Madison.

Galtsoff, Paul S. 1956. Ecological changes affecting the productivity of oyster grounds. Trans. N. A. Wildl. Conf., 21:408–419.

Garren, Kenneth H. 1943. Effects of fire on the vegetation of the southeastern United States. Bot. Rev., 9:617–654.

Gause, G. F. 1932. Ecology of populations. Quart. Rev. Biol., 7:27–46. (See also Quart. Rev. Biol. 11:320–336, 1936.)

——. 1934. The Struggle for Existence. Williams & Wilkins, Baltimore.

——. 1934a. Experimental analysis of Vito Volterra's mathematical theory of the struggle for existence. Science, 79:16–17.

Geiger, R. 1957. The Climate Near the Ground. 2nd Ed., revised by M. N. Stewart. Harvard University Press, Cambridge, Mass.

Gessner, F. 1949. Der chlorophyllgehalt in see und seine photosynthetische Valenz als geophysikalishes problem. Schweizer Zeit. f. Hydrologie, 11: 378–410.

Glasstone, Samuel (Editor.) 1957. The Effects of Nuclear Weapons. U. S. Atomic Energy Commission, Washington.

Glueckauf, E. 1955. Chemical aspects of the atomic industry. Endeavor, 14:83–89.

——. 1956. Long-term aspect of fission product disposal. Proc. Int. Conf. Peaceful Uses Atomic Energy, Vol. 9:3 8.

Good, Ronald D. 1953. The Geography of Flowering Plants. Longmans, Green & Co., New York.

Goodall, D. W. 1952. Quantitative aspects of plant distribution. Biol. Rev., 27:194–245.

——. 1953. Objective methods for classification of vegetation, II. Fidelity and indicator value. Australian J. Bot., 1:434–456.

Graham, Edward H. 1944. Natural Principles of Land Use. Oxford University Press, New York.

Graham, S. A. 1951. Developing forests resistant to insect injury. Scient. Monthly, 73:235–244.

——. 1952. Principles of Forest Entomology (Rev. Ed.). McGraw-Hill Book Co., Inc., New York.

Grandfield, C. O. 1945. Alfalfa seed production as affected by organic reserves, air temperature, humidity and soil moisture. J. Agr. Res., 70:123–132.

Griggs, Robert F. 1956. Competition and succession on a rocky mountain fellfield. Ecol., 37:8–28.

Gross, A. O. 1947. Cyclic invasion of the snowy owl and the migration of 1945–46. Auk, 64:584–601.

Gunter, Gordon, 1941. Death of fishes due to cold on the Texas coast, January, 1940. Ecol., 22:203–208.

——. 1956. Some relations of faunal distributions to salinity in estuarine waters. Ecol., 37:616–619.

Haagen-Smit, A. J.; Darley, E. F.; Zaitlin, E. F.; Hull, M.; and Noble, W. 1952. Investigation of injury to plants from air pollution in the Los Angeles area. Plant Physiol., 27:18–34.

Hamilton, William J. 1937. The biology of microtine cycles. J. Agr. Res., 54:784–789.

Hammer, K. C. 1940. Interaction of light and darkness in photoperiodic induction. Bot. Gaz., 101:658–687.

Hanson, H. C. 1950. Ecology of the grassland. II. Bot. Rev., 16:283–360.

Hanson, W. C., and Kornberg, H. A. 1956. Radioactivity in terrestrial animals near an atomic energy site. Proc. Int. Conf. Peaceful Uses Atomic Energy, 13:385–388.

Hardy, Ross. 1945. Breeding birds of the pigmy conifers in the Book Cliff region of Eastern Utah. Auk, 62:523–542.

Harley, J. L. 1956. The mycorrhiza of forest trees. Endeavour, 15:43–48.

Harvey, H. W. 1950. On the production of living matter in the sea off Plymouth. J. Mar. Biol. Assoc. U.K. n.s. 29:97–137.

———. 1955. The Chemistry and Fertility of Sea Water. Cambridge University Press, Cambridge, England.

Haskell, E. F. 1949. A clarification of social science. Main Currents in Modern Thought, 7:45–51.

Haurwitz, Bernhard, and Austin, J. M. 1944. Climatology. McGraw-Hill Book Co., Inc., New York.

Haviland, Maud D. 1926. Forest, Steppe and Tundra. Cambridge University Press, Cambridge, England.

Hawkins, Arthur S. 1940. A wildlife history of Faville Grove, Wisconsin. Tr. Wisc. Acad. Sc., Arts, Lets., 32:29–65.

Hawley, Amos H. 1950. Human Ecology: A Theory of Community Structure. Ronald Press, New York.

Hayes, F. R., and Coffin, C. C. 1951. Radioactive phosphorus and exchange of lake nutrients. Endeavour, 10:78–81.

Hazard, T. P., and Eddy, R. E. 1950. Modification of the sexual cycle in the brook trout (*Salvelinus fontinalis*) by control of light. Tr. Am. Fish Soc., 80:158–162.

Hedgpeth, Joel W. 1951. The classification of estuarine and brackish waters and the hydrographic climate, in Report No. 11 of National Research Council Committee on a Treatise on Marine Ecology and Paleoecology, pp. 49–56. See Ladd, Harry S.

———. (Editor.) 1957. Treatise on Marine Ecology and Paleoecology. Vol. 1. Ecology. The Geological Society of America, New York.

Hegner, Robert. 1938. Big Fleas Have Little Fleas, or Who's Who among the Protozoa. Williams & Wilkins Co., Baltimore.

Heinicke, A. J., and Childers, N. F. 1937. The daily rate of photosynthesis of a young apple tree of bearing age. Mem. Cornell Univ. Agr. Exp. Sta., 201:3–52.

Hellmers, Henry; Bonner, J. F.; and Kelleher, J. M. 1955. Soil fertility: a watershed management problem in the San Gabriel Mountains of southern California. Soil Sc., 80:180–197.

Henrici, A. T. 1939. The distribution of bacteria in lakes. Publ. Am. Assoc. Adv. Sc., 10:39–64.

Hewitt, E. J. 1957. Some aspects of micro-nutrient element metabolism in plants. Nature, 180:1020–1022.

Heyward, Frank, 1939. The relation of fire to stand composition of longleaf pine forests. Ecol., 20:287–304.

Heyward, Frank, and Barnette, R. M. 1934. Effect of frequent fires on the chemical composition of forest soils in the longleaf pine region. Univ. Fla. Agr. Exp. Sta. Bull. No. 265.

Hickey, Joseph J. 1943. A Guide to Bird Watching. Oxford University Press, London and New York.

Hickling, C. F. 1948. Fish farming in the Middle and Far East. Nature, 161: 748–751.

Hills, G. A. 1952. The classification and evaluation of site for forestry. Res. Rep. No. 24, Ontario Dept. Lands and Forests.

Hjort, John. 1926. Fluctuations in the year classes of important food fishes. J. du Conseil Permanent Internationale pour L'Exploration de la Mer, 1:1–38.

Hocker, Harold W., Jr. 1956. Certain aspects of climate as related to distribution of loblolly pine. Ecol., 37:824–834.

Hoffmann, C. H., and Linduska, J. P. 1949. Some considerations of the biological effects of DDT. Scient. Monthly, 69:104–114.

Hogetsu, K., and Ichimura, S. 1954. Studies on the biological production of Lake Suwa. VI. The ecological studies on the production of phytoplankton. Japanese J. Bot., 14:280–303.

Hollaender, A. (Editor.) 1954. Radiation Biology. Vol. I. High Energy Radiation. Vol. II. Ultraviolet and Related Radiation. Vol. III. Visible and Near-visible Light. McGraw-Hill Book Co., Inc., New York.

Hollingshead, A. B. 1940. Human ecology and human society. Ecol. Monogr., 10:354–366.

Holloway, James K. 1957. Weed control by insects. Scient. Am., 197(1): 56–62.

Hooker, H. D. 1917. Liebig's law of minimum in relation to general biological problems. Science, 46:197–204.

Huffaker, C. B. 1957. Fundamentals of biological control of weeds. Hilgardia, 27:101–167.

Humphrey, R. R. 1949. Field comments on the range condition method for forage survey. J. Range Mgt., 2:1–10.

Hunter, W. S., and Vernberg, W. B. 1955. Studies on oxygen consumption of digenetic trematodes. II. Effects of two extremes in oxygen tension. Exper. Parsit., 4:427–434.

Huntington, E. 1945. Mainsprings of Civilization. John Wiley & Sons, Inc., New York.

Hursh, C. R. 1948. Watershed management research Coweeta Experimental Forest, Macon County, North Carolina. U.S.D.A., Southeastern Forest Exp. Sta., Asheville, N. C.

——. 1948a. Local climate in the Copper Basin of Tennesseee as modified by the removal of vegetation. U.S.D.A. Circular No. 774.

Hutchinson, G. E. 1944. Limnological studies in Connecticut: critical examination of the supposed relationship between phytoplankton periodicity and chemical changes in lake waters. Ecol., 25:3–26.

——. 1944a. Nitrogen in the biogeochemistry of the atmosphere. Am. Sci., 32:178–195.

——. 1948. Circular causal systems in ecology. Ann. N. Y. Acad. Sc., 50: 221–246.

——. 1948a. On living in the biosphere. Scient. Monthly, 67:393–398.

——. 1957. A Treatise on Limnology. Vol. 1. John Wiley & Sons, Inc., New York.

Hutchinson, G. E., and Bowen, V. T. 1948. A direct demonstration of phosphorus cycle in a small lake. Proc. Nat. Acad. Sc., 33:148–153.

——. 1950. Limnological studies in Connecticut: quantitative radiochemical study of the phosphorus cycle in Linsley Pond. Ecol., 31:194–203.

Hutchinson, G. E., and Deevey, E. S., Jr. 1949. Ecological studies on populations. Surv. Biol. Progress, 1:325–359.

Huxley, Julian. 1935. Chemical regulation and the hormone concept. Biol. Revs., 10:427.

Ichimura, Shun-ei. 1954. Ecological studies on the plankton in paddy fields. I. Seasonal fluctuations in the standing crop and productivity of plankton. Japanese J. Bot., 14:269–279.

Ivlev, V. S. 1934. Eine Mikromethode zur Bestimmung des Kaloriengehalts von Nahrstoffen. Biochem. Ztschr., 275:49–55.

Jacot, A. P. 1940. The fauna of the soil. Quart. Rev. Biol., 15:28–58.

Jenkins, Dale W. 1957. Radioisotopes in entomology. In: Atomic Energy and Agriculture, pp. 195–229. (See Comar, 1957.)

Jenny, Hans. 1941. Factors in Soil Formation. McGraw-Hill Book Co., Inc., New York.

Jewell, M. E., and Brown, H. W. 1929. Studies on northern Michigan bog lakes. Ecol., 10:427–475.

Johnston, David W., and Odum, Eugene P. 1956. Breeding bird populations in relation to plant succession on the Piedmont of Georgia. Ecol., 37:50–62.

Jones, E. W. 1951. Laboratory studies on the moisture relations of *Limonius* (Coleoptera; Elateridae). Ecol., 32:284–293.

Jones, J. R. Erichsen. 1949. A further ecological study of a calcareous stream in the 'Black Mountain' district of south Wales. J. Anim. Ecol., 18:142–159.

Juday, Chancey. 1940. The annual energy budget of an inland lake. Ecol., 21:438–450.

——. 1942. The summer standing crop of plants and animals in four Wisconsin lakes. Tr. Wis. Acad. Sc., 34:103–135.

Kalela, Olavi. 1949. Changes in geographic ranges in the avifauna of northern and central Europe in relation to recent changes in climate. Bird-Banding, 20:77–103.

Kamen, Martin D. 1953. Discoveries in nitrogen fixation. Sc. Am., 188:38–42.

Kamen, Martin D., and Gest, H. 1949. Evidence for a nitrogenase system in the photosynthetic bacterium *Rhodospirillum rubrum*. Science, 109:560.

Keever, Catherine. 1950. Causes of succession on old fields of the Piedmont, North Carolina. Ecol. Monogr., 20:229–250.

——. 1955. *Heterotheca latifolia,* a new and aggressive exotic dominant in Piedmont old-field succession. Ecol., 36:732–739.

Kellogg, Charles E. 1948. Modern soil science. Amer. Sci., 36:517–535.

Kendeigh, S. Charles. 1934. The role of environment in the life of birds. Ecol. Monogr., 4:299–417.

Kevan, D. Keith McE. (Editor.) 1955. Soil Zoology. Butterworths Scientific Publications. London.

Kimball, James W. 1948. Pheasant population characteristics and trends in the Dakotas. Tr. 13th N. A. Wildl. Conf., 13:291–314.

King, Ralph T. 1942. Is it a wise policy to introduce exotic game birds? Aud. Mag., 44:136–145; 230–236.

Kinne, Otto. 1956. Uber den Einfliss des Salzgehaltes und der temperatur auf Wachstum, Form und Vermehrung bei dem Hydroidpolypen *Cardylophora caspia* (Pallas), Thecata, Clavidae. Zool. Jahrb., 66:565–638.

Kittredge, J., Jr. 1939. The forest floor of the Chaparral of the San Gabriel Mountains, California. J. Agric. Res., 58:521–535.

Klages, K. H. W. 1942. Ecological Crop Geography. The Macmillan Co., New York.

Kleitman, Nathaniel. 1949. Biological rhythms and cycles. Physiol. Revs., 29:1–30.

Kluijver, H. N. 1951. The population ecology of the great tit, *Parus m. major* L. Ardea, 39:1–135.

Kohler, Fred. 1952. Evolution and Human Destiny. Philosophical Library, New York.

Kohn, Alan J., and Helfrich, Philip. 1957. Primary organic productivity of a Hawaiian Coral Reef. Limnol. and Oceanogr., 2:241–251.

Koritz, H. G., and Went, F. W. 1956. Physiological action of smog on plants. I. Initial growth and transpiration studies. Plant Physiol., 28:50–62.

Korringa, P. 1952. Recent advances in oyster biology. Quart. Rev. Biol., 27:266–308; 339–365.

Krumholz, Louis A. 1954. A summary of findings of the ecological survey of White Oak Creek, Roane County, Tennessee, 1950–1953. U. S. Atomic Energy Comm., Publ. ORO–132.

Krutch, Joseph W. 1955. The Voice of the Desert. William Sloane Associates, New York.

Kühnelt, W. 1950. Bodenbiologie mit besunderer Berucksichtigung der Tierwelt. Wien.

Kulp, J. L.; Eckelmann, W. R.; and Schulert, A. P. 1957. Strontium-90 in man. I. Science, 125:219. II. Science, 127:266–274.

Kuntz, J. E., and Riker, A. J. 1955. The use of radioactive isotopes to ascertain the role of root grafting in the translocation of water, nutrients, and disease-inducing organisms among forest trees. Proc. Int. Conf. Peaceful Uses Atomic Energy, 12:144–148.

Lack, David. 1945. Ecology of closely related species with special reference to cormorant (*Phalacrocorax carbo*) and shag (*P. aristotelis*). J. Anim. Ecol., 14:12–16.

———. 1951. Population ecology in birds; a review. Proc. Xth International Orn. Congress, Uppsala, Stockholm, pp. 409–448.

———. 1954. The Natural Regulation of Animal Numbers. Oxford University Press.

Ladd, Harry S. (Chairman). 1951. Report No. 11 of the National Research Council Committee on a Treatise on Marine Ecology and Paleoecology, 1950–51. National Research Council, Washington. (83 pp., mimeographed.)

Lalou, C. 1957. Studies on bacterial precipitation of carbonates in sea water. J. Sed. Pet., 27:190–195.

Lane, J. A. 1954. Nuclear fuel requirements for large-scale industrial power Nucleonics, 12(10):65.

Lang, R., and Barnes, O. K. 1942. Range forage production in relation to time and frequency of harvesting. Wyo. Agr. Exp. Sta. Bull. No. 253.

Langlois, T. H. 1945. Water, fishes, and cropland management. Tr. 10th N. A. Wildl. Conf., 10:190–196.

Laskey, Amelia R. 1939. A study of nesting eastern bluebirds. Bird-Banding, 10:23–32.

Leitch, James L. 1951. Summary of the radiobiological findings in animals from biological surveys of 1947, 1948, 1949, and 1950. Univ. Calif. Los Angeles Atomic Energy Project Rept., No. 111.

Leonard, Warren H. 1957. World population in relation to potential food supply. Scient. Monthly, 85:113–125.

Leopold, Aldo. 1933. Game Management. Charles Scribner's Sons, New York.

———. 1936. Farm game management in Silesia. Am. Wildl., 1936:81–91.

———. 1941. Lakes in relation to terrestrial life patterns, in A Symposium on Hydrobiology (pp. 17–22). University of Wisconsin Press, Madison.

——. 1942. Land use and democracy. Aud. Mag., 44:259–265.

Leopold, Aldo, and Jones, S. E. 1947. A phenological record for Sauk and Dane Counties, Wisconsin, 1935–1945. Ecol. Monogr., 17:81–122.

Leopold, Luna B., and Maddock, Thomas. 1954. The Flood Control Controversy: Big Dams, Little Dams, and Land Management. The Ronald Press, New York.

Leslie, P. H. 1945. On the use of matrices in certain population mathematics. Biometrika, 33:183–212.

Leslie, P. H., and Park, Thomas. 1949. The intrinsic rate of natural increase of *Tribolium castaneum* Herbst. Ecol., 30:469–477.

Leslie, P. H., and Ranson, R. M. 1940. The mortality, fertility, and rate of natural increase of the Vole (*Microtus agrestis*) as observed in the laboratory. J. Anim. Ecol., 9:27–52.

Levi, Herbert W. 1952. Evaluations of wildlife importations. Scient. Monthly, 74:315–322.

Libby, W. F. 1955. Radiocarbon Dating. University of Chicago Press.

——. 1956. Radioactive fallout and radioactive strontium. Science, 123:657–658.

Liebig, Justus. 1840. Chemistry in Its Application to Agriculture and Physiology. Taylor and Walton, London. (4th Ed. 1847.)

Lindeman, Raymond L. 1941. Seasonal food-cycle dynamics in a senescent lake. Am. Midl. Nat., 26:636–673.

——. 1942. The trophic-dynamic aspect of ecology. Ecol., 23:399–418.

Loosanoff, V. L. 1954. New advances in the study of bivalve larvae. Am. Sc., 42:607–624.

Lotka, A. J. 1925. Elements of Physical Biology. Williams & Wilkins, Baltimore.

Loutit, J. F. 1956. The experimental animal for the study of biological effects of radiation. Proc. Int. Conf. Peaceful Uses Atomic Energy, 11:3–6.

Lowman, Frank G.; Palumbo, Ralph F.; and South, Dorothy J. 1957. The occurrence and distribution of radioactive non-fission products in plants and animals of the Pacific Proving Ground. Applied Fish. Lab. Univ. Washington Report No. 51:1–61.

Lucas, C. E. 1947. The ecological effects of external metabolites. Biol. Rev. Cambr. Phil. Soc., 22:270–295.

Luck, J. Murray. 1957. Man against his environment: the next 100 years. Science, 126:903–908.

Ludwig, H. F.; Oswald, W. J.; Gatoos, H. B.; and Lynch, V. 1951. Algae symbiosis in oxidation ponds. I. Growth characteristics of *Euglena gracilis* cultured in sewage. Sewage and Industrial Wastes, 23:1337–1355.

Lundegårdh, H. 1954. Klima und Boden in ihrer Wirkung auf das Pflanzenleben. Gustav Fischer Verlag, Jena.

Lynch, D. L., and Cotnoir, L. J., Jr. 1956. The influence of clay minerals on the breakdown of certain organic substances. Soil Sc. Proc., 20:367–370.

MacFadyen, A. 1949. The meaning of productivity in biological systems. J. Anim. Ecol., 17:75–80.

——. 1957. Animal Ecology. Aims and Methods. Sir Isaac Pitman and Sons, London.

MacFarlane, Constance. 1952. A survey of certain seaweeds of commercial importance in southwest Nova Scotia. Canadian J. Bot., 30:78–97.

MacLulich, D. A. 1937. Fluctuations in the numbers of the varying hare (*Lepus americanus*). Univ. Toronto Studies, Biol. Ser., No. 43.

Major, Jack. 1951. A functional, factorial approach to plant ecology. Ecol., 32:392–412.

Malin, James C. 1953. Soil, animal and plant relations of the grassland, historically reconsidered. Scient. Monthly, 76:207–220.

———. 1956. The Grasslands of North America: Prolegomena to its history. 3rd printing, with addenda. Lawrence, Kan. (Privately printed by the author.)

Malthus, T. R. 1798. An Essay on the Principle of Population. Johnson, London. (Reprinted in Everyman's Library, 1914.)

Manning, W. M., and Juday, R. E. 1941. The chlorophyll content and productivity of some lakes in northeastern Wisconsin. Trans. Wisc. Acad. Sc. Arts. Lett., 33:363–393.

Marinelli, L. D.; Quimby, Edith H.; and Hine, G. L. 1948. Dosage determination with radioactive isotopes. II. Practical considerations in therapy and protection. Am. J. Roentgenology and Radium Therapy, 59:260–280.

Marshall, N. B. 1954. Aspects of Deep Sea Biology. Philosophical Library, New York.

Marshall, S. M., and Orr, A. P. 1955. The Biology of a Marine Copepod *Calanus finmarchicus* (*Gunnerus*). Oliver and Boyd, London.

Mason, H. L., and Langenheim, J. H. 1957. Language analysis and the concept environment. Ecol., 38:325–340.

Matheson, Colin. 1953. Some aspects of urban zoology in Great Britain. Scient. Monthly, 74:29–32.

Matthews, G. V. L. 1955. Bird Navigation. Cambridge University Press, New York.

Maynard, L. A. 1954. Animal species that feed mankind: the role of nutrition. Science, 120:164–166.

McMillan, Calvin. 1956. Nature of the plant community, 1. Uniform garden and light period studies of five grass taxa in Nebraska. Ecol., 37:330–340.

Mellanby, Helen. 1938. Animal Life in Fresh Water. Methuen, London.

Mericle, L. W., and Mericle, Rae Phelps. 1957. Irradiation of developing plant embryos, 1. Effect of external irradiation (x-rays) on barley embryology, germination and subsequent seedling development. Am. J. Bot., 44:747–756.

Merriam, C. Hart. 1894. Laws of temperature control of the geographic distribution of terrestrial animals and plants. Natl. Geogr. Mag., 6:229–238. (See also Life zones and crop zones. U. S. D. A. Bull. No. 10, 1899.)

Merrimam, Daniel. 1949. Biological problems of the ocean. Scient. Monthly, 68:12–16.

Miller, Alden H. 1955. Breeding cycles in a constant equatorial environment in Colombia, South America. Acta XI Congr. Inter. Orn., Basal, pp. 495–503.

Miller, Richard S. 1957. Observations on the status of ecology. Ecol., 38: 353–354.

Milthrope, F. L. 1956. The Growth of Leaves. Butterworths Publications, London.

Mohr, Carl O. 1940. Comparative populations of game, fur and other mammals. Am. Midl. Nat., 24:581–584.

Monsi, M., and Oshima, Y. 1955. A theoretical analysis of the succession of plant community based on the production of matter. Jap. J. Bot., 15:60–82.

Moran, P. A. P. 1949. The statistical analysis of the sunspot and lynx cycles. J. Anim. Ecol., 18:115–116.

Moreau, R. E. 1952. Africa since the mesozoic. Proc. Zool. Soc. London, 121:869–913.

Mori, Syuiti. 1957. Daily rhythmic activity of the sea-pen, *Cavernularia obesa valenciennes*. XV. Controlling the activity by light. Seto. Mar. Biol. Lab., 6:89–98.

Morrison, Frank B. 1947. Feeds and Feeding (20th ed.). Morrison, Ithaca, New York.

Mortimer, C. H., and Hickling, C. F. 1954. Fertilizers in fish ponds. Colonial Office Fishery Publ. No. 5:1–155. London.

Mukerjee, R. 1945. Social Ecology. Longmans, Green, New York.

Murie, Adolph. 1944. Dall Sheep, Chapter 3 in: Wolves of Mount McKinley. Nat. Parks Service Fauna No. 5, Washington.

Murneek, A. E., and Whyte, R. O. 1948. Vernalization and Photoperiodism: A Symposium. Chronica Botanica Co., Waltham, Mass.

Murphy, Robert C. 1936. Oceanic birds of South America. The Macmillan Co., New York. 2 Vols.

Myers, J. 1949. The pattern of photosynthesis in Chlorella. In: J. Franck, and W. E. Loomis, Photosynthesis in Plants, pp. 349–364. Iowa State College Press, Ames.

——. 1954. Basic remarks on the use of plants as biological gas exchangers in a closed system. J. Aviation Medicine, 25:407–411.

Needham, James G., and Needham, Paul R. 1941. A Guide to the Study of Fresh-water Biology. Comstock, Ithaca, New York.

Neess, John C. 1946. Development and status of pond fertilization in central Europe. Tr. Am. Fish. Soc., 76:335–358.

Nice, Margaret M. 1937. Studies in the life history of the song sparrow I. Tr. Linn. Soc. of New York, 4:1–247.

——. 1941. The role of territory in bird life. Am. Midl. Nat., 26:441–487.

Nicholson, A. J. 1933. The balance of animal populations. J. Anim. Ecol., 2:132–178.

——. 1954. An outline of the dynamics of animal populations. Australian J. Zool., 2:9–65.

Nielsen. (See Overgaard-Nielsen and Steeman-Nielsen.)

Nishita, H., and Larson, K. H. 1957. Summary of certain trends in soil-plant relationship studies of the biological availability of fall-out debris. Univ. Calif. Los Angeles, Atomic Energy Project Report No. 401:1–67.

Norman, A. G. 1957. Soil-plant relationships and plant nutrition. Am. J. Bot., 44:67–73.

Nutman, P. S. 1956. The influence of the legume in root-nodule symbiosis. Biol. Rev., 31:109–151.

Oberlander, G. T. 1956. Summer fog precipitation on the San Francisco Peninsula. Ecol., 37:851–852.

Odum, Eugene P. 1943. The vegetation of the Edmund Niles Huyck Preserve, New York. Am. Midl. Nat., 29:72–88.

——. 1945. The concept of the biome as applied to the distribution of North American birds. Wilson Bull., 57:191–201.

——. 1956. Ecological aspects of waste disposal. Atomic Energy Commission Rept., TID-7512:95–103.

——. 1956a. Consideration of the total environment in power reactor waste disposal. Proc. Int. Conf. Peaceful Uses Atomic Energy, 13:350–353.

——. 1957. Ecology and the atomic age. Assoc. Southeastern Biologists Bull., 4:27–29.

——. 1957a. The ecosystem approach in the teaching of ecology illustrated with sample class data. Ecol., 38:531–535.

——. 1959. Organic production and turnover in old field succession. (In press.)

Odum, Eugene P., and Burleigh, Thomas D. 1946. Southward invasion in Georgia. Auk, 63:388–401.

Odum, Eugene P., and Johnston, David W. 1951. The house wren breeding in Georgia: an analysis of a range extension. Auk, 68:357–366.

Odum, Eugene P.; Kuenzler, E. J.; and Blunt, Marion X. 1958. Uptake of P^{32} and primary productivity in marine benthic algae. Limnol. and Oceanogr., 3:340–345.

Odum, E. P., and Odum, H. T. 1957. Zonation of corals on Japtan Reef, Eniwetok Atoll. Atoll Res. Bull., 52:1–3.

Odum, Eugene P., and Smalley, Alfred E. 1957. Trophic structure and productivity of a salt marsh ecosystem. Progress report to Nat. Sc. Foundation (mimeo).

——. 1959. Population energy flow of two invertebrate species in a salt marsh ecosystem. (In press.)

Odum, Howard Thomas. 1951. The stability of the world strontium cycle. Science, 144:407–411.

——. 1956. Primary production in flowing waters. Limnol. and Oceanogr., 1:102–117.

——. 1956a. Efficiencies, size of organisms, and community structure. Ecol., 37:592–597.

——. 1957. Trophic structure and productivity of Silver Springs, Florida. Ecol. Monogr., 27:55–112.

——. 1957a. Primary production measurement in eleven Florida springs and a marine turtle-grass community. Limnol. and Oceanogr., 2:85–97.

Odum, H. T., and Odum, E. P. 1955. Trophic structure and productivity of a windward coral reef community on Eniwetok Atoll. Ecol. Monogr., 25:291–320.

——. 1956. Corals as producers, herbivores, carnivores and possibly decomposers. Ecol., 38:385.

Odum, H. T., and Pinkerton, R. C. 1955. Times speed regulator, the optimum efficiency for maximum output in physical and biological systems. Am. Sc., 43:331–343.

Odum, Howard W. 1951. The promise of regionalism, Chapter 15 in: Regionalism in America, Merrill Jensen (Ed.) University of Wisconsin Press, Madison.

——. 1953. Folk sociology as a subject for the historical study of total human society and the empirical study of group behavior. Social Forces, 31:193–223.

Odum, Howard W., and Moore, Harry E. 1938. American Regionalism. Henry Holt & Co., Inc., New York.

Oosting, Henry J. 1942. An ecological analysis of the plant communities of Piedmont, North Carolina. Am. Midl. Nat., 28:1–126.

——. 1956. The Study of Plant Communities. (2nd Ed.) W. H. Freeman, San Francisco.

Ordway, Samuel D., Jr. 1953. Resources and the American Dream. Ronald Press, New York.

Overgaard-Nielsen, C. 1949. Studies on soil microfauna. II. The soil inhabiting nematodes. Natura Jutlandica, 2:1–131.

——. 1949a. Freeliving nematodes and soil microbiology. Proc. Fourth Inter. Congr. Microbiology, Copenhagen 1947, pp. 283–484.

——. 1955. Studies on Enchytraeidae; 2. field studies. Natura Jutlandica, 4:5–58.

Ovington, J. D. 1957. Dry matter production by *Pinus sylvestris*. Annals Bot. n.s., 21:287–314.

Ovington, J. D., and Pearsall, W. H. 1956. Production Ecology. II. Estimates of average production by trees. Oikos, 7:202–205.

Packard, Charles. 1935. The relation between age and radiosensitivity of *Drosophila eggs*. Radiology, 25:223–230.

——. 1945. Roentgen radiations in biological research. Radiology, 45:522–533.

Palmgren, P. 1949. Some remarks on the short-term fluctuations in the numbers of northern birds and mammals. *Oikos*, 1:114–121.

Park, Robert E.; Burgess, E. W.; and McKenzie, R. D. 1925. The City. University of Chicago Press, Chicago.

Park, Thomas. 1934. Studies in population physiology: effect of conditioned flour upon the productivity and population decline of *Tribolium confusum*. J. Exp. Zool., 68:167–182.

——. 1939. Analytical population studies in relation to general ecology. Am. Midl. Nat., 21:235–255. (See also Quart. Rev. Biol., 16:274–293; 440–461, 1941.)

——. 1948. Experimental studies of interspecific competition. I. Competition between populations of flour beetles *Tribolium confusum* Duval and *T. castaneum* Herbst. Ecol. Monogr., 18:265–308.

——. 1954. II. Temperature, humidity and competition in two species of Tribolium. Physiol. Zool., 27:177–238.

Park, Thomas; Ginsburg, B.; and Horwitz, S. 1945. Ebony: a gene affecting the body color and fecundity of *Tribolium confusum* Duval. Physiol. Zool., 18:35–52.

Parker, J. R. 1930. Some effects of temperature and moisture upon *Melanoplus mexicanus* and *Camnula pellucida* Scudder (Orthoptera). Bull. Univ. Mont. Agr. Exp. Sta., 223:1–132.

Parker, M. W.; Hendricks, S. B.; Borthwick, H. A.; and Jenner, C. E. 1952. Photo-periodic responses of plants and animals. Nature, 169:242–244.

Patrick, Ruth. 1949. A proposed biological measure of stream conditions based on a survey of the Conestoga Basin, Lancaster County, Pennsylvania. Proc. Acad. Nat. Sc. Phila., 101:277–341.

Patrick, R.; Hohn, M. H.; and Wallace, J. H. 1954. A new method of determining the pattern of the diatom flora. Notula Naturae, Acad. Nat. Sc., Phila. No. 259:1–12.

Pearl, Raymond. 1930. The Biology of Population Growth. Knopf, New York.

Pearl, Raymond, and Parker, S. L. 1921. Experimental studies on the duration of life: introductory discussion of the duration of life in *Drosophila*. Am. Nat., 55:481–509.

Pearse, A. S. 1939. Animal Ecology (2nd Ed.). The McGraw-Hill Book Co., Inc., New York.

——. 1946. Observations on the microfauna of the Duke forest. Ecol. Monogr., 16:127–150.

Pearse, A. S.; Humm, H. J.; and Wharton, G. W. 1942. Ecology of sand beaches at Beaufort, N. C. Ecol. Monogr., 12:136–190.

Pendleton, Robert C. 1949. The rain shadow effect on the plant formations of Guadalcanal. Ecol. Monogr., 19:75–93.

——. 1956. Labeling animals with radioisotopes. Ecol., 37:686–689.

Pendleton, Robert C., and Grundmann, A. W. 1954. Use of P^{32} in tracing some insect-plant relationships of the thistle, *Cirsium undulatum*. Ecol., 35:187–191.

Penfound, William T. 1956. Primary production of vascular aquatic plants. Limnol. and Oceanogr., 1:92–101.

Penman, H. L. 1956. Weather and water in the growth of grass. In: The Growth of Leaves. (See Milthrope, 1956.)

Pennak, Robert W. 1939. The microscopic fauna of the sandy beaches. Publ. Am. Assoc. Adv. Sc., 10:94–106.

———. 1953. Fresh-water Invertebrates of the United States. Ronald Press, New York.

———. 1955. Comparative limnology of eight Colorado mountain lakes. Univ. of Colorado Studies, Ser. Biol., 2: 1–74.

Pequegnat, Willis E. 1958. Whales, plankton, and man. Sc. Am. 198:84–90.

Petersen, C. G. J. 1914; 1915; 1918. The animal associations of the sea-bottom in the North Atlantic. Kobenhavn Ber. Biol. Sta., 22:89–98; 23:1–28; 26:1–62.

Peterson, Elmer T. 1952. Insoak is the answer. Land, 11:83–88.

Petrides, George A. 1950. The determination of sex and age ratios in fur animals. Am. Midl. Nat., 43:355–382.

Philip, J. P. 1955. Note on the mathematical theory of animal population dynamics and a recent fallacy. Australian J. Zool., 3:287–294.

Pirt, S. J. 1957. The oxygen requirement of growing cultures of an Aerobacter species determined by means of the continuous culture technique. J. Gen. Microbiol., 16:59–75.

Pitelka, Frank A. 1941. Distribution of birds in relation to major biotic communities. Am. Midl. Nat., 25:113–137.

———. 1951. Ecologic overlap and interspecific strife in breeding populations of Anna and Allen Hummingbirds. Ecol., 32:641–661.

Pitelka, F. A.; Tomich, P. Q.; and Treichel, G. W. 1955. Ecological relations of jaegers and owls as lemming predators near Barrow, Alaska. Ecol. Monogr., 25:85–117.

Pittendrigh, Colin S. 1958. Perspectives in the study of biological clocks. In: Perspectives in Marine Biology, pp. 239–268. University of California Press, Berkeley.

Platt, Robert B. 1957. Field installation for automatic recording of micro-environmental gradients. Trans. Am. Geo. Union, 38:160–170.

Platt, Robert B., and Wolfe, James N. 1950. General uses and methods of thermistors in temperature investigations, with special reference to a technique for high sensitivity contact temperature measurement. Plant. Physiol., 25:507–512.

Pomeroy, Lawrence R. 1959. Algal productivity in salt marshes of Georgia. Limnol. and Oceanogr., 4. (In press.)

Potash, Milton. 1956. A biological test for determining the potential productivity of water. Ecol., 37:631–639.

Preston, F. W. 1948. The commonness and rarity of species. Ecol., 29:254–283.

Proctor, Vernon W. 1957. Studies of algal antibiosis using *Hematococcus* and *Chlamydomonas*. Limnol. and Oceanogr., 2:125–139.

Provasoli, L., and Pintner, I. J. 1953. Ecological implications of in vitro nutritional requirements of algal flagellates. Ann. N. Y. Acad. Sc., 56:839–851.

Puck, Theodore T., and Marcus, P. I. 1956. Action of x-rays on mammalian cells. J. Exp. Med., 103:653–666.

Quinn, James A. 1950. Human Ecology. Prentice-Hall, Inc., New York.

Rabinowitch, E. I. 1951. Photosynthesis and Related Processes. Vol. II (1): 603–1208 Interscience, New York.

Rafter, T. A., and Fergusson, G. J. 1957. The atom bomb effect: recent increase in the C^{14} content of the atmosphere, biosphere, and surface waters of the ocean. New Zealand J. Sc. and Tech., 38:871–883.

Ragotzkie, Robert A., and Pomeroy, Lawrence R. 1957. Life history of a dinoflagellate bloom. Limnol. and Oceanogr., 2:62–69.

Raunkaier, C. 1934. The Life Form of Plants and Statistical Plant Geography. Clarendon Press, Oxford.

Rawson, D. S. 1952. Mean depth and the fish production of large lakes. Ecol., 33:513–521.

——. 1956. Algal indicators of trophic lake types. Limnol. and Oceanogr., 1:18–25.

Redfield, Alfred C. 1958. The biological control of chemical factors in the environment. Am. Sc., 46:205–221.

Revelle, Roger. 1951. Paleoecology and deep sea exploration, in Report No. 11 of National Research Council Committee on a Treatise on Marine Ecology and Paleoecology, pp. 57–70. See Ladd, Harry S.

——. (Editor.) 1957. The Effects of Atomic Radiation on Oceanography and Fisheries. Pub. No. 551. Nat. Acad. Sci., National Research Council, Washington.

Rice, E. L., and Kelting, R. W. 1955. The species-area curve. Ecology, 36:7–11.

Rice, E. L., and Penfound, Wm. T. 1954. Plant succession and yield of living plant material in a plowed prairie in central Oklahoma. Ecol., 35:176–180.

Rice, T. R. 1954. Biotic influences affecting population growth of planktonic algae. Fishery Bull. (U. S. Fish and Wildlife Service), 87:227–245.

Richards, F. A., and Thompson, T. G. 1952. The estimation and characterization by pigment analysis. II. A spectrophotometric method for the estimation of plankton pigments. J. Mar. Res., 11:156–172.

Richards, P. W. 1952. The Tropical Rain Forest. Cambridge University Press.

Ricker, W. E., and Forester, R. E. 1948. Computation of fish production. Bull. Bingham Oceanographic Coll., 11:173–211.

Rigler, R. L. 1956. A tracer study of phosphorus cycle in lake water. Ecol., 37:550–556.

Riley, Gordon A. 1939. Plankton studies: the western North Atlantic, May-June, 1939. J. Marine Res., 2:145–162.

——. 1941. Plankton studies: Long Island Sound. Bull. Bingham Oceanographic Coll., 7:1–89.

——. 1943. Physiological aspects of spring diatom flowering. Bull. Bingham Oceanographic Coll., 8:1–53.

——. 1944. The carbon metabolism and photosynthetic efficiency of the earth. Am. Sc., 32:132–134.

——. 1952. Phytoplankton of Block Island Sound, 1949. Bull. Bingham Oceanographic Coll., 13:40–64.

——. 1952a. Biological Oceanography. In: Survey of Biological Progress, 2:79–104. Academic Press, N. Y.

——. 1956. Oceanography of Long Island Sound, 1952-54. IX. Production and utilization of organic matter. Bull. Bingham Oceanographic Coll., 15:324–344.

——. 1957. Phytoplankton of the north central Sargasso Sea. Limnol. and Oceanogr., 2:252–270.

Riley, Gordon A.; Strommel, H.; and Bumpus, D. F. 1949. Quantitative ecology of the plankton of the western Atlantic. Bull. Bingham Oceanographic Coll., 12:1–169.

Robertson, J. S. 1957. Theory and use of tracers in determining transfer rates in biological systems. Physiol. Revs., 37:133–154.

Rodhe, W. 1955. Can plankton production proceed during winter darkness in subarctic lakes? Proc. Int. Assoc. Theoret. and Appl. Limnol., 12:11̃.–122.

Romney, E. M.; Neel, J. W.; Nishita, H.; Olafson, J. H.; and Larson, K. H. 1957. Plant uptake of Sr90, Y91, Ru106, Cs137 and Ce144 from soils. Soil Science, 83:369–376.

Rounsefell, G. A. 1946. Fish production in lakes as a guide for estimating production in proposed reservoirs. Copeia, 1946:29–40.

Rübel, Eduard. 1935. The replaceability of ecological factors and the law of the minimum. Ecol., 16:336–341.

Rudd, Robert L., and Genelly, R. E. 1956. Pesticides: their use and toxicity in relation to wildlife. Calif. Dept. Fish and Game, Game Bull., No. 7:1–209.

Rugh, Roberts, and Wolff, Joan. 1958. Increased radioresistance through heterosis. Science, 127:144–145.

Russell, E. John. 1954. World Population and World Food Supplies. George Allen and Unwin, London.

———. 1957. The World of the Soil. The New Naturalist: a survey of British Natural History. William Collins Sons and Co., London.

Russell, E. J., and Russell, E. W. 1950. Soil Conditions and Plant Growth. 8th Ed. Longmans, Green & Co., New York.

Russell, E. S. 1942. The Overfishing Problem. Cambridge University Press, Cambridge, England.

Ruttner, Franz. 1953. Fundamentals of Limnology. University of Toronto Press, Toronto.

Ryther, John H. 1954. The ecology of phytoplankton blooms in Moriches Bay and Great South Bay, Long Island, New York. Biol. Bull., 106:198–209.

———. 1954a. The ratio of photosynthesis to respiration in marine plankton algae and its effect upon measurement of production. Deep-Sea Res., 2: 134–139.

———. 1956. Photosynthesis in the ocean as a function of light intensity. Limnol. and Oceanogr., 1:61–70.

———. 1956a. The measurement of primary production. Limnol. and Oceanogr., 1:72–84.

Ryther, J. H., and Yentsch, C. S. 1957. The estimation of phytoplankton production in the ocean from chlorophyll and light data. Limnol. and Oceanogr., 2:281–286.

Sampson, Arthur W. 1952. Range Management, Principles and Practices. John Wiley & Sons., New York.

Sanderson, Ivan T. 1945. Living Treasure. Viking, New York.

Sauer, C. O. 1950. Grassland, climax, fire and man. J. Range Mgt., 3:16–21.

Saunders, George W. 1957. Interrelations of dissolved organic matter and phytoplankton. Bot. Rev., 23:389–409.

Schmid, Calvin F. 1950. Generalizations concerning the ecology of the American City. Am. Soc. Rev., 40:264–281.

Schmidt-Nielsen, Bodil, and Schmidt-Nielsen, Knut. 1949. The water economy of desert mammals. Scient. Monthly, 69:180–185.

Schmidt-Nielsen, Knut. 1956. Animals and arid conditions; physiological aspects of productivity and management. In: The Future of Arid Lands, Amer. Assoc. Adv. Sc. Wash., pp. 368–382.

Scott, J. P. (Editor.) 1956. Allee Memorial number. Series of papers on social organization in animals. Ecol., 37:211–273.

Sears, Paul B. 1935. Deserts on the March. University of Oklahoma Press, Norman.

———. 1950. Conservation in theory and practice. Ohio J. Science, 50:149–155.

———. 1957. The Ecology of Man. Condon Lectures. Univ. Oregon Press. (60 pages.)

Seligman, Henry, and Dunster, H. J. 1956. The discharge of radioactive waste products into the Irish Sea. Proc. Int. Conf. Peaceful Uses Atomic Energy, 9:701–104.

Seymour, Allyn; Held, Edward E.; Lowman, Frank G.; Donaldson, John R.; and South, Dorothy J. 1957. Survey of radioactivity in the sea and in pelagic marine life west of the Marshall Islands, Sept. 1-20, 1956. U. S. Atomic Energy Comm. Rept. UWFL-47.

Shantz, H. L. 1911. Natural vegetation as an indicator of the capabilities of land for crop production in the great plains area. U. S. Dept. Agr., Bureau of Plant Industry, Bull. 201.

———. 1917. Plant succession on abandoned roads in eastern Colorado. J. Ecol. 5:19–42.

———. 1942. The desert vegetation of North America. Bot. Rev., 8:195–246.

Shelford, V. E. 1911. Physiological animal geography. J. Morphol., 22:551–618.

———. 1911a. Ecological succession: stream fishes and the method of physiographic analysis. Biol. Bull., 21:9–34.

———. 1911b. Ecological succession: pond fishes. Biol. Bull., 21:127–151.

———. 1913. Animal Communities in Temperate America. University of Chicago Press, Chicago.

———. 1919. Nature's mobilization. Nat. Hist., 19:205–210.

———. 1929. Laboratory and Field Ecology. William & Wilkins Co., Baltimore.

———. 1943. The abundance of the collared lemming in the Churchill area, 1929–1940. Ecol., 24:472–484.

———. 1951. Fluctuations of forest animal populations in east central Illinois. Ecol. Monogr., 21: 183–214.

Shelford, V. E., and Olson, Sigurd. 1935. Sere, climax and influent animals with special reference to the transcontinental coniferous forest of North America. Ecol., 16:375–402.

Shields, Lora M. 1953. Nitrogen sources of seed plants and environmental influences affecting the nitrogen cycle. Bot. Rev., 19:321–376.

Shields, Lora M.; Mitchell, Charles; and Drouet, Francis. 1957. Alga- and lichen-stabilized surface crusts as soil nitrogen sources. Am. J. Bot., 44: 489–498.

Siivonen, Lauri. 1957. The problem of the short-term fluctuations in numbers of tetranoids in Europe. Papers on Game Res. (Finnish Game Foundation) No. 19:1–44.

Simonson, Roy W. 1951. The soil under natural and cultural environment. J. Soil & Water Conserv., 6:63–69.

Siu, R. G. H., and Reese, E. T. 1953. Decomposition of cellulose by microorganisms. Bot. Rev., 19:377–416.

Smith, L. 1942. Hereditary susceptibility to x-ray injury in *Tsiticum monococcum*. Am. J. Bot., 29:189–191.

Solomon, M. E. 1949. The natural control of animal populations. J. Anim. Ecol., 18:1–32.

Sparrow, A. H., and Christensen, E. 1953. Tolerance of certain higher plants to chronic exposure to gamma radiation from Cobalt-60. Science, 118:697–698.

Sparrow, A. H., and Robin, B. A. 1952. Effects of radiations on biological systems. Surv. Biol. Progr., 2:1–52.

Springer, Leonard M. 1950. Aerial census of interstate antelope herds of California, Idaho, Nevada and Oregon. J. Wildl. Mgt., 14:295–298.

Springer, Paul F. 1956. Insecticides—boon or bane? Audubon Mag., 58:128–130; 176–178.

Steemann-Nielsen, E. 1952. The use of radioactive carbon (C^{14}) for measuring organic production in the sea. J. Cons. Int. Explor. Mer., 18:117–140.

——. 1954. On organic production in the ocean. J. Cons. Int. Explor. Mer., 49:309–328.

——. 1955. The production of organic matter by phytoplankton in a Danish lake receiving extraordinary amounts of nutrient salts. Hydrobiologia, 7: 68–74.

Stephenson, T. A., and Stephenson, Anne. 1949. The universal features of zonation between tide-marks on rocky coasts. J. Ecol., 37:289–305.

——. 1952. Life between tide-marks in North America: Northern Florida and the Carolinas. J. Ecol., 40:1–49.

Stern, W. L., and Buell, M. F. 1951. Life-form spectra of New Jersey pine barren forest and Minnesota jack pine forest. Bull. Torry Bot. Club, 78:61–65.

Stewart, Paul A. 1952. Dispersal, breeding, behavior, and longevity of banded barn owls in North America. Auk, 69:277–285.

Stickel, Lucille F. 1950. Populations and home range relationships of the box turtle, *Terrapene c. carolina* (Linnaeus). Ecol. Monogr., 20:351–378.

Stickel, Lucille F., and Springer, P. F. 1957. Pesticides and wildlife. U. S. Fish and Wildl. Serv., Wildl. Leaflet No. 392:1–12.

Stoddard, Herbert L. 1932. The Bobwhite Quail, Its Habits. Preservation and Increase. Charles Scribner's Sons, New York.

——. 1936. Relation of burning to timber and wildlife. Proc. 1st N. A. Wildl. Conf., 1:1–4.

Stoddart, Laurence A., and Smith, Arthur D. 1955. Range Management. (2nd Ed.) McGraw-Hill Book Co., Inc., New York.

Strode, G. (Editor.) 1951. Yellow Fever. McGraw-Hill Book Co., Inc., New York.

Struxness, E. G.; Morton, R. J.; and Straub, C. P. 1956. Disposal of high level liquid wastes in terrestrial pits. Proc. Int. Conf. Peaceful Uses Atomic Energy, 9:684–691.

Studhalter, R. A. 1955. Tree growth. I. Some historical chapters. Bot. Rev., 21:1–72.

Summerhayes, V. S., and Elton, C. S. 1923. Contributions to the ecology of Spitsbergen and Bear Island. J. Ecol., 11:214–286.

Svardson, Gunnar. 1949. Competition and habitat selection in birds. Oikos, 1:157–174.

Sverdrup, H. U.; Johnson, Martin, W.; and Fleming, Richard, 1942. The Oceans, Their Physics, Chemistry, and General Biology. Prentice-Hall, Inc., New York. (Second printing, 1946.)

Sweeney, James R. 1956. Responses of vegetation to fire. Univ. of California. Publ. Bot., 28:143–250.

Swingle, H. S. 1952. Farm pond investigations in Alabama. J. Wildl. Mgt., 16:243–249.

Swingle, H. S., and Smith, E. V. 1947. Management of farm fish ponds (Rev. Ed.). Alabama Polytechnic Inst. Ag. Exp. Sta. Bull. No. 254.

Taber, R. D., and Dasmann, Raymond. 1957. The dynamics of three natural populations of the deer, *Odocoileus hemionus columbianus*. Ecol., 38:233–246.

Tadros, T. M. 1957. Evidence of the presence of an edapho-biotic factor in the problem of serpentine tolerance. Ecol., 38:14–23.

Tamiya, Hiroshi. 1957. Mass culture of algae. Ann. Rev. Plant Physiol., 8: 309–334

Tansley, A. G. 1935. The use and abuse of vegetational concepts and terms. Ecol., 16:284–307.

Taylor, Clyde C.; Bigelow, Henry B.; and Graham, Herbert W. 1957. Climatic trends and the distribution of marine animals in New England. Fisheries Bull. U. S. Fish and Wildlife Service 115. Vol. 57:293–343.

Taylor, Harden F. 1951. Survey of Marine Fisheries of North Carolina. University of North Carolina Press, Chapel Hill.

Taylor, Walter P. 1934. Significance of extreme or intermittent conditions in distribution of species and management of natural resources, with a restatement of Liebig's law of the minimum. Ecol., 15:274–379.

Teal, John M. 1957. Community metabolism in a temperate cold spring. Ecol. Monogr., 27:283–302.

——. 1958. Distribution of fiddler crabs in Georgia salt marshes. Ecol., 39: 185–193.

Thienemann, August. 1926. Limnologie. Jedermanns Bücherei, Breslau.

——. 1926a. Der Nahrungskreislauf im Wasser. Verh. deutsch. Zool. Ges., 31:29–79.

——. 1939. Grundzüge einer allgemeinen Oekologie. Arch. Hydrobiol., 35: 267–285.

Thomas, Moyer D. 1955. Effect of ecological factors on photosynthesis. Annual Rev. Plant Physiol., 6:135–156.

Thomas, Moyer D., and Hill, George R. 1949. Photosynthesis under field conditions in photosynthesis in plants. Edited by James Franck and Walter E. Loomis. Iowa State College Press, Ames, pp. 19–52.

Thomas, William L. (Editor.) 1956. Man's Role in Changing the Face of the Earth. University of Chicago Press.

Thompson, D'Arcy W. 1942. On Growth and Form. Cambridge University Press, Cambridge, England.

Thompson, David H., and Bennett, G. W. 1939. Fish management in small artificial lakes. Tr. 4th N. A. Wildl. Conf., 4:311–317.

Thompson, David H., and Hunt, Francis D. 1930. The fishes of Champaign County: a study of the distribution and abundance of fishes in small streams. Ill. Nat. Hist. Surv. Bull., 19:1–101.

Thompson, W. R. 1956. The fundamental theory of natural and biological control. Ann. Rev. Ent., 1:379–402.

Thornthwaite, C. W. 1931. The climates of North America according to a new classification. Geogr. Rev., 21:633–655.

——. 1933. The climates of the earth. Geogr. Rev., 28:433–440.

——. 1948. An approach to a rational classification of climate. Geogr. Rev., 38:55–94.

——. 1955. Discussions on the relationships between meteorology and oceanography. J. Mar. Res., 14:510–515.

Thornton, H. G. 1956. The ecology of microorganisms in soil. Proc. Royal Soc. London Ser. B., 145:364–374.

Thorson, Gunnar. 1955. Modern aspects of marine level-bottom animal communities. J. Mar. Res., 14:387–397. (See also Tr. N. Y. Acad. Sc., 18:693–700. 1956.)

Tischler, Wolfgang. 1955. Synokologie der Landtiere. Gustav Fischler Verlag, Stuttgart.

Transeau, E. N. 1926. The accumulation of energy by plants. Ohio J. Sc., 26:1–10.

Trautman, Milton B. 1942. Fish distribution and abundance correlated with stream gradients as a consideration in stocking programs. Tr. 7th N. A. Wildl. Conf., 7:221–223.

Tribe, H. T. 1957. Ecology of microorganisms in soil as observed during their development upon buried cellulose film. In: Microbial Ecology (See Williams and Spicer, 1957).

Trippensee, R. E. 1948. Wildlife Management. McGraw-Hill Book Co., Inc., New York.

Turner, H. J., *et al.* 1948-51. Report on investigations of the propagation of the soft-shelled clam *Mya arenaria*. Commonwealth Mass. Dept. Conservation, Div. Marine Fishes. Boston. Four reports.

Tuxen, S. L. 1944. The hot springs of Iceland, in The Zoology of Iceland. Ejnar Munksgaard, Copenhagen.

Twomey, Arthur C. 1936. Climographic studies of certain introduced and migratory birds. Ecol., 17:122–132.

UNESCO. 1955. Arid Zone Research. VI. Plant Ecology. Reviews of research. Paris.

UNESCO. 1957. Arid Zone Research. VIII. Human and Animal Ecology, Paris.

United States Department of Agriculture. 1938. Soils and Men. Yearbook of Agriculture for 1938.

——. 1948. Grass. Yearbook of Agriculture for 1948.

Utida, Syunro. 1957. Cyclic fluctuations of population density intrinsic to the host-parasite system. Ecol., 38:442–449.

Uvarov, B. P. 1957. The aridity factor in the ecology of locust and grasshoppers of the old world. In: Human and Animal Ecology. Arid Zone Res. VIII. UNESCO, Paris.

Vallee, Bert L. 1951. The function of trace elements in biology. Scient. Monthly, 72:368–376.

Varley, G. C. 1947. The natural control of population balance in the knapweed gall-fly (*Urophora jaceana*). J. Anim. Ecol., 16:139–187.

——. 1949. Population changes in German forest pests. J. Anim. Ecol., 18: 117–122.

——. 1953. Ecological aspects of population regulation. Tr. 9th Int. Congr. Ent., 2:210–214.

——. 1957. Ecology as an experimental science. J. Anim. Ecol., 26:251–261.

Varley, G. C., and Edwards, R. I. 1957. The bearing of parasite behaviour on the dynamics of insect host and parasite populations. J. Anim. Ecol., 26: 471–477.

Verduin, Jacob. 1956. Primary production in lakes. Limnol. and Oceanogr., 1:85–91.

Vernadsky, W. I. 1944. Problems in biogeochemistry. II. Tr. Conn. Acad. Arts, Sc., 35:493–494.

——. 1945. The biosphere and the noosphere. Am. Sc., 33:1–12.

Vestal, A. G. 1949. Minimum areas for different vegetations. Illinois Biol. Monogr., 20:1–129.

Viosca, Percy, Jr. 1935. Statistics on the productivity of inland waters, the master key to better fish culture. Tr. Am. Fish Soc., 65:350–358.

Vlasyuk, P. A. 1955. The effect of nuclear radiations on plants. Conf. Acad. Sci. USSR on Peaceful Uses of Atomic Energy; Session Div. Biol. Sci. Moscow. (English translation US AEC Report, 1956.)

Vogt, William. 1948. Road to Survival. Sloane, New York.

Voute, A. D. 1946. Regulation of the density of the insect-populations in virgin-forests and cultivated woods. Arch. Neerlandaises de Zool., 7:435–470. (Review by Varley, J. Anim. Ecol., 17:82–83.)

Waksman, Selman A. 1932. Principles of Soil Microbiology (2d Ed.). Williams & Wilkins, Co., Baltimore.

——. 1941. Aquatic bacteria in relation to the cycle of organic matter in lakes, in Symposium on Hydrobiology (pp. 86–105). University of Wisconsin Press, Madison.

——. 1952. Soil Microbiology. John Wiley & Sons, Inc., New York.

Wallis, G. W., and Wilde, S. A. 1957. Rapid method for determination of carbon dioxide evolved from forest soils. Ecol., 38:359–361.

Walter, H. 1954. Le facteur eau dans les regions arides et sa signification pour l'organisation de la vegetation dans les contrees sub-tropicales. In: Les Division Ecologiques du Monde. Centre National de la Recherche Scientifique, Paris, pp. 27–39.

Wangersky, P. J., and Cunningham, W. J. 1957. Time lag in population models. Cold Spring Harbor Sym. Quant. Biol., 22:329–338.

Watson, D. J. 1956. Leaf growth in relation to crop yield. In: The Growth of Leaves. (See Milthrope, 1956.)

Weaver, J. E. 1954. North American Prairie. Johnsen Publ. Co., Lincoln, Nebraska.

Weaver, J. E., and Albertson, F. W. 1956. Grasslands of the Great Plains: Their Nature and Use. Johnsen Publ. Co., Lincoln, Nebraska.

Weaver, J. E., and Clements, F. E. 1929. Plant Ecology. McGraw-Hill Book Co., Inc., New York. (2d ed. 1938.)

Weaver, J. E., and Zink, E. 1946. Annual increase of underground materials in three range grasses. Ecol., 27:115–127.

Wellington, W. G. 1957. Individual differences as a factor in population dynamics: the development of a problem. Canadian J. Zool., 35:293–323.

Wells, B. W. 1928. Plant communities of the coastal plain of North Carolina and their successional relations. Ecol., 9:230–242.

Went, Fritz W. 1957. The Experimental Control of Plant Growth. Chronica Botanica Co., Waltham, Mass.

Weston, William. 1941. The role of aquatic fungi in hydrobiology. In: Symposium on Hydrobiology (pp. 129–151). University of Wisconsin Press, Madison.

Whitehead, F. H. 1957. Productivity in alpine vegetation (abstract). J. Anim. Ecol., 26:241.

——. 1957a. The importance of experimental ecology to the study of British Flora. In: Progress in the Study of British Flora. Edited by J. E. Lousley. Arbroath, T. Buncle & Co., London, pp. 56–60.

Whittaker, R. H. 1951. A criticism of the plant association and climatic climax concepts. Northwest Sc., 25: 17–31.

——. 1953. A consideration of climax theory; the climax as a population and pattern. Ecol. Monogr., 23:41–78.

——. 1953a. Removal of radiophosphorus contaminant from the water in an aquarium community. AEC Document HW-28636.

——. (Editor.) 1954. The ecology of serpentine soils. Ecol., 35:258–288.

——. 1954a. Plant populations and the basis of plant indication. In: Angewandte Pflanzensoziologie, Veroffentlichungen des Karntner Landesinstituts fur angewandte Pflanzensoziologie in Klagenfurt, Festschrift Aichinger, Vol. 1.

——. 1957. The kingdoms of the living world. Ecol., 38:536–538.

Williams, R. E. O., and Spicer, C. C. (Editors). 1957. Microbial Ecology. 7th Symposium of the Soc. Gen. Microbiology. Cambridge University Press.

Williamson, M. H. 1957. An elementary theory of interspecific competition. Nature, 180:1–7.

Willstatter, R., and Stroll, A. 1918. Untersuchungen uber die Assimilation der Koblensaure. Julius Springer, Berlin.

Wilson, D. P. 1952. The influence of the nature of the substratum on the metamorphosis of the larvae of marine animals, especially the larvae of *Ophelia bicornis*, Ann. Inst. Oceanogr., 27:49–156.

Winogradsky, S. 1949. Microbiologie du Sol. Masson and Cie., Paris.

Wirth, Louis. 1928. The Ghetto. University of Chicago Press, Chicago.

———. 1945. Human ecology. Am. J. Sociol., 50:483–488.

Wittwer, S. H. 1957. Nutrient uptake with special reference to foliar absorbtion. In: Comar, C. L. Atomic Energy and Agriculture. Am. Assoc. Adv. Sc. Publ. No. 49:139–164.

Wolcott, G. N. 1937. An animal census of two pastures and a meadow in northern New York. Ecol. Monogr., 7:1–90.

Wolfanger, Louis A. 1930. The Major Soil Divisions of the United States. John Wiley & Sons, Inc., New York.

Wolfe, John N.; Wareham, Richard T.; and Scofield, Herbert T. 1949. Microclimates and macroclimates of Neotoma, a small valley in central Ohio. Ohio State University Publication, 8:1–267 (Bull. No. 41).

Wolfenbarger, D. O. 1946. Dispersion of small organisms. Am. Midl. Nat., 35:1–152.

Wood, Roy. 1951. The significance of managed water levels in developing the fisheries of large impoundments. J. Tenn. Acad. Sc. 26:214–235.

Woodbury, Angus M. 1947. Distribution of pigmy conifers in Utah and northeastern Arizona. Ecol., 28:113–126.

Woodruff, L. L. 1912. Observations on the origin and sequence of the protozoan fauna of hay infusions. J. Exp. Zool., 12:205–264.

Woytinsky, W. S., and Woytinsky, E. S. 1953. World Population and Production. The Twentieth Century Fund, New York.

Yeatter, R. E. 1950. Effect of different preincubation temperatures on the hatchability of pheasant eggs. Science, 112:529–530.

Yonge, C. M. 1940. The biology of reef-building corals. Rept. Great Barrier Reef Expedition, 1:135–176.

Yount, James L. 1956. Factors that control species numbers in Silver Springs, Florida. Limnol. and Oceanogr., 1:286–295.

Zeuthen, E. 1953. Oxygen uptake and body size in organisms. Quart. Rev. Biol., 28:1–12.

Zhezhel, N. G. 1955. Effect of natural radioactive substances on the yield of agricultural crops, pp. 149–161 in Meetings of Div. Biol. Sc. Sess. of Acad. Sc. USSR on Peaceful Uses of Atomic Energy, July 1-5, 1955. Moscow. (In Russian; English translation by USAEC, 1956.)

ZoBell, Claude E. 1946. Marine Microbiology. Chronica Botanica, Waltham, Mass.

ZoBell, Claude E.; Sisler, F. D.; and Oppenheimer, C. H. 1953. Evidence of biochemical heating of Lake Meade mud. J. Sed. Petrol., 23:13–17.

Index with reference glossary

Numbers in **boldface type** indicate pages on which terms and concepts are most fully defined and explained. Scientific names are *italicized*. In some cases scientific names are included in the index and referred to pages on which only vernacular names appear. Only names of persons not accompanied by a specific literature reference in the text are listed in this index; see bibliography for other names. Organisms in lengthy tables are not indexed.

Grasshopper(s). See also LOCUSTS.
  in dune succession, 260-261
  and overgrazing, 446
  population energy flow of, 211-213
    (Fig. 61)
Grasshopper eggs, variable temperature and, 105
Grassland, 120
  biomes, 396-402
  chlorphyll in, 86
  drought, 90
  historical aspects, 447
  mammals of, 400-402
  management, 444-447
  overgrazing in, 445 (Fig. 143)
  productivity of, 73-75, 445-446
  rainfall in, 95, 120
  soils in, 130-132 (Figs. 32, 33)
  succession, 264
  temperate, 396-401
Grayia, 405, 478
Grouse, ruffed (*Bonasa*), 170
Growth rate. See POPULATION.
  substances, 23
Guano, 36, 330
Gulf Stream, 329, 330
Gull, herring, survivorship curve, 167
Gumbo limbo (*Bursera*), 396
Gymnodinium, 341
Gyrinidae, 304

H

Habitat(s), **27-30**
  approach, 289-290
  fresh-water, 291-294
  improvement, in wildlife manage-
    ment, 433
  lotic and lentic comparison of, 316-
    319
  marine, 328-333
  terrestrial, 367-368
Hadal zone, 334
Haeckel, Ernst, 3, 336
Half-life (of radioisotope), **457-459**
"Hammocks" of Florida, 396
Hare, snowshoe (*Lepus americanus*),
    194 (Fig. 55)
  cycle of abundance, 193-194, 200
Harvest, method of productivity
  measurement, 73, **80-81**
Hay, productivity of, 73

Heat. See also TEMPERATURE.
  latent, 292
  loss in food chains, 43, 46, 47 (Fig
    11)
  specific, 292
Helianthus, 400
Helisoma, 302
Helocordulia, 302
Hemi-cryptophytes, 372-373
Herbivores, 46-48, 52, 63, 65
Heron (*Ardea*), changes in abun-
  dance, 192
Herring (Clupeidae), 351-352
  age distribution, 175 (Fig. 46),
    177
Heterospilus, 199
Heterotrophic, **10**
Hexagenia, 321
Hibernal (season), 276
Hierarchies, social, 220-221
Hippocrates, 3
Histidine, 23
Historical approach, and biome con-
  cept, 418
Holocoen, 10
Holoplankton, 308, **341,** 342
Homeostasis, **25-27,** 41
  mechanisms, **7**
Horizons, soil, 129
Hormone(s), environmental, 23-24
  external diffusion, 22
Human ecology, 487-496. See also
  MAN.
  geography, 487
Humidity, **112**
  absolute, **112**
  and climographs, 119, 122
  measurement of, 112
  relative, **112**
Humification, 20, **130**
Humus, **20**
  content of soils, 130
Hurricanes, 128
Hydra, survivorship curve, 168
Hydracarina, 302
Hydroclimographs, 331
Hydropsyche, 50, 321, 322
Hydrosphere, 128
Hygrograph, 112
Hypericum, 426

14 · Radiation ecology*

Radiation ecology is concerned with radioactive substances, radiation and the environment. There are two rather distinct phases of radioecology which require different approaches. On the one hand we are concerned with the effects of radiation on individuals, populations, communities and ecosystems. The other important phase of radiation ecology concerns the fate of radioactive substances released into the environment and the manner by which the ecological communities and populations control the distribution of radioactivity. The rapid development of atomic energy for military and peaceful purposes and the spread of potentially dangerous materials into the environments have made radiation ecology of major concern.

Materials like radioactive strontium and radioactive iodine are falling from the skies after atomic blasts. Elsewhere such materials are going into soils and natural waters as atomic wastes. Many organisms take up these substances and concentrate them in their tissues. In high concentrations such substances and their radiations have biological effects including induction of mutation, cancers and death. In the extremely dilute amounts now found in many environments effects are little known and presumed to be negligible, but there is much controversy. In this chapter are presented some of the aspects of a new subject in its infancy.

* This chapter is a revised version of a previous article (E. P. Odum, 1956) and was prepared while the author held a National Science Foundation Senior Fellowship which enabled him to take part in research programs at several of the Atomic Energy Installations.

side, which, as we have already indicated, often does more harm than good.

Probably the greatest problem in public health in the near future is not the control of specific diseases but the control of pollution of the general environment (water, air, soil), which can bring with it ill-health of all kinds. Irritating and toxic air-borne substances or "smog" is already a health factor in all large cities, and is especially serious in certain regions, such as southern California. Smog in the latter area has even been shown to inhibit photosynthesis and plant growth, some varieties of plants being especially sensitive (Koritz and Went, 1953). Radioactive pollutants, of course, are becoming a major problem, as will be discussed in the next chapter. At the same time, radioactive "tracers" can be extremely useful in the detection of pollution of all types. Ely (1957), for example, reports that the radioactive isotope scandium-46 mixed with sewage effluent and discharged into the sea off southern California made possible a rapid determination of dispersal patterns and the detection of very minute amounts of effluent on the beaches. As a result, the design of the disposal system was corrected long before beach pollution became a hazard to people.